Recent Progress in

HORMONE RESEARCH

The Proceedings of the Laurentian Hormone Conference

VOLUME 38

RECENT PROGRESS IN
HORMONE RESEARCH

Proceedings of the
1981 Laurentian Hormone Conference

Edited by
ROY O. GREEP

VOLUME 38

PROGRAM COMMITTEE

G. D. Aurbach	B. W. O'Malley
J. C. Beck	J. E. Rall
H. Friesen	K. Savard
R. O. Greep	N. B. Schwartz
E. E. McGarry	J. L. Vaitukaitis

1982

ACADEMIC PRESS
A Subsidiary of Harcourt Brace Jovanovich, Publishers

New York London
Paris San Diego San Francisco São Paulo Sydney Tokyo Toronto

ACADEMIC PRESS, INC.
111 Fifth Avenue, New York, New York 10003

United Kingdom Edition published by
ACADEMIC PRESS, INC. (LONDON) LTD.
24/28 Oval Road, London NW1 7DX

LIBRARY OF CONGRESS CATALOG CARD NUMBER: Med. 47–38

ISBN 0–12–571138–7

PRINTED IN THE UNITED STATES OF AMERICA

82 83 84 85   9 8 7 6 5 4 3 2 1

CONTENTS

v

LIST OF CONTRIBUTORS AND DISCUSSANTS

G. Aguilera
K. Ahren
R. N. Andersen
L. D. Anderson
N. Aronin
G. D. Aurbach
A. L. Barofsky
E. R. Barrack
C. W. Beattie
H. P. J. Bennett
A. Biegon
H-C. Blossey
H. L. Bradlow
G. P. Budzik
L. P. Bullock
G. V. Callard
G. T. Campbell
C. P. Channing
M. C. Charlesworth
R. Chatterton
C.-L. C. Chen
K. Cheng
G. P. Chrousos
J. H. Clark
L. E. Closs
D. S. Coffey
M. A. Conkling
S. Creacy
W. F. Crowley
G. B. Cutler
P. G. Davis
E. R. DeSombre
D. J. Diamond
B. M. Dobyns
P. K. Donahoe
L. J. Dorflinger
R. W. Downs
R. Dubler
J. F. Dunn
J. H. Eberwine
M. J. Q. Evinger
L. E. Faber
R. E. Fellows
C. Ferris
J. K. Findlay

B. G. Forget
J. E. Fortune
H. G. Friesen
A. Fuller, Jr.
G. Galasko
C. Gee
J. Geller
A. G. Gilman
S. R. Glasser
H. M. Goodman
R. R. Grady
G. L. Greene
R. O. Greep
G. L. Hammond
A. Hayashi
G. A. Hedge
E. Herbert
D. J. Hoover
B. Hudson
J. M. Hutson
H. Ikawa
E. V. Jensen
R. Jewelewicz
V. C. Jordan
D. B. Jump
J. Kallos
M. Katz
J. Keller
K. Kikuchi
J. Kolena
L. C. Krey
R. W. Kuhn
J. Larner
W. W. Leavitt
S. E. Leeman
R. Levine
D. M. Linkie
H. Lipner
V. N. Luine
D. MacLaughlin
B. S. McEwen
M. Y. McGinnis
A. R. Means
G. W. Moll, Jr.
C. Monder

D. D. Moore
I. Mowszowicz
W. Moyle
M. Mudgett-Hunter
J. T. Murai
B. E. P. Murphy
M. Nadji
M. I. New
C. S. Nicoll
M. B. Nikitovitch-Winer
J. A. Nisker
J. M. Nolin
J. K. Northup
P. J. Olsiewski
J. H. Oppenheimer
K. G. Osteen
C. M. Paden
H. Papkoff
B. Parsons
J. R. Pasqualini
O. H. Pearson
E. J. Peck, Jr.
J. C. Penhos
A. J. Perlman
J. Pierce
S. R. Plymate
D. K. Pomerantz
S. H. Pomerantz
C. Pullin
B. M. Raaka
T. C. Rainbow
M. H. G. Raj
J. E. Rall
W. J. Raymoure

G. S. Richardson
H. J. Ringold
B. Robaire
J. L. Roberts
Z. Rosenwaks
A. K. Roy
M. Rush
M. Saffran
H. H. Samuels
K. Savard
C. T. Sawin
B. S. Schachter
C. Schwartz
N. B. Schwartz
J. Shapiro
D. Shields
P. K. Siiteri
M. D. Smigel
S. Solomon
S. W. Spaulding
F. Stanley
K. Sterling
S. Tamura
K. Tanabe
R. Trelstad
D. Tulchinsky
J. E. A. Tyson
N. Varsano-Aharon
M. D. Walker
T. H. Wise
K. Yoshinaga
E. A. Zimmerman
U. Zor

PREFACE

Despite much bewailing of current constraints on the financial support of biomedical research, the pace of progress continues to mount with unprecedented rapidity. This is due chiefly to the remarkable technological advances that have made available instruments and techniques for the rapid obtainment of precise, accurate, and reliable information. Methods are the unsung partners of ideas, but together they form the core of research.

Startling advances are now such commonplace phenomena that they tend to be taken for granted. Indeed, it is difficult to realize how rapidly progress is being made without reviewing the data of only a decade or two ago. This was especially evident in Elwood Jensen's Gregory Pincus Memorial Lecture, Receptors Reconsidered: A 20-Year Perspective, and was reemphasized throughout the remainder of the 1981 Laurentian Hormone Conference by the dazzling presentations of progress in a variety of other active fields of hormone research. The proceedings of that Conference constitute this thirty-eighth volume of *Recent Progress in Hormone Research*. Never has that title seemed more apt for this serial publication. What needs to be underscored is the word *"Recent."*

Lively discussions followed each formal presentation and appear in this volume as edited by each discussant. Those chairing each session were selected for their relevant expertise and served to keep the interchanges between speaker and discussant brief and on an even keel. For their services in this capacity we are indebted to Drs. Earl A. Zimmerman, James H. Clark, Murray Saffran, J. Edward Rall, John G. Pierce, Rachmiel Levine, Jack Oppenheimer, and Lutz Birnbaumer.

It is my pleasure to thank our executive secretary Miss Martha Wright for her unstinting labor throughout the year in arranging the Conference, tending to all the correspondence, and helping to make every aspect of the Conference an enjoyable and rewarding experience. Our gratitude goes also to Lucy Felicissimo and Linda Carsagnini for transcribing the discussion with amazing alacrity and to the staff of Academic Press for their friendly cooperation and expertise in the timely production of this volume.

Roy O. Greep

Errata
Recent Progress in Hormone Research, Volume 37

The Regulation of the Mammalian Corpus Luteum

I. ROTHCHILD

Page 188, line 10 *should read*: (Moore *et al.*, 1969; Stabenfeldt *et al.*, 1969; Pant *et al.*, 1978), and during more than 4 months in the roe deer (Hoffmann *et al.*, 1978).

Page 188, line 18: monestrous *should read*: polyestrous.

Receptors Reconsidered: A 20-Year Perspective[1]

ELWOOD V. JENSEN, GEOFFREY L. GREENE, LISELOTTE E. CLOSS,
EUGENE R. DESOMBRE, AND MEHRDAD NADJI[2]

*Ben May Laboratory for Cancer Research, The University of Chicago,
Chicago, Illinois*

I. Introduction

Largely because of the interest of Gregory Pincus, at the Laurentian Hormone Conference in 1961 we had the privilege of describing our early studies on the uptake and binding of radioactive steroidal estrogens to receptor substances in reproductive tissues. Although there had been earlier reports of the estrogen-binding phenomenon, both from our laboratory (Jensen, 1960; Jensen and Jacobson, 1960) and elsewhere (Glascock and Hoekstra, 1959), it was the presentation at the Laurentian Hormone Conference and its subsequent publication (Jensen and Jacobson, 1962) that served to awaken the interest of endocrinologists in studying estrogen–receptor interaction as an approach to the mechanism of steroid hormone action. Now, 20 years later, it is a special pleasure to deliver a lecture honoring the memory of Gregory Pincus, who was the founder of this Conference and to whom we are grateful for valuable encouragement and support during our early investigations of estrogen receptors.

In this Pincus Memorial Lecture I shall attempt to survey some of the progress toward understanding steroid hormone action that has resulted during the past two decades from experiments in which a radioactively labeled steroid has been employed to follow the course of its interaction with the target cell. I shall then describe the preparation and properties of specific antibodies to receptor proteins, which provide an alternative approach to receptor recognition and permit the application of immunochemical techniques for the study of steroid hormone receptors and their role in hormone action. For the most part, discussion will be limited to estrogen receptors and their antibodies, with the realization that much of the information discovered about estrogen receptors has had application to receptors for other classes of steroid hormones and, conversely,

---

[1] The Gregory Pincus Memorial Lecture.
[2] Department of Surgical Pathology, University of Miami, Miami, Florida.

1

studies of other hormone receptors have provided information of importance in the better understanding of estrogen receptors and their function.

II. Receptor Recognition by Hormone Binding

A. EARLY STUDIES OF HORMONE BINDING IN TARGET TISSUES

The original discovery of steroid hormone receptors and essentially all information concerning their interaction and function in target cells have depended on experiments in which a radioactive steroid serves as a marker for the receptor protein to which it binds. That the female reproductive tissues, such as uterus, vagina, and anterior pituitary, contain a characteristic estrogen-binding component (estrophilin) was first indicated by their striking ability to take up and retain tritiated hexestrol (Glascock and Hoekstra, 1959) and estradiol (Jensen and Jacobson, 1960) after the administration of physiological doses of these substances to immature animals (Fig. 1). It is now recognized that most if not all mam-

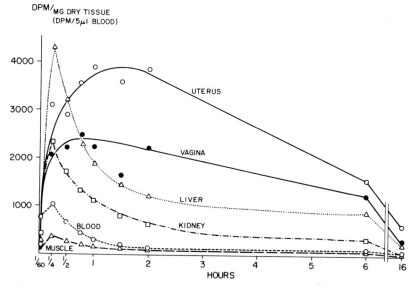

FIG. 1. Selective uptake and retention of tritiated estradiol by reproductive tissues. Concentration of radioactivity in dried tissues of 23-day-old rats after single subcutaneous injection of 98 ng (11.5 mCi) [6,7-³H]estradiol in 0.5 ml saline. Blood data plotted as dpm/5 μl. Radioactivity incorporation patterns paralleling that of blood were observed in bone, adrenal, ovary, lung, diaphragm, hypothalamus, and cerebrum (Jensen and Jacobson, 1960).

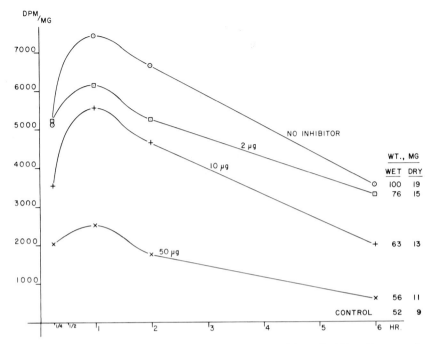

FIG. 2.   Inhibition of estradiol binding and uterine growth by nafoxidine. Concentration of radioactivity in dried uterine tissue of 23-day-old rats after single subcutaneous injection of 40 ng (7.3 μCi) [6,7-^{3}H]estradiol in 0.5 ml saline. Some animals were also given varying amounts of nafoxidine by intraperitoneal injection in 0.1 ml glycerol 30 minutes before the estradiol. For growth experiments, nonradioactive estradiol (50 ng) and different amounts of nafoxidine were administered in the same manner daily on the twenty-third through the twenty-seventh day of life, and the uteri excised and weighed on day 28 (Jensen, 1965).

malian tissues contain small amounts of estrogen receptor, and that the unique characteristic of the hormone-dependent tissues is the magnitude of their estrophilin content. Despite extensive metabolic transformation of estradiol by the liver and the presence in the blood of free as well as conjugated metabolites, estradiol was found to combine reversibly with the receptor and initiate growth of the immature rat uterus without itself undergoing chemical change (Jensen and Jacobson, 1962), suggesting that the action of the hormone involves its influence on macromolecules rather than participation in reactions of steroid metabolism as had once been assumed.

The specific uptake and retention of estradiol by target tissues are inhibited by a class of estrogen antagonists (clomiphene, nafoxidine, Parke-Davis CI-628, tamoxifen) which are themselves very weak estrogens but which prevent the uterotrophic action of the natural hormone. The correlation observed between the reduction in hormone incorporation and the inhibition of uterine growth when different amounts of nafoxidine were administered along with estradiol to the immature rat first provided evidence that binding of hormone to receptor actually is involved in its biological action (Fig. 2). In contrast, actinomycin-D and puromycin, substances found to prevent uterine growth response to estradiol (Mueller *et al.*, 1961; Ui and Mueller, 1963), show no inhibition of the uptake and retention of estradiol (Jensen, 1965), suggesting that the binding of hormone to the receptor is an early step in the uterotrophic process, initiating a sequence of biochemical events that can be blocked at later stages by inhibitors of RNA and protein synthesis.

After the uptake of estrogenic hormones by female reproductive tissues had been established in the living animal, it was found that similar affinity could be demonstrated *in vitro* (Stone and Baggett, 1965; Jungblut *et al.*,

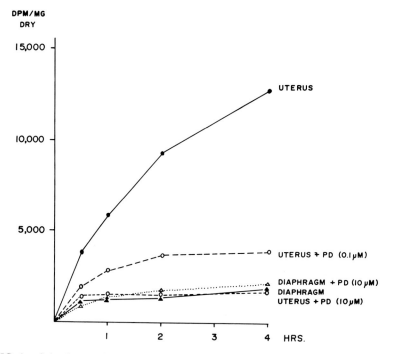

FIG. 3. Selective uptake of estradiol by rat uteri *in vitro*. Tritium levels in slit uterine horns and hemidiaphragms of immature rats after exposure to 0.12 n*M* tritiated estradiol (57 Ci/mmol) at 37°C in Krebs–Ringer–Henseleit glucose buffer, pH 7.3, in the presence of different concentrations of the estrogen antagonist Parke-Davis CI-628 (PD) (Jensen *et al.*, 1972a).

1965; Terenius, 1966). When excised target tissues are exposed to dilute solutions of tritiated estradiol at physiological temperature *in vitro*, an interaction of hormone with receptor takes place that shows all the characteristics of that observed *in vivo*, including sensitivity to inhibitors and, as found later, formation of the same estradiol–receptor complexes that are produced *in vivo*. As indicated in Fig. 3, estrogen antagonists such as nafoxidine or Parke Davis CI-628 provide a useful means of distinguishing the specific binding of hormone to receptor from the nonspecific binding that estradiol shows with all tissues under *in vitro* conditions. These observations not only provided simplified systems for studying the effect of various reagents on hormone–receptor interaction, but they set the stage for extensive investigations in many laboratories of the reaction of steroid hormones with components of broken cell preparations.

B. ESTROGEN–RECEPTOR INTERACTION

The biochemical mechanism by which the reaction of estradiol and other estrogenic hormones with receptor substances elicits hormonal response has been the subject of extensive investigation. Complete documentation of the accumulated information related to this subject is beyond the scope of this report. Considered here are the principal observations that led to the formulation of the currently accepted two-step pathway of intracellular interaction, illustrated schematically in Fig. 4,

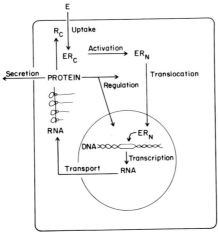

FIG. 4. Schematic representation of the estrogen interaction pathway and biochemical responses in target cells. The hormone (E) enters the cell and binds to an extranuclear receptor protein (Rc), inducing its conversion to an activated form (Rn) that is bound in the nucleus where the hormone–receptor complex enhances the production of preribosomal and messenger RNAs involved in the synthesis of constituent and/or secreted proteins.

along with some of the uncertainties and deficiencies in our knowledge that call for further investigation, perhaps by novel experimental approach. More extensive discussion with detailed references to specific reports can be found in the many reviews on this subject (Jensen and DeSombre, 1972, 1973; O'Malley and Means, 1974; O'Malley and Schrader, 1976; Gorski and Gannon, 1976; Yamamoto and Alberts, 1976; Jensen, 1978; Muldoon, 1980).

It is generally accepted that estrogens, as well as other classes of steroid hormones, enter their respective target cells and associate with an extranuclear receptor protein, inducing its conversion to a new form that has marked affinity for chromatin, DNA, and other polyanions. The "activated" steroid–receptor complex is "translocated" to the nucleus where it binds to chromatin and in some way modulates RNA synthesis, which appears to be characteristically restricted in hormone-dependent tissues. This two-step interaction pathway (Fig. 4) was originally developed for the immature rat uterus, a tissue in which most (70–80%) of the incorporated estrogen becomes localized in the nucleus but which before exposure to hormone contains essentially all its specific binding capacity in the cytosol fraction of a tissue homogenate.

Progress toward an understanding of the intracellular pathway of estrogen–receptor interaction was greatly enhanced when Toft and Gorski (1966) introduced the technique of sucrose density gradient ultracentrifugation for detecting and characterizing estradiol–receptor complexes. For the first time it was possible to go beyond the mere demonstration of binding and to identify estrophilin by a specific property, its sedimentation coefficient. In sucrose gradients of low ionic strength, the hormone in the cytosol fraction of uterine homogenates from rats receiving a physiological dose of tritiated estradiol was found to sediment as a discrete band (Toft and Gorski, 1966), originally considered to be 9.5 S but later shown to be closer to 8 S (Fig. 5). It was then observed that in gradients of higher ionic strength (0.3–0.4 M KCl) the 8 S complex is reversibly dissociated into a 4 S binding subunit (Erdos, 1968; Korenman and Rao, 1968), which, by careful sedimentation in salt-containing sucrose gradients can be differentiated (Jensen *et al.*, 1969) from the 5 S estradiol–receptor complex extracted by salt solutions from the uterine nuclei of estrogen-treated rats (Jungblut *et al.*, 1967; Puca and Bresciani, 1968). This small difference in sedimentation properties provided the first criterion for recognizing the phenomenon of receptor activation. Another technique that has proved of great value in receptor localization studies is dry-mount autoradiography, developed by Stumpf and Roth (1966) and used as a complement to centrifugal fractionation of homogenates to establish the relative amounts of nuclear and extranuclear binding in target cells (Stumpf, 1968, 1969).

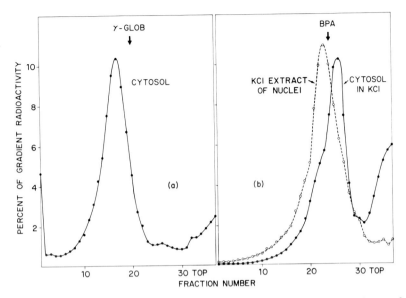

FIG. 5. Sedimentation patterns of radioactive estradiol–receptor complexes of rat uterine cytosol and nuclear extract (400 mM KCl) from uteri of immature rats excised 1 hour after the subcutaneous injection of 100 ng (20.8 μCi) tritiated estradiol in saline. To saturate its receptor capacity, the cytosol fraction was made 5 nM with additional tritiated estradiol. γ-GLOB and BPA indicate respective positions of bovine immunoglobulin (7.0 S) and bovine plasma albumin (4.6 S) markers. Gradients are: (a) 10 to 30% sucrose without added salt; (b) 5 to 20% sucrose containing 400 mM KCl (Jensen and DeSombre, 1973).

Some of the observations leading to and supporting the concept of the two-step activation mechanism of estradiol–receptor interaction are listed in Table I. A relation between nuclear and extranuclear estrogen binding was first suggested by observations that a given dose of nafoxidine *in vivo* inhibits cytosol and nuclear incorporation to the same degree (Jensen *et al.*, 1967a) and that more radioactivity is bound to isolated uterine nuclei when they are incubated with tritiated estradiol in uterine cytosol than in buffer alone (Brecher *et al.*, 1967). When it was found that there is a difference in saturability between the initial uptake of estradiol by the rat uterus *in vivo* and its longer term retention (Jensen *et al.*, 1967a) and that the 8 S extranuclear complex can be produced in surprisingly large amounts by adding the hormone directly to uterine cytosol (Jungblut *et al.*, 1967; Toft *et al.*, 1967) it was suggested that the extranuclear 8 S protein might serve as an uptake receptor, bringing the hormone to the nucleus where it is retained in limited amount by a nuclear receptor (Jensen *et al.*, 1967b). Shortly thereafter it was proposed that the nuclear receptor actually is an altered form of the cytosol receptor that has be-

TABLE I

Evidence for Extranuclear Origin of Nuclear Receptor Complex

Equal inhibition by nafoxidine of nuclear and extranuclear binding	*In vivo*
Difference in saturability of uptake vs retention	*In vivo*
Cytosol dependence of nuclear complex formation	*In vitro*
Hormone-induced depletion of cytosol receptor	*In vivo* and *in vitro*
Temperature-dependent intracellular redistribution	*In vitro*
Hormone-induced, temperature-dependent conversion of cytosol receptor to nuclear form	*In vitro*
Enhanced binding to nuclei by activated cytosol receptor	*In vitro*
Tissue-specific effect of activated or nuclear complex on RNA synthesis	*In vitro*
Immunochemical similarity between nuclear and cytosol complexes	*In vivo* and *in vitro*

come associated with the nucleus (Gorski *et al.*, 1968; Jensen *et al.*, 1968). This translocation hypothesis was based on three further observations: (1) when excised rat uteri are exposed to estradiol solutions at 37°C, most hormone becomes localized in the nucleus, but at 2°C the estradiol is predominantly extranuclear, shifting to the nucleus as the tissue is warmed to physiological temperature; (2) the characteristic 5 S complex, extractable from uterine nuclei of rats injected with tritiated estradiol, can be produced by treating isolated uterine nuclei directly with estradiol but only if uterine cytosol containing 8 S receptor is also present; and (3) less total 8 S complex is produced on adding excess tritiated estradiol to uterine cytosol from rats injected with a large dose of tritiated estradiol than from those receiving a smaller dose suggesting hormone-induced depletion of extranuclear receptor. As further evidence of receptor depletion resulting from transfer to the nucleus, the progressive diminution and subsequent restoration of cytosol receptor content after a physiological dose of hormone was described (Jensen *et al.*, 1969; Sarff and Gorski, 1971).

With the finding that warming uterine cytosol in the presence but not the absence of estrogenic hormone causes the gradual conversion of the hormone–receptor complex from a 4 S to a 5 S form (Jensen *et al.* 1971b; Gschwendt and Hamilton, 1972) and that this "transformed" complex, like that extracted from uterine nuclei of estradiol-treated animals, has a greatly increased affinity for nuclei (Jensen *et al.*, 1972b), chromatin (McGuire *et al.*, 1972) and DNA (Milgrom *et al.*, 1973), it was recognized that the temperature-dependent process involved in nuclear localization of estradiol in whole tissues is the hormone-induced conversion of the 4 S binding unit of the native cytosol receptor to an activated form that can bind in the nucleus. Although the exact molecular basis of receptor activation remains to be elucidated, detailed studies of this phenomenon indicate that the 5 S complex is a dimer of a modified form of the native 4 S receptor (Little *et al.*, 1975; Notides *et al.*, 1975, 1981). The importance of receptor transformation or activation, as it is now generally called, in the biological action of the hormone was emphasized by observations that the stimulation of RNA polymerase activity in isolated uterine nuclei, previously observed after incubation with estradiol–cytosol mixtures (Raynaud-Jammet and Baulieu, 1969), could be elicited by the activated 5 S form of the estradiol–receptor complex but not by the native 4 S form (Mohla *et al.*, 1972). The importance of nuclear binding of estradiol in biological action has since been demonstrated in experiments showing that full uterotrophic response requires the continued presence of estrogen–receptor complex in the nucleus for a period of several hours (Gorski and Raker, 1974; Anderson *et al.*, 1975).

More recently it was found that monoclonal antibodies raised against the nuclear form of calf uterine estrophilin react with the cytosol form (Greene *et al.*, 1980a), whereas antibodies generated against the extranuclear receptor of MCF-7 human breast cancer cells recognize the nuclear receptor of reproductive tissues from many species (Greene *et al.*, 1980b). Though immunochemical similarity does not prove that the nuclear receptor actually is derived from extranuclear estrophilin, the observed cross reactivity is consistent with this concept.

C. UNRESOLVED PROBLEMS

Despite the variety of experimental evidence on which the formulation of the two-step translocation mechanism is based and the large amount of subsequent experimental data consistent with this concept, there are certain observations suggesting that the interaction of estrogens and other steroid hormones with their target cells may be more complex than implied by the simple scheme of Fig. 4. Moreover, there are many aspects of hormone–receptor interaction and subsequent biological response for which our understanding is deficient and the elucidation of which may require experimental approaches different from those now commonly used.

Among the challenging questions is the intracellular location of the "extranuclear" receptor that appears in the cytosol of tissue homogenates. Although nuclei of the immature rat uterus show little if any specific estrogen-binding components before hormone treatment, in certain other tissues, such as rat pituitary tumor (Sonnenschein *et al.*, 1976), MCF-7 human breast cancer cells (Zava and McGuire, 1977), and chick and toad liver (Mester and Baulieu, 1972; Ozon and Belle, 1973), the nuclei contain substantial amounts of unoccupied estrophilin, even before exposure to hormone. Also it has been reported (Shao *et al.*, 1975) that it is the nucleus and not the cytoplasm of vaginal epithelium cells that contains a specific receptor for 5-androstene-3β,17β-diol, a C_{19} steroid that elicits an estrogen-like effect in this tissue. Earlier autoradiographic evidence that the radioactive steroid incorporated by rat uteri on exposure to tritiated estradiol at 2°C *in vitro* is mostly extranuclear (Jensen *et al.*, 1968) has recently been challenged on the basis of similar autoradiographic studies in which binding in the cold appeared to be predominantly nuclear (Sheridan *et al.*, 1979). These and other findings suggest that the native receptor may be distributed throughout the target cell, possibly freely diffusible among various liquid compartments until hormone-induced conversion to the activated form causes its fixation in the nucleus. The amount of estrophilin recovered in the cytosol fraction of a homogenate may depend on the ease of extraction from the nuclear compartment of that particular tissue as well as the experimental conditions used for homogenization. To resolve these uncertainties, which do not invalidate the two-step translocation mechanism but may suggest some modification or refinement, there is need for a method of receptor detection that does not depend on the labeled steroid which causes perturbation of the intracellular distribution pattern.

A related question, unresolved at present, is where in the target cell does receptor activation occur. The fact that hormone-induced conversion of native estrophilin to the nuclear form can be effected in the absence of nuclei does not preclude the possibility that, in the living cell, this process takes place preferentially in the nucleus, either from the interaction of the hormone with native receptor already present in the nuclear compartment or from 4 S complex originating in the cytoplasm and diffusing through the nuclear envelope more readily than would the larger 5 S complex. The finding of both 4 S and 5 S complexes in the nuclei of immature rat uteri shortly after exposure to estradiol *in vivo* or *in vitro* with progressive increase in the proportion of 5 S complex (Linkie and Siiteri, 1978), as well as observations that DNA increases the rate of the activation process (Yamamoto and Alberts, 1972), suggest that in the intact cell receptor activation may be a nuclear event. Although the enhanced affinity of the activated receptor for chromatin has been considered responsible for the accumulation of steroid–receptor complex in the nucleus, this simple concept does not explain the finding that the ratio of nuclear to extranuclear binding, either *in vivo* (Jensen *et al.*, 1967a; Williams and Gorski, 1972) or *in vitro* (Gannon *et al.*, 1976), remains constant over a wide range of estradiol concentrations. If, as indicated by the saturability of nuclear retention in rat target cells by hyperphysiological doses of estradiol *in vivo* (Jensen *et al.*, 1967a; Anderson *et al.*, 1975), the number of nuclear acceptor sites that bind activated complex is limited, one would expect the ratio of extranuclear to nuclear steroid to increase at higher hormone doses where most of the acceptor becomes occupied. To explain these observations it has been proposed (Gannon *et al.*, 1976) that accumulation of estrogen–receptor complex in the nucleus may not result simply from the selective affinity of the chromatin for activated estrophilin but from a "cytoplasmic exclusion" process in which excluded solute is distributed in accordance with the volume of intracellular solution to which it has free access.

Although it appears that regulation of target cell function by estrogens results in large part from the association of an activated steroid–receptor complex with the genome, the nature of the acceptor site where the complex binds in the nucleus and the molecular basis for the resulting enhancement of gene function remain obscure. The conclusion from early studies that nuclear estradiol is associated with chromatin (King *et al.*, 1966; Maurer and Chalkley, 1967; Teng and Hamilton, 1968) is generally accepted, but the precise location of this binding is still uncertain. Indications from nuclear fractionation experiments that estradiol is bound in the nucleolus (Arnaud *et al.*, 1971; Bieri-Bonniot *et al.*, 1977) are at variance with autoradiographic studies that show no evidence of nucleolar localization of hormone (Stumpf, 1969). The number of estradiol–receptor complexes translocated to the nucleus by a physiological dose of hormone has been variously estimated as 6000 (Anderson *et al.*, 1975), 10,000 (Mulvihill and Palmiter, 1977), and 14,000 (Jensen *et al.*, 1971b), a finding that is not consistent with a concept of a limited number of acceptor sites involved in the regulation of a few specific genes. It has been suggested that many of the hormone–receptor complexes in the nucleus may be bound nonspecifically (Yamamoto and Alberts, 1975) and that there may be a rate-limiting transfer of receptor from initial, nonproductive binding sites to the actual productive sites in the chromatin (Palmiter *et al.*, 1976). Treatment of rat uterine nuclei with micrococcal nuclease indicates that estradiol–receptor complexes may be bound in two regions of the chromatin, one associated with nu bodies and the other with a portion of chromatin that is digested by the nuclease (Senior and Frankel, 1978), but the contribution of either site to biological action remains to be elucidated.

Studies of the intracellular interactions of estrogen antagonists illustrate the complex nature of the effect of receptors on nuclear processes. Though it was first assumed that these substances exert their antiuterotrophic effects simply by competing for the receptor (Figs. 2 and 3), it was later found that, like estradiol, these antagonists form complexes with the receptor that are translocated and bound in the nucleus (Rochefort *et al.*, 1972; Clark *et al.*, 1973; Ruh and Ruh, 1974; Katzenellenbogen and Ferguson, 1975). This nuclear interaction appears to differ somehow from that which takes place when estradiol is associated with the receptor, for only a small degree of growth is induced, and the replenishment of cytosol receptor that ordinarily follows its depletion with estradiol is not seen with nafoxidine (Clark *et al.*, 1974). The growth response induced by nafoxidine and similar compounds is seen principally in the uterine epithelium, with greater antagonistic activity observed in the stroma and myometrium (Clark and Peck, 1979). It has been suggested that complex of the receptor with antiestrogen binds to a different acceptor site in the nucleus than does the estradiol–receptor complex (Ruh and Baudendistel, 1978; Gardner *et al.*, 1978), but little is known as to how the sites differ. Understanding of the interaction of estrogen–receptor complexes in the nucleus is further complicated by observations that, in addition to the originally observed 5 S receptor extracted from the nuclei of rat uteri exposed to estradiol *in vivo* or *in vitro*, there is another type of binding substance in the nucleus which has higher capacity but lower affinity for estradiol and which is induced by estradiol treatment (Eriksson *et al.*, 1978; Markaverich and Clark, 1979). Despite the fact that the affinity of these "type II" binders is such that few would be occupied by physiological concentrations of estradiol, there is evidence to suggest that their level in the nucleus is more closely related to actual uterine growth than are the classical type I sites.

While the use of radioactive steroid as a marker for the receptor protein has furnished a wealth of information about the biochemical pathway by which estrogenic hormones interact with target cells to become incorporated into the nucleus, it has told us relatively little about how the hormone leaves the cell and what happens to the receptor after its biological action is complete. There is evidence that at least some of the nuclear receptor returns to the cytoplasm and recycles, inasmuch as the replenishment of cytosol receptor in rat uterus that follows its initial depletion after estradiol administration (Jensen *et al.*, 1969; Sarff and Gorski, 1971) is only partially inhibited by cycloheximide (Mester and Baulieu, 1975; Cidlowski and Muldoon, 1978). In the case of certain short acting estrogens, such as 2-hydroxyestradiol (Martucci and Fishman, 1979) or estradiol-16α (Kassis and Gorski, 1981), replenishment is extremely rapid, and, in the latter case, the entire restoration of the cytosol receptor level is cycloheximide-insensitive and appears to be due to recycling. Studies with MCF-7 cancer cells have shown that estrophilin can leave the nucleus by another mechanism that leads to loss of receptor activity and which has been called "receptor processing" (Horwitz and McGuire,

1978a). This processing step, which is inhibited by actinomycin-D (Horwitz and McGuire, 1978b), appears to be involved in biological action as indicated by the synthesis of progesterone receptor; translocation of receptor to the nucleus as a complex with an antiestrogen such as nafoxidine or tamoxifen is not followed by receptor processing, nor is the synthesis of progesterone receptor induced (Horwitz and McGuire 1978c, 1980).

D. HORMONE DEPENDENCY OF BREAST CANCER

In addition to furnishing nearly all our current information about hormone–receptor interaction in target cells, the use of labeled steroid as a marker for the receptor protein has had important clinical application in the selection of therapy for advanced breast cancer. It has long been known that some human breast cancers are hormone-dependent, in that they undergo striking regression when deprived of supporting hormone by removal of the ovaries (Beatson, 1896), adrenals (Huggins and Bergenstal, 1952), or pituitary (Luft and Olivecrona, 1953; Pearson et al., 1956), or on altering the hormonal milieu by the administration of androgens (Nathanson, 1952), large doses of estrogen (Haddow et al., 1944), or antiestrogens such as tamoxifen (Cole et al., 1971; Ward, 1973). For those patients who respond, endocrine manipulation by either ablative or additive means represents the best treatment now available for advanced breast cancer. However only 25–30% of the patients have tumors of the hormone-dependent type, so there has been need for a means to distinguish these individuals, who are favorable candidates for endocrine therapy, from the larger group whose cancers are unresponsive to hormonal treatment and who should be placed directly on chemotherapy.

Soon after the original demonstration of estrogen-binding components in female reproductive tissues, it was found that breast cancers of patients who respond favorably to adrenalectomy take up more radioactivity after the parenteral administration of tritiated hexestrol than do tumors in unresponsive patients (Folca et al., 1961). It was also shown that experimental mammary tumors in the rat resemble uterus in their uptake of tritiated estradiol (King et al., 1965; Jensen, 1965) and that the small proportion of tumors that continue to grow in the ovariectomized animal take up much less radioactive hormone than do the majority of the tumors, which are hormone-dependent and regress after ovariectomy (Mobbs, 1966).

With the development of techniques for the study of estrogen–receptor interaction in vitro, it became possible to determine the estradiol uptake and later the estrophilin content in excised specimens of breast cancer and to correlate these results with response of the patient to endocrine therapy. The initial finding (Jensen *et al.*, 1971a) that breast cancers show-ing low estrogen binding or lacking cytosolic estrogen receptor rarely respond to endocrine therapy, whereas most but not all patients with receptor-containing tumors receive objective benefit from such treatment, was soon confirmed and extended by other investigators (Maass *et al.*, 1972; Engelsman *et al.*, 1973; Leung *et al.*, 1973, Savlov *et al.*, 1974; McGuire *et al.*, 1975). As the sensitivity of methods for the detection and estimation of estrophilin was improved, it became apparent that many breast cancers that previously would have been considered to lack recep-tor actually contain low levels of this protein. The clinical correlation data in Fig. 6 show clearly that tumors with low but definite estrophilin content rarely respond to endocrine therapy and should be classified with those lacking detectable receptor. We have found it helpful to replace the earlier classification of receptor-positive and receptor-negative with the terms

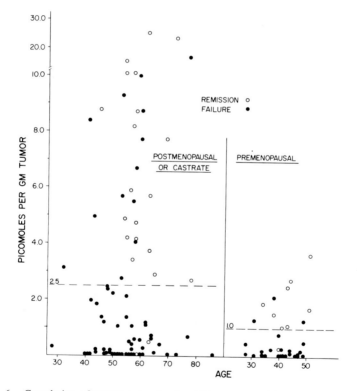

FIG. 6. Correlation of tumor cytosol estrophilin content with response to endocrine therapy for 133 patients with advanced breast cancer. Estrophilin was determined by sedimentation analysis of tumor cytosol using 0.5 n*M* tritiated estradiol, and results were corrected to total binding capacity as described elsewhere (Jensen *et al.*, 1976).

"receptor-rich" and "receptor-poor," with a dividing line determined empirically on the basis of clinical experience (Jensen *et al.*, 1976; Jensen, 1981). This critical estrophilin level appears to be lower in patients with ovarian function, probably because they produce more endogenous estrogen that masks some of the receptors.

As illustrated in Table II, approximately two-thirds of the patients with receptor-rich cancers in our study responded objectively to one or another type of endocrine ablation, in contrast to very few remissions in the receptor-poor group (Jensen *et al.*, 1976; Jensen, 1981). The results with additive hormonal therapy are similar except the rate of response among the receptor-rich group is slightly lower. Of all the primary and metastatic breast cancer specimens we have examined, most contain some detectable estrophilin but only one-third contain a sufficient level to be classified as receptor-rich. Because the estrogen receptor assay predicts clinical response correctly in approximately two-thirds of the patients with receptor-rich tumors and in essentially all of those in the receptor-poor group, the overall accuracy is approximately 85%.

The failure of one-third of the patients with receptor-rich cancers to respond to endocrine therapy is probably due in some cases to tumor heterogeneity and in others to the fact that receptor may be present but nonfunctional. It has been suggested (Horwitz *et al.*, 1975) that determining the tumor content of progesterone receptor, which in normal reproductive tissues is known to depend on estrogenic stimulation and thus on functioning estrophilin, might serve to identify tumors with functioning receptor. Subsequent experience has shown that breast cancers that contain substantial amounts of both estrogen and progesterone receptors show a significantly higher response rate, so that measuring both recep-

TABLE II

Objective Remissions to Endocrine Ablation[a]

	Tumor classification	
Treatment	Receptor-rich	Receptor-poor
Adrenalectomy	4/6	0/20
Adrenalectomy plus oophorectomy	14/19	1/17
Hypophysectomy	2/4	0/9
Castration	9/12	1/30
Total: 117 cases	29/41	2/76
	71%	3%

[a] Values are number of patients with remission/total patients in that group.

tors can increase the accuracy of the predictive assay (McGuire, 1978). However, some cancers with high levels of both receptors still do not benefit from hormonal therapy, while many containing only estrogen receptor do respond. At the present state of knowledge, progesterone receptor assay can complement but not substitute for estrogen receptor determination.

In many patients with metastatic breast cancer, assay of hormone receptors is precluded by the lack of a readily accessible tumor specimen. Preliminary findings in our laboratory indicate that an estrogen receptor analysis of the primary tumor, carried out at the time of mastectomy, will predict response to subsequent endocrine therapy if metastatic disease appears at a later time (Block *et al.*, 1978; DeSombre and Jensen, 1980). It was also shown that the estrophilin content of the primary tumor provides valuable information as to the probability and rapidity of recurrence of metastatic disease (Knight *et al.*, 1977). In patients with comparable lymph node involvement, receptor-rich primary tumors show less frequent recurrence with a longer disease-free interval than do receptor-poor primary tumors. Thus, as a guide to both prognosis and therapy there is general consensus that determination of estrogen receptors, and when possible progesterone receptors as well, be carried out on all patients with primary as well as metastatic breast cancer (DeSombre *et al.*, 1979).

Unfortunately, the present methods for estrophilin measurement are not well suited to routine analysis on a large scale. All methods now in use depend on the radioactive steroid as a marker for the receptor protein, and these have several inherent disadvantages. Especially in premenopausal or estrogen-treated patients, some of the receptors in the tumor may be occupied with nonradioactive estrogen and remain undetected (Fig. 6), unless an exchange procedure is carried out. The binding of steroid to receptor, though strong, is noncovalent, and the radioactive marker is subject to displacement by dissociation, by exposure to heavy metal ions, or by degradation of the labile receptor protein during storage and manipulation of the specimen. The two analytical procedures most commonly used for separating the receptor-bound steroid from the excess unbound hormone (sucrose gradient ultracentrifugation and Dextran-coated charcoal with Scatchard plot) are costly in terms of laboratory time and instrumentation and usually require a tumor specimen larger than may be available, especially with metastatic cancers. Thus, there is need for analytical procedures that are simpler, more accurate, and less expensive and sensitive to error than those now in use. As described in the next section, the preparation of monoclonal antibodies to estrophilin of human origin should provide immunochemical assay procedures that have significant advantages over current methods.

III. Receptor Recognition by Specific Antibodies

As described in the foregoing section, current procedures for the detection, measurement, and study of estrogen receptors in normal and malignant tissues all depend on the binding of a radioactively labeled steroid. Valuable as these techniques have been, there has been need for other means of detecting receptor protein that do not depend on the binding of hormone and which may provide a novel approach to some of the unresolved problems of the biochemical mechanism of estrogen action and to the simplified analysis of receptor in breast cancers. Specific antiestrophilin antibodies that recognize the receptor whether or not it is complexed with hormone provide such an approach.

A. POLYCLONAL ANTIBODIES TO ESTROPHILIN

After several years work by many collaborators in our laboratory, we developed a procedure for purifying the nuclear form of the estradiol–receptor complex of calf uterus to yield a product with about 20% of the specific radioactivity expected for a pure complex containing one molecule of tritiated estradiol for each molecule of receptor protein. This material proved immunogenic in rabbits (Greene *et al.*, 1977) and a goat (Greene *et al.*, 1979), when administered by an intradermal procedure (Vaitukaitis *et al.*, 1971). The antibodies obtained were found to react with extranuclear as well as nuclear estrophilin from calf uterus and also with estrogen receptor from reproductive tissues and tumors from every animal species tested, including the nonmammalian tissue, hen oviduct (Table III). Similar crossreacting antibodies have been produced in rabbits or sheep immunized with partially purified preparations of trypsin-treated

TABLE III

Cross Reactivity of Rabbit i-Ig with Estrophilin of Various Species

Receptor	Tissue	Species
Nuclear	Uterus	Calf, rat, rabbit, sheep
	Breast cancer	Human, MCF-7 cell
	Endometrial tumor	Rat
	Pituitary tumor	Rat
Cytosol	Uterus	Calf, rat, rabbit, sheep, mouse, guinea pig, monkey
	Oviduct	Monkey, hen
	Breast cancer	Rat, human, MCF-7 cell
	Endometrial tumor	Rat
	Pituitary tumor	Rat

estradiol–receptor complex of calf uterine cytosol (Radanyi *et al.*, 1979) or the cytosol complex from rat mammary tumor (Al-Nuaimi *et al.*, 1979) or human myometrium (Coffer *et al.*, 1980). Thus, there appears to be a common antigenic determinant that is conserved across a wide variety of animals species. Reactivity is specific for estrogen receptors; our antibodies show no tendency to react with androgen or progesterone receptors from various sources.

Although the interaction of estrophilin with these antibodies does not require the presence of estrogen, the antibody does not prevent the binding of hormone to receptor, so the radioactive steroid can serve as a convenient marker for the association of receptor with antibody. Because of the antiestrophilin antibodies thus far obtained all form nonprecipitating immune complexes, the usual immunodiffusion gel precipitation methods are not applicable, although double antibody precipitation techniques, as well as the binding of the estradiol–receptor complex to Sepharose-linked antibody or to immobilized *Staphylococcus aureus* protein-A in the

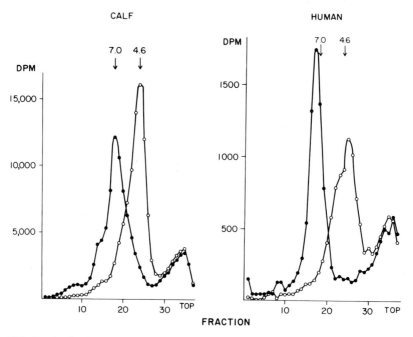

FIG. 7. Antibody–receptor interaction demonstrated by increase in sedimentation rate of estradiol–receptor complex (E*R). Sedimentation patterns in 10 to 30% sucrose/400 m*M* KCl gradients of calf uterine cytosol and human breast cancer cytosol, each containing tritiated estradiol, in the presence of immunoglobulin from an immunized (●) or control (○) rabbit (Greene *et al.*, 1977).

presence of the antibody, can be used to detect the presence of antiestrophilin in immune serum or immunoglobulin preparations (Greene *et al.*, 1977). A convenient criterion for demonstrating antiestrophilin antibodies is their ability to increase the size of the soluble estradiol–receptor complex, as evident either by an acceleration of its elution on gel filtration or an increase in its rate of sedimentation on ultracentrifugation in a sucrose gradient.

The sucrose gradient sedimentation technique has proved especially informative in detecting these antibodies and in recognizing different patterns of interaction with receptors. The nonprecipitating immune complexes formed usually consist of one molecule of immunoglobulin associated with each receptor protein molecule, as indicated by the shift in the sedimentation constant of the tritiated estradiol–receptor complex (E^*R) of calf uterine cytosol from 4 S to 7.5–8 S (Fig. 7) in the presence of immunoglobulin from an immunized animal (i-Ig) but not from a control animal (n-Ig). In some instances more than one immunoglobulin molecule appears to associate with each receptor, as in the reaction of rabbit i-Ig with the nuclear form of estrophilin from many species (Greene *et al.*, 1977). Similarly goat i-Ig causes a much greater shift in the sedimentation peak of E^*R from calf uterus as compared to that from other species (Greene *et al.*, 1979), suggesting that this immunoglobulin preparation contains antibodies that recognize an antigenic determinant characteristic of the calf uterine estrophilin used as the immunogen, as well as the determinant that appears to be common to estrophilin from all species.

B. MONOCLONAL ANTIBODIES TO ESTROPHILIN

The hormone specificity and crossreactivity of the antiestrophilin antibodies generated in the rabbit or the goat against estradiol–receptor complexes of calf uterus make them attractive as probes for studying receptor structure and function and as reagents for immunochemical purification, assay, and intracellular localization of receptors. For many of these purposes, however, the usefulness of these antibody preparations is limited by their heterogeneity. To obtain antiestrophilin uncontaminated by other immunoglobulins, we have employed the technique of Köhler and Milstein (1975), as modified by McKearn *et al.* (1979), to obtain monoclonal hybridoma cell lines secreting specific antibodies to estrophilin.

1. Monoclonal Antibodies to Calf Uterine Estrophilin

When hybridization of mouse myeloma cells with lymphocytes of an immunized rabbit proved unsuccessful, a Lewis rat was immunized with partially purified calf uterine receptor and its splenic lymphocytes fused with cells of three different myeloma lines, (P3-X63-Ag8, P3-NSI/1-Ag4-1, and Sp2/0-Ag14) to yield proliferating hybridomas in over half (485/912) of the original microtiter wells (Greene *et al.*, 1980a). Nearly 10% of the derived hybridoma lines (44/485) secreted antiestrophilin antibody as determined by double antibody precipitation, using goat anti-Lewis rat immunoglobulin with crude nuclear E*R from calf uterus as the labeled antigen. Hybrid lines were successfully derived from all three mouse myeloma lines, although the P3 and NSI myelomas produced more viable hybrids than did the Sp2/0. However, hybridomas from the Sp2/0 myeloma have the advantage that this line does not synthesize any mouse myeloma immunoglobulin (Shulman *et al.*, 1978), so the antibody secreted by Sp2/0 hybridomas is entirely that derived from the rat lymphocytes.

Several of the hybrids, including lines derived from all three myeloma mutants, were cloned by limiting dilution. About 15% of the total wells (79/528) produced viable clusters of hybridomas, and approximately 70% of these proliferating clones (56/79) secreted antiestrophilin. Several of the clones were expanded in suspension culture, producing milligram amounts of rat immunoglobulin. Viable antibody-secreting hybridomas have been recovered after storage in liquid nitrogen for at least 6 months.

Three of the expanded antiestrophilin-secreting clones, all derived from the Sp2/0 myeloma, were found to secrete rat IgG of the γ2a subclass (Bazin *et al.*, 1974). Seven additional expanded clones, derived from all three myeloma lines, were found to secrete IgM. The monoclonal i-IgG, like the original Lewis rat i-Ig, reacts with either the 4 S cytosol or 5 S nuclear E*R of calf uterus to produce 8 S immune complexes, whereas i-IgM formed complexes sedimenting at 12–13 S with both cytosol and nuclear E*R (Fig. 8). Monoclonal antiestrophilin of the IgG class shows comparable affinity for both the cytosol and nuclear forms of calf uterine estrophilin, whereas the IgM antiestrophilin reacts preferentially with the nuclear receptor, so higher antibody concentrations must be employed to demonstrate reaction with cytosol E*R. These monoclonal antibodies do not interfere with the binding of estradiol to the Ig–receptor complex, as demonstrated by postlabeling (with E*) fractions from sucrose gradients containing unoccupied receptor and either IgG or IgM.

By inclusion of [^{35}S]methionine in the culture medium of an IgG-secreting hybridoma clone, we have obtained radiolabeled antiestrophilin, recognized by sedimentation of the isotope at 7 S (Fig. 9). When treated with an excess of calf nuclear E*R, the sedimentation peak of the [^{35}S]IgG is completely shifted to the 8–9 S region, along with that portion of the excess E*R that reacted. This observation, as well as the fact that, on repeated cloning, antiestrophilin antibody is produced by 100% of the

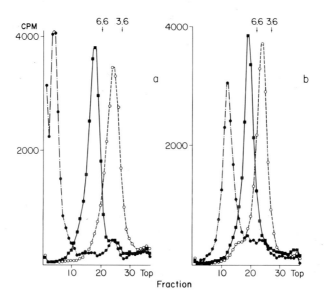

FIG. 8. Reaction of monoclonal IgG and IgM with calf uterine estrophilin. Sedimentation pattern in sucrose gradients containing 400 mM KCl of E*R (0.6 pmol) from: (a) calf uterine cytosol (10–30% sucrose) and (b) calf uterine nuclei (10–50% sucrose), in the presence of Lewis rat n-Ig (○), 20 μg clonal i-IgG (■), or clonal i-IgM (●), 200 μg in (a) and 20 μg in (b) (Greene *et al.*, 1980a).

recloned cultures, indicates that the hybridoma cell lines obtained are actually monoclonal. Biosynthetic labeling with [^{35}S]methionine is a convenient means of preparing radioactive antiestrophilin that is especially useful for identifying gel electrophoresis bands that correspond to receptor or receptor fragments.

Like the total i-IG from the serum of the parent Lewis rat, the monoclonal antiestrophilin antibodies secreted by all these hybridoma cell lines were found to react specifically with estrogen receptors from calf tissues but not with receptors from other species. Thus, these monoclonal antibodies provide useful reagents for investigations with calf uterine estrophilin, but they cannot be used for the study of receptors in target tissues of other species, in particular for the assay of estrophilin in human breast cancers. For that reason attention was directed toward the preparation of antibodies raised against estrogen receptor from human sources.

2. Monoclonal Antibodies to Human Estrophilin

Development of an improved affinity chromatography procedure, using a novel adsorbent (Greene *et al.*, 1980b) and a combination of dimethylformamide (Musto *et al.*, 1977) and sodium thiocyanate (Sica and Bres-

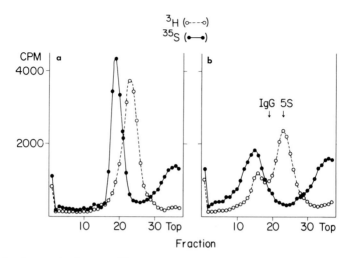

FIG. 9.   Interaction between ^{35}S-labeled monoclonal antiestrophilin and excess calf nuclear E*R. Sedimentation pattern in 10 to 30% sucrose gradient containing 400 mM KCl of nuclear calf uterine E*R (O) and a limiting amount of monoclonal [^{35}S]IgG (●): (a) in separate tubes and (b) after incubation together for 1 hr at 4°C. The arrows in (b) indicate the sedimentation positions of E*R (5 S) and labeled IgG (7 S) corresponding to the peaks in (a) (Greene *et al.*, 1980a).

ciani, 1979) to facilitate elution from the column, made possible the use of MCF-7 human breast cancer cell cytosol as a source of purified receptor for immunization. The adsorbent, which consists of estradiol linked the Sepharose 6B via a substituted di-*n*-propyl thioether bridge in the 17α-position of the steroid, has a high capacity for uncomplexed estrophilin of either calf uterus or MCF-7 cells, binding as much as 10 nmol of receptor per ml of packed adsorbent. In a typical purification sequence, 630 ml of cytosol from a homogenate of MCF-7 cells, containing 7.3 nmol of receptor, was passed through a 2-ml column of adsorbent. The column retained 79% of the available estrophilin. Elution with E* in the presence of 10% dimethylformamide and 0.5 M sodium thiocyanate, following by removal of excess reagents by gel filtration, gave partially purified E*R that sedimented at 3.5 S in salt-containing sucrose gradients and as a mixture of 3.5 S and 7 S components in low-salt gradients. The recovery of receptor ranged from 40 to 50% (90% in one experiment), and purification factors approaching 1000-fold could be achieved in a single step. Receptor purity was generally 5 to 10% of the specific radioactivity expected for one E* bound to a receptor protein of M_r about 65,000.

Serum from a male Lewis rat immunized with this partially purified estradiol–receptor complex contained antiestrophilin antibodies that reacted not only with nuclear and extranuclear E*R from MCF-7 cells, but with estrophilin from human, monkey, calf, and rat uterus, hen oviduct, and human breast cancers (Table IV). The interaction of these antibodies with estrophilin was detected and characterized both by sucrose density gradient centrifugation and by double-antibody precipitation, using E* as a marker for the receptor. The interaction of Lewis rat antiserum with cytosol E*R from MCF-7 of cells and human breast cancers increased its sedimentation rate in salt-containing sucrose gradients from 3.5 S to a broad band at 10–12 S (Fig. 10), suggesting that the serum contains a mixture of antibodies recognizing different determinants in the human estrophilin molecule. Where tested, the rat antiserum reacted with nuclear and cytosol forms of estrophilin from other animal species to give 8 S immune complexes.

Splenic lymphocytes from the rat immunized with purified receptor from MCF-7 breast cancer cells were fused with cells of two different mouse myeloma lines (P3-X63-Ag8 and Sp2/0-Ag14) to yield hybridoma cultures (Greene et al., 1980b). Virtually all of the P3 and 22% of the Sp2/0 microtiter wells contained proliferating hybridomas, approximately 2% of which initially secreted antiestrophilin antibody, as determined by double antibody precipitation with crude cytosol E*R from MCF-7 cells as the labeled antigen. Of five hybridoma lines selected for cloning, three were successfully cloned and recloned by limiting dilution and expanded in suspension culture to produce milligram quantities of monoclonal antibody (Table IV). The line derived from the Sp2/0 myeloma, (D547Spγ, secreting IgG2a) has been grown repeatedly in athymic mice to produce ascitic fluid containing more than 500 times the concentration of antibody present in suspension culture medium. Because 8 to 9 ml of fluid can be

TABLE IV

Reactivity[a] of Rat Antiserum and Monoclonal Antibodies

	Receptor source						
	Breast cancer		Uterus				Oviduct
Antibody	MCF-7[b]	Human	Human	Monkey	Calf[b]	Rat	Hen
Rat serum	+	+	+	+	+	+	+
D58P3μ	+	+	+	+	+	+	−
D75P3γ	+	+	+	+	−	−	−
D547Spγ	+	+	+	+	+	+	−

[a] Reactivity determined by effect on sedimentation of E*R complex, confirmed in some instances by double antibody precipitation.

[b] Cytosol and nuclear E*R tested; others cytosol only.

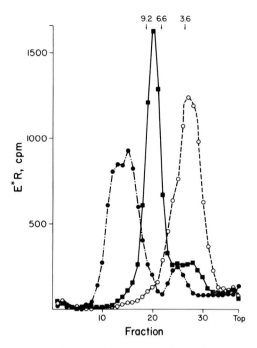

FIG. 10.   Sedimentation profiles in 10–30% sucrose/400 mM KCl gradients of E*R (0.5 pmol) from human breast cancer cytosol in the presence of 25 μg of Lewis rat n-Ig (○), 25 μg of D547Spγ monoclonal IgG (■), or 10 μl of Lewis rat antiserum (●) (Greene *et al.*, 1980b).

collected from one mouse over a period of several days, this system provides an efficient source of monoclonal antiestrophilin. When expanded in athymic mice, the two P3-derived hybridomas (D58P3μ, secreting IgM; and D75P3γ, secreting IgG2a) lost the ability to produce functional antibody, although they continued to yield antiestrophilin in suspension culture. By repeated cloning of D75P3γ a more stable hybridoma line has been obtained that apparently no longer synthesizes the heavy chain of mouse immunoglobulin. After storage in liquid nitrogen, viable antibody-producing hybridomas have been recovered from all three lines. The IgG2a antibodies react with cytosol E*R from human breast cancer (Fig. 10) and with cytosol and nuclear E*R from other sources to give 8 S immune complexes in salt-containing sucrose gradients, whereas the IgM antibodies interact with cytosol and nuclear E*R to form immune complexes sedimenting at 18–19 S.

Whereas the serum of the rat contained antibodies that reacted with estrophilin from all sources tested including hen oviduct, none of the isolated monoclonal antibodies derived from its spleen cells recognized

cytosol receptor from hen oviduct. All three monoclonal antibodies recognized cytosol receptor from human breast cancer and from human and
monkey uterus. When tested against receptor from calf and rat uterus,
interesting differences in crossreactivity among the three monoclonal antibodies were observed. For Sp2/0-derived clone (D547Spγ), the titer of
the secreted IgG was found to be considerably lower against calf and rat
receptor than against MCF-7 receptor, although in the presence of excess
antibody complete reaction with calf and rat estrophilin takes place. In
contrast, the IgG from the P3-derived clone (D75P3γ) shows little if any
affinity for calf or rat estrophilin, whereas the IgM antibody (D58P3μ)
crossreacts strongly with receptor from all mammalian species tested.
Each of the three monoclonal antibody preparations appears to recognize
a different antigenic determinant in the human receptor molecule. Any
combination of two of these monoclonal antibodies reacts additively with
estrophilin MCF-7 cytosol as indicated by an additional displacement of
the sedimentation peak when the second antibody is added (Fig. 11).

The foregoing findings indicate that, in addition to the common antigenic determinant(s) recognized by rabbit and goat antiestrophilin and

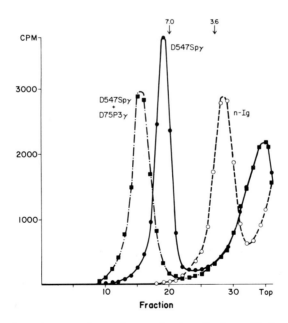

FIG. 11. Independent reactions of monoclonal antibodies with human estrophilin.
Sedimentation profiles in 10–50% sucrose gradients containing 400 mM KCl of MCF-7 cell
cytosol E*R (0.5 pmol) in the presence of 50 μg of Lewis rat n-Ig (○), 40 μg D547Spγ clonal
IgG (●), or 40 μg D547 IgG followed by 50 μg D75 IgG (■).

the calf-specific determinant recognized by the monoclonal antibodies generated against calf receptor, there is a determinant in mammalian estrophilin that is not present or available in hen receptor. They also suggest that there may be determinants characteristic of primate receptor that are either absent or modified in estrophilin from calf or rat uterus. The availability of an assortment of antiestrophilin antibodies with different specificities should provide valuable tools for investigating similarities and differences among estrophilins of different animals species.

The monoclonal antiestrophilin antibodies can be readily prepared in radioactive form, either by chemical labeling with ^{125}I or biosynthetically by growing the hybridoma cells in culture medium containing [^{35}S]methionine. They should prove useful in the purification of receptor proteins by immunoadsorption; for the precise localization of receptors in target cells, before and after translocation to the nucleus, by a combination of immunocytochemical and electron microscopic techniques; and as a new approach to some of the unsolved problems of estrogen–receptor interaction discussed earlier. Experiments in many of these areas are now underway in our laboratory. The remainder of this presentation will concentrate on an important practical use of these antibodies in the immunoradiometric and immunocytochemical estimation of estrogen receptors in human breast cancers.

C. IMMUNORADIOMETRIC ASSAY OF ESTROPHILIN

As discussed earlier, determination of estrogen receptors in human breast cancers provides valuable clinical information as a guide to prognosis and therapy, but when applied on a routine basis, the assay methods currently available leave much to be desired. Immunochemical analysis using monoclonal antibodies should overcome many of these difficulties.

Because each of the three preparations of monoclonal antibodies to human estrophilin recognizes a different antigenic determinant on the receptor molecule, a combination of two such antibodies can be used in a sandwich technique for the immunoradiometric (IRMA) or enzyme-linked immunosorbent (ELISA) determination of estrophilin in tissue extracts. In this procedure, illustrated schematically in Fig. 12, one antibody serves to immobilize the receptor on a supporting surface, such as a polystyrene bead, and a second antibody, suitably labeled, is used to measure the amount of receptor bound to the first antibody. We have found that an especially favorably combination is one in which D547Spγ is used as the adsorbing antibody (ab$_1$) and D75P3γ, labeled either with ^{125}I or with peroxidase enzyme, serves as the marker (ab$_2$). When different amounts of MCF-7 cell cytosol, containing tritiated estradiol as label for the recep-

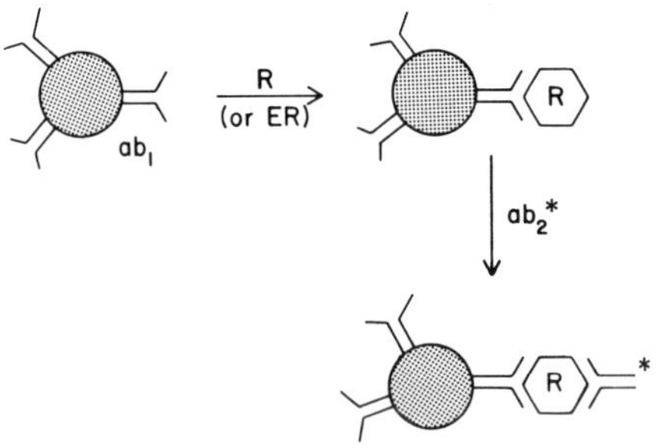

FIG. 12. System for the immunochemical determination of estrogen receptors. A polystyrene bead, coated with one monoclonal antiestrophilin preparation, (D547Spγ) adsorbs the unoccupied (R) or occupied (ER) receptor from the tissue or tumor extract. The receptor thus bound adsorbs a second monoclonal antibody (D75P3γ) which has been labeled (*) either with ^{125}I for immunoradiometric assay (IRMA) or with an enzyme that serves as the basis for a colorimetric assay (ELISA).

tor protein, are analyzed by this IRMA system, the amount of ^{125}I-labeled second antibody bound is directly proportional to the amount of receptor added over a large range. Using the tritiated estradiol–receptor complex of MCF-7 cells as a calibrating reference, a series of 18 human breast cancer cytosols was analyzed by the IRMA procedure and the results compared with those obtained with the same cytosols by the sucrose gradient sedimentation procedure. As seen in Fig. 13, the agreement between the two procedures appears to be good, although confirmation with a much larger series of patients is necessary before complete confidence in the immunometric procedure can be established. Commercial development of this assay procedure is now underway, and it is hoped that, before long, a simple diagnostic kit will be available that will permit the determination of estrophilin on breast cancers with high accuracy, low cost, and without the need for hospitals or clinics to ship their tumor specimens to a central analytical facility.

D. IMMUNOCYTOCHEMICAL DETECTION OF ESTROPHILIN

Though a simple immunoradiometric method for the determination of estrogen receptors in breast cancer cytosols offers many advantages over procedures now in use, there is one difficulty inherent in any biochemical assay: the problem of knowing whether the sample taken for analysis is truly representative of the tumor as a whole. The availability of monoclonal antiestrophilin antibodies suggests the possibility of employing an immunocytochemical procedure, such as the immunoperoxidase technique (Sternberger, 1974), to obtain an indication of the receptor content

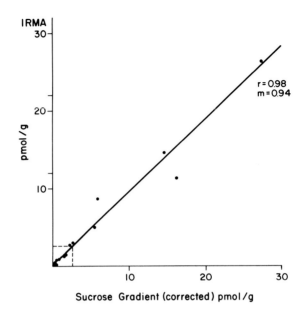

FIG. 13. The estrophilin contents of eighteen human breast cancer cytosols as determined by the IRMA technique, compared with the results obtained by sucrose gradient ultracentrifugation. In the sedimentation procedure, using 0.5 nM tritiated estradiol which does not saturate all the receptor, the results have been corrected to total binding capacity, under which conditions the distinction between receptor-rich and receptor-poor tumors in postmenopausal patients occurs at a level of 2.5 pmol per gram tumor (Fig. 6).

of the individual cancer cells as well as an estimate of the proportion of cancer cells in the tumor specimen.

Initial attempts, both in our laboratory and elsewhere, to identify estrophilin immunocytochemically in fixed or frozen sections of either uterus or breast tumor met with little success, possibly because the soluble immune complexes formed were easily extracted from the tissues. More recently we have found that the immunoperoxidase method employed at the University of Miami (Nadji, 1980) appears to work well with our antibodies and fixed sections of mammary tumors.

As illustrated in Fig. 14, the immunoperoxidase technique clearly shows the presence of extranuclear receptor in MCF-7 breast cancer cells. Exposure of the antibody solution to immobilized purified human receptor to preadsorb the antiestrophilin completely eliminates the extranuclear staining. Similar negative results are obtained when calf-specific monoclonal antibody, produced by hybridoma cells derived from the rat immunized with calf uterine receptor, is substituted for the D75P3γ antibody. Figure 15 illustrates the difference in staining between receptor-rich

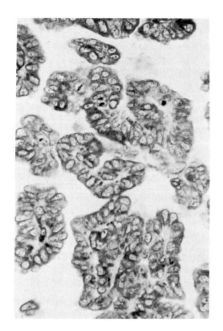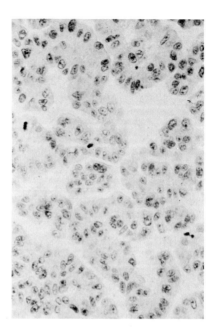

FIG. 14.   Immunocytochemical demonstration of estrophilin in MCF-7 cells. Confluent
MCF-7 cells were harvested from culture flasks, pelleted by centrifugation, and fixed in
Bouin fluid. Paraffin embedded sections (4 μm thick) were incubated (left) with D75P3γ or
(right) with D75P3γ previously adsorbed with estrophilin bound to an estradiol affinity
column, followed by goat antibody to rat IgG and finally rat peroxidase–antiperoxidase
complex (PAP). After staining with aminoethylcarbazole, sections were counterstained with
hematoxylin (Nadji *et al.*, 1982).

and receptor-poor human breast cancers, previously analyzed for estrophilin content by the sucrose gradient sedimentation procedure. Here
again, in contrast to the D547Spγ antibody, a calf-specific monoclonal
antibody failed to elicit any significant staining.

Although the foregoing results are still preliminary and correlation of
staining intensity with actual receptor levels remains to be established,
the immunoperoxidase technique using our monoclonal antiestrophilin antibodies promises to provide a useful system for the immunocytochemical
demonstration of estrogen receptor in individual cancer cells. A combination of quantitative immunoradiometric assay of estrophilin in breast
cancer cytosol with a semiquantitative immunocytochemical estimation of
the receptor content of individual cells should be an especially precise
way to characterize the receptor status of breast tumors. Preliminary
studies of 20 cases suggest that the immunocytochemical procedures may
have the further advantage of being applicable for the retrospective analy-

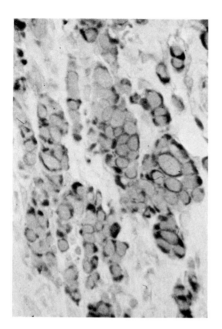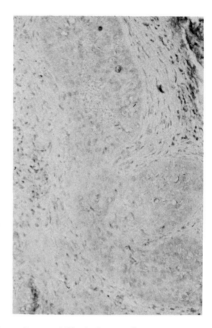

FIG. 15. Immunocytochemical demonstration of estrophilin in human breast cancers. Formalin fixed, paraffin-embedded sections (4 μm) of receptor-rich (left) and receptor-poor (right) human mammary infiltrating ductal carcinomas were incubated with D547Spγ IgG. Bound antibodies were visualized as described for Fig. 14. Estrogen receptor levels in these tumors were determined independently in fresh tumor cytosol by sucrose density gradient centrifugation with [^{3}H]estradiol (Nadji et al., 1982).

sis of fixed embedded primary tumors from patients who now have advanced disease with no accessible metastases and who did not have receptor analysis at the time of mastectomy.

IV. Summary

During the past 20 years our knowledge about estrogen receptors and their function in target cells has been gained largely from experiments in which the radioactively labeled steroid hormone serves as a marker for the receptor protein to which it binds. This approach has produced extensive information about the nature of receptor proteins and their intracellular interactions, as well as providing a valuable means of characterizing human breast cancers as a guide to prognosis and therapy. The recent preparation of specific antibodies to estrogen receptors and the development of hybridoma cell lines secreting various types of monoclonal antibodies to human and calf estrophilin represents a novel approach to problems that have resisted elucidation from hormone-binding techniques and promises to provide simple, improved assay procedures for the determination of estrogen receptors in breast cancer specimens.

During the past two decades endocrinologists have devoted an intense effort to hormone-binding studies, and no doubt this approach will continue to yield informative results. But in all probability the next decade will see a proliferating effort in immunoreceptorology furnishing information to complement that obtained from ligand receptorology, thus bringing us closer to a complete understanding of the mechanism of steroid hormone action, a subject that was dear to the heart of Gregory Goodwin Pincus.

ACKNOWLEDGMENTS

These investigations were supported by research grants from the American Cancer Society (BC-86) and Abbott Laboratories, by a research grant (CA-02897) and contract (CB-43969) from the National Cancer Institute, and by the Women's Board of the University of Chicago Cancer Research Foundation.

REFERENCES

Al-Nuaimi, N., Davies, P., and Griffiths, K. (1979). *Cancer Treat. Rep.* **63**, 1147.

Anderson, J. N., Peck, E. J., Jr., and Clark, J. H. (1973). *Endocrinology* **92**, 1488.

Anderson, J. N., Peck, E. J., Jr., and Clark, J. H. (1975). *Endocrinology* **96**, 160.

Arnaud, M., Beziat, Y., Guilleux, J. C., and Mousseron-Canet, M. (1971). *C. R. Acad. Sci. Paris, Ser. D* **272**, 635.

Bazin, H., Beckers, A., and Querinjean, P. (1974). *Eur. J. Immunol.* **4**, 44.

Beatson, G. T. (1896). *Lancet* ii, 104.

Bieri-Bonniot, F., Joss, U., and Dierks-Ventling, C. (1977). *FEBS Lett.* **81**, 91.

Block, G. E., Ellis, R. S., DeSombre, E., and Jensen, E. V. (1978). *Arch. Surg.* **188**, 372.

Brecher, P. I., Vigersky, R., Wotiz, H. S., and Wotiz, H. H. (1967). *Steroids* **10**, 635.

Cidlowski, J. A., and Muldoon, T. G. (1978). *Biol. Reprod.* **18**, 234.

Clark, J. H., and Peck, E. J., Jr..(1979). "Female Sex Steroids: Receptors and Function." Springer-Verlag, Berlin and New York.

Clark, J. H., Anderson, J. N., and Peck, E. J., Jr. (1973). *Steroids* **22**, 707.

Clark, J. H., Peck, E. J., Jr., and Anderson, J. N. (1974). *Nature (London)* **251**, 446.

Coffer, A. I., King, R. J. B., and Brockas, A. J. (1980). *Biochem. Int.* **1**, 126.

Cole, M. P., Jones, C. T. A., and Todd, I. D. H. (1971). *Br. J. Cancer* **25**, 270.

DeSombre, E. R., and Jensen, E. V. (1980). *Cancer* **46**, 2783.

DeSombre, E. R., Carbone, P. P., Jensen, E. V., McGuire, W. L., Wells, S. A., Jr., Wittliff, J. L., and Lipsett, M. B. (1979). *New Engl. J. Med.* **301**, 1011.

Engelsman, E., Persijn, J. P., Korsten, C. B., and Cleton, F. J. (1973). *Br. Med. J.* ii, 750.

Erdos, T. (1968). *Biochem. Biophys. Res. Commun.* **37**, 338.

Eriksson, H., Upchurch, S., Hardin, J. W., Peck, E. J., Jr., and Clark, J. H. (1978). *Biochem. Biophys. Res. Commun.* **81**, 1.

Folca, P. J., Glascock, R. F., and Irvine, W. T. (1961). *Lancet* ii, 796.

Gannon, F., Katzenellenbogen, B., Stancel, G., and Gorski, J. (1976). *In* "The Molecular Biology of Hormone Action" (J. Papaconstantinou, ed.), pp. 137–149. Academic Press, New York.

Gardner, R. M., Kirkland, J. I., and Stancel, G. M. (1978). *Endocrinology* **103**, 1583.

Glascock, R. F., and Hoekstra, W. G. (1959). *Biochem. J.* **72**, 673.

Gorski, J., and Gannon, F. (1976). *Annu. Rev. Physiol.* **38**, 425.

Gorski, J., and Raker, B. (1974). *Gynecol. Oncol.* **2**, 249.

Gorski, J., Toft, D., Shyamala, G., Smith, D., and Notides, A. (1968). *Recent Prog. Horm. Res.* **24**, 45.

Greene, G. L., Closs, L. E., Fleming, H., DeSombre, E. R., and Jensen, E. V. (1977). *Proc. Natl. Acad. Sci. U.S.A.* **74**, 3681.

Greene, G. L., Closs, L. E., DeSombre, E. R., and Jensen, E. V. (1979). *J. Steroid Biochem.* **11**, 333.

Greene, G. L., Fitch, F. W., and Jensen, E. V. (1980a). *Proc. Natl. Acad. Sci. U.S.A.* **77**, 157.

Greene, G. L., Nolan, C., Engler, J. P., and Jensen, E. V. (1980b). *Proc. Natl. Acad. Sci. U.S.A.* **77**, 5115.

Gschwendt, M., and Hamilton, T. (1972). *Biochem. J.* **128**, 611.

Haddow, A., Watkinson, J. M., and Patterson, E. (1944). *Br. Med. J.* **ii**, 393.

Horwitz, K. B., and McGuire, W. L. (1978a). *J. Biol. Chem.* **253**, 2223.

Horwitz, K. B., and McGuire, W. L. (1978b). *J. Biol. Chem.* **253**, 6319.

Horwitz, K. H., and McGuire, W. L. (1978c). *J. Biol. Chem.* **253**, 8185.

Horwitz, K. B., and McGuire, W. L. (1980). *J. Biol. Chem.* **255**, 9699.

Horwitz, K. B., McGuire, W. L., Pearson, O. H., and Segaloff, A. (1975). *Science* **189**, 726.

Huggins, C., and Bergenstal, D. M. (1952). *Cancer Res.* **12**, 134.

Jensen, E. V. (1960). *Proc. Int. Congr. Biochem., 4th, Vienna, 1958* **15**, 119.

Jensen, E. V. (1965). *Can. Cancer Conf.* **6**, 143.

Jensen, E. V. (1978). *Pharmacol. Rev.* **30**, 477.

Jensen, E. V. (1981). *Cancer* **47**, 2319.

Jensen, E. V., and DeSombre, E. R. (1972). *Annu. Rev. Biochem.* **41**, 203.

Jensen, E. V., and DeSombre, E. R. (1973). *Science* **182**, 126.

Jensen, E. V., and Jacobson, H. I. (1960). *In* "Biological Activities of Steroids in Relation to Cancer" (G. Pincus and E. P. Vollmer, eds.), pp. 161–178. Academic Press, New York.

Jensen, E. V., and Jacobson, H. I. (1962). *Recent Prog. Horm. Res.* **18**, 387.

Jensen, E. V., DeSombre, E. R., and Jungblut, P. W. (1967a). *Proc. Int. Congr. Hormonal Steroids, 2nd, Milan, 1966* pp. 492–500.

Jensen, E. V., DeSombre, E. R., Hurst, D. J., Kawashima, T., and Jungblut, P. W. (1967b). *Arch. Anat. Microsc. Morphol. Exp.* **56** (Suppl.), 547.

Jensen, E. V., Suzuki, T., Kawashima, T., Stumpf, W. E., Jungblut, P. W., and DeSombre, E. R. (1968). *Proc. Natl. Acad. Sci. U.S.A.* **59**, 632.

Jensen, E. V., Suzuki, T., Numata, M., Smith, S., and DeSombre, E. R. (1969). *Steroids* **13**, 417.

Jensen, E. V., Block, G. E., Smith, S., Kyser, K., and DeSombre, E. R. (1971a). *Natl. Cancer Inst. Monogr.* **34**, 55.

Jensen, E. V., Numata, M., Brecher, P. I., and DeSombre, E. R. (1971b). *Biochem. Soc. Symp.* **32**, 133.

Jensen, E. V., Jacobson, H. I., Smith, S., Jungblut, P. W., and DeSombre, E. R. (1972a). *Gynecol. Invest.* **3**, 108.

Jensen, E. V., Mohla, S., Gorell, T. A., and DeSombre, E. R. (1972b). *J. Steroid Biochem.* **3**, 445.

Jensen, E. V., Smith, S., and DeSombre, E. R. (1976). *J. Steroid Biochem.* **7**, 911.

Jungblut, P. W., Morrow, R. I., Reeder, G. L., and Jensen, E. V. (1965). *Meet. Endocrine Soc., 47th, New York* p. 56 (Abstr.).

Jungblut, P. W., Hätzel, I., DeSombre, E. R., and Jensen, E. V. (1967). *Colloq. Ges. Physiol. Chem.* **18**, 58.

Kassis, J. A., and Gorski, J. (1981). *J. Biol. Chem.* **256**, 7378.

Katzenellenbogen, B. S., and Ferguson, E. R. (1975). *Endocrinology* **97**, 1.

King, R. J. B., Cowan, D. M., and Inman, D. R. (1965). *J. Endocrinol.* **32**, 83.

King, R. J. B., Gordon, J., Cowan, D. M., and Inman, D. R. (1966). *J. Endocrinol.* **36**, 139.

Knight, W. A., Livingston, R. B., Gregory, E. J., and McGuire, W. L. (1977). *Cancer Res.* **37**, 4669.

Köhler, G., and Milstein, C. (1975). *Nature (London)* **256**, 495.

Korenman, S. G., and Rao, B. R. (1968). *Proc. Natl. Acad. Sci. U.S.A.* **61**, 1028.

Leung, B. S., Fletcher, W. S., Lindell, T. D., Wood, D. C., and Krippaehne, W. W. (1973). *Arch. Surg.* **106**, 515.

Linkie, D. M., and Siiteri, P. K. (1978). *J. Steroid Biochem.* **9**, 1071.

Little, M., Szendro, P., Teran, C., Hughes, A., and Jungblut, P. W. (1975). *J. Steroid Biochem.* **6**, 493.

Luft, R., and Olivecrona, H. (1953). *J. Neurosurg.* **10**, 301.

Maass, H., Engel, B., Hohmeister, H., Lehmann, F., and Trams, G. (1972). *Am. J. Obstet. Gynecol.* **113**, 377.

McGuire, W. L. (1978). *Semin. Oncol.* **5**, 428.

McGuire, W. L., Huff, K., and Chamness, G. C. (1972). *Biochemistry* **11**, 4562.

McGuire, W. L., Carbone, P. P., and Vollmer, E. P., eds. (1975). "Estrogen Receptors in Human Breast Cancer." Raven, New York.

McKearn, T. J., Fitch, F. W., Smilek, D. E., Sarmiento, M., and Stuart, F. P. (1979). *Immunol. Rev.* **47**, 91.

Markaverich, B. M., and Clark, J. H. (1979). *Endocrinology* **105**, 1458.

Martucci, C. P., and Fishman, J. (1979). *Endocrinology* **105**, 1288.

Maurer, H. R., and Chalkley, R. (1967). *J. Mol. Biol.* **27**, 431.

Mester, J., and Baulieu, E. E. (1972). *Biochim. Biophys. Acta* **261**, 236.

Mester, J., and Baulieu, E. E. (1975). *Biochem. J.* **146**, 617.

Milgrom, E., Atger, M., and Baulieu, E. E. (1973). *Biochemistry* **12**, 5198.

Mobbs, B. G. (1966). *J. Endocrinol.* **36**, 409.

Mohla, S., DeSombre, E. R., and Jensen, E. V. (1972). *Biochem. Biophys. Res. Commun.* **46**, 661.

Mueller, G. C., Gorski, J., and Aizawa, Y. (1961). *Proc. Natl. Acad. Sci. U.S.A.* **47**, 164.

Muldoon, T. G. (1980). *Endoc. Rev.* **1**, 339.

Mulvihill, E. R., and Palmiter, R. D. (1977). *J. Biol. Chem.* **252**, 2060.

Musto, N. A., Gunsalus, G. L., Miljkovic, M., and Bardin, C. W. (1977). *Endocr. Res. Commun.* **4**, 147.

Nadji, M. (1980). *Acta Cytol.* **24**, 442.

Nadji, M., Morales, A., Greene, G. L., and Jensen, E. V. (1982). (in press).

Nathanson, I. T. (1952). *Cancer* **5**, 754.

Noteboom, W. D., and Gorski, J. (1965). *Arch. Biochem. Biophys.* **111**, 559.

Notides, A. C., Hamilton, D. E., and Auer, H. E. (1975). *J. Biol. Chem.* **250**, 3945.

Notides, A. C., Lerner, N., and Hamilton, D. E. (1981). *Proc. Natl. Acad. Sci. U.S.A.* **78**, 4926.

O'Malley, B. W., and Means, A. R. (1974). *Science* **183**, 610.

O'Malley, B. W., and Schrader, W. T. (1976). *Sci. Am.* **234**, 32.

34 ELWOOD V. JENSEN ET AL.

Ozon, R., and Belle, R. (1973). *Biochim. Biophys. Acta* **297**, 155.
Palmiter, R. D., Moore, P. B., Mulvihill, E. R., and Emtage, S. (1976). *Cell* **8**, 557.
Pearson, O. H., Ray, B. S., Harrold, C. C., West, C. D., Li, M. C., MacLean, J. P., and Lipsett, M. (1956). *J. Am. Med. Assoc.* **161**, 17.
Puca, G. A., and Bresciani, F. (1968). *Nature (London)* **218**, 967.
Radanyi, C., Redeuilh, G., Eigenmann, E., Lebeau, M. C., Massol, N., Secco, C., Baulieu, E. E., and Richard-Foy, H. (1979). *C. R. Acad. Sci. Paris Ser. D* **288**, 255.
Raynaud-Jammet, C., and Baulieu, E. E. (1969). *C. R. Acad. Sci. Paris Ser. D* **268**, 3211.
Rochefort, H., Lignon, F., and Capony, F. (1972). *Biochem. Biophys. Res. Commun.* **47**, 662.
Ruh, T. S., and Baudendistel, L. J. (1978). *Endocrinology* **102**, 1838.
Ruh, T. S., and Ruh, M. F. (1974). *Steroids* **24**, 209.
Sarff, M., and Gorski, J. (1971). *Biochemistry* **10**, 2557.
Savlov, E. D., Wittliff, J. L., Hilf, R., and Hall, T. C. (1974). *Cancer* **33**, 303.
Senior, M. B., and Frankel, F. R. (1978). *Cell* **14**, 857.
Shao, T. C., Castaneda, E., Rosenfield, R. L., and Liao, S. (1975). *J. Biol. Chem.* **250**, 3095.
Sheridan, P. J. Buchanan, J. M., Anselmo, V. C., and Martin, P. M. (1979). *Nature (London)* **282**, 579.
Shulman, M., Wilde, C. D., and Köhler, G. (1978). *Nature (London)* **276**, 269.
Sica, V., and Bresciani, F. (1979). *Biochemistry* **18**, 2369.
Sonnenschein, C., Soto, A. M., Colofiore, J., and Farookhi, R. (1977). *Exp. Cell. Res.* **101**, 15.
Sternberger, L. A. (1974). "Immunocytochemistry." Prentice-Hall, New York.
Stone, G. M., and Baggett, B. (1965). *Steroids* **5**, 809.
Stumpf, W. E. (1968). *Endocrinology* **83**, 777.
Stumpf, W. E. (1969). *Endocrinology* **85**, 31.
Stumpf, W. E., and Roth, L. J. (1966). *J. Histochem. Cytochem.* **14**, 274.
Teng, C. S., and Hamilton, T. H. (1968). *Proc. Natl. Acad. Sci. U.S.A.* **60**, 1410.
Terenius, L. (1966). *Acta Endocrinol.* **53**, 611.
Toft, D., and Gorski, J. (1966). *Proc. Natl. Acad. Sci. U.S.A.* **55**, 1574.
Toft, D., Shyamala, G., and Gorski, J. (1967). *Proc. Natl. Acad. Sci. U.S.A.* **57**, 1740.
Ui, H., and Mueller, G. C. (1963). *Proc. Natl. Acad. Sci. U.S.A.* **50**, 256.
Vaitukaitis, J., Robbins, J. B., Nieschlag, E., and Ross, G. T. (1971). *J. Clin. Endocrinol. Metab.* **33**, 988.
Ward, H. W. C. (1973). *Br. Med. J.* **i**, 13.
Williams, D., and Gorski, J. (1972). *Proc. Natl. Acad. Sci. U.S.A.* **69**, 3464.
Yamamoto, K. R., and Alberts, B. M. (1972). *Proc. Natl. Acad. Sci. U.S.A.* **69**, 2105.
Yamamoto, K. R., and Alberts, B. M. (1975). *Cell* **4**, 301.
Yamamoto, K. R., and Alberts, B. M. (1976). *Annu. Rev. Biochem.* **45**, 721.
Zava, D. T., and McGuire, W. L. (1977). *J. Biol. Chem.* **252**, 3703.

DISCUSSION

S. Spaulding: This was a very beautiful presentation. I wonder whether you have performed any physiological histocytochemical studies utilizing the hybridoma-generated receptor antibodies to determine whether estrogen treatment does, in fact, cause translocation of cytoplasmic receptor to the nucleus?

E. V. Jensen: We have not done this as yet with the peroxidase technique. Earlier, before we were able to see any staining at all in tissue sections, Thomas Allen in our laboratory found that using fluorescent-labeled antibody he could demonstrate fluorescence in the extranuclear region of intact MCF-7 cells grown in the absence of estrogen. With cells that had been incubated with estradiol to translocate the receptor to the nucleus, Dr. Allen observed very little fluorescence in the cytoplasm. However, there was no appearance of fluorescence in the nucleus but only a narrow halo around the periphery of the nucleus. We interpreted these results to mean one of three things: (1) Though it appears that the antibody can enter the cytoplasm of MCF-7 tumor cells in culture, it may not be able to penetrate the nucleus; (2) association of the receptor with chromatin renders the antigenic determinant(s) unaccessible to the antibody; or (3) translocation of the activated estrogen–receptor complex actually does not occur into the nucleus but rather onto the nucleus. This will have to be sorted out, and I think we can do it better now with the immunoperoxidase technique where we are actually working on sections and the nuclei have been sliced through.

J. H. Clark: You mentioned the quantitative aspects of receptor assays earlier in your talk and implied that the antibodies to receptor would facilitate such measurements. It seems to me that saturation analysis with ^{3}H-labeled estrogens will still be necessary to derive quantitative data and that immunomethods can only give rough quantitative information. Would you care to comment on this point?

E. V. Jensen: The one figure with 18 breast cancers was an attempt to show that we are getting essentially the same quantitative results by the sucrose gradient assay and by the immunoradiometric assay for the cytosol. The immunocytochemical assay can only be semiquantitative; that is $1^+, 2^+$, etc. Empirically we will just have to get some kind of feeling for the different degrees of color. I suppose the pathologists will take this over from the biochemists.

J. H. Clark: I feel that it should be made clear that at this point in time one cannot differentiate biologically active receptor from inactive receptor by the antibody technique. Therefore, experiments on receptor synthesis and replenishment will have to be interpreted with caution. Investigators who use your antibody in such experiments will be obliged to demonstrate that the receptor which is measured by your method is capable of nuclear translocation and subsequent biological response.

E. V. Jensen: Of course we do not know for sure whether there may be inactivated receptor or even a proestrophilin that does not yet bind hormone but which still might have an antigenic determinant. How that might relate to clinical response will have to be established, though it seems to me that the final criterion will be how well the assays using the antibody correlate with the response of the patient. This is the same thing we had to do in the beginning for the ligand assays. You are certainly right; we can't make assumptions until correlations have been established.

P. K. Siiteri: I enjoyed your talk very much. As you well know with receptor binding assays we are plagued with the problem of tissue contamination by serum proteins and particularly the sex hormone binding globulin which binds estrogen in human serum. I was wondering whether you have in fact tested the immunocytochemical reagents against serum binding proteins?

E. V. Jensen: That is something we have not done as yet for the immunocytochemical test and something that should be done. We have tested the original polyclonal antibodies with these hormone-binding proteins and see no reaction at all. In other words, these antibodies don't seem to recognize the transport proteins in the way they recognize receptor. But you are certainly right; especially in the immunocytochemical technique we have to do more of these experiments as a safeguard.

G. S. Richardson: I wonder if the immunocytochemical techniques are going to tell us whether the tumors with intermediate levels of receptors are composed of cells some of which are receptor rich and which some have no receptor at all. In other words, are we looking at a situation in which there are tumors of mixed clonal nature in which some of the cells are simply not hormone-responsive? For example, when a patient has recurrent cancer after a period of hormonal response, are we seeing the growth of cells that by your test are going to turn out to be receptor-poor? Up to the present time we are usually told that receptor levels tend to be fairly consistent over periods of time. Do you have any forecast on that? Or do you have data already?

E. V. Jensen: We don't have many data. There are a few sections that Dr. Nadji has shown us where there are some cells that have a red halo around the nucleus and others that do not. Of course there will be some tumor specimens that will have normal cells and noncellular material in the sections as well as cancer cells, and we must depend on the pathologists to sort that out. I am sure there will be some tumor specimens that are polyclonal and will have receptor-containing and nonreceptor-containing cells in the same specimen. Whether this will be usual or exceptional is too early to tell. That is one of the attractive things about the immunocytochemistry, it enables one to examine the question of specimen heterogeneity, whereas in looking at the cytosol of a homogenized specimen, you are unaware of the actual composition of that tissue.

G. S. Richardson: The fact that breast cancers are often histologically different looking in different areas of the same tumor suggests they may also prove to show differences in your histochemical assay.

E. V. Jensen: I would agree.

L. E. Faber: There is an interesting paradox developing from work on the mammalian progesterone receptor, concerning the biological work from several laboratories suggesting that the preactivated 7 S complex may be biologically significant. For instance McGuire used the detection of the 7 S progesterone receptor as the end point in his breast cancer studies. Raynaud and his colleagues during the development of their super progestational agents, such as R5020, were able to correlate the biological potency of a synthetic progestin with the ability to bind in the 7 S complex. Finally in our laboratories we find that the hormone impedes the process of *in vitro* activation, and this occurs in relation to the biological potency of the progestin. All of these studies imply that the 7 S or larger forms of receptors are biologically important. Would you care to comment on this?

E. V. Jensen: What you call 7 S I guess our laboratory would call 8 S, whether it be with progesterone or R5020. Is this 7 S in a high salt gradient?

L. E. Faber: Low salt.

E. V. Jensen: In a low salt gradient it is hard to tell the difference between activated and nonactivated receptor in the estrogen case, because both the 4 S and the 5 S forms of the uterine receptor sediment at 8 to 9 S. For that reason we have depended on high salt gradients if we are going to use sedimentation to tell us anything about native and activated forms.

L. E. Faber: Have you used molybdate to study activation? I am thinking of the work of Bunzo Sato and the Osaka group where they were able to demonstrate that degradation of estrogen, glucocorticoid, and androgen receptors paralleled the process of *in vitro* activation.

E. V. Jensen: We use molybdate routinely now. This has been a valuable contribution. It has been shown by others that in the presence of molybdate activation does not take place. When you remove the molybdate the receptor can be activated. There is no question that molybdate is protecting the receptor against what may be a number of degradative steps.

L. E. Faber: Your answer then, is that you feel that experiments utilizing Tris gradients containing 300 mM KCl are biologically more relevant than experiments utilizing low salt gradients.

E. V. Jensen: In the case of estrogen receptor, we feel that high salt gradients are more informative in distinguishing between different forms of the receptor that can be correlated with different biological actions. Of course what we see in a high salt gradient, or in any gradient, may not represent the actual form of the receptor in the cell.

H. G. Friesen: I wonder if you could answer the question that Dr. Gordan posed 20 years ago at this meeting; namely, why are estrogen receptors apparently absent in normal mammary epithelial cells. With your immunocytochemical technique are the normal mammary epithelial cells positive or negative and if positive, how do they react in comparison to breast cancer cells.

E. V. Jensen: That is a good question that we ought to be able to answer soon. In the effort to obtain a practical immunoassay for breast cancers, we haven't done this as yet, but I would think that the immunocytochemical technique ought to provide an answer.

J. M. Nolin: Relative to this last point, maybe we could have a go at looking at estrogen receptor in normal breast tissue with one of your antiestrophilins since immunocytochemistry of the breast is a routine procedure in our laboratory. The question I want to ask is: in light of evidence that antiinsulin receptor and now, apparently, antiprolactin receptor, can in fact mimic the actions of the respective hormones, do you have any thoughts on, or perhaps plans to investigate, the possibility that antiestrophilin might mimic the action of estradiol?

E. V. Jensen: We have carried out two experiments in which the original rabbit antibody was administered to immature rats, either alone or with physiological doses of estradiol, to see whether the antibody itself had any uterotrophic properties or whether it could block the action of the hormone. In these experiments the antibody showed no effect whatsoever. Of course, unlike the insulin receptors which are in the plasma membrane, the estradiol receptors appear to be intracellular, and the immunoglobulin may not penetrate the uterine cell *in vivo*. These experiments should be repeated using the Fab fragments of the immunoglobulins, which, in the case of monoclonal antibodies, we have prepared labeled with [^{35}S]methionine, so one can actually determine if they get into the target cell.

J. M. Nolin: I hope you will do that experiment but may I remind you that some estrogen targets are unquestionably capable of immunoglobulin uptake into the cell. The target is one of them. Also, I might add that in situations involving antiprotein hormone receptor, high concentrations inhibit, but low concentrations can mimic, hormone action.

E. V. Jensen: The whole antibody had no biological effect that we can determine.

L. P. Bullock: I may have found a slight crack with the last question. Most of what you talked about focused on the various aspects of steroid actions mediated through the two-step mechanism of a soluble receptor and nuclear transfer. I am comfortable with this concept of steroid action. What I am bothered about, however, is the continuous trickle of information that I see regarding steroid–membrane interactions be they on the cell wall or intracellularly. Would you comment on what role you think this type of an interaction has in mediating steroid effects?

E. V. Jensen: This trickle of information that you refer to suggests that estrogens may have actions in target cells or maybe in cells in general, in addition to the receptor-mediated gene activation in the nucleus. The evidence is quite convincing that histamine release in response to estrogen action, whether it be from the target cell or from mast cells or eosinophils, may be involved in water imbibition and hyperemia, and that these phenomena probably do not involve the receptor mechanism. In regard to an action on the plasma membrane of the uterine or the mammary cell that results in some of the biological phenomena we associate with estrogens, I don't know. But I think we would do well to keep our minds open to these possibilities. The fact that we concentrate on the gene activation nuclear mechanism does not mean that we won't let ourselves be convinced by good evidence that other actions do exist.

H. C. Blossey: There are still 12% of the tumors that are receptor positive and do not respond to endocrine therapy and I think as far as I know from the literature it is very difficult to explain this phenomenon. Do you think it might be that due to the fact that the cancer cells are genetically altered, that they may produce a protein which binds specifically estrogens or steroids, generally, but does not function as a receptor?

E. V. Jensen: That is a possibility, and it would be interesting to test this now that one has a whole battery of antibodies recognizing different antigenic determinants. Perhaps the receptors of these recalcitrant patients may have a different spectrum of antibody recognition than the so-called normal receptors. However, I think one can explain these anomalous patients in two other ways. One is tumor heterogeneity. In those instances when we are able to get several metastases from the same patient, usually they are all receptor rich or receptor-poor, but occasionally one finds a patient that will have both receptor-rich and receptor-poor metastases. If the surgeon had given us only a receptor-containing metastasis to analyze, we would classify that patient receptor-rich, but because she also had receptor-poor metastases that are unresponsive to endocrine therapy, this patient will be a failure. Many of our so-called failures in the high receptor group do show what we call subjective remissions in which some of the metastases regress and others do not. So I do think tumor heterogeneity is one cause for nonresponding positives. On the other hand, I am convinced that some autonomous breast cancers synthesize estrophilin even though they don't need it. When a mammary cell escapes from hormone dependency, during neoplastic transformation or possibly at some later stage, usually that cell shuts down its synthesis of estrogen receptor. But, as was nicely shown by Gene DeSombre and Loretta Arbogast (*J. Natl. Cancer Inst.* **54**, 483, 1975) with DMBA-induced mammary tumors in the Sprague–Dawley rat, occasionally one finds an autonomous tumor, whose nuclei are insensitive to stimulation by estrogen–receptor complex, but which continues to produce substantial amounts of apparently superfluous estrophilin.

R. O. Greep: I saw a paper recently suggesting some similarity in steroid receptor content between normal and pathological tissue (IRCS, *J. Med. Sci.* **9**, 445, 1981).

E. V. Jensen: That I don't know. We have not worked with normal breast tissue, and we have not done much with neoplastic uterine tissue, although Gene DeSombre is now examining endometrial cancers in a study that I am not associated with. Certainly very few human breast cancers have a receptor content, either per unit of DNA or per gram of tissue, that even approaches that of immature rat uterus.

B. E. Murphy: You used the terms "ligand binding receptorology" and "ligand binding assay." Since the word "ligand" comes from the Latin *ligare* and means "something which is bound," it seems to me that you are just saying the same thing twice. Why not just say "ligand assay" or "ligand receptorology" rather than saying the same thing in two languages.

E. V. Jensen: Good suggestion; I can make my paper shorter now.

R. N. Andersen: Mohammad Eldeib, a graduate student working in my laboratory, is studying progesterone receptors in human uterine tissues. He has evidence of a 10 S progesterone receptor which upon binding ligand is converted to 8 S. Basically, he pulverizes his tissue under liquid nitrogen and prepares a 105,000 g cytosol with only minimal homogenization. If he does the usual sucrose density gradient analysis with prelabeling of the cytosol, he sees 4 S and 7.7 S receptor with endometrium. He has to include lupeptin in order to have very much 8 S from myometrium and fibroid. We were initially using protamine sulfate to try to do Scatchard analysis. Once we got curious as to what forms of receptor the protamine sulfate might precipitate, that is in terms of the S forms. He has found that it precipitates 4 S essentially not at all; it precipitates 8 S very poorly and the 10 S form somewhat better. The 10 S form of receptor is found only when cytosol is centrifuged on gradients without having included any exogenous steroid. In that situation he finds a big peak of 10 S, but in the cases where he has prelabeled with steroid, he sees only 7.7 or 4 S. This phenomenon is dose dependent. That is, he varied the dose of R5020 and showed increasing amounts of 8 S receptor proportional to the dose of R5020. He can only do a semiquantitative estimate of the 10 S form because the protamine sulfate does not precipitate it quantitatively. Hydroxylapatite will precipitate it quantitatively, but then he has the problem that there is 8 S present and the two are not completely resolved; one goes to fraction 16 and the other to 19 or 20. So they are well enough resolved that one can say they are different, but they are not resolved so well that one can quantify 10 S reliably following hydroxylapatite precipitation. The 10 S receptor demonstrates specific binding; excess radioinert R5020 completely displaces bound labeled R5020. Have you used your antibody system to look for larger molecular weight forms of estrogen receptors? Or do you have any data from your estrogen receptor work that would tend to confirm our finding with progesterone receptors?

E. V. Jensen: We have studied the reaction of our antibodies with both cytosol and nuclear receptors in low salt gradients as well as in high salt gradients. In low salt gradients the antibody causes a shift in the 8 S peak up to something like 10 or 11 S, but we have not looked to see if there is any difference whether or not steroid is bound to the receptor.

M. H. G. Raj: Dr. Jensen, I got the impression that all the antibodies that you have made thus far, including the monoclonal antibody, did not interfere with the estrogen binding receptor. Do you speculate whether it means that the estrogen binding site on the receptor does not fulfill the minimum requirements to being an immunologic determinant?

E. V. Jensen: I must admit that we have loaded the dice in favor of antibodies that don't interfere with the binding, because we use the binding of the labeled hormone as a marker when we screen to select clones that are making antiestrophilin antibody. If we had antibodies that prevent the binding, these clones would be considered negative. I think it is possible that there are antibodies that recognize determinants so close to the receptor site that they would interfere with binding, but we have not found these as yet.

M. H. G. Raj: Also, would you expect that only if you use an antibody that is directed toward the binding site, only such an antibody could be a blocking neutralizing antibody.

E. V. Jensen: I don't know. I think it possible that the antibody reacts with the receptor in such a way as to perturb its structure enough to weaken its binding ability. We do have evidence of this. I didn't mention that there is something interesting about the antibody raised against calf estrophilin in the goat. Not only does it recognize a common determinant, that appears to be present in receptors from all species, but in addition it seems to recognize something specific for calf estrophilin. With calf receptor the goat antibody shifts the sedimentation peak to 14 S rather than to 8 S the way it does with rat or rabbit uterine receptors. It is definite that the goat antibody but not the rabbit antibody lowers the affinity of the calf receptor for estradiol as indicated by the slope of a Scatchard plot in which antibody and receptor interact in the presence of different concentrations of estradiol (Greene *et al.*, 1979). It appears that if you put several antibody molecules on a single receptor, which usually does not happen, you may so perturb the protein structure that steroid binding will be weaker.

S. R. Glasser: When you assay your immunocytochemistry and give a score of 3+, are you scoring the intensity of an individual cell or do you introduce a factor for the number of cells staining versus the number of cells that are not staining in this subjective calculation?

E. V. Jensen: We have not reached that stage yet, although we shall have to face this question soon. All this is relatively recent. I just showed you examples of cancers with high receptor content and with very low receptor content. Dr. Nadji who runs the surgical pathology lab at the University of Miami, does have a formula that they use for other systems that looks as if it might be applicable here. We have not really settled on anything yet, but if we are going to do something semiquantitative we shall have to consider this point you raise.

S. R. Glasser: But at the present time considering those cells you already have scored would the one and two pluses fall in your category of receptor poor and the three and four pluses in your category of receptor rich?

E. V. Jensen: I showed one example of a cancer that was strongly receptor rich, and two cases that were essentially receptor negative. We shall have to examine a lot more specimens at all different receptor levels before we can come up with any kind of semiquantitative scoring.

O. H. Pearson: I can attest to the usefulness of the estrogen receptor in breast cancer specimens for the management of patients both in terms of predicting response to endocrine treatment as well as in prognosis. However, I think it has a limited value in terms of understanding what makes breast cancer grow, because there are tumors that have estrogen receptors, progesterone receptors; obviously estrogen gets in and it can initiate progesterone receptor synthesis and yet its growth has no relationship to taking estrogen away or giving an antiestrogen and this is very vividly true in the animal tumor models. So it seems to me that after 20 years we have only gotten to the first step, the binding of estrogen. The next step seems to me to find out how estrogens get into the nucleus and turn on a protein that stimulates mitogenesis. Is that what you think is happening, and if so, why don't we identify that protein that stimulates cell growth. Then we would have the marker that would tell us which tumors are responsive and which ones aren't?

E. V. Jensen: You are certainly right; we don't have all the answers yet, and in fact I would be willing to say we don't even have most of the answers. But I think you may be overly simplifying the situation by considering that there may be a single protein that is responsible for stimulating mitogenesis. I think most people working in the field would feel that what estrogen–receptor complex is doing is activating not just a single gene to make a single protein but is relieving a restriction on the function of many genes that are associated with the synthesis of messenger RNAs for many proteins as well as ribosomal RNA for the machinery to translate them.

O. H. Pearson: Yes, but that was the point. In other words, you can have all of this going on without any stimulation of growth. So there must be another factor, another protein that is made that turns on cell division and growth. Don't you think that must be the case?

E. V. Jensen: It may be. I don't know that it has to be the case, but I would agree that perhaps it is. I am sure there are many key factors we don't recognize, and perhaps this is an especially important one.

S. R. Plymate: Dr. Hurayamd has suggested that the level of sex hormonal binding globulin in the serum correlates well with response to antiestrogen therapy in breast cancer compared to the use of the estrogen receptor. We also have found a correlation between estrogen receptor levels and sex hormone binding globulin in some cancer patients. This would suggest that it is not just the estrogen receptor in the tumor but in other tissues as well, e.g., liver, that is determining the response to antiestrogen therapy. Do you have any data relating to this.

E. V. Jensen: I don't think it is the presence of receptor in the tumor that determines response to hormone therapy. I think the basis of hormone dependency lies in the nucleus, in some restriction on gene function imposed during differentiation. The presence or absence of the receptor is only an associated phenomenon; if the tumor is hormone dependent it must have the receptor so the hormone can work. However, just because the receptor is there doesn't mean that the tumor is dependent. As I mentioned earlier, the receptor can be there and yet the nucleus can get along fine without the estrogenic stimulation as apparently some autonomous rat mammary tumors do. Now the presence or the level of sex steroid binding globulin in the serum is interesting, and that again can be an associated phenomenon. All these may be an indication of the nature of something in the nucleus that presumably changes either during neoplastic transformation or sometime after the original tumor cells grow out.

RECENT PROGRESS IN HORMONE RESEARCH, VOL. 38

Steroid Hormones: Humoral Signals Which Alter Brain Cell Properties and Functions

Bruce S. McEwen, Anat Biegon, Paula G. Davis, Lewis C. Krey, Victoria N. Luine, Marilyn Y. McGinnis, Charles M. Paden, Bruce Parsons, and Thomas C. Rainbow

The Rockefeller University,
New York, New York

I. Introduction

That steroid hormones influence the brain to affect behavior has been known in principle since the experiments of Berthold (1849) examined the consequences of castration for sexual and aggressive behavior of the rooster. Beginning in the 1930s, the subject of hormonal influences on behavior developed into a systematic area of research, in large measure through the pioneering work and scholarship of Frank Beach, W. C. Young, and Daniel Lehrman (Beach, 1948; Young, 1961; Lehrman, 1964) and their colleagues and students. However, information about sites and mechanisms of hormone action in brain has been very recent in coming. So recent was our ignorance that in the early 1960s, almost concurrently with the publication of initial information about uterine estrogen receptors (Jensen and Jacobson, 1962), the late W. C. Young wrote the following analysis of knowledge about the mechanisms and sites of steroid hormone action on the brain responsible for the regulation of mating behavior:

> Little to nothing is known about the mechanisms whereby gonadal hormones stimulate mating behavior. At the molecular level the likelihood that such information will be revealed in the near future is not great. . . . Furthermore, the neural tissues mediating mating behavior have not been identified in the sense that attention can be directed to cells in which change or changes in response to hormonal stimulation could be correlated with the expression of sexual behavior. We suggest, however, that when the mechanism of hormone action has been worked out for the more accessible tissues, such as the uterine epithelium . . . , much of the knowledge will be applicable to the tissues mediating mating behavior (Young, 1961, p. 1204).

41

Therefore in 1981, when the progress of the steroid receptor field is reviewed by Jensen (this volume), it is gratifying that there should be an
opportunity to summarize the rapid increase in our knowledge of the
mechanism of steroid hormone action on neural tissue, which was nur-
tured by the steroid receptor story as it developed in "the more accessible" nonneural tissues.

During the 1960s and early 1970s, three types of experimentation
catalyzed the development of this area of research on the brain. First was
the use of crystalline hormone implants into particular brain regions to
mimic systemic hormone treatment (Harris *et al.*, 1958; Lisk, 1960, 1962;
Rodgers and Law, 1968; Chambers and Howe, 1968; Dörner *et al.*, 1968).
This type of work revealed brain sites which mediate estrogen-dependent
behaviors. Second, ^{3}H steroids were used to delineate biochemically the
temporal and regional profiles of hormone uptake and retention by particular brain regions (reviewed by McEwen *et al.*, 1972a). This approach,
patterned after the studies of Jensen and Jacobson (1962) in the uterus,
resulted in the identification of estrogen "retention" sites in the
hypothalamus, preoptic area, amygdala, and pituitary (Eisenfeld and
Axelrod, 1965; Kato and Villee, 1977; McEwen and Pfaff, 1970) and
glucocorticoid "retention" sites in hippocampus, amygdala, and septum
(McEwen *et al.*, 1968, 1969; Knizley, 1972). Subsequent work (see Table I)
has characterized cytosol and cell nuclear receptors in the various brain
regions where retention is highest. Third, ^{3}H steroid autoradiography was
utilized to map the brain for cell groupings containing high levels of
steroid receptors (Michael, 1965; Pfaff, 1968a,b; Stumpf, 1968; Anderson
and Greenwald, 1969; Attramadal, 1970; Warembourg, 1970a,b; Gerlach
and McEwen, 1972).

The identification, characterization, and mapping of steroid receptors in
neural structures has provided brain sites as well as an experimental
rationale for studies of steroid action. The story which has emerged from
these and subsequent work will be summarized below in three parts. The
first section of this article deals with intracellular steroid receptors in
neural tissue: their anatomical distribution and properties, their role in
carrying hormone to the cell nucleus, and their effects upon gene expression. The second section describes direct effects of steroids upon neural
tissue which do not appear to be mediated by intracellular steroid receptors. The third section provides a more integrated picture of how steroid
hormones influence patterns of behavior during development and in adult
life, using as an example the effects of estradiol in the rat brain. The
conclusion of the article looks toward the future of this kind of investigation by considering the neurochemistry underlying hormone action.

II. Neural Steroid Receptors and Consequences of their Functioning

A. CYTOSOL RECEPTORS AND NUCLEAR TRANSLOCATION

The brain contains receptor sites for all five classes of steroid hormones. To the extent that they have been characterized physicochemically and for steroid specificity, these receptors resemble those found in nonneural target tissues (Table I).

Brain regions that contain such cytosol steroid receptors also display translocation of labeled hormone to the cell nuclear compartment (Table I), and this phenomenon underlies autoradiographic localization of steroid hormone concentrating cells, since the presence of label over the cell nucleus provides a visually striking and quantifiable endpoint: i.e., a collection of silver grains over the nuclear region which must be at least 3–5 times background to be recognized (Arnold, 1980).

Cell nuclear translocation of steroid hormones in neural tissues is not necessarily accompanied by extensive cytosol receptor depletion even when nuclear sites are loaded to capacity. Estrogen receptor depletion by estradiol of about 50% or less is found in hypothalamus, preoptic area, and amygdala, after an estradiol dose which produces near capacity nuclear estradiol levels. This same dose loads pituitary nuclei and produces

TABLE I

Neural and Pituitary Steroid Receptors[a]

Class of steroid	Cytosol[b]	Nuclear[b]	Brain regions
Estrogen	≈8 S (1–3)	4–5 S (4–7)	Hyp, POA, Amyg, Pit
Progestin	6–9 S (8–10)	5 S (9,11–13)	Hyp, POA, Pit, Ctx
Androgen	≈7 S (14–16)	3–4 S (17)	Hyp, POA, Sep, Amyg, Pit
Glucocorticoid	≈7 S (18–20)	U (21)	Hippo, Amyg, Sep, Pit
Mineralocorticoid	U (22–24)	U	Similar to glucocorticoid

[a] Hyp, hypothalamus; POA, preoptic area; Amyg, amygdala; Pit, pituitary; Ctx, cerebral cortex; Sep, septum; Hippo, hippocampus.

[b] Estimates of sedimentation (S) coefficient given where available. Values for low ionic strength in cytosol and 0.4 M KCl in nuclear extracts. U, S value unknown. Numbers in parentheses refer to references listed: (1) Eisenfeld (1970); (2) Ginsburg *et al.* (1977); (3) McEwen (1978, review); (4) Zigmond and McEwen (1970); (5) Chader and Villee (1970); (6) Linkie (1977); (7) Fox (1977); (8) MacLusky and McEwen (1980a); (9) Kato *et al.* (1978); (10) Moguilewsky and Raynaud (1977); (11) Blaustein and Wade (1978); (12) Blaustein and Feder (1979); (13) McGinnis *et al.* (1981); (14) Barley *et al.* (1975); (15) Fox (1975); (16) Chamness *et al.* (1979); (17) Lieberburg *et al.* (1977a); (18) Chytil and Toft (1972); (19) Grosser *et al.* (1971); (20) McEwen *et al.* (1972b); (21) McEwen and Plapinger (1970); (22) Anderson and Fanestil (1976); (23) Moguilewsky and Raynaud (1980); (24) Veldhuis *et al.* (1982).

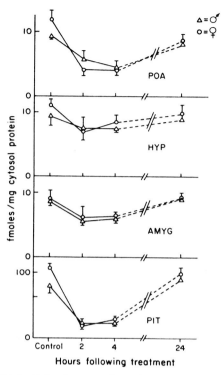

FIG. 1.   Levels of high affinity, low capacity E_2 binding measured by LH-20 gel filtration in cytosols prepared from various brain regions of gonadectomized–adrenalectomized male and female rats at 0 (control, uninjected), 2, 4, and 24 hours after iv injection of 2.7 μg/kg ^{3}H which produce near-capacity cell nuclear occupation. The results also illustrate the similarity of estrogen receptor levels in male and female brains and pituitary. Incubations were performed with 10^{-9} M [^{3}H]E_2 of the same specific activity as used in the injection. Binding values depicted were mathematically corrected for nonspecific binding. Reprinted from Lieberburg *et al.* (1980a) by permission.

a depletion of 80% or more of pituitary cytosol estrogen receptors (Fig. 1; Lieberburg *et al.*, 1980a). Depletion of less than 20–30% of cytosol capacity is reported for neural and pituitary progestin receptors during nuclear loading by progesterone (Parsons *et al.*, 1981b). It appears from these results that neural estrogen and progestin receptors are present in excess over what is needed for translocation to the nucleus. As in peripheral tissues like uterus, replenishment of neural cytosol estrogen and progestin receptors occurs within 24 hours (Cidlowski and Muldoon, 1974; Lieberburg *et al.*, 1980a; Parson *et al.*, 1981b). In contrast to the foregoing examples for estradiol and progesterone, there is no apparent depletion of cytosol glucocorticoid receptors in the hippocampus, the major neural glucocorticoid target site, even at steroid doses capable of saturating nuclear receptor sites (Turner and McEwen, 1980). To explain this strange result, it was postulated that a pool of "cryptic" receptor exists from which functional receptors are rapidly generated to replace those entering the nucleus.

In general, biochemical demonstrations of steroid receptors have revealed distributions of target cells in brain that are consistent with but sometimes broader than what is revealed by autoradiography. That is to say, not all brain areas where steroid receptors can be demonstrated by biochemical means contain steroid-concentrating cells which can be readily visualized by autoradiography. This is the case for progestin receptors in cerebral cortex (Warembourg, 1978; MacLusky and McEwen, 1978) and for glucocorticoid receptors in glial cells of the optic nerve (Meyer and McEwen, 1982). In both tissues nuclear translocation *in vivo* appears to be low relative to cytosol receptor content. Thus too little nuclear translocation may preclude detection of steroid receptors by autoradiography. One important lesson from this discrepancy is that negative data from autoradiography do not preclude the existence of receptors in a particular group of cells; rather, negative biochemical data are also required.

B. GENE ACTIVATION IN NEURAL TARGETS

According to the well-accepted model of steroid hormone action, nuclear translocation of hormone–receptor complexes results in genomic activation. There are two instances where such activation has been directly demonstrated in recognized steroid target regions of the brain. The first case is the finding that estradiol administration results in a transient activation of hypothalamic cell nuclear RNA polymerase II activity (Kelner *et al.*, 1980). These authors note that in contrast to uterus, the adult hypothalamus lacks a sustained activation of RNA polymerase II and shows no change in RNA polymerase I. They correlate this with the absence in adult brain of estrogen-induced hypertrophy and hyperplasia. A second instance of genomic activation is the finding that corticosterone application to hippocampal slices results within 30–60′ in a selective increase in the incorporation of [^{3}H]uridine into polyadenylic acid-rich nuclear RNA (Dokas, 1979).

There are other, indirect demonstrations of genomic involvement in steroid action on the brain. These include the ability of the RNA synthesis inhibitor, actinomycin D, to block estrogen action on female sexual behavior (Quadagno *et al.*, 1971; Terkel *et al.*, 1973), and preovulatory LH release (Jackson, 1972; Kalra, 1975).

C. INDUCTION OF GENE PRODUCTS IN NEURAL TISSUE

The end result of genomic activation by steroids is believed to be the induction of gene products such as enzymes and other cell proteins which are the actual agents that manifest the hormone action. That such a mechanism is applicable to hormone action in brain is indicated by two kinds of evidence. The first is that protein synthesis inhibitors block steroid hormone actions to facilitate certain behaviors. These kinds of data will be summarized below in Section IV,C. The second kind of evidence is that steroid hormones appear to induce neural gene products which are concerned with the process of neurotransmission as well as with aspects of hormonal sensitivity and the metabolism of glial cells.

There are a number of examples which illustrate the diversity of such steroid actions upon neural targets. Estrogens, for example, regulate progestin receptor levels in hypothalamus and pituitary gland (see Section II,D). Glucocorticoids regulate levels of specific proteins in glia and neurons (Table II). In oligodendroglial cells (Leveille *et al.*, 1980), they induce glycerol phosphate dehydrogenase (DeVellis and Inglish, 1968; McGinnis and DeVellis, 1978). In neurons of Ammon's horn and dentate gyrus of hippocampus, they induce protein I, a neuron-specific synaptic phosphoprotein (Nestler *et al.*, 1981a,b). One interesting difference between these two phenomena is that the synthetic glucocorticoid, dexamethasone, induced GPDH and not protein I (Table II). This finding parallels the extensive uptake of [³H]dexamethasone by the neuropil, consisting in large part of glial cells, but not by hippocampal neurons (e.g., Warembourg, 1975; Rhees *et al.*, 1975; deKloet *et al.*, 1975). Dexa-

TABLE II

Glucocorticoid Regulation of Neuronal and Glial Properties in the Hippocampus[a]

Treatment	Glial GPDH[b]	Neuronal protein I[c]
Control ADX	410 ± 27	56.8 ± 0.9
+ 100% Cort	628 ± 27*	74.2 ± 2.3*
+ 25% Dex	594 ± 54*	56.4 ± 1.1

[a] GPDH, glycerol phosphate dehydrogenase; treatment consisted of implantation subcutaneously into adrenalectomized (ADX) rats 80–100 μg pellets containing either 100% corticosterone or 25% dexamethasone, 75% cholesterol.

[b] Meyer *et al.* (1979); micromoles/gram protein/hour.

[c] Nestler *et al.* (1981a); nanomoles/gram protein.

* Significantly different from control, $p < 0.05$, Student's t test.

methasone, in contrast to corticosterone, appears to reach neural tissue not by crossing the blood–brain barrier but rather by reaching the ventricles and diffusing into the brain from the CSF (Rees *et al.*, 1975). For unknown reasons, dexamethasone does not reach neuronal glucocorticoid receptors very well when it enters via this route even though it seems to bind to these receptors *in vitro* (McEwen *et al.*, 1976).

Steroid hormones induce gene products linked to neurotransmission. In the Zebra finch and canary, testosterone induces cholinergic properties of the tracheosyringealis (Ts) branch of the hypoglossal nerve and of the syrinx muscle group which it innervates (Luine *et al.*, 1980a; see Fig. 2). The motoneurons of the Ts nerve and the muscle both contain putative androgen receptor sites (Zigmond *et al.*, 1973; Arnold *et al.*, 1976; Lieberburg and Nottebohm, 1979). Besides regulating choline acetyltransferase (CAT) and acetylcholinesterase activities (Fig. 2), androgens also regulate syrinx muscle mass (Luine *et al.*, 1980a) and nicotinic cholinergic receptor levels (Bleisch and Luine, 1981). These findings are of particular interest because androgens regulate song in male songbirds and because the syrinx is the song-producing organ (Nottebohm, 1980). They provide an example of the connection between steroid hormones and neurochemical features associated with neurotransmission and illustrate the type of changes which steroids may induce centrally in the hypothalamus or other hormone-sensitive brain regions.

Indeed, in the rat preoptic area, estradiol induces an increase in choline

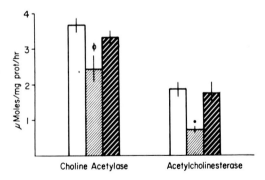

FIG. 2. Effect of castration and testosterone replacement therapy on enzyme activities in tracheosyringealis nerve from adult male zebra finches. Adults were castrated or left intact; 1 week later castrates were implanted with Silastic containing either cholesterol or testosterone. Four to five weeks after castration all groups were sacrificed. Entires are average ± SEM for 4 birds in intact, open bars; castrate + C, light striped bars; and castrate + T, dark striped bars. Differences between groups tested by Newman–Keuls procedure; ϕ different from intact, $p < 0.05$; *different from other two groups, $p < 0.05$. Reprinted from Luine *et al.* (1980a) by permission.

acetyltransferase activity (Fig. 3). This increase occurs within 24 hours and represents an increase in enzyme amount, as demonstrated by immunotitration with an antiserum against CAT (Fig. 4). That this induction may be related to sexually dimorphic processes such as ovulation or feminine sexual behavior is suggested by the fact that estrogen induction of CAT does not occur in the preoptic area of male rats, which do not show preovulatory LH release or feminine sexual behavior in response to estradiol plus progestin treatment (Luine *et al.*, 1975). In contrast, the androgen effect upon cholinergic properties of the syrinx occurs in females as well as males even though androgen-dependent song occurs predominantly, if not exclusively, in the male (Luine *et al.*, 1980a).

Adrenal steroids can also affect neurotransmitter-related functions. Adrenalectomy increases and glucocorticoids suppress high affinity GABA uptake in hippocampus (Miller *et al.*, 1978). This effect, which requires days of hormone treatment *in vivo*, is not detected in cerebellum or cortex. It may help explain the increased seizure susceptibility of the rat which occurs over days after adrenalectomy (Feldman and Robinson, 1968). The basis of this suggestion is that a more efficient GABA reuptake resulting from adrenalectomy would reduce the efficacy of GABA as an inhibitory transmitter.

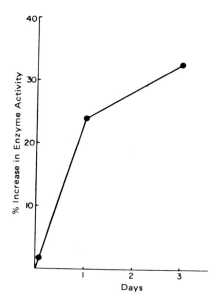

FIG. 3.   Time course of the effect of estradiol on CAT activity in preoptic area. Enzyme activity is expressed as percentage increase in estrogen-treated rats over control rats. Reprinted from Luine *et al.* (1980b) by permission.

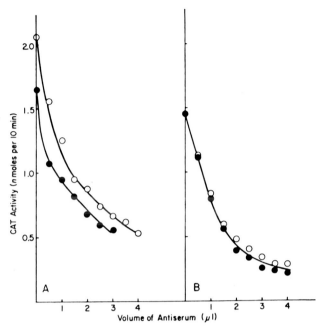

FIG. 4. Immunochemical titration curves of CAT in the preoptic area from control (closed circles) and experimental (open circles) rats. (A) Equal amounts of supernatants from 3 day EB- or saline-injected rat preoptic areas were immunotitrated and the equivalence point was shifted to the right. (B) Equivalent CAT activity of control and experimental supernatants was immunochemically titrated and the curves overlapped one another. Reprinted from Luine *et al.* (1980b) by permission.

D. EVENTS ASSOCIATED WITH STEROID RECEPTORS

Identification and mapping of steroid receptor systems in the brain (Table I) was a stimulus for the investigation of steroid receptor-associated events such as testosterone metabolism and the synergism between estradiol and progesterone. The conversion of testosterone to 5α-dihydrotestosterone in neural and pituitary tissue (Sholiton *et al.*, 1966; Denef *et al.*, 1973; Martini, 1976) provides androgens which associate with intracellular androgen receptors (Lieberburg and McEwen, 1977). The aromatization of testosterone to estradiol (Naftolin *et al.*, 1975) provides a source of estradiol which interacts *in vivo* with intracellular estrogen receptor sites (Lieberburg and McEwen, 1977). In the rat, such conversion appears to be important for the process of brain sexual differentiation (see below) and for the activation of masculine sexual behavior (Christensen and Clemens, 1974; Davis and Barfield, 1979). In both developing and adult rat brain, aromatization appears to be associated with (i.e., provide estradiol to) about half of the available estrogen-concentrating sites of the limbic brain and hypothalamus (Krey *et al.*, 1980). Newborn and adult male rats produce testosterone at a level which occupies those estrogen receptors accessible to the aromatizing enzymes to about half of their capacity (Figs. 5 and 6). In the adult rat brain, some cells which aromatize also appear able to produce progestin receptors via an estrogen-dependent

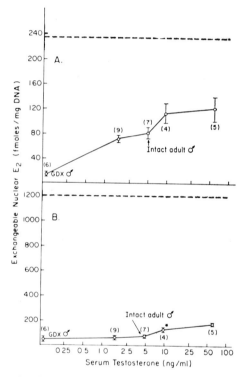

FIG. 5.   Semilogarithmic plot of serum testosterone levels vs exchangeable cell nuclear estradiol in hypothalamus and preoptic area (A) and pituitary (B) from adult male rats. Rats were grouped according to treatment and mean serum testosterone levels were castrate (gdx) males, 0.11 ± 0.3 ng/ml (mean $\pm$ SEM); gdx + testosterone capsules, 1.64 ± 0.18; intact males, 4.69 ± 0.68; intact + testosterone capsules, 9.60 ± 1.02; intact + high testosterone capsules, 59.4 ± 4.8. Error bars for each data point indicate the SEM; the number of determinations is indicated in parentheses. The data were subjected to one-way analyses of variance: (A) $F(4/26) = 12.000$, $p < 0.001$ and (B) $F(4/26) = 41.287$, $p < 0.001$. *In vivo* estrogen receptor capacities are presented as dashed lines at the top of each panel; the shaded area abutting this line represents the SE of the mean (number of determinations: HYP-POA, 4; pituitary, 5). Reprinted from Krey *et al.* (1980) by permission.

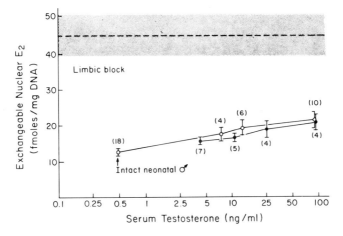

FIG. 6. Semilogarithmic plot of serum testosterone levels vs exchangeable cell nuclear estradiol in the limbic block (containing hypothalamus, preoptic area, and amygdala) of neonatal male and female rats of 3–4 days of age. Rats were grouped according to treatment and mean serum testosterone levels were females (solid circles) 50 μg TP, 4.5 ± 0.6 ng/ml (mean ± SE); 100 μg TP, 10.7 ± 0.9; 200 μg TP, 25.3 ± 6.5; 500 μg TP, 93.4 ± 2.2 ($n = 4$); males (open circles) 50 μg TP, 7.5 ± 1.1; 100 μg TP, 13.2 ± 1.6; 500 μg TP, 91.9 ± 22.6. Error bars representing SEM are indicated for each data point. The data for males were subjected to a one-way analysis of variance [$F(3/32) = 2.969, p < 0.05$]. Estrogen receptor capacity is presented as a dashed line at the top of the figure. Shaded area abutting the line represents the SEM (number of determinations = 6). Reprinted from Krey et al. (1980) by permission.

process, because testosterone administration increases progestin receptor levels in hypothalamus and preoptic area of male Tfm rats which are deficient in androgen receptors (Krey et al., 1981).

Progestin receptor induction by estradiol is a major feature associated with estrogen-sensitive neurons of the hypothalamus and pituitary (see McEwen et al., 1982, for review). This induction occurs following a time course of hours (Fig. 7) within certain hypothalamic and preoptic area estrogen-sensitive cell groupings and is absent in estrogen-sensitive areas of the amygdala. Decay of induced progestin receptors following removal of an estrogen stimulus occurs by first order kinetics with a half-time of around 24 hours (Fig. 8; Parsons et al., 1980). Neural progestin receptor induction thus appears to be another example of a neural gene product, production of which is regulated by steroid hormones. In the female rat, progestin receptor induction is very closely correlated with the ability of the animal to display feminine sexual behavior; progestin receptors in the estrogen-sensitive ventromedial hypothalamus appear to be essential (see Sections IV,C,2 and 3).

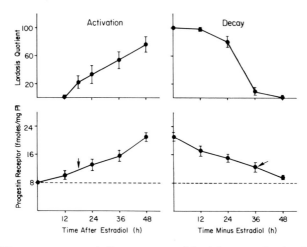

FIG. 7. The appearance and disappearance of feminine reproductive behavior and cytosol [³H]R5020 binding to the MBH-POA after E_2 treatment and E_2 withdrawal. Reproductive behavior was measured as the LQ, and [³H]R5020 binding is expressed as femtomoles of [³H]R5020 per mg protein. After implantation of 5 mm E_2 Silastic capsules, LQ values and [³H]R5020 binding increase with time. The increase in [³H]R5020 binding is significant for MBH-POA from 24 hours onward ($p < 0.01$, by Student's t test). After the removal of E_2 capsules, LQ values and [³H]R5020 binding decrease with time. Arrows mark the level of [³H]R5020 binding at the time sexual receptivity was first and last observed. For behavioral measurements, each data point represents a minimum of 6 animals (mean ± SE). For progestin receptor measurements, each data point represents 5–7 observations (mean ± SE; 10–14 animals, pools of tissues from 2 animals). Reprinted from Parsons *et al.* (1980) by permission.

III. Direct Effects of Steroid Hormones Which May Operate on Neural Membranes

As noted above, many actions of steroids on neural tissue are delayed in onset and prolonged in duration and appear to involve intracellular receptors operating via the genome. Other steroid effects are rapid and direct and may be operating at or near the cell surface. In some cases, they have been reproduced on isolated synaptosomes or membranes. One of the most striking direct actions is the alteration of diencephalic neuronal discharge rates which occurs within seconds after iontophoretic administration of estradiol-17β hemisuccinate; estradiol-17α hemisuccinate is ineffective (Kelly *et al.*, 1977). Likewise, iontophoretically applied cortisol alters the response of hypothalamic neurons to stimulation via afferents or glutamate (Mandelbrod *et al.*, 1981). Another type of direct steroid action is the rapid inhibition of release of corticotropin releasing factor, which

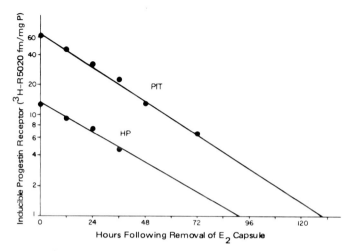

FIG. 8. The time course of decay of estrogen-inducible [³H]R5020-binding molecules in the MBH-POA and pituitary (PIT) after the removal of 5 mm E_2 Silastic capsules. The amount of [³H]R5020 binding present in control animals was subtracted from those levels after estrogenic stimulation. The $\log_{10}$ of those values which were greater than those of unstimulated animals was used to mathematically generate a function of the form $y = mx + b$. The coefficient of regression was found to be -0.993 for brain samples and -0.998 for pituitary samples, the slope was -0.012 for brain samples and -0.014 for pituitary samples, and the y intercept was 1.124 for brain samples and 1.815 for pituitary samples (antilog: brain, 13.30 fmol/mg protein; pituitary 65.31 fmol/mg protein). For progestin receptor measurements, each data point represents the mean of 5–7 observations (10–14 animals, pools of tissues from 2 animals). Reprinted from Parsons *et al.* (1980) by permission.

occurs following corticosterone application to hypothalamic fragments or synaptosomes *in vitro* (Edwardson and Bennett, 1974; Jones *et al.*, 1977). A third type of direct steroid action appears to involve certain neurotransmitter receptors. Estradiol-17β given *in vitro* causes an acute decrease in the number of serotonin₁ receptor sites assayed *in vitro;* and this effect can be reproduced entirely *in vitro* on washed brain membranes with submicromolar concentrations of estradiol-17β (McEwen and Biegon, 1981). This effect is illustrated for a high 2-hydroxy estradiol concentration in Fig. 9. Estradiol-17α is less effective, and progesterone, corticosterone, and testosterone are without effect. Higher concentrations of estradiol-17β or 2-hydroxy estradiol-17β (≈ 10–$100\ \mu M$) will also selectively compete for α_1 adrenergic and dopaminergic receptor sites in brain membranes (Paden *et al.*, 1981; McEwen *et al.*, 1981). Data for α_1 adrenergic receptors are presented in Fig. 10.

With the likely exception of this last cited estradiol effect, each of the direct steroid effects noted above may occur *in vivo* under more or less

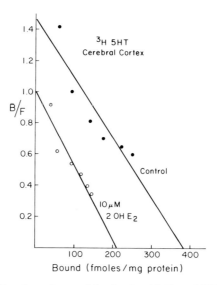

FIG. 9. Concentration dependence of the *in vitro* binding of [³H]serotonin to cerebral cortical membranes from ovariectomized rats in the presence or absence of 2-hydroxyestradiol-17β (2-OHE₂) at 10^{-5} M. Data are presented according to the method of Scatchard (1949). The method for 5HT binding is that described by Biegon *et al.* (1980). Reprinted from McEwen *et al.* (1981) by permission.

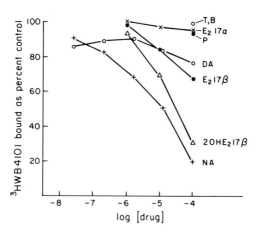

FIG. 10. Displacement curves for *in vitro* [³H]WB4101 binding to cerebral cortical membranes from ovariectomized rats. Results are expressed as percentage of total binding without drugs at 0.25 nM [³H]WB4101 vs log of unlabeled drug concentration. NA, noradrenaline; DA, dopamine; 2-OHE₂17β, 2-hydroxy 17β-estradiol; E₂17α, estradiol-17α; E₂17β, estradiol-17β; T, testosterone; B, corticosterone; P, progesterone. Reprinted from McEwen *et al.* (1981) by permission.

physiological conditions. For example, rapid electrical effects have been recorded *in vivo* following intravenous estradiol administration (Yagi, 1973); and glucocorticoids are known to exert rapid feedback effects on ACTH secretion *in vivo* (cf. Dallman and Yates, 1969; Jones *et al.*, 1977). With respect to serotonin, rat hypothalamic serotonin$_1$ receptors decrease on proestrus at the time of maximum elevation of estradiol in blood (Biegon *et al.*, 1980).

Although the identification of putative membrane steroid receptors by binding assays is at best sketchy and preliminary (cf. Towle and Sze, 1978; Schaeffer and Hseuh, 1979), each of the above cited functional studies provides some indication of the specificity of the putative membrane receptors which mediate them. For example, as noted above, the iontophoretic effects of estradiol are stereospecific for the 17β as 17α enantiomer as are also the effects of $5HT_1$ receptors. Moreover, steroid effects on serotonin$_1$ receptors and inhibition of CRF release show a high degree of selectivity for estrogens and certain glucocorticoids, respectively (McEwen and Biegon, 1981; Jones *et al.*, 1977).

At the present time, although it is possible to point to *in vivo* action of steroids via a putative membrane receptor, we do not yet know whether such direct actions constitute a major means of influencing brain function and behavior. It is conceivable that direct membrane effects may be a means by which catechol estrogens exert effects on neuroendocrine function (see Ball and Knuppen, 1980; MacLusky *et al.*, 1982, for review of this area).

IV. Toward Understanding How Steroid Hormones Act to Regulate Behavior

A. BACKGROUND

Steroid hormones circulating in the blood influence brain function and behavior and do so by acting upon specific brain regions. Since 1961, considerable information has been obtained pertaining to the brain sites and mechanisms of hormone action underlying these functional and behavioral changes. Isolated examples have been given in the first two sections of this article, but these have focused upon the cellular and molecular aspects of steroid action. The intent of this section of the article is to provide a more integrated picture of how steroid hormones control behavior by focusing upon the role of estrogens in brain sexual differentiation (called "organization"; see Young, 1961) and in the "activation" of feminine sexual behavior and ovulation in the rat. One reason for discussing "organization" as well as "activation" is that the same type of estrogen receptors appear to be involved in both processes, and yet the consequences of their function in each process are quite different. Not only do the consequences of estrogen action in "organization" and "activation" differ from each other at the cellular level, they are also different in their consequences for sexual behavior and ovulation. That is, during the "organizational" phase, estradiol defeminizes (i.e., suppresses) the rat's ability to display feminine sexual behavior and ovulation, whereas estradiol "activates" (i.e., facilitates) feminine sexual behavior in adult female rats which have not been defeminized.

B. ORGANIZATIONAL EFFECTS

1. Definitions

Organizational effects of gonadal steroids are those which operate during a limited and thus "critical" period of brain development to alter permanently neural circuitry or the response characteristics of neurons to electrical or chemical stimulation. Like the morphological sex differences in the reproductive tract, brain sex differences in mammals arise, through the developmental actions of testicular secretions. Male rats castrated at birth fail to develop a complete male reproductive tract and also are deficient in masculine reproductive behavior, even after replacement with testosterone in adulthood (Feder, 1981a,b). Such neonatally castrated male rats also display feminine sexual behavior and a preovulatory LH "surge" after priming with estradiol plus progesterone as adults. In contrast, male rats castrated as adults and given estradiol followed by progesterone rarely, if ever, show LH "surges" and display very little feminine sexual behavior. Female rats can be made to respond like adult castrated male rats if, as neonates, they are given a single testosterone injection (Gorski, 1979). This suppression of feminine characteristics is known as "defeminization," whereas the enhancement of masculine characteristics by testosterone is known as "masculinization" (Beach, 1975).

Defeminization in rats is produced by estrogens as well as by testosterone given neonatally (e.g., Whalen and Nadler, 1963). This finding, together with the ineffectiveness of 5α reduced androgens (McDonald *et al.*, 1970; for review see Plapinger and McEwen, 1978), led to the demonstration that defeminization in the rat is mediated by estrogen receptors after the conversion of testosterone to estradiol within target cells of the brain (Fig. 11). Masculinization, on the other hand, appears to be the result of both aromatization of testosterone and estrogen receptors, on the one hand, and androgen-receptor mediated effects on the other (reviewed

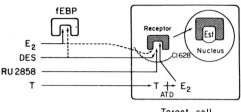

Target cell

FIG. 11. Model of estrogen and testosterone action in the brain of the newborn rat, showing the protective role of α-fetoprotein (fEBP) toward estradiol but not toward diethylstilbestrol (DES), moxestrol (RU2858), and testosterone (T). The figure also indicates the presence of sites of antagonism of testosterone action by androstatriene-3,17-dione (ATD) and by nitromiphene citrate (CI628). Est, estrogens bound to receptors in nuclei. Reprinted from McEwen *et al.* (1975) by permission.

by McEwen, 1981). We shall briefly summarize the story of aromatization, estrogen receptors, and defeminization.

2. The Role of Aromatization

The brain possesses enzymes which are capable of converting testosterone and androstenedione to estradiol and estrone (Naftolin *et al.*, 1975). This capability exists in the neonatal rat brain (Reddy *et al.*, 1974; Weisz and Gibbs, 1974) along with the capacity to produce 5α reduced androgens (Denef *et al.*, 1974). That this capability *in vitro* actually results in significant metabolism of testosterone *in vivo* was revealed by experiments of Lieberburg and co-workers (1977b) in our laboratory (Table III). Especially noteworthy is that the purified cell nuclear pellet of the whole forebrain (control N, Table III) contains 25% of its radioactivity as [³H]estradiol (E_2) and 10% as 5α-dihydrotestosterone (DHT). In a brain sample consisting of hypothalamus, preoptic area, and amygdala, approximately 50% of nuclear radioactivity after [³H]testosterone injection is [³H]estradiol (Lieberburg and McEwen, 1975).

Another means of demonstrating estradiol production from testosterone in the neonatal rat brain is by means of an exchange assay for occupied estrogen receptors translocated to brain cell nuclei. Exchange assays reveal that about half of the maximal estrogen receptor translocation occurs in hypothalamic nuclei at circulating testosterone levels (Fig. 6, Krey *et al.*, 1980). Table IV shows that forebrain cell nuclear estrogen receptor occupation in male rat pups is decreased equally by castration and by the competitive aromatase inhibitor, 1,4,6-androstatriene 3,17-dione (ATD) (Schwarzel *et al.*, 1973). The ATD effect on [³H]estrogen production from [³H]testosterone is also evident in Table III. Note also in Table III that the

TABLE III

Effect of CI628 or ATD Pretreatment on in Vivo Formed Testosterone Metabolites Recovered from Neonatal Female Brain Homogenates and Purified Cell Nuclear Fractions (Expressed as fmol/mg Protein in That Fraction $\pm$ SEM, $n = 8$)[a,b]

Pre-treatment	Fraction	Total	A_0	Diol	T	DHT	A	a	E_2	E_1
Control	WH	631 ± 64	58.1 ± 15.6	16.6 ± 2.0	69.5 ± 7.6	13.9 ± 2.5	30.2 ± 3.1	4.57 ± 0.72	1.40 ± 0.04	0.83 ± 0.09
	N	6.43 ± 0.57	0.58 ± 0.07	0.29 ± 0.05	1.54 ± 0.16	0.65 ± 0.05	0.64 ± 0.08	0.23 ± 0.02	1.78 ± 0.35	U
CI-628	WH	681 ± 49	64.2 ± 14.7	19.0 ± 1.0	76.6 ± 4.6	14.2 ± 0.8	33.8 ± 2.8	5.04 ± 0.52	1.19 ± 0.12	1.01 ± 0.09
	N	5.37 ± 0.59	0.57 ± 0.05	0.30 ± 0.05	1.52 ± 0.14	0.63 ± 0.04	0.33 ± 0.09*	0.21 ± 0.01	0.36 ± 0.03**§	U
ATD	WH	646 ± 80	68.4 ± 18.3	14.3 ± 3.0	83.4 ± 12.9	20.0 ± 2.6	37.6 ± 5.5	8.71 ± 1.49*	0.82 ± 0.06***§	0.08 ± 0.04***§§
	N	4.71 ± 0.37*	0.59 ± 0.07	0.30 ± 0.05	1.50 ± 0.18	0.72 ± 0.07	0.36 ± 0.11	0.34 ± 0.06	0.32 ± 0.06***§	U

[a] Reprinted from Lieberburg et al. (1977b) by permission.

[b] WH, whole tissue homogenate; N, purified cell nuclei. Radioactivity was analyzed according to the method of Lieberburg and McEwen (1975) which involves double isotope dilution, toluene extraction, phenolic separation, separation of neutral steroids (androgens) on silica gel plates with two developments in $CHCl_3$–ether 20:1 (v/v), methylation of estrogens, and separation of estrogen-3-methyl ethers on silica gel plates with one development in benzene–ethanol 95:5 (v/v). A_0 = radioactivity recovered from the origin of the neutral steroids plate ($CHCl_3$–ether 20:1), probably representing very polar androgens; Diol, radioactivity recovered from the spot containing $3\alpha + 3\beta$-androstanediol; T, testosterone; DHT, 5α-dihydrotestosterone; A, androstenedione; a, androstanedione; E_2, estradiol-17β; E_1, estrone. U signifies undetectable.

* $p < 0.05$.

** $p < 0.01$.

*** $p < 0.001$, significantly different from control (t test).

§ $p < 0.025$.

§§ $p < 0.005$, significantly different from control (Dunnett).

TABLE IV
Neonatal Treatment Effects: Male Rats on Day 5[a,b]

Treatment	N	Serum T (pg/ml)	n	Cell nuclear E_2[c] (fmol/mg DNA)
Control	13	454 ± 107	11	2.35 ± 0.19
Castrate (day 4)	5	31 ± 2	12	0.57 ± 0.10*
ATD (days 2–5)	10	432 ± 105	9	0.67 ± 0.11*
CA (days 2–5)	13	426 ± 109	14	1.86 ± 0.13**

[a] Reprinted from McEwen *et al.* (1979b) by permission.

[b] Serum testosterone (T) levels measured by radioimmunoassay after chromatography. Cell nuclear estrogen receptor occupation, measured by exchange assay on soluble 0.4 M KCl extracts.

[c] Whole forebrain.

* $p < 0.01$ vs control.

** $p < 0.05$ vs control.

estrogen antagonist CI628 reduces cell nuclear content of [³H]estradiol to the same extent as ATD without affecting tissue levels of [³H]estrogens.

We established the efficacy of ATD and CI628 as blockers of cell nuclear estrogen receptor occupation resulting from testosterone in order to use these drugs in an attempt to interfere with defeminization. In females given testosterone in neonatal life, both ATD and CI628 antagonized the defeminizing effects of this steroid (Table V). CI628, but not ATD, at-

TABLE V
Lordosis Quotients of Adult Female Rats Treated as Neonates with Indicated Substances

Number	Treatment	LQ
1	Control	89 ± 3
2	Testosterone	18 ± 7
3	ATD	86 ± 4[a]
4	T + ATD	82 ± 5[a]
5	T + CI628	52 ± 7[a,b]
6	Estradiol	13 ± 3
7	Estradiol + ATD	8 ± 8
8	CI628	66 ± 5[a,b]
9	Estradiol + CI628	56 ± 7[a,b]

[a] Significantly different from rows 2, 6, and 7.

[b] Significantly different from rows 1, 4, and 5.

Data compiled from McEwen *et al.* (1977, 1979b).

tenuated the defeminizing action of estradiol benzoate (Table V), in agreement with the predicted action of these drugs. In Table V it can be seen that CI628, acting presumably as a weak estrogen, has a small defeminizing effect and reduces feminine sexual behavior scores when given by itself to newborn female rats. Yet this effect is not so strong as to preclude CI628 acting as an antagonist to the more potent effects of testosterone and estradiol benzoate (Table V). In newborn male rats, both ATD and CI628 interfered with the defeminization normally produced by testicular secretions (McEwen et al., 1977, 1979b). The effects of ATD are not due to a suppression of testosterone levels during the time of treatment (Table IV).

Studies of ATD action revealed another aspect of rat brain sexual differentiation, namely, that one can block defeminization without affecting masculinization. In fact male rats treated with ATD as neonates showed the same degrees of masculine sexual behavior as control males, while also being able to display feminine sexual responses, even prior to castration as adults (Table VI). Many of these rats were strongly "bisexual" and displayed alternately masculine and feminine sexual responses when put into a choice situation with male and female partners at opposite ends of a runway (Davis et al., 1979a). They did not, however, display an altered preference for male over female partners.

3. Androgen Insensitive (Tfm) Mutant

Support for the exclusive role of aromatization and estrogen receptors in rat brain defeminization has come from studies of the androgen-insensitive (Tfm) mutation (Beach and Buehler, 1977; Olsen, 1979a,b; Shapiro et al., 1980; Krey et al., 1981). Although deficient in androgen receptors and markedly insensitive to various androgen actions, Tfm males are defeminized and this defeminization can be prevented by castration on postnatal day 2 (Fig. 12). Significantly, estrogen receptors and aromatizing capability of Tfm brains appear normal (Krey et al., 1981). It can be seen in Fig. 12 that both testosterone and estradiol are capable of priming both feminine sexual behavior and preovulatory LH release in neonatally castrated Tfm males. This finding supports the notion that aromatizing enzymes may exist in or very near neurons which make progestin receptors and which control these events.

4. Gonadal Steroid Receptors

The importance of estradiol as a mediator of the defeminizing action of testosterone demanded that we find out more about the ontogeny of the estrogen receptor system of the rat brain. Some estrogen and androgen receptors are present in the fetal rodent hypothalamus during the last

TABLE VI

Feminine Sexual Behavior of ATD (n = 14) and Control (n = 12) Males Observed under Endogenous and Exogenous Hormonal Conditions[a]

	$\bar{X}$ mounts received	Number of responders	$\bar{X}$ LQ responders	Number soliciting
Precastration				
Test 1–3				
ATD	24.7	7	21	0
Control	14.5	0	—	—
Test 4				
ATD	10	9	77	7[b]
Control	10	2	55	0
Postcastration				
Test 1–2				
ATD	20	14	85	11
Control	20	5	59	1

[a] Reprinted from Davis *et al.* (1979a) by permission.
[b] One ATD male exhibited solicitation behaviors but no lordosis.

trimester of gestation (Vito and Fox, 1979, 1982; Vito *et al.*, 1979) about the time of final neuronal cell divisions (Ifft, 1972). However, we found that estrogen receptor levels in the male and female rat brain increase markedly beginning shortly before birth (MacLusky *et al.*, 1979a),

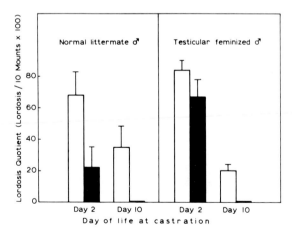

FIG. 12. Effects of neonatal castration (day 2) compared to castration or postnatal day 10 on the ability of normal male and testicular-feminized male rats to respond to estradiol plus progesterone replacement (open bars) or testosterone + progesterone replacement (black bars) for the activation of feminine sexual receptivity (expressed as the lordosis quotient, lordosis/10 mounts × 100). Data from Krey *et al.* (1981).

whereas androgen receptor levels increase markedly around 1 week after birth (Lieberburg et al., 1980b; Attardi and Ohno, 1976). These developmental profiles are summarized in Fig. 13. As their levels increase, estrogen receptors in near-term male rat fetuses are occupied by estradiol and translocated to the nucleus (Fig. 14). The sex difference of receptor occupation is maintained during the postnatal critical period (Lieberburg et al., 1979).

Since the perinatal rise of estrogen receptors begins just at the start of the period of sensitivity to the defeminizing actions of testosterone, it seemed reasonable to suppose that the onset of this "critical period" may be determined by the rapid rise in estrogen receptor levels (MacLusky et al., 1979a). What is suggested by these results is perhaps analogous to the rapid appearance of ecdysone sensitivity in imaginal disks (precursors of exoskeleton in insects) that is believed to be the final event which determines the onset of ecdysone action to promote differentiation of the disks

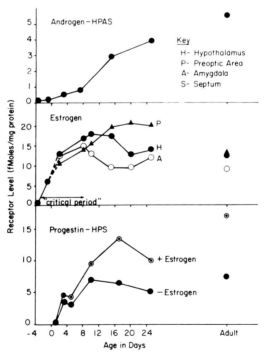

FIG. 13.   Developmental time course of cytosol androgen, estrogen, and progestin receptors in regions of rat brains. Androgen receptor data are from Lieberburg et al. (1980b); estrogen receptor data from MacLusky et al. (1979a); progestin receptor data from MacLusky and McEwen (1980b).

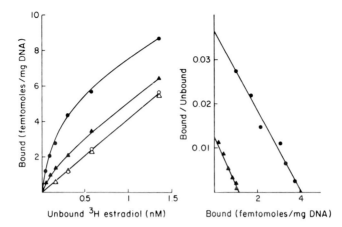

FIG. 14. Left-hand panel: isotherms for the binding of [³H]estradiol in 0.4 *M* KCl extracts of purified cell nuclei from fetal rat brain tissue. Cell nuclei were prepared from limbic brain tissue of male (○) or female (△) fetuses taken on day 21 of gestation. Estrogen receptor complexes were extracted from the nuclei as described in the text, and equilibrated with a range of [³H]estradiol concentrations for 4 hours at 25°C, in the presence (open symbols) or absence (closed symbols) of 0.3 *μM* unlabeled moxestrol. Bound radioactivity was measured in each incubate using Sephadex LH-20 gel filtration. Right-hand panel: limited capacity binding, calculated from the data presented in the left-hand panel as the difference between the results in the presence and absence of unlabeled moxestrol, and represented by the method of Scatchard (1949). Reprinted from MacLusky *et al.* (1979) by permission.

in the course of moulting and metamorphosis (Nöthiger, 1972; Oberlander, 1972).

Regarding neural steroid receptor development, one unanswered question concerns the nature of signals which control the first appearance and subsequent perinatal increase of estrogen, progestin, and androgen receptors (Fig. 13), as well as the testosterone-metabolizing enzymes in both male and female brains. Presumably, estrogen and progestin receptor development does not depend on endogenous steroids since receptor development was apparently normal after transplanting fetal hypothalamus to the choroidal pia of ovariectomized–adrenalectomized or intact female hosts (Steveni *et al.*, 1980; Paden *et al.*, 1980). Even more remarkable in these experiments was that hypothalamic transplants developed an organized dopamine-fluorescing median eminence-like structure (Stenevi *et al.*, 1980).

The ontogenesis of gonadal steroid receptor profiles in rat brain contains two other interesting pieces of information. The first is that progestin receptors develop according to a pattern similar to estrogen receptors, but their initial increase is delayed by several days (Fig. 13). When

progestin receptors appear, estrogen inducibility is not immediately evident in brain (Fig. 13), although it occurs very early in pituitary gland (Mac-
Lusky and McEwen, 1980b). The emergence of estrogen inducibility takes
place after the end of the critical period, and it coincides with the maturation of components of the lordosis response and proceptive behavior in
female neonates (see MacLusky and McEwen, 1980b, for discussion).

The second observation is that estrogen and progestin receptors develop in the neonatal cerebral cortex at the same time as the receptors in
the hypothalamus (compare Fig. 13 and Fig. 15). During this period, there
is no significant estrogen inducibility of progestin receptors (Fig. 15).
Moreover, estrogen receptor levels decline markedly in the cortex in the
third postnatal week of life, whereas progestin receptors decrease to a
lesser extent (Fig. 15). The reason for the decline is currently under investigation.

The presence of progestin receptors in the neonatal rat brain provides a
possible target for actions of progesterone which attenuate the defeminizing actions of estradiol and testosterone (Kincl and Maqueo, 1965; Mc-

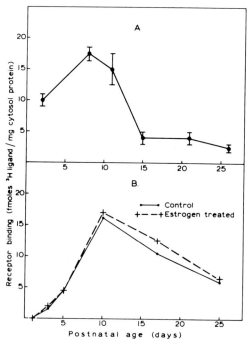

FIG. 15.   Developmental profile of estrogen receptors (A) and progestin receptors (B) in
rat cerebral cortex. Data from MacLusky *et al.* (1979b) and MacLusky and McEwen
(1980b).

Ewen *et al.*, 1979b). Both the potent progestin R5020 and the progestogenic antiandrogen cyproterone acetate bind to progestin receptors in the neonatal brain and attenuate defeminization produced in neonatal males by endogenous testosterone (MacLusky and McEwen, 1980b; McEwen *et al.*, 1979b).

5. α-Fetoprotein

Before ending this discussion of the role of estrogens in defeminization, it should be noted that in the late fetal and neonatal period, the rat contains an important serum protein, α-fetoprotein (AFP), which binds estradiol (Raynaud *et al.*, 1971; Nunez *et al.*, 1971). This protein functions to retard endogenous or exogenous estradiol from defeminizing normal female rats (Fig. 11) and from stimulating growth of the developing reproductive tract (Raynaud, 1973; Whalen and Olsen, 1978; Mizejewski *et al.*, 1980). α-Fetoprotein does not bind synthetic estrogens such as moxestrol (Raynaud *et al.*, 1971; Raynaud, 1973), and low levels of [^{3}H]moxestrol, in contrast to [^{3}H]estradiol, gains ready access to neonatal brain estrogen receptor sites (Table VII). Moxestrol will also stimulate uterine growth in neonatal rats (Raynaud, 1973) and defeminizes these animals (Doughty *et al.*, 1975) when given in minute amounts. Although AFP is present in serum, an AFP-like substance is also found in neural tissue (Fig. 16). Whereas some of this AFP occurs in cerebrospinal fluid (Plapinger *et al.*, 1973), it has recently become apparent that some AFP exists inside brain cells, including neurons, within certain brain regions (Benno and Williams, 1978; Toran-Allerand, 1980b). Thus speculation has arisen that AFP may have a role in brain development besides its protective function (Toran-Allerand, 1980b).

TABLE VII

Comparison of Serum Binding and Brain Cell Nuclear Translocation of [^{3}H]Estradiol and [^{3}H]Moxestrol[a]

Estrogen	Serum binding[b] (fmol/ml)	Cell nuclear retention *in vivo* (fmol/mg DNA)[c]
[^{3}H]Estradiol	≈9000	5.4 ± 0.5
[^{3}H]Moxestrol	70	190 ± 19

[a] Data from McEwen *et al.* (1975).

[b] Binding in a 1:50 dilution of serum from 2–5 day male and female rats measured after 1 hour of incubation with [^{3}H]estrogen by means of gel filtration on Sephadex G-25 minicolumns.

[c] Female rats were given subcutaneously [^{3}H]estrogen at a dose of 3–4 nmol/kg and were killed 2 hours later for assay of cell nuclear retention of ^{3}H label in pooled hypothalamus, preoptic area, and amygdala.

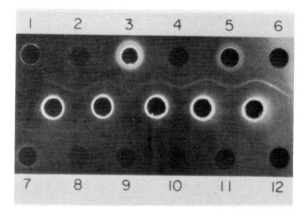

FIG. 16. Photograph of Ouchterlony plate. The center wells were filled with rabbit antiserum, against fetoneonatal rat serum, absorbed with adult rat serum. Well 1 contained a 1 : 10 dilution of adult rat serum. Wells 2, 4, 6, 8, 10, and 12 contained day 3 female rat serum at the following total protein concentrations: 2.1, 0.5, 0.21, 0.11, and 0.05 mg/ml. Wells 3, 5, 7, 9, and 11 contained cytosol prepared from pooled, perfused, day 3 male and female rat whole brains, at the following total protein concentrations: 23, 6.8, 3.4, 1.7, and 1.0 mg/ml. Reprinted from Plapinger and McEwen (1975) by permission.

6. Growth-Promoting Effects of Estradiol

Although for many years the brain and not the pituitary was presumed to be the primary site of testosterone-induced differentiation of neuroendocrine function (see Harris and Jacobsohn, 1952; Barraclough and Gorski, 1961), it is only quite recently that there has been real progress in understanding what happens to the brain during sexual differentiation. Much of this progress has come from neuroanatomical studies. The first studies revealed sex differences in nucleolar and cell nuclear size in brains of gonadally intact (Pfaff, 1966) and hormone-treated adult rodents (Dörner and Staudt, 1969a,b) and primates (Bubenik and Brown, 1973). The studies of Raisman and Field (1973), using the electron microscope, revealed a sex difference in synaptic patterns within adult rat preoptic area which is influenced by early testosterone exposure. The Raisman and Field paper triggered a series of recently reported observations at the light and electron microscopic level which revealed sex differences in brain morphology in songbirds (Nottebohm and Arnold, 1976; Gurney and Konishi, 1980) and rodents (Greenough et al., 1977; Gorski et al., 1978; Rethelyi, 1979; Matsumoto and Arai, 1980; Breedlove and Arnold, 1980; Loy and Milner, 1980; Arimatsu et al., 1981; Nishizuka and Arai, 1981; Ross et al., 1981). Differences in cell number and cell size in addition to different patterns of synapses are characteristic of these sex differences (e.g., Arnold and Saltiel, 1979; Breedlove and Arnold, 1980; Gorski *et al.*, 1980; Jacobson *et al.*, 1980; Gurney and Konishi, 1980; Nishizuka and Arai, 1981).

How do these sex differences arise during the critical period of early perinatal neural development in mammals and birds? One of the most attractive mechanisms currently under investigation is hormone-stimulated neurite outgrowth, which has been demonstrated to result from estradiol and testosterone administration to explants of newborn mouse preoptic area and amygdala in organ culture (Toran-Allerand, 1976, 1978, 1980a, 1981). The neurite outgrowth is not produced by 5α-dihydrotestosterone and it is blocked by the antiestrogen CI628 (Toran-Allerand, 1980a). Since the outgrowth does not occur in all parts of the preoptic area or hypothalamus, but rather appears to be related to particular loci, we collaborated with Dr. Toran-Allerand to trace the estrogen-sensitive neurons in these explants (Toran-Allerand *et al.*, 1980). In spite of some morphological rearrangements resulting from organ culture, the pattern of estrogen concentrating cells revealed by [^{3}H]estrogen autoradiography of the explants was reminiscent of the topographic pattern described for neonatal rat (Sheridan *et al.*, 1974) and mouse (Gerlach, McEwen, and Toran-Allerand, unpublished). By comparing neurite outgrowth with the autoradiographic maps of the same planes of section in parallel culture, it was possible to show that the selective and localized pattern of the neuritic response to estradiol in several instances appears to emanate from regions which contain estrogen-accumulating neurons (Fig. 17). This finding suggests that estrogen action on neurite outgrowth is a primary effect of the hormone acting alone or in combination with other growth factors upon estrogen-sensitive neurons.

C. ACTIVATIONAL ACTIONS OF ESTRADIOL AND PROGESTERONE

1. Background

The "activational effects" of hormones are reversible actions which lead, for example, to ovulation and sexual or aggressive behavior as well as vocalization (e.g., song in birds). Such effects operate on a neural substrate which may have been subject to "organizing" actions of the same hormones. For example, testosterone acts in development to organize permanently the neural substrate controlling vocalization in songbirds (Nottebohm, 1980) and masculine sexual behavior in rats and other mammals; and it also activates these behaviors in the mature animal

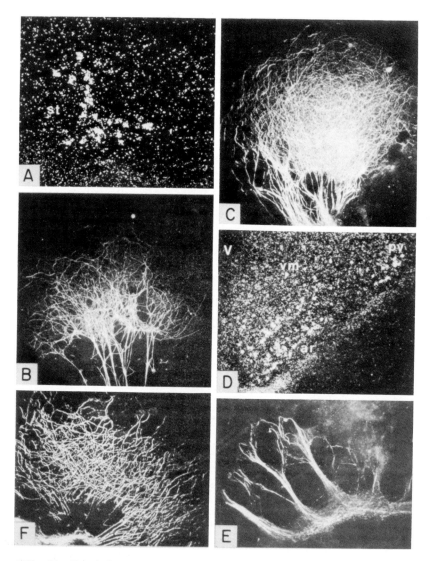

FIG. 17. Correlation of the neuritic response to estradiol with the presence of [³H]estradiol-labeled cells. Steroid responsive neuritic outgrowth (B, C, E, F) (Holmes' silver impregnation) is localized only to explant regions which contain labeled cells (A). Regions with few or no labeled cells are nonresponsive. (A) POA, n. interstitialis striae terminalis (×63); (B) control, estradiol endogenous to serum; (C) estradiol (50 ng/ml), 13 days *in vitro* (×16), dark-field; (D) infundibular/premammillary level, nn. arcuatus/ventromedialis/premamillaris ventralis (×40); (E) control, endogenous estradiol; (F) estradiol (50 ng ml), 19 days *in vitro* (×25), dark-field. St, n. interstitialis striae terminalis; vm, n. ventromedialis; ar, n. arcuatus; pv, n. premamillaris ventralis. Reprinted from Toran-Allerand *et al.* (1980) by permission.

(see Goy and McEwen, 1980, Chapter 1, for discussion). Moreover, as noted above, testosterone, acting via its conversion to estradiol, defeminizes the rat brain and suppresses its ability to respond to estradiol and progesterone with respect to ovulation and feminine sexual behavior. In this section, we shall examine some of the characteristics of estradiol and progesterone action on the normal female rat brain, as an illustration of activational effects and how the mechanism and site of hormone action can be studied.

2. Temporal Aspects of Estradiol and Progesterone Action

One of the major advantages of studying estradiol and progesterone action on feminine sexual behavior in rats is that both hormones act within hours, rather than minutes or days, to activate the behavior. Estradiol priming is required for progesterone to stimulate mating behavior, which consists of "receptivity" (the lordosis response) and "proceptivity" (hop-darting and ear-wiggling) (see Beach, 1976, for definition of terms). The behavioral endpoints used in assessing mating behavior are reliable and clearcut and amenable to quantitation (e.g., Hardy and DeBold, 1971; Pfaff, 1980). As a result there has been considerable recent progress in elucidating the neural circuitry for lordosis as well as neurophysiological mechanisms (Pfaff, 1980).

The sequential administration of estradiol and progesterone mimics the natural sequence of secretion of these two hormones: rising titers of estradiol over several days are followed on the afternoon of proestrus by a large peak of progesterone secretion coincident with the preovulatory LH surge (Smith et al., 1975), and this in turn is followed within a few hours by the onset of behavioral estrus.

Estradiol effects on feminine sexual behavior are manifested after a lag period of ≈ 18 hours; these effects never occur in less than 18 hours and they become clearly evident by 24 hours (Green et al., 1970; Parsons et al., 1980) (see Fig. 7). Progesterone acts more rapidly than estradiol, with an onset latency for sexual behavior of an hour or less (Meyerson, 1972; Kubli-Garfias and Whalen, 1977; McGinnis et al., 1981) (see Fig. 18).

Estradiol and progesterone actions on mating behavior both appear to involve the stimulation of protein synthesis, as indicated by studies with macromolecular synthesis inhibitors. Estradiol facilitation of mating is blocked reversibly by the RNA synthesis inhibitor, actinomycin D (Quadagno et al., 1971; Terkel et al., 1973), and by protein synthesis inhibitors, cycloheximide (Quadagno and Ho, 1975) and anisomycin (Rainbow et al., 1980a). The effects of estradiol on protein synthesis required for mating behavior are complex. When estradiol is applied continuously via Silastic capsules, a 6-hour period of treatment is just as good as a continuous 24 hour exposure in activating behavior (Rainbow et al.,

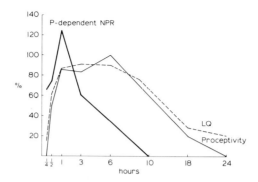

FIG. 18.   Effects of progesterone administration to estrogen-primed ovariectomized rats. Comparison between proceptivity and lordosis quotient (LQ) scores and nuclear progestin receptor levels expressed as percentage elevation above control. Reprinted from McGinnis *et al.* (1981) by permission.

1980a; Parsons *et al.*, 1981a). Moreover, anisomycin applied at the beginning of the 6 hour estrogen exposure is far more effective than when it is applied at the end of this 6-hour period (Rainbow *et al.*, 1980a). However, if the estrogen stimulus is broken into two 1-hour segments, two such exposures which are not less than 4 hours or more than 14 hours apart are sufficient to activate sexual behavior measured at 24 hours (Parsons *et al.*, 1981a) (see Fig. 19). Under these conditions, anisomycin is effective in blocking estrogen action when given before the first 1-hour period, between the first and second exposure, or just before the second 1-hour period; it is not effective when given 2 hours or more after the second 1 hour estradiol treatment (Parsons *et al.*, 1981a; see Fig. 19). These results are consistent with the notion that estradiol action to facilitate lordosis may involve a "cascade" of protein synthesis in which the early protein synthetic events prepare the system for later estrogen action. Such a "cascade" sequence has been postulated to explain "early" and "late" puffs (representing gene activation) resulting from the action of the steroid hormone, ecdysone, on giant polytene chromosomes of *Drosophila* (Clever, 1964; Ashburner, 1974; Ashburner and Berendes, 1978).

The later actions of estradiol may occur within a few hours of the initial estrogenic stimulus (i.e., when the two stimuli are 4 hour apart) but they may also be delayed until 14 hours after the initial stimulus, which is also 9 hours before behavior is tested. We do not know which time interval is more important: i.e., whether the 9-hour period indicates a minimum latency for the later synthesized proteins to reach a functional location or whether the 14 hours after the first estrogen exposure indicates the decay of the synthetic products triggered by that initial treatment.

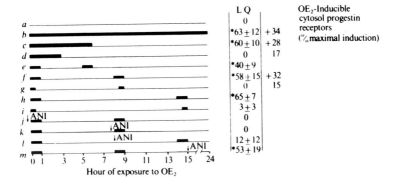

FIG. 19. The effects of estradiol (OE₂) and anisomycin (ANI) on the lordosis quotient (LQ) and on the induction of cytosol progestin receptors (CPRs) in the mediobasal hypothalamus-preoptic area (MBH-POA) of the female rat. Biochemical results are expressed as percentage maximal induction (see text). For behavior, animals were tested with an experienced male 24 hours after the initiation of estradiol treatment. Four hours before testing, each animal received 500 μg progesterone (sc in oil). In some behavioral experiments, animals received sc injections of the protein synthesis inhibitor, anisomycin, dissoved 20 mg ml^{-1} in saline. For CPR measurements, animals were killed 24 hours after the insertion of Silastic capsules. No exogenous progesterone was given before death. The temporal paradigms for these experiments are as follows: (a) No OE₂, control group; (b) OE₂ 0–24 hours; (c) OE₂ 0–6 hours; (d) OE₂ 0–3 hours; (e) OE₂ 0–1 hour and 5–6 hours; (f) OE₂ 0–1 hour and 8–9 hours; (g) OE₂ 0–0.5 hour and 8.5–9 hours; (h) OE₂ 0–1 hour and 14–15 hours; (i) OE₂ 0–0.5 hour and 14.5–15 hours; (j) OE₂ 0–1 hour and 8–9 hours, ANI at −0.25 hour; (k) OE₂ 0–1 hour and 8–9 hours, ANI at 8.75 hours; (l) OE₂ 0–1 hour and 14–15 hours, ANI at 8 hours; (m) 0–1 hour and 8–9 hours, ANI at 15 hours. We conclude that a discontinuous exposure to estradiol, in two 1-hour segments, is sufficient to activate the lordosis reflex and to increase CPRs in the female rat. ANI experiments demonstrate that protein synthesis essential for the activation of the lordosis reflex occurs during the period bounded by and including these two 1-hour segments of OE₂ treatment. CPR levels are (fmol [³H]R5020 per mg protein): (a) 8.1 ± 0.3; (b) 12.7 ± 0.7; (c) 11.8 ± 1.2; (d) 10.3 ± 0.7; (f) 13.3 ± 1.1; (g) 10.0 ± 0.6. CPR levels in animals which receive estradiol benzoate for 3 days before death (15 μg per day) are 21.1 ± 1.2 fmol [³H]5020 per mg protein. *LQ scores in groups a–m were compared with each other using a one-way analysis of variance. A significant treatment effect was seen ($F = 11.21$, $p < 0.01$). Comparisons of individual means using the Newman–Kuels tests revealed that groups b, c, e, f, and h were statistically different from the control group ($p < 0.01$). ⁺Cytosol progestin receptor levels in groups a–d, f, and g were compared with each other using a one-way analysis of variance. A significant treatment effect was seen ($F = 4.91$, $p < 0.05$). Comparisons of individual means using the Newman–Kuels tests revealed that groups b, c, and f were significantly different from the control group ($p < 0.05$). Reprinted from Parsons et al. (1981a) by permission.

Progesterone action to facilitate feminine sexual behavior is also blocked by anisomycin (Rainbow et al., 1980a). The proteins synthesized under stimulation by progesterone appear to have a rapid turnover—this is inferred from the fact that anisomycin applied after progesterone has already activated sexual behavior will inhibit this behavior within 1 hour. In contrast, the effects of estradiol, once established (see above), are resistant to anisomycin treatment (Rainbow *et al.*, 1980a; Parsons *et al.*, 1981a). Besides stimulating the formation of proteins involved in facilitating sexual behavior, progesterone also appears to promote formation of proteins which have a delayed effect to inhibit sexual behavior. This is revealed by experiments in which anisomycin treatment 3–10 hours after progesterone administration blocks the "sequential inhibition" by progesterone of sexual behavior 24 hours later (Parsons and McEwen, 1981).

An event linking estradiol and progesterone action in the brain is the induction of progestin receptors by estradiol (Moguilewsky and Raynaud, 1977; MacLusky and McEwen, 1978; Blaustein and Wade, 1978). In the rat brain, progestin receptor induction occurs in the hypothalamus and preoptic area, and it is temporally correlated with the activation of feminine sexual behavior (Parsons *et al.*, 1980). A "threshold level" of 30% of maximal induction in hypothalamus-preoptic area has been associated with the potential to display lordosis behavior; i.e., below 30% of maximal induction progesterone administration has no significant effect in activating lordosis responding (Parsons *et al.*, 1980, 1981a). Further support for the importance of progestin receptor induction by estradiol in sexual behavior is that the induction is attenuated by treatment with an antiestrogen, CI628 (Roy *et al.*, 1979) and by anisomycin (Rainbow *et al.*, 1980a) under conditions which also block activation of feminine sexual behavior.

3. Spatial Aspects of Estradiol and Progesterone Action

Besides the temporal characteristics of estradiol and progesterone action and the involvement of protein synthesis in their effects upon feminine sexual behavior, the question of site or sites of action in the brain is also very important. This question has been answered by means of localized implantation of estradiol (e.g., Lisk, 1960, 1962; Rodgers and Law, 1968; Chambers and Howe, 1968; Dörner *et al.*, 1968; Barfield and Chen, 1977; Davis *et al.*, 1979b; Rubin and Barfield, 1980) and progesterone (see McEwen *et al.*, 1979a, Table 12, for summary) in various brain areas. When the dose of estradiol is minimized by diluting it with cholesterol so as to apply nanogram, rather than microgram quantities, the most consistent brain site for eliciting lordosis behavior in ovariectomized rats is the ventromedial nucleus of the hypothalamus (Davis *et al.*, 1979b; Rubin and Barfield, 1980). When [^{3}H]estradiol is used in the implants, measurements of spread of isotope (Table VIII) reveal that occupancy of estrogen receptors in pituitary, preoptic area, and amygdala is negligible ($\leq 0.05\%$ of capacity), whereas receptor labeling in basomedial hy-

TABLE VIII

Comparison of Cell Nuclear Receptor Occupancy Resulting from
[³H]Estradiol Implants with Capacities of Cell Nuclear Binding in
Brain and Pituitary[a]

Tissue	Estimated capacity (fmol/mg DNA)	Occupation (fmol/mg DNA)	Percentage capacity
Hypothalamus	700	30.5	4.5
POA	1100	0.5	0.04
Amygdala	350	0.2	0.05
Pituitary	3200	1.8	0.05

[a] Reprinted from Davis et al. (1979a) by permission.

pothalamus is significant ($\approx$4.5% of capacity). Further analysis of the basomedial hypothalamus of such implanted animals by autoradiography reveals a high degree of localization of radioactivity in a steep gradient around the ventrolateral ventromedial nucleus (Davis et al., 1981). The ventrolateral ventromedial nucleus is a locus of estrophilic neurons (Pfaff and Keiner, 1973), as well as of progestin-concentrating neurons (Warembourg, 1978; McEwen et al., 1982). Therefore, it is particularly important that when the intracranial dose of progesterone is minimized by dilution with cholesterol, the ventromedial nuclei are, once again, the most sensitive sites for activation of lordosis responding in estrogen-treated rats (Rubin and Barfield, unpublished).

Since all earlier published work was done with 100- to 1000-fold larger amounts of steroid, it is attractive to suppose that other intracranial sites where estradiol and progesterone have been reported to elicit some lordosis behavior (see McEwen et al., 1979a, for review) are spurious due to leakage of steroid to the ventromedial nuclei. However, it is also conceivable that there may be other brain sites from which estrogen and progesterone action may be capable of influencing behavior.

The case for the ventromedial nuclei having an essential role in lordosis behavior is very strong. Lesions of this region abolish the behavior and electrical stimulation of this area facilitates the lordosis response (Pfaff, 1980). Introduction of anisomycin into the ventromedial hypothalamus reversibly blocks the effects of systemically administered estradiol and also of progesterone in activating sexual behavior (Rainbow et al., 1980b). The anisomycin effect upon protein synthesis is reversible, thus ruling out brain lesions as a reason for the inhibition. Moreover, these anisomycin effects are limited to the hypothalamus. Within the hypothalamus they are confined for the first 2 hours to the ventromedial region, although by 4 hours after ANI implantation, there is some spread of drug into the more dorsal aspect of the hypothalamus (Rainbow *et al.*, 1980b). Taken together with the data on intracranial estradiol and progesterone implantation, the results with intracranial ANI lend strong support to a primary, if not exclusive role, of the ventromedial hypothalamus in the hormonal control of feminine sexual behavior in the rat.

V. Conclusions

In view of the preceding detailed discussions of the organizational and activational modes of estradiol action, it is possible to speculate on the potential cellular and molecular events in hormone-induced modulations of behavior.

Regarding "organizational" effects, the predominant view is that certain neural circuits are permanently modified by early hormone exposure. According to this view, these modified circuits are then either better able (as in masculinization) or less capable (as in defeminization) of mediating a particular behavior or neuroendocrine function. Indeed, the evidence for hormonally controlled morphological sex differences in localized regions of the brain is accumulating rapidly (see Section IV,B above). When and how these morphological sex differences arise during brain development are matters of great interest (e.g., Jacobson *et al.*, 1980; Gurney, 1981). Work summarized in this article provides several insights regarding the nature of primary events in brain sexual differentiation. First, the acquisition of sufficient levels of hormone (e.g., estrogen) receptors by certain neuronal groupings may be both the rate-limiting and final step which signals the onset of the critical period (e.g., for defeminization in a rat or mouse). Second, the primary effects of testosterone or estradiol to trigger neurite outgrowth in the system of Toran-Allerand (see Fig. 17) may be sufficient in terms of hormonal input to account for the differences in synaptic connections and, possibly, in neuronal cell number and cell body size, the major morphologic features of the brain sex differences so far described (Section IV,B,6) (see Fig. 20). It would, however, be premature to overlook other possible actions of testosterone or estradiol on other cellular events which may be involved in neuronal differentiation. Some of these are listed in Table IX. Among the most intriguing of these possibilities is the notion that hormones may influence the expression of a particular neurotransmitter phenotype. Such a possibility is suggested by observations that glucocorticoids promote adrenergic and not cholinergic expression in developing sympathetic neurons (McLennan *et al.*, 1980; Fukada, 1980; see also Patterson, 1978).

In contrast to "organizational" effects, the "activational" effects of steroids on behavior appear to be mediated by a reversible induction of

COULD NEURITE GROWTH BE THE PRIMARY STEROID SENSITIVE EVENT?

Growth of neurites - E or A dependent

↓

Increased contacts / more "good" synapses

↓

Increased cell survival (cell number)

and

Increased cell body size

FIG. 20. Hypothetical sequence for hormone action leading to morphological sex differences in hormone-sensitive brain regions. E, estrogen; A, androgen. This designation refers to presence of estrogen or androgen receptors in neurons from which outgrowth emanates.

gene products which are involved in neurotransmission or other aspects of nerve cell function. According to this view, hormones might regulate behavior by modifying levels of synaptic constituents involved in neurotransmission and thereby alter the response of the neural circuit to a triggering stimulus (for example the male mounting the female which elicits a lordosis response). The most specific examination of this notion concerns the action of estradiol followed by progesterone on the hypothalamic

TABLE IX

Possible Control Points for Gonadal Steroid Action[a]

Neurite growth
Programs of differentiation (e.g., dendritic spines; neurotransmitter phenotype)
Production of stabilizing factors (like nerve growth factor)
Production of cell recognition factors
Programmed cell loss[b]
Reinitiation of cell division

[a] With the exception of neurite growth (see text), most of the possible control points listed above lack specific examples involving gonadal steroid action. For discussion of each possibility, see McEwen (1981).

[b] Programmed cell loss refers to the notion that, as a primary action, hormones might trigger neurons to self-destruct. However, this category also includes hormone-dependent loss or absence of a target for neurons like a muscle or other neuronal group. Such a loss would lead to atrophy of the primary afferent neurons and lead to a reduction in neuronal cell number. The loss of neurons of the spinal nucleus of the bulbocavernosus, in relation to the failure of development of muscles of the penis, may represent an example of this type (Breedlove and Arnold, 1980).

ventromedial nucleus to facilitate feminine sexual behavior in the rat. The finding that hormone action in this brain area is sufficient to promote behavior (Section IV,C,3) is an enormous advantage for future research on neurochemical mechanisms. The recent work of Pfaff (Pfaff and Sakuma, 1979a,b; Sakuma and Pfaff, 1979a,b, 1980a,b,c) argues forcefully for neural projections from the ventromedial nuclei to a mesencephalic control center for a "reflex arc" mediating lordosis. Electrical stimulation of the ventromedial nuclei potentiates lordosis responding beyond the termination of the stimulating current (Pfaff and Sakuma, 1979b). This effect implies a long-lasting synaptic modulation by a substance which may be produced and released by ventromedial neurons. Recently, Cohen and Pfaff (1981) have presented electron microscopic evidence for an estrogen-induced change in morphology of the endoplasmic reticulum that implies enhanced formation of neurosecretory material and perhaps other cellular proteins.

Besides stimulating the formation of neurosecretory material to be released at ventromedial synapses in the midbrain, estradiol (and also progesterone) may also modify other features of the ventromedial neurons, such as their sensitivity to afferent neural input (Fig. 21). For example, these hormones may increase the sensitivity to incoming stimulatory neural inputs and/or decrease the sensitivity to incoming inhibitory neural inputs and thus tip the balance toward activation of the ventromedial neurons to exert their influence on the midbrain. Several neurochemical

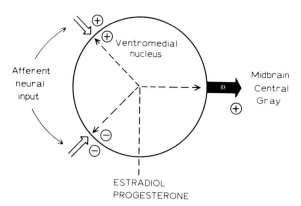

FIG. 21.   Hypothetical scheme for control points of estrogen and progesterone action in the ventromedial nucleus of hypothalamus which would lead to activation of sexual behavior. In particular, hormone action may enhance effect of stimulatory afferent neural input and/or decrease effect of inhibitory neural input. It may also alter output of ventromedial neurons to midbrain central grey, as suggested by the experiments of Pfaff and co-workers (see text).

changes are already known which fit this description. Estrogen treatment increases the level of muscarinic cholinergic receptors in the ventromedial nuclei (Rainbow *et al.*, 1980c); and muscarinic cholinergic neurotransmission appears to have a facilitative effect on feminine sexual behavior (Clemens and Dohanich, 1980; Clemens *et al.*, 1980). Estrogen treatment also decreases the activity of glutamic acid decarboxalase (GAD) in the ventromedial nuclei (Wallis and Luttge, 1980); and the GABA which is produced by GAD action is an inhibitory neurotransmitter and may have an inhibitory effect on sexual behavior (D. W. Pfaff, personal communication). Finally, direct estrogen effects on serotonin$_1$ receptors (see Section III) might result in decreased serotonin effects during the peak of estrogen titers in the blood. Such an action of estradiol would help to explain the decreased serotonin binding to hypothalamic membranes which has been reported to occur on the afternoon of proestrus (Biegon *et al.*, 1980). Decreased serotonin receptor sensitivity might tend to release the lordosis-mediating neurons from a serotonergic influence which is generally regarded as inhibitory for this behavior (Meyerson, 1964; Everitt *et al.*, 1975; Ward *et al.*, 1975; Foreman and Moss, 1979). Taken together, these various hints regarding neurochemical consequences of estradiol action point to a multiplicity of possible regulatory events within the rather circumscribed domain of the ventromedial nuclei, any one or all of which might be sufficient for the behavior to occur. Further research may reveal which event plays a predominant role in estradiol action on lordosis behavior. A major step in this direction will be to find which events are influenced by progesterone, as well as by estradiol, since under normal estrogen priming conditions, feminine sexual behavior is almost entirely dependent on exposure to progesterone.

As with all speculations of this kind, the main purpose of those contained in Figs. 20 and 21 and discussed above is to focus thinking and catalyze further research. The wealth of information regarding sites and modes of steroid hormone action in the brain gathered since 1961 should make such future investigations especially productive and rewarding.

ACKNOWLEDGMENTS

Research support was obtained from USPHS Grants NS07080 (BMc), HD12011 (VNL), and HD10168 (LCK) and by an institutional grant RF70095 from the Rockefeller Foundation for research in reproductive biology. The senior author acknowledges with great appreciation the important contribution of former laboratory associates (Drs. Carl Denef, Ivan Lieberburg, Neil MacLusky, Jerrold Meyer, Linda Plapinger, Edward Roy, and Richard Zigmond) and present and past technical assistants (Claude Chaptal, Valerie DeGroff, John Gerlach, Jaqueline Kass, Carew Magnus, Marie Nicolas, Joan Nicholson, Lenore Snyder, Barbara Sue Stephenson, and Ghislaine Wallach) to the research described herein. A number of collaborators from other institutions have added greatly to the work: Dominique

Toran-Allerand (Columbia); Ernest J. Peck (Baylor); Eric Nestler and Paul Greengard (Yale); Tong Joh and Donald Reis (Cornell); and Ulf Stenevi and Anders Björklund (Lund). Very special thanks also go to two colleagues at Rockefeller for their cooperation and collaboration over a number of years: Professors Donald Pfaff and Fernando Nottebohm. Mrs. Oksana Wengerchuk assisted greatly with editorial matters and typing.

REFERENCES

Anderson, C. H., and Greenwald, S. S. (1969). *Endocrinology* **85**, 1160.
Anderson, N. S., III, and Fanestil, D. D. (1976). *Endocrinology* **98**, 676.
Arimatsu, Y., Seto, A., and Amano, T. (1981). *Brain Res.* **213**, 432.
Arnold, A. P. (1980). *J. Comp. Neurol.* **189**, 421.
Arnold, A. P., and Saltiel, A. (1979). *Science* **205**, 702.
Arnold, A. P., Nottebohm, F., and Pfaff, D. W. (1976). *J. Comp. Neurol.* **165**, 487.
Ashburner, M. (1974). *Dev. Biol.* **39**, 141.
Ashburner, M., and Berendes, H. D. (1978). *In* "The Genetics and Biology of Drosophila" (M. Ashburner and T. R. F. Wright, eds.), pp. 315–395. Academic Press, New York.
Attardi, B., and Ohno, S. (1976). *Endocrinology* **99**, 1279.
Attramadal, A. (1970). *Z. Zellforsch.* **104**, 572.
Ball, P., and Knuppen, R. (1980). *Acta Endocrinol.* **93** (Suppl.), 232, 233.
Barfield, R. J., and Chen, J. J. (1977). *Endocrinology* **101**, 1716.
Barley, J., Ginsburg, M., Greenstein, B. D., MacLusky, N. J., and Thomas, P. J. (1975). *Brain Res.* **100**, 383.
Barraclough, C. A., and Gorski, R. A. (1961). *Endocrinology* **68**, 68.
Beach, F. A. (1948). *In* "Hormones and Behavior: A Study of Interrelationships between Endocrine Secretions and Patterns of Overt Response." Hoeber, New York.
Beach, F. A. (1975). *Psychoneuroendocrinology* **1**, 3.
Beach, F. A. (1976). *Horm. Behav.* **7**, 105.
Beach, F. A., and Buehler, M. G. (1977). *Endocrinology* **100**, 197.
Benno, R. H., and Williams, T. H. (1978). *Brain Res.* **142**, 182.
Berthold, A. A. (1849). *Arch. Anat. Physiol. Wiss. Med.* **16**, 42.
Biegon, A., Bercovitz, H., and Samuel, D. (1980). *Brain Res.* **187**, 221.
Blaustein, J. D., and Feder, H. H. (1979). *Brain Res.* **169**, 481.
Blaustein, J. D., and Wade, G. N. (1978). *Brain Res.* **140**, 360.
Bleisch, W. V., and Luine, V. N. (1981). *Soc. Neurosci. Abstr.* **259** (5), 805.
Breedlove, S. M., and Arnold, A. P. (1980). *Science* **210**, 564.
Bubenik, G. A., and Brown, G. M. (1973). *Experientia* **29**, 619.
Chader, G. J., and Willee, C. A. (1970). *Biochem. J.* **118**, 93.
Chambers, W. F., and Howe, G. (1968). *Proc. Soc. Exp. Biol. Med.* **128**, 292.
Chamness, G. C., King, T. W., and Sheridan, P. J. (1979). *Brain Res.* **161**, 267.
Christensen, L. W., and Clemens, L. G. (1974). *Endocrinology* **95**, 984.
Chytil, F., and Toft, D. (1972). *J. Neurochem.* **19**, 2877.
Cidlowski, J. A., and Muldoon, T. G. (1974). *Endocrinology* **95**, 1621.
Clemens, L. G., and Dohanich, G. P. (1980). *Pharmacol. Biochem. Behav.* **13**, 89.
Clemens, L. G., Humphrys, R. R., and Dohanich, G. P. (1980). *Pharmacol. Biochem. Behav.* **13**, 81.
Clever, U. (1964). *Science* **146**, 794.
Cohen, R. S., and Pfaff, D. W. (1981). *Cell Tissue Res.* **217**, 451.
Dallman, M. F., and Yates, F. E. (1969). *Ann. N.Y. Acad. Sci.* **156**, 696.
Davis, P. G., and Barfield, R. J. (1979). *Neuroendocrinology* **28**, 217.

Davis, P. G., Chaptal, C. V., and McEwen, B. S. (1979a). *Horm. Behav.* **12**, 12.
Davis, P. G., McEwen, B. S., and Pfaff, D. W. (1979b). *Endocrinology* **104**, 898.
Davis, P. G., McEwen, B. S., and Pfaff, D. W. (1981). *Conf. Reprod. Behav.* (*Abstr.*)
DeKloet, R., Wallach, G., and McEwen, B. S. (1975). *Endocrinology* **96**, 598.
Denef, C., Magnus, C., and McEwen, B. S. (1973). *J. Endocrinol.* **59**, 605.
Denef, C., Magnus, C., and McEwen, B. S. (1974). *Endocrinology* **94**, 1265.
deVellis, J., and Inglish, D. (1968). *J. Neurochem.* **15**, 1061.
Dokas, L. A. (1979). *Soc. Neurosci. Abstr.* **1498**, 443.
Dörner, G., and Staudt, J. (1969a). *Neuroendocrinology* **4**, 278.
Dörner, G., and Staudt, J. (1969b). *Neuroendocrinology* **5**, 103.
Dörner, G., Döcke, F., and Moustafa, S. (1968). *J. Reprod. Fertil.* **17**, 583.
Doughty, C., Booth, J. E., McDonald, P. G., and Parrott, R. F. (1975). *J. Endocrinol.* **67**, 419.
Edwardson, J. A., and Bennett, G. W. (1974). *Nature* (*London*) **251**, 425.
Eisenfeld, A. J. (1970). *Endocrinology* **86**, 1313.
Eisenfeld, A. J., and Axelrod, J. (1965). *J. Pharmacol. Exp. Ther.* **150**, 469.
Everitt, B. J., Fuxe, K., Hökfelt, T., and Jonsson, G. (1975). *J. Comp. Physiol. Psychol.* **89**, 556.
Feder, H. H. (1981a). *In* "Neuroendocrinology of Reproduction" (N. Adler, ed.), pp. 89–126. Plenum, New York.
Feder, H. H. (1981b). *In* "Neuroendocrinology of Reproduction" (N. Adler, ed.), pp. 127–157. Plenum, New York.
Feldman, S., and Robinson, S. (1968). *J. Neurol. Sci.* **6**, 1.
Foreman, M. M., and Moss, R. L. (1979). *Physiol. Behav.* **22**, 283.
Fox, T. O. (1975). *Proc. Natl. Acad. Sci. U.S.A.* **72**, 4303.
Fox, T. O. (1977). *Brain Res.* **120**, 580.
Fukada, K. (1980). *Nature* (*London*) **287**, 553.
Gerlach, J. L., and McEwen, B. S. (1972). *Science* **175**, 1133.
Ginsburg, M., MacLusky, N., Morris, I. D., and Thomas, P. J. (1977). *Br. J. Pharmacol.* **59**, 397.
Gorski, R. A. (1979). *In* "The Neurosciences: 4th Study Program" (F. O. Schmitt, ed.), pp. 969–982. MIT Press, Cambridge, Massachusetts.
Gorski, R. A., Gordon, J. H., Shryne, J. E., and Southam, A. M. (1978). *Brain Res.* **148**, 333.
Gorski, R. A., Harlan, R. E., Jacobson, C. D., Shryne, J. E., and Southam, A. M. (1980). *J. Comp. Neurol.* **193**, 529.
Goy, R. W., and McEwen, B. S., eds. (1980). *In* "Sexual Differentiation of the Brain," p. 211. MIT Press, Cambridge, Massachusetts.
Green, R., Luttge, W. G., and Whalen, R. E. (1970). *Physiol. Behav.* **5**, 137.
Greenough, W. T., Carter, C. S., Steerman, C., and DeVoogd, T. (1977). *Brain Res.* **126**, 63.
Grosser, B. I., Stevens, W., Bruenger, F. W., and Reed, D. J. (1971). *J. Neurochem.* **18**, 1725.
Gurney, M. E. (1981). *J. Neurosci.* **1**, 658.
Gurney, M. E., and Konishi, M. (1980). *Science* **208**, 1380.
Hardy, D. F., and DeBold, J. F. (1971). *Horm. Behav.* **2**, 287.
Harris, G. W., and Jacobsohn, D. (1952). *Proc. R. Soc. London Ser. B* **139**, 263.
Harris, G. W., Michael, R. P., and Scott, P. P. (1958). *In* "Ciba Foundation Symposium on the Neurological Basis of Behavior" (G. E. Wolstenholme and C. M. O'Connor, eds.), pp. 236–251. Little Brown, Boston.
Ifft, J. D. (1972). *J. Comp. Neurol.* **144**, 193.
Jackson, G. L. (1972). *Endocrinology* **91**, 1284.

Jacobson, C. D., and Gorski, R. A. (1981). *J. Comp. Neurol.*, **196**, 519.
Jacobson, C. D., Shryne, J. E., Shapiro, F., and Gorski, R. A. (1980). *J. Comp. Neurol.* **193**, 541.
Jensen, E. V., and Jacobson, H. I. (1962). *Recent Prog. Horm. Res.* **18**, 387.
Jones, M. T., Hillhouse, E. W., and Burden, J. L. (1977). *J. Endocrinol.* **73**, 405.
Kalra, S. P. (1975). *Neuroendocrinology* **18**, 333.
Kato, J., and Villee, C. A. (1967) *Endocrinology* **80**, 567.
Kato, J., Onouchi, T., and Okinaga, S. (1978). *J. Steroid Biochem.* **9**, 419.
Kelly, M. J., Moss, R. L., and Dudley, C. A. (1977). *Exp. Brain Res.* **30**, 53.
Kelner, K. L., Miller, A. L., and Peck, E. J., Jr. (1980). *J. Receptor Res.* **1**, 215.
Kincl, F. A., and Maqueo, M. (1965). *Endocrinology* **77**, 859.
Knizley, H., Jr. (1972). *J. Neurochem.* **19**, 2737.
Krey, L. C., Kamel, F., and McEwen, B. S. (1980). *Brain Res.* **193**, 277.
Krey, L. C., Lieberburg, I., MacLusky, N. J., and Davis, P. G. (1981). *Endocrine Soc. Abstr.* **607P**, 234.
Kubli-Garfias, C., and Whalen, R. E. (1977). *Horm. Behav.* **9**, 380.
Lehrman, D. S. (1964). *Sci. Am.* **211** (5), 48.
Leveille, P. J., McGinnis, J. F., Maxwell, D. S., and DeVellis, J. (1980). *Brain Res.* **196**, 287.
Lieberburg, I., and McEwen, B. S. (1975). *Brain Res.* **85**, 165.
Lieberburg, I., and McEwen, B. S. (1977). *Endocrinology* **100**, 588.
Lieberburg, I., and Nottebohm, F. (1979). *Gen. Comp. Endocrinol.* **37**, 286.
Lieberburg, I., MacLusky, N. J., and McEwen, B. S. (1977a). *Endocrinology* **100**, 598.
Lieberburg, I., Krey, L. C., and McEwen, B. S. (1979). *Brain Res.* **178**, 207.
Lieberburg, I., Wallach, G., and McEwen, B. S. (1977b). *Brain Res.* **128**, 176.
Lieberburg, I., MacLusky, N. J., and McEwen, B. S. (1980a). *Brain Res.* **193**, 487.
Lieberburg, I., MacLusky, N. J., and McEwen, B. S. (1980b). *Brain Res.* **196**, 125.
Linkie, D. M. (1977). *Endocrinology* **101**, 1862.
Lisk, R. D. (1960). *J. Exp. Zool.* **145**, 197.
Lisk, R. D. (1962). *Am. J. Physiol.* **203**, 493.
Loy, R., and Milner, T. A. (1980). *Science* **208**, 1282.
Luine, V. N., Khylchevskaya, R. I., and McEwen, B. S. (1975). *Brain Res.* **86**, 293.
Luine, V. N., Nottebohm, F., Harding, C., and McEwen, B. S. (1980a). *Brain Res.* **192**, 89.
Luine, V. N., Park, D., John, T., Reis, D., and McEwen, B. S. (1980b). *Brain Res.* **191**, 273.
McDonald, P., Beyer, C., Newton, F., Brien, B., Baker, R., Jan, H. S., Sampson, C., Kitching, P., Greenhill, R., and Pritchard, D. (1970). *Nature (London)* **227**, 964.
McEwen, B. S. (1978). *In* "Hormone Receptors, Vol. I, Steroid Hormones" (B. O'Malley and L. Birnbaumer, eds.), pp. 353–400. Academic Press, New York.
McEwen, B. S. (1981). *In* "Molecular Approaches to Neurobiology" (I. Brown, ed.), Academic Press, New York.
McEwen, B. S., and Biegon, A. (1981). *Soc. Neurosci. Abstr.* **262**(11), 818.
McEwen, B. S., and Pfaff, D. W. (1970). *Brain Res.* **21**, 1.
McEwen, B. S., and Plapinger, L. (1970). *Nature (London)* **226**, 263.
McEwen, B. S., Weiss, J. M., and Schwartz, L. (1968). *Nature (London)* **220**, 911.
McEwen, B. S., Weiss, J. M., and Schwartz, L. S. (1969). *Brain Res.* **16**, 227.
McEwen, B. S., Zigmond, R. E., and Gerlach, J. L. (1972a). *In* "Structure and Function of Nervous Tissue" (G. H. Bourne, ed.), pp. 205–291. Academic Press, New York.
McEwen, B. S., Magnus, C., and Wallach, G. (1972b). *Endocrinology* **90**, 217.
McEwen, B. S., Plapinger, L., Chaptal, C., Gerlach, J., and Wallach, G. (1975). *Brain Res.* **96**, 400.
McEwen, B. S., De Kloet, R., and Wallach, G. (1976). *Brain Res.* **105**, 129.

McEwen, B. S., Lieberburg, I., Chaptal, C., and Krey, L. C. (1977). *Horm. Behav.* **9**, 249.

McEwen, B. S., Davis, P. G., Parsons, B., and Pfaff, D. W. (1979a). In "Annual Review of Neuroscience" (M. Cowan, ed.), pp. 65–112. Annual Reviews, Palo Alto, California.

McEwen, B. S., Lieberburg, I., Chaptal, C., Davis, P. G., Krey, L. C., MacLusky, N. J., and Roy, E. J. (1979b). *Horm. Behav.* **13**, 269.

McEwen, B. S., Biegon, A., Rainbow, T., Paden, C., Snyder, L., and DeGroff, V. (1981). In "Steroid Hormone Regulation of the Brain" (K. Fuxe *et al.,* eds.), pp. 15–30. Pergamon, Oxford.

McEwen, B. S., Davis, P. G., Gerlach, J. L., Krey, L. C., MacLusky, N. J., McGinnis, M. Y., Parsons, B., and Rainbow, T. C. (1982). In "Progesterone and Progestins" (C. W. Bardin, P. Mauvais-Jarvis, and E. Milgrom, eds.). Raven, New York, in press.

McGinnis, J. F., and deVellis, J. (1978). *J. Biol. Chem.* **252**, 8483.

McGinnis, M. Y., Parsons, B., Rainbow, T. C., Krey, L. C., and McEwen, B. S. (1981). *Brain Res.* **218**, 365.

McLennan, I. S., Hill, C. E., and Hendry, I. A. (1980). *Nature (London)* **283**, 206.

MacLusky, N. J., and McEwen, B. S. (1978). *Nature (London)* **274**, 276.

MacLusky, N. J., and McEwen, B. S. (1980a). *Endocrinology* **106**, 192.

MacLusky, N. J., and McEwen, B. S. (1980b). *Brain Res.* **189**, 262.

MacLusky, N. J., Lieberburg, I., and McEwen, B. S. (1979a). *Brain Res.* **178**, 129.

MacLusky, N. J., Chaptal, C., and McEwen, B. S. (1979b). *Brain Res.* **178**, 143.

MacLusky, N. J., Clark, C. R., Paden, C. M., and Naftolin, F. (1982). In "Mechanisms of Steroid Action" (G. P. Lewis, R. J. Flower, M. Ginsburg, and H. P. Rany, eds.), Macmillan, New York, in press.

Mandelbrod, I., Feldman, S., and Werman, R. (1981). *Brain Res.* **218**, 115.

Martini, L. (1976). In "Subcellular Mechanisms in Reproductive Neuroendocrinology" (F. Naftolin, K. J. Ryair, and J. Davies, eds.), pp. 327–355. Elsevier, Amsterdam.

Matsumoto, A., and Arai, Y. (1980). *Brain Res.* **190**, 238.

Meyer, J. S., and McEwen, B. S. (1982). *J. Neurochem.,* in press.

Meyer, J. S., Micco, D. J., Stephenson, B. S., Krey, L. C., and McEwen, B. S. (1979). *Physiol. Behav.* **22**, 867.

Meyerson, B. J. (1964). *Arch. Int. Pharmacodyn.* **150**, 4.

Meyerson, B. J. (1972). *Horm. Behav.* **3**, 1.

Michael, R. P. (1965). *Br. Med. Bull.* **21**, 87.

Miller, A. L., Chaptal, C., McEwen, B. S., and Peck, E. J., Jr. (1978). *Psychoneuroendocrinology* **3**, 155.

Mizejewski, G. J., Vonnegut, M., and Simon, R. (1980). *Brain Res.* **188**, 273.

Moguilewsky, M., and Raynaud, J.-P. (1977). *Steroids* **30**, 99.

Moguilewsky, M., and Raynaud, J.-P. (1980). *J. Steroid Biochem.* **12**, 309.

Naftolin, F., Ryan, K. J., Davies, I. J., Reddy, V. V., Flores, F., Petro, Z., Kuhn, M., White, R. J., Takaoka, Y., and Wolin, I. (1975). *Recent Prog. Horm. Res.* **31**, 291.

Nestler, E. J., Rainbow, T. C., McEwen, B. S., and Greengard, P. (1981a). *Science* **212**, 1162.

Nestler, E. J., Rainbow, T. C., McEwen, B. S., and Greengard, P. (1981b). In "Steroid Hormone Regulation of the Brain" (K. Fuxe *et al.,* eds.), pp. 205–216. Pergamon, Oxford.

Nishizuka, M., and Arai, Y. (1981). *Brain Res.* **212**, 31.

Nöthiger, R. (1972). In "The Biology of Imaginal Disks" (H. Ursprung and R. Nöthiger, eds.), pp. 1–34. Springer-Verlag, Berlin and New York.

Nottebohm, F. (1980). In "Progress in Psychobiology and Physiological Psychology" (J. M. Sprague and A. N. Epstein, eds.), pp. 85–124. Academic Press, New York.

Nottebohm, F., and Arnold, A. P. (1976). *Science* **194**, 211.

Nunez, E., Engelmann, F., Benassayag, C., Savu, L., Crepy, O., and Jayle, M. F. (1971). *C. R. Acad. Sci. (Paris, Ser. D* **272**, 2396.

Oberlander, H. (1972). *In* "The Biology of Imaginal Disks" (H. Ursprung and R. Nöthiger, eds.), pp. 155–172. Springer-Verlag, Berlin and New York.

Olsen, K. L. (1979a). *Nature (London)* **279**, 238.

Olsen, K. L. (1979b). *Horm. Behav.* **13**, 66.

Paden, C. M., Silverman, A.-J., McEwen, B. S., Stenevi, U., Björklund, A., and Thorngren, K. G. (1980). *Peptides* **1**, 117.

Paden, C. M., Snyder, L., DeGroff, V., and McEwen, B. S. (1981). *Soc. Neurosci. Abstr.* **137**(3), 424.

Parsons, B., and McEwen, B. S. (1981). *J. Neurosci.* **1**, 527.

Parsons, B., MacLusky, N. J., Krey, L. C., Pfaff, D. W., and McEwen, B. S. (1980). *Endocrinology* **107**, 774.

Parsons, B., Rainbow, T. C., Pfaff, D. W., and McEwen, B. S. (1981a). *Nature (London)* **292**, 58.

Parsons, B., McGinnis, M. Y., and McEwen, B. S. (1981b). *Brain Res.* **221**, 149.

Patterson, P. H. (1978). *Annu. Rev. Neurosci.* **1**, 1.

Pfaff, D. W. (1966). *J. Endocrinol.* **36**, 415.

Pfaff, D. W. (1968a). *Endocrinology* **82**, 1149.

Pfaff, D. W. (1968b). *Science* **161**, 1355.

Pfaff, D. W. (1980). "Estrogens and Brain Function," pp. 281. Springer-Verlag, Berlin and New York.

Pfaff, D. W., and Keiner, M. (1973). *J. Comp. Neurol.* **151**, 121.

Pfaff, D. W., and Sakuma, Y. (1979a). *J. Physiol. (London)* **288**, 203.

Pfaff, D. W., and Sakuma, Y. (1979b). *J. Physiol. (London)* **288**, 189.

Plapinger, L., and McEwen, B. S. (1973). *Endocrinology* **93**, 1119.

Plapinger, L., and McEwen, B. S. (1975). *Steroids* **26**, 255.

Plapinger, L., and McEwen, B. S. (1978). *In* "Biological Determinants of Sexual Behavior" (J. Hutchinson, ed.), pp. 193–218. Wiley, New York.

Plapinger, L., McEwen, B. S., and Clemens, L. E. (1973). *Endocrinology* **93**, 1129.

Quadagno, D. M., and Ho, G. K. W. (1975). *Horm. Behav.* **6**, 19.

Quadagno, D. M., Shryne, J., and Gorski, R. A. (1971). *Horm. Behav.* **2**, 1.

Rainbow, T. C., Davis, P. G., and McEwen, B. S. (1980a). *Brain Res.* **194**, 548.

Rainbow, T. C., Davis, P. G., McGinnis, M., and McEwen, B. S. (1980b). *Soc. Neurosci. Abstr.* **293**(4), 862.

Rainbow, T. C., DeGroff, V., Luine, V. N., and McEwen, B. S. (1980c). *Brain Res.* **198**, 239.

Raisman, G., and Field, P. M. (1973). *Brain Res.* **54**, 1.

Raynaud, J.-P. (1973). *Steroids* **21**, 249.

Raynaud, J.-P., Mercier-Bodard, C., and Baulieu, E. (1971). *Steroids* **18**, 767.

Reddy, V. V. R., Naftolin, F., and Ryan, K. J. (1974). *Endocrinology* **94**, 117.

Rees, H. D., Stumpf, W. E., and Sar, M. (1975). *In* "Anatomical Neuroendocrinology" (W. E. Stumpf and L. D. Grant, eds.), pp. 262–269. Karger, Basel.

Rethelyi, M. (1979). *Neuroendocrinology* **28**, 82.

Rhees, R. W., Grosser, B. I., and Stevens, W. (1975). *Brain Res.* **100**, 151.

Rodgers, C. H., and Law, O. T. (1968). *Physiol. Behav.* **3**, 241.

Ross, D. W., Glick, S. D., and Meibach, R. C. (1981). *Proc. Natl. Acad. Sci. U.S.A.* **78**, 1958–1961.

Roy, E. J., MacLusky, N. J., and McEwen, B. S. (1979). *Endocrinology* **104**, 1333.

Rubin, B. S., and Barfield, R. J. (1980). *Endocrinology* **106**, 504.

Sakuma, Y., and Pfaff, D. W. (1979a). *Am. J. Physiol.* **237**(5), R278.

Sakuma, Y., and Pfaff, D. W. (1979b). *Am. J. Physiol.* **237**(5), R285.

Sakuma, Y., and Pfaff, D. W. (1980a). *J. Neurophysiol.* **44**, 1002.

Sakuma, Y., and Pfaff, D. W. (1980b). *J. Neurophysiol.* **44**, 1012.

Sakuma, Y., and Pfaff, D. W. (1980c). *Exp. Neurol.* **70**, 269.

Scatchard, G. (1949). *Ann. N.Y. Acad. Sci.* **51**, 660.

Schaeffer, J. M., and Hsueh, A. J. (1979). *J. Biol. Chem.* **254**, 5606.

Schwarzel, W. C., Kruggel, W. G., and Brodie, H. J. (1973). *Endocrinology* **92**, 866.

Shapiro, B. H., Levine, D. C., and Adler, N. T. (1980). *Science* **209**, 418.

Sheridan, P. J., Sar, M., and Stumpf, W. E. (1974). *Endocrinology* **94**, 1386.

Sholiton, L. J., Marnell, R. T., and Werk, E. E. (1966). *Steroids* **8**, 265.

Smith, M. S., Freeman, M. E., and Neill, J. D. (1975). *Endocrinology* **96**, 219.

Stenevi, U., Björklund, A., Kromer, L. F., Paden, C. M., Gerlach, J. L., McEwen, B. S., and Silverman, A. J. (1980). *Cell Tissue Res.* **209**, 217.

Stumpf, W. E. (1968). *Science* **162**, 1001.

Terkel, A. S., Shryne, J., and Gorski, R. A. (1973). *Horm. Behav.* **4**, 377.

Toran-Allerand, C. D. (1976). *Brain Res.* **106**, 407.

Toran-Allerand, C. D. (1978). *Am. Zool.* **18**, 553.

Toran-Allerand, C. D. (1980a). *Brain Res.* **189**, 413.

Toran-Allerand, C. D. (1980b). *Nature (London)* **286**, 733.

Toran-Allerand, C. D. (1981). *In* "Bioregulators of Reproduction" (G. Jagiello and H. J. Vogel, eds.), pp. 43–57. Academic Press, New York.

Toran-Allerand, C. D., Gerlach, J. L., and McEwen, B. S. (1980). *Brain Res.* **184**, 517.

Towle, A. C., and Sze, P. Y. (1978). *Soc. Neurosci. Abstr.* **1141**, 356.

Turner, B. B., and McEwen, B. S. (1980). *Brain Res.* **189**, 169.

Veldhuis, H. D., Van Koppen, C., van Ittersum, M., and deKloet, E. R. (1982). *Brain Res.*, in press.

Vito, C. C., and Fox, T. O. (1979). *Science* **204**, 517.

Vito, C. C., and Fox, T. O. (1982). *Dev. Brain Res.* **2**, 97.

Vito, C. C., Wieland, S. J., and Fox, T. O. (1979). *Nature (London)* **282**, 308.

Wallis, C. J., and Luttge, W. G. (1980). *J. Neurochem.* **34**, 609.

Ward, I. L., Crowley, W. R., Zemlan, F. P., and Margules, D. L. (1975). *J. Comp. Physiol. Psychol.* **88**, 53.

Warembourg, M. (1970a). *C. R. Soc. Biol.* **164**, 126.

Warembourg, M. (1970b). *C. R. Acad. Sci. (Paris)* **270**, 152.

Warembourg, M. (1975). *Cell Tissue Res.* **161**, 183.

Warembourg, M. (1978). *Mol. Cell. Endocrinol.* **12**, 67.

Weisz, J., and Gibbs, C. (1974). *Endocrinology* **94**, 616.

Whalen, R. E., and Nadler, R. D. (1963). *Science* **141**, 273.

Whalen, R. E., and Olsen, K. L. (1978). *Behav. Biol.* **24**, 549.

Yagi, K. (1973). *Brain Res.* **53**, 343.

Young, W. C. (1961). *In* "Sex and Internal Secretion" (W. C. Young, ed.), Vol. II, 3rd ed., pp. 1173–1239. Williams & Wilkins, Baltimore, Maryland.

Zigmond, R. E., and McEwen, B. S. (1970). *J. Neurochem.* **17**, 889.

Zigmond, R. E., Nottebohm, F., and Pfaff, D. W. (1973). *Science* **179**, 1005.

DISCUSSION

E. J. Peck, Jr.: I'd like to make a comment about your observations on translocation of receptor to the nucleus in the hypothalamus and pituitary. Katrina Kelner and I presented at the 1981 Endocrine Meetings the observation that the estrogen receptor system in the brain is less sensitive to circulating levels of steroid than any of the peripheral targets, including the pituitary. In line with this observations for receptors, for a given dose of estradiol, either implanted or injected, you see the same differential sensitivity with respect to biochemical and physiologic responses. I'm not certain that I would use your term "spare receptors" here. We know that there are spare receptors; however, I think the same fraction of receptor occupation may be required for a given level of response. However, all brain tissues seem to require higher levels of steroid for a given response than do the peripheral targets.

B. S. McEwen: I'm sure that's right, but what I was trying to relate our data to, was the fact that we knew in our experiment that we had produced about 80–90% of the occupation of the nuclear receptor sites that could possibly occur. Under those circumstances we could not see more than about 50% depletion of cytosol receptors, in some cases apparently less, in the brain. Whereas in the pituitary where we were dealing also with about 85–90% of nucleus capacity, we could see an 80% depletion of cytosol receptors.

E. J. Peck: Does this mean that the number of total receptors is actually changing as a function of time in that experiment?

B. S. McEwen: Well, when we gave a pulse, the receptor goes in and out of the nucleus.

E. J. Peck: I mean total receptor, that is, cytoplasmic plus nuclear.

B. S. McEwen: No, cytosol plus nuclear receptor does not appear to change. It's just that a smaller fraction of the total seems to go to the nucleus under a dose of [^{3}H]estradiol that translocates near maximum amounts to the nucleus.

E. J. Peck: There may be a difference in methodology there, because using extraction you may be losing receptors whereas with the assay we use we measure them all. I don't know, but there is definitely a difference in what we're seeing with the dynamics of the receptor system in the case of the brain.

B. S. McEwen: Our study was not an exchange study. We used [^{3}H]estradiol to label receptors *in vivo* and *in vitro* and did not extract the nuclear receptor. But you made a very important point as well, because I'm sure that the brain is less sensitive—it's also less sensitive in terms of, say, the antiestrogens; that is, CI628 is accumulated less extensively by the brain and once it goes in, it seems to come out more rapidly, so the antagonistic effects wear off more rapidly than it does, for example, in the pituitary.

E. J. Peck: Is the region that Toran-Allerand observed sprouting in the preoptic area the same as the sexually dimorphic region that Roger Gorski reported or is it nearby?

B. S. McEwen: That nucleus is closer to the area that Raisman and Field described as being sexually dimorphic—it's above Gorski's nucleus. As far as I can tell Toran Allerand's observations cannot be related directly to either of those areas. That is, she's studying areas that happened by the proximity to the surface of the culture to be able to show the outgrowth response. She can't so easily study the deeper structures where presumably there is outgrowth, but it is internalized.

D. K. Pomerantz: A few points about the aromatization of androgen in the hypothalamus. Is there information about the ontogenic development of that aromatizing capacity—it seems to me that you have very nicely shown that the hypothalamus acquires responsiveness to estrogen, at least the receptors there at the appropriate time for sexual differentiation of the brain. When does the brain develop the ability to make the estrogen to activate those receptors?

B. S. McEwen: Neil MacLusky has at Yale done this sort of developmental study and since he's mentioned it in print, I guess I can refer to the fact that as early as 15 or 16 days of gestation, he can see substantial aromatase activity already in the rat hypothalamus. This accompanies elevated testosterone production, so that's why I made the statement that I did that the elevation of estrogen receptors seems to be a relatively late and possibly crucial event in the onset of the critical period for defeminization.

D. K. Pomerantz: Is the cell that possesses the estrogen receptor the same cell that is doing the aromatizing of the androgen to the estrogen? A similar phenomenon would appear to exist in the testis in which the Leydig cell both aromatizes androgen and possesses estrogen receptor.

B. S. McEwen: Well it is either the same cell or something very close, and our evidence for this is as follows: that is, the pituitary gland of the rat doesn't possess aromatase activity and it serves as a very sensitive index of how much estrogens are circulating in the blood due to, say, peripheral aromatization. Indeed when you give very high doses of testosterone you can demonstrate some peripheral aromatization which results in some limited occupation of the pituitary–estrogen receptors. But everything that we normally do, and certainly in the physiologic range of testosterone, is such that there would be very little peripheral aromatization. So what we see with normal levels of testosterone in the male rat is that the estrogen receptors of the hypothalamus and preoptic area and amygdala are occupied to about 25% of capacity determined by giving exogenous estradiol—50% of the capacity if you determine the maximum which testosterone can label via aromatization. So we have used that evidence to infer that about half of estrogen-sensitive cells have aromatase either in them or closely associated with them.

D. K. Pomerantz: If you'll permit me to push an analogy a bit—I'm not trying to claim that the testes function as a brain, but you may have a similar situation in which in the testes of the young rat, estrogen formed by the Sertoli and Leydig cell may alter Leydig cell function and that estrogen produced by glial or other surrounding tissue as well as by hypothalamic neurons may alter function of those neurons.

W. Leavitt: I'm interested in what you think the mechanism is for progesterone modulation of sex behavior—do you feel that it is mediated by way of the progesterone receptor and RNA and protein synthesis or is it possible that it works indirectly by modulating the estrogen receptor itself? The reason I ask is that we've recently discovered in work on the uterus that progesterone induces a factor that regulates the retention of the estrogen receptor in the nucleus (Evans and Leavitt, *Proc. Natl. Acad. Sci. U.S.A.* **77,** 5856–5860, 1980; Okulicz *et al., Steroids* **37,** 463–470, 1981).

B. S. McEwen: I'm well aware of your work, and I don't believe that the paradigm that you used in that study has ever been specifically tried in the brain. Under the conditions in which estrogens and then progestins normally facilitate sexual behavior it has been demonstrated that the sequential application of progesterone after estradiol has no effect on estrogen receptor occupation. Furthermore, the progestin application occurs after the time when the estrogen effects on protein synthesis have already taken place. Because we can demonstrate progestin receptor translocation to the nucleus occurring very rapidly, just prior to the onset of sexual behavior, and because we can block progestin facilitation with protein synthesis inhibitors, we infer that the normal genomic protein synthetic mechanism is operating even though the progestin action is very rapid.

W. Leavitt: If I can comment on that last point—inhibitors of RNA and protein synthesis will also block the progesterone-induced regulatory factor that works on the estrogen receptor. When you block the progesterone effect with protein synthesis inhibitors, you don't rule out the possibility that progesterone is working on the estrogen receptor by way of the estrogen-receptor regulatory factor.

B. S. McEwen: However, since we have already established that estrogen action is no longer required, I don't see how that is a very likely possibility—I think that what you suggest is a possibility, for example, in sequential inhibition. We have also demonstrated recently that protein synthesis is involved in that progestin inhibition of subsequent sexual receptivity can be relieved by the application of anisomycin to block protein synthesis. The mechanism you describe might be applicable there and I think it would be well worth looking into.

R. Grady: I'd like to ask a question about the organizing effects of estrogen during the perinatal period, but not with regard to defeminization but rather to feminization. There's been some recent work by Klaus Döhler which suggest that estrogen also has a role in feminization. However, your data, if I'm correct, show that estrogen binding, at least in the nucleus, is not detectable during the neonatal period. Are we looking at a process that is not regulated by estrogen receptor, or are we looking too late? Does this occur during the prenatal period, or do you have data which would give an alternate hypothesis?

B. S. McEwen: Maybe I should say first what Döhler has been talking about are effects of antiestrogens, tamoxifen, in particular, which on the face of it seemed to antagonize the defeminization process. But then they apparently can be reversed by the application of certain estrogens.

R. Grady: I believe so.

B. S. McEwen: There are two aspects to the data. It is very complicated and there is not a lot of it yet. So, I think, anything can happen. But a larger part of the data is perfectly compatible with the interpretation that I gave, because we can block defeminization with CI628 which works similarly to tamoxifen. But then if it really is true that estrogens will reverse the effect of the tamoxifen, then you have to consider a different sort of mechanism. My own view of it is that something may occur, perhaps in addition to what I was talking about. That is, there may be a very low level of some extremely high affinity estrogen receptors that we haven't seen yet which are operative in a range that we cannot measure by an exchange assay in the female. Those might normally be required for the process of feminization that for so many years has been thought to be independent of gonadal steroids; I think that is a very valid point that really has not been experimentally tested yet, and Döhler and also Toran-Allerand are two people who are trying to work on this. But it invalidates the conclusions about defeminization which occurs in a range of estrogen receptor occupation that can be measured by the techniques I was describing.

J. K. Findlay: Dr. Ian Clarke and I have been interested for some time in the feedback effects of estrogens on gonadotropin secretion and in particular whether the feedback effects of estrogens are genomic, or non-genomic. Could I show some data (I. J. Clarke, J. W. Funder, and J. K. Findlay, *J. Reprod. Fertil.,* 1982, in press) and then ask you to comment. We did an experiment in the ovariectomized ewe in which we injected 100 μg of estradiol-17β iv, a very large dose for the sheep, but nevertheless, one which ensures that you get both negative and positive feedback on gonadotropin secretion. In Fig. A you see the effect on plasma LH concentration and you'll note that within 4 to 6 hours of the estrogen injectin LH levels were significantly decreased followed later by the positive feedback effects. I should point out here that the sheep is obviously different from the monkey in that you only need a single bolus of estradiol in order to get the positive feedback effects, whereas in the monkey you need a more continuous exposure to estrogen (T. Yamaji, D. J. Tierschke, J. Hotchkiss, A. N. Bhatachanya, A. H. Surve, and E. Knobil, *Endocrinology* **89,** 1034–1041, 1971). We've also measured the estrogen receptors in the pituitary tissue across the early part of this period and the data are shown in Fig. B. The percentage of receptors which are nuclear was maximal at the 1 hour point, but by 6 hours the levels in the nucleus were back to those prior to injection. So we are left with a dilemma I think as to whether the negative feedback effect of estrogen on LH secretion is a genomic or a nongenomic effect. I don't think we can differentiate it in this model. I wonder if you might comment on this.

B. S. McEwen: Can we go back to Fig. A, I just want to get the temporal relationships. Where is the negative feedback occurring?

J. K. Findlay: The LH levels are suppressed significantly by about 4–6 hours after injection.

B. S. McEwen: Yes, and during that time you can see intracellular estrogen receptor occupation?

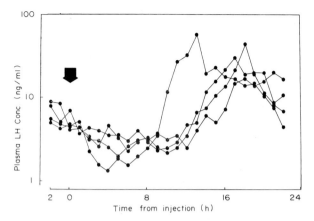

FIG. A. Plasma LH levels in 4 ovariectomized ewes from 2 hours before until 22 hours after a single intravenous injection of 100 μg estradiol-17β (from Clarke *et al.*, 1982).

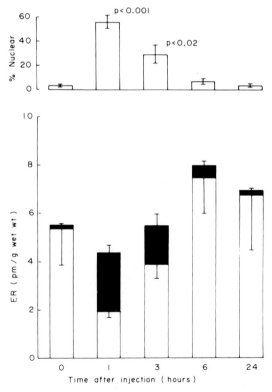

FIG. B. Pituitary estrogen receptor (ER) levels in cytosol and nuclei after intravenous injection of 100 μg estradiol-17β in ovariectomized ewes (from Clarke *et al.*, 1982).

J. K. Findlay: There is maximum occupation of nuclear sites at 1 hour, but it's already declining by 3 hours.

B. S. McEwen: If we give a pulse injection of estradiol which is sufficient to activate lordosis behavior, the effect doesn't appear until 24 hours and that's long after the estrogen receptor's occupation has come back to very low levels. There's a limited protein synthetic period within the first 6 hours. The dissociation in time is one of the important points about inferring genomic effects. Now what you're talking about is the very rapid negative feedback effects. In the rat, Lewis Krey and a number of other investigators have been able to study the suppression of pulsatile LH release and show that there is an estrogen effect that can be blocked for example by CI628 administration. It has all the characteristics of a short latency genomically mediated effect. Of course with all of the interest in catechol estrogens has been that the possibility that they might be involved in some of these shorter latency effects. So far, to my knowledge, there isn't really any clear evidence that the catechol estrogens are producing a unique effect over and above their estrogenic potency.

J. K. Findlay: We would agree with that in the sheep too (I. J. Clarke, and J. K. Findlay, *J. Endocrinol.* **85,** 503–509, 1980) unless there's some local effect of catechol estrogens which we cannot observe.

B. S. McEwen: And yet beyond that, I would say the kind of evidence that, if one would do the kind of thing that Mortyn Jones did with glucocorticoids and hypothalamic CRF, incubate hypothalamic fragment cells and show that there was a very rapid suppression of CRF release by glucocorticoids, that could even be produced in isolated synaptosomes—that would be presumptive evidence that there was a nongenomic mechanism.

P. K. Siiteri: Dr. Ryan has recently demonstrated that the aromatase enzyme of human placenta has a K_m value of about 10 nM rather than 1 μM which my laboratory and others have reported. I would suggest that if you're looking in regions where there are very low aromatase enzyme concentrations, it might be easy to confuse testosterone binding to the enzyme with receptor binding. The question I have relates to your model for the organizational effects of testosterone which is dependent upon intracellular aromatization. You indicated that this mechanism would avoid the problem of estradiol binding to α-fetoprotein. Toran-Allerand has found α-fetoprotein within cells and neurons of the developing rat brain. I wonder how you reconcile the presence of intracellular α protein and the sex differences you are proposing.

B. S. McEwen: One feature of Toran-Allerand's work however is that the areas that have the intracellular receptors that are for example labeled by moxestrol, which does not bind AFP, are the mirror image of the localization of the intracellular AFP. In other words, it tends not to be present in the preoptic area, basal hypothalamus, and corticomedial amygdala where these intracellular receptors are located. So AFP is absent in the cells that have the receptors that are implicated in the growth effect. In answer to your first question, when one is doing Scatchard plots and you see low affinity binding sites in the 1 to 10 nM range, the aromatase could certainly be a candidate. But what most people measure and call estrogen receptor is something that has a 0.1 or 0.2 nM K_D and so is an order of magnitude or two removed from the aromatase affinity.

J. Geller: I would like to ask about androgen and its role in mammal sexual behavior. Now, you showed that the process of defeminization was induced by testosterone and inhibited by estrogens, and I am just wondering if the androgen receptor plays any role in either the organizational effects or activational effects of male sexual behavior; is there any role for the androgen receptor in either male sexual behavior or defeminization? If you gave a pure antiandrogen or a 5α reductase inhibitor, what would happen?

B. S. McEwen: Well, in the first place, yes there appears to be an involvement that has not been totally worked out in male sexual behavior, that is, the activation of male sexual behavior. One of the likely sites of action is in a certain group of motor neurons in the spinal cord which innervate muscles of the penis and recently Art Arnold at UCLA and a couple of his graduate students have described androgen receptors in this nucleus. It's a nucleus which is absent in the TFM, androgen insensitive, animal, and it doesn't appear to have estrogen receptors. The development of this nucleus may also be involved in the organizing actions of the androgens on male sexual behavior. The process of masculinization, as I noted, is not blocked by the administration of ATD or CI628, so that's evidence that androgen receptor mechanisms may be involved. I also noted that there was also involvement of aromatization as well that has not been very extensively studied. As far as defeminization, it takes place in the androgen insensitive mutant of both the mouse and the rat. It can be prevented in the TFM male by neonatal castration, just as a wild type male. It seems to have all the characteristics of a process that involves only the aromatization—the inhibitors that block estrogen receptor occupation, CI628 and ATD, do not interfere with 5α-DHT production or DHT levels in the nucleus. I should add that cyproterone acetate attenuates defeminization and its ability probably to do this is explained by two factors: its ability to inhibit aromatase weakly and also its ability to act as a progestin. Progestins will antagonize defeminization, perhaps by acting through progestin receptor sites which are elaborated just about the time the critical period starts. The only thing that is a little bit confusing is that flutamide under certain circumstances will also antagonize defeminization. Again it's not a very strong effect and it has not been ruled out that flutamide may have some peculiar ability to interfere with either estrogen receptor mechanisms or aromatization but it remains a fly in the ointment.

J. R. Pasqualini: I would like to know if you have some information in the estradiol metabolism itself, particularly in this perinatal period in which you found a big increase in the estrogen receptor level.

B. S. McEwen: I really can't make any comments about that. We haven't studied it and about the only thing I can say is that when you look at the receptor that is the nuclear bound, it contains unchanged estradiol. Metabolism may of course have regulatory influence in the amount of estradiol that can reach receptors, but I am not aware of any studies that speak to that point.

J. R. Pasqualini: Do you have information on the estrogen receptors ontogenesis in other species?

B. S. McEwen: Estrogen receptor ontogeny? No we don't.

R. E. Fellows: Your suggestion that estradiol causes morphological development in neurons, that is, neurite development, is very interesting. Does estradiol also cause neurite sprouting in dissociated neurons in primary cell culture?

B. S. McEwen: Not to my knowledge. That is, I know people who have been trying. This is something that is maybe very difficult to obtain in a dissociated cell system (a) because you may lose or dilute out the cells that are responsive; (b) because they may lose the estrogen receptor in the culture environment or not acquire them, and (c) because of course there may be an involvement of other cellular elements to express the full effect. That is, by saying that estrogen effect on outgrowth is a primary effect on the target cell, it doesn't rule out the existence or participation of other growth factors.

J. E. Rall: You noted, I think, that dexamethasone bound to certain specific areas containing glial cells, whereas glucocorticoids bound to the neurons in the same areas. Furthermore, there were differences between these two steroids in induction of protein 1 versus α-glycerophosphate dehydrogenase. This is quite interesting because most people working on the glucocorticoid receptor in liver generally expect that if they use labeled dex or affinity labeled the receptor with some derivative of dex, that they are looking at the glucocorticoid receptor and you are suggesting that there really are different receptors at least in some aspects of brain tissue for the two different steroids. I wonder if there are any behavioral differences between dexamethasone and corticosterone which would support a real difference between these two steroids. In general, my impression has been that there are no gross biochemical differences between these two steroids.

B. S. McEwen: I am glad you asked that question. In the first place, to take the second part first, we have some evidence and Ron DeKloet in Holland has some evidence for behavioral effects of glucocorticoids that are produced by corticosterone and not by dexamethasone. In several instances we have chosen our behavioral paradigms to emphasize those that have a heavy dependence on the hippocampus. So we infer from that that this is an expression of this selective action of corticosterone versus dexamethasone. However, as to the interpretation of this selective uptake of the hormone, we do not subscribe to the idea that it is a separate receptor, because extensive studies *in vitro* have failed to show physicochemical differences in receptor profiles. For example, the enucleated optic nerve preparation consisting predominantly of glial cells in which you can demonstrate GPDH induction has receptors that have identical behavior in low and high ionic strength gradients and in other features like heat inactivation to the receptors of the hippocampus, which of course emphasizes the neuronal element. There is another explanation which is very interesting, and that is that autoradiographic studies published in 1975 by Howard Rees show that when you look at short time intervals after giving a pulse of [^{3}H]dexamethasone you see label first in the ventricles. And then it diffuses into the brain tissue. Whereas corticosterone does not do this. The implication of that is that dexamethasone doesn't really cross the blood–brain barrier directly but enters the ventricles and then diffuses into the brain. Corticosterone, however, crosses directly into the brain. That tells us something about the role of glial cells in relation to the blood–brain barrier and in relation to the ventricles.

J. E. Rall: I would guess then the answer would be to isolate the separate cells and look at their receptors.

E. A. Zimmerman: It is very important in clinical neurology. Glucocorticoids in high doses are commonly given to patients with various neurologic disorders. It has recently been shown that glucocorticoids induce astrogliosis as well as inhibit regeneration or sprouting in the brain. Would you like to comment on this?

B. S. McEwen: The fact that glial cells now can be recognized as glucocorticoid targets of course begins to raise questions about, for example, the role of glucocorticoids in myelin formation as well as effects on neuronal growth and sprouting. There seem to be any number of possibilities; as you said glucocorticoids will apparently by some mechanism inhibit neuronal sprouting and will also inhibit proliferation of the glioblasts that give rise to the Schwann or oligodendroglial cells. They may also in adult animals have some influence on the formation of myelin without necessarily affecting glial cell proliferation.

E. A. Zimmerman: Possible receptor differences in astroglia because of their participation in the blood brain barrier and cerebral edema.

E. J. Peck: A comment relative to Figs. A and B: In the attempt to correlate negative feedback, I think it is really dangerous to do this. If you study a biochemical response which is very closely coupled to receptor translocation, as RNA polymerase activation which we did a couple of years ago, then, yes, you can see a direct relationship or correlation. If, however, you move away from that immediate biochemical response and study subsequent physiologic responses, it is more difficult, you might achieve that correlation if you do different doses, i.e., you do a dose response of your feedback system versus receptor translocation. Even so, you must pick a peak time of receptor translocation to relate to your response. Alternatively you might use some pharmacologic agents, as antiestrogens, to study blockade, or protein synthesis inhibitors to demonstrate that you have activated genomic mechanism. What we have shown is that you can complete 80–90% of the negative aspects of feedback, that is, suppression of serum LH in the ovariectomized rat, before you have translocated the first receptor in the hypothalamus. At the same time the pituitary has 95% of its receptors translocated, suggesting that the site of negative feedback is the pituitary, even in the rat. However, this doesn't prove that we have a genomic mechanism operating since the translocation of receptor to the genome is only a measure of total circulating levels of free steroid.

J. H. Clark: I would like to make a comment about your reference to the work with CI628. This drug is a mixed estrogen agonist–antagonist, and like other triphenylethylene drugs, it has both estrogenic and antiestrogenic properties. Neonatal exposure to such drugs causes a syndrome in rats which resembles the persistent estrus condition. Therefore, some of the actions of these drugs are mimicking estrogen action. This may not hold for the behavioral aspects; however. I feel that caution should be used on interpreting their action as strictly antiestrogenic.

B. S. McEwen: Well, it is not invalid because we were able to see the partial defeminization of both ovulation and lordosis behavior by CI628, and yet it was still able to relieve the more profound defeminization produced either by estradiol or by testosterone. Because of the fact that it is a weak agonist and weakly defeminizes, CI628 is not as good a choice for these kinds of blocking experiments as ATD which doesn't have any apparent side effects of its own.

G. V. Callard: I would like to say a few words in support of the idea that the primary effect of estrogen on the brain is one of growth. This would explain why, in very early development in mammals, estrogen receptors as well as aromatase activity are found outside of known brain reproductive centers, as well as in preoptic, hypothalamic, and limbic regions. It might also explain why such high levels of CNS aromatizing activity are found in lower vertebrates in which the brain continues to grow throughout life. I would also like to comment on a question raised earlier concerning the brain cell type in which aromatase is located. Although there is still no direct evidence showing a neuronal versus nonneuronal location, my colleagues at Harvard have reported that neurotoxic agents in brain cell cultures will reduce aromatizing activity whereas cytosine arabinoside, an agent which inhibits nonneuronal cell proliferation, enhances aromatizing activity (Canick, Vaccaro, Ryan, and Leeman, *Endocrinology* **100**, 250–253, 1977; Livingston, Canick, Vaccaro, Ryan, and Fox, Soc. for Neurosciences Abstr. No. 153.7, 1980). In the same fetal rat system, dopamine pretreatment appears to inhibit aromatizing activity (Vaccaro, Canick, Livingston, Fox, Ryan, and Leeman. Endocrine Soc. Abstr. No. 127, 1980).

B. S. McEwen: So you are subscribing to the fact that it it a neuronal function and not a glial function?

G. V. Callard: It may be premature to reach a conclusion based on indirect evidence. I am simply reporting data that may be relevant. I do think we will have to test the aromatizing potential of both cell types directly since many agents will change estrogen yields in brain cell cultures. For example, in our reptilian system, estrogen yields increase after pretreatment with cyclic AMP, a substance known to inhibit proliferation and induce differentiated functions in both neuronal and glial cultures (Callard, *Brain Res.* **204**, 461–463, 1981). A variety of natural and synthetic steroids will also alter estrogen yields in the same system (Callard, Petro, and Ryan, *Brain Res.* **202**, 117–130, 1980). One problem with interpretation of data from mixed cell cultures is that aromatase-positive cells may be indirectly affected by changes in other cell types. Under these circumstances, morphological criteria would be misleading.

D. M. Linkie: A comment about the positive and negative feedback effects of estrogen on the anterior pituitary. This target tissue is a heterogeneous population of cell types; 80–90% of the cells contain estrogen receptor according to autoradiography, but only 5% of the cells are gonadotropes. Homogenization of the tissue makes anonymous any contribution of a given cell type to the total receptor population. It may be premature to attempt to relate receptor movements in the whole gland and subsequent genomic effects to the event of LH secretion. One should really strive to examine receptors in purified gonadotrope populations.

Substance P and Neurotensin

Susan E. Leeman,* Neil Aronin,*,† and Craig Ferris*

Departments of *Physiology and †Medicine,
University of Massachusetts Medical School,
Worcester, Massachusetts

I. Introduction

During the course of an attempt to purify a corticotropin releasing factor from bovine hypothalamic extracts, two substances were discovered while screening column eluates for biological activity. The first, a sialogogic peptide, was subsequently characterized as substance P. A more detailed account of this work may be found in a volume on substance P (von Euler and Pernow, 1977). The second, which like substance P has vasoactive properties, was named neurotensin (Carraway and Leeman, 1973). Both these peptides were isolated, their amino acid sequences determined, and synthetic material prepared, permitting a wealth of morphological, biochemical, and physiological studies by many different laboratories. Substance P and neurotensin are widely distributed throughout the central and peripheral nervous system and the gastrointestinal tract and no doubt subserve multiple physiological functions. This present article will focus on only a few selected studies in which this laboratory has participated.

II. Substance P: Discovery, Isolation, and Chemical Characterization

In 1931, von Euler and Gaddum found a substance(s) in extracts of equine brain and intestine that caused a transient hypotension when injected into anesthetized rabbits and stimulated the contraction of intestinal tissue *in vitro* (von Euler and Gaddum, 1931). Since pretreatment with atropine did not prevent these responses, the effects could not be ascribed to acetylcholine. An extract designated "P" in the laboratory of origin was standardized; the active principle was referred to as substance P (P for preparation) by Gaddum and Schild (1934). The use of this noncommittal term has persisted. In 1967, Leeman and Hammerschlag reported the discovery of a sialogogic peptide in extracts of bovine hypothalami (Fig.

93

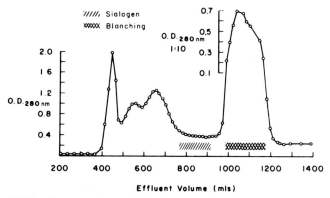

FIG. 1. Gel filtration on a column of G-75 Sephadex of bovine hypothalamic extract: 1.9 g was applied in 60 ml of column buffer to a 4.7 × 69 cm column run in 0.1 M pyridine acetate, pH 2.8, at room temperature; 16-ml fractions were collected at a rate of 60 ml/hour. The region of effluent volume from which sialogogic activity was recovered and the region containing material that caused cutaneous blanching in the test rats are indicated. From Leeman and Hammerschlag (1967).

TABLE I

Summary of Purification of Sialogogic Peptide[a]

Purification step	Total protein (mg)	Total sialogogic doses[b] (mg^{-1})	Sialogogic doses (mg^{-1})
Initial extraction	100,000	30,000	0.3[c]
First gel filtration on Sephadex G-25	2,000	25,000	12[c]
Second gel filtration on Sephadex G-25	1,000	20,000	20[c]
Chromatography on sulfoethyl Sephadex	5	8,000	1,300[c]
Chromatography on Cm-cellulose	1	5,000	5,000[d]
Paper electrophoresis	0.150	2,000	13,000[d]

[a] The starting material was 20 kg of frozen hypothalami. The total sialogogic doses reported are those recovered after each purification step.

[b] Testing for sialogogic activity was done according to the procedure of Leeman and Hammerschlag (1967). A sialogogic dose is defined as the amount of material required to stimulate the secretion of approximately 50 μl of saliva when injected intravenously into an anesthetized rat weighing approximately 100 g.

[c] Protein was determined by the method of Lowry *et al.* (1951).

[d] Protein was calculated from quantitative amino acid analyses.

1). Shortly afterward it was suggested by Lembeck and Starke (1968) that the sialogogic substance and substance P might be identical.

In 1970, a method for obtaining the sialogogic peptide in pure form was reported from our laboratory (Chang and Leeman, 1970). The purification steps are summarized in Table I. The best evidence for the purity of the peptide was that the molar ratios of the constituent amino acids were integral and remained constant after reelectrophoresis at several different pHs (Table II). The molecular weight estimated by gel permeation chromatography was in good agreement with that calculated by its amino acid composition. Spectrophotometric analysis confirmed the lack of a tyrosine and established the lack of tryptophan in the molecule.

Until that time, all attempts to isolate substance P had met with only partial success; thus substance P had only a biological definition. It was a

TABLE II

Electrophoresis of Pure Sialogogic Peptide at pH 6.5; Distribution of Activity and Amino Acid Composition[a]

Amino acid	Condition A[b]		Condition B[b]	
	Composition (μmol)	Molar ratio	Composition (μmol)	Molar ratio
Lysine	3.9	1.0	4.2	1.0
Arginine	4.2	1.1	3.8	0.9
Glutamic acid	7.9	2.0	9.7	2.2
Proline	7.9	2.0	8.7	2.0
Glycine[c]	5.8	1.5	8.6	2.0
Methionine[d]	2.1	0.5	1.3	0.3
Leucine	3.7	0.9	4.6	1.1
Phenylalanine	6.6	1.7	8.1	1.9
Serine	1.3	0.3	1.6	0.4
Alanine	0.9	0.2	Trace	Trace

[a] Another 50 sialogogic doses were distributed over the region of paper presenting and electrophoretic mobility of 0.15 to 0.45 (mobility: lysine, 1.00).

[b] Condition A: 0.65 to 0.75 mobility (mobility: lysine, 1.00), 120 doses recovered; 60 doses per analysis; Condition B: 0.45 to 0.65 mobility (mobility: lysine, 1.00); 150 doses recovered; 75 doses per analysis.

[c] Elevated glycine values were due to contamination during electrophoresis. Blank strips of paper eluted as controls yielded glycine and smaller amounts of serine and alanine, respectively. The contamination problem was negligible when larger amounts of material were used.

[d] The low methionine value is in part explained by the fact that the methionine sulfone and methionine sulfoxide peaks were unusually high in this sample. When these peaks were calculated as part of the value for methionine, the molar ratio of methionine increased to at least 0.6.

substance that even in the presence of atropine could (a) cause acute hypotension and (b) stimulate the contraction of various smooth muscle preparations including rat duodenal tissue. The pure sialogogic peptide was then shown to have these properties as well as other chemical and physical properties reported for substance P (Chang and Leeman, 1970).

The amino acid sequence of the sialogogic peptide was first determined in collaboration with the group at the Endocrine Unit, Massachusetts General Hospital, directed by Dr. John Potts, Jr. and in particular, with Dr. Hugh Niall. Because of the scarcity of pure material, the sequence of the sialogogic peptide was deduced on unseparated mixtures of the peptide and its fragments using a combination of Edman degradation and selected enzymatic cleavages (Chang *et al.*, 1971). Total enzymatic digestion indicated that both the glutamyl residues in the molecule were amidated. The unique sequence was found to be Arg-Pro-Lys-Pro-Gln-Gln-Phe-Phe-Gly-Leu-Met-NH$_2$. The glutamine in the fifth position was established by inference. Confirmatory evidence that the sialogogic peptide and substance P are identical was provided by Studer *et al.* (1973) who, starting with a crude preparation of substance P from equine intestine, isolated a peptide that had the identical amino acid sequence of that obtained in our initial studies. An additional study was done by Carraway and Leeman (1979) on substance P isolated from bovine hypothalami. A mixture of fragments was generated by papain digest, the fragments isolated, and direct evidence for the positioning of each residue obtained. The amino acid sequence determined here (Fig. 2) demonstrates that bovine

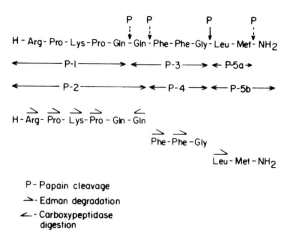

FIG. 2. The complete amino acid sequence of substance P and the alignment of the fragments obtained by digestion with papain (P). Arrows and broken arrows mark the sites of cleavage and partial cleavage. From Carraway and Leeman (1979).

hypothalamic substance P is identical to that of substance P from bovine colliculi and equine intestine.

The first solid phase synthesis of substance P was accomplished by Tregear *et al.* (1971). This provided large quantities of pure substance P for biological studies, as well as for the development of antisera for radioimmunoassay (Powell *et al.*, 1973; Mroz and Leeman, 1979) and immunohistochemical studies (see below).

III. Substance P in Brain and Spinal Cord

Radioimmunoassay and immunohistochemistry have proved to be useful methods in the detection of substance P-like peptides in brain and spinal cord. The specificity of both techniques is limited, in part, by the ability of the antiserum used to recognize a portion of the substance P molecule. Since it is possible that several immunoreactive species with structures similar to substance P may cross-react with the substance P antiserum, the term substance P-like immunoreactivity (SPLI) is used to describe results from radioimmunoassay and immunohistochemistry.

The widespread distribution of SPLI in the central nervous system in the rat (Brownstein *et al.*, 1976; Kanazawa and Jessell, 1976) and human (Gale *et al.*, 1978; Emson *et al.*, 1980; Cooper *et al.*, 1981), as measured by radioimmunoassay, is shown in Table III. Especially high concentrations

TABLE III
Regional Distribution of Substance P in the CNS[a]

Region	Rat (pmol/10 mg[b] wet weight)	Rat (pmol/mg protein[c])	Human (pmol/10 mg[d] wet weight)	Human (pmol/mg protein[e])
Somatosensory system and cortex				
Dorsal root ganglia	0.6			
Dorsal horn	9.4			
Trigeminal nucleus	12.1			
Dorsal column	1.1			
Dorsal column nucleus	1.5			
Thalamic nucleus	0.2			
Lateral dorsal			0.12	
Lateral posterior			0.03	
Dorsal medial			0.35	
Somatosensory cortex	0.2			
Cerebral cortex				
Frontal			0.08	
Parietal			0.07	

(*Continued*)

TABLE III (*Continued*)

Region	Rat (pmol/10 mg[b] wet weight)	Rat (pmol/mg protein[c])	Human (pmol/10 mg[d] wet weight)	Human (pmol/mg protein[e])
Uncal			0.12	
Entorhinal			0.15	
			0.34	
Cingulate			0.11	
Striate			0.046	
Visual system				
Optical nerve			0.06	
Lateral				
geniculate body	0.7	0.9	0.36	
Superior colliculus			1.25	
Visual cortex	0.2			
Basal ganglia				
Striatum		0.9		
Caudate	2.2		1.13	3.7
Putamen			0.81	3.3
Globus pallidus	2.9			18.0
Internal			5.18	
External			1.24	
Subthalamic nucleus	2.0		0.21	
Substantia nigra	15.1		9.22	
Pars compacta		2.9		47.2
Pars reticulata		11.38		47.9
Pars lateralis		3.0		
Hypothalamus		2.1		5.2
Anterior			1.22	
Posterior			1.35	
Medial	5.5			
Middle	4.5			
Lateral	4.3			
Medial preoptic nucleus		4.4		
Lateral preoptic nucleus		3.3		
Periventricular nucleus		3.3		
Suprachiasmatic nucleus		1.6		
Supraoptic nucleus		1.6		
Anterior hypothalamic nucleus		3.2		
Paraventricular nucleus		3.1		
Arcuate nucleus		2.5		
Ventromedial nucleus		2.5		
Dorsomedial nucleus		3.5		
Perifornical nucleus		2.9		
Mammillary bodies	1.8		0.83	
Ventral premammillary nucleus		3.3		
Dorsal premammillary nucleus		1.7		

(*Continued*)

TABLE III (*Continued*)

Region	Rat (pmol/10 mg[b] wet weight)	Rat (pmol/mg protein[c])	Human (pmol/10 mg[d] wet weight)	Human (pmol/mg protein[e])
Posterior premammillary nucleus		2.8		
Medial forebrain bundle, anterior		3.1		
Medial forebrain bundle, posterior		2.3		
Median eminence		1.0	1.34	
Limbic system				
Olfactory bulb	0.5	0.2	0.41	
Olfactory tubercle	2.6			
Olfactory cortex	0.4			
Amygdala	3.3	3.4	0.26	
Hippocampus	0.3			
Habenula	3.3			
Interpeduncular nucleus	5.2	5.9		
Septum	3.5	1.2		
Dorsal septal nucleus		2.8		
Lateral septal nucleus		3.6		
Interstitial nucleus of stria terminalis		3.3		
Nucleus accumbens	2.4			
Anterior thalamic nucleus	1.9			
Other regions				
Locus coeruleus			1.99	
Raphe nuclei			0.71	
Area postrema			1.14	
Inferior olive			0.078	
Red nucleus		1.3	0.76	
Medial geniculate		0.8		
Inferior colliculus		1.2	2.34	
Central gray		2.9		
Periaqueductal gray			1.30	
Cerebellum	<0.1	<0.1		0.2
Cortex			0.003	
Dentate nucleus			0.014	
Pineal	<0.1[f]		0.01	0.5

[a] Values measured by radioimmunoassay. No standard errors are presented. All values have been converted to either pmol/10 mg wet weight or pmol/mg protein. These values may be comparable, since nervous tissue contains approximately 10% protein.

[b] Kanazawa and Jessell (1976).

[c] Brownstein *et al.* (1976).

[d] Cooper *et al.* (1981).

[e] Gale *et al.* (1978).

[f] M. H. Fernstrom and S. E. Leeman (unpublished).

are found in the substantia nigra, the dorsal horn of the spinal cord, the trigeminal nucleus of the medulla, the hypothalamus, and, in the human unlike the rat, the globus pallidus. The presence of SPLI in such diverse systems (neuroendocrine, extrapyramidal, somatosensory) underscores the likelihood that SPLI may have a variety of physiologic roles.

Immunohistochemical studies by the fluorescence method (Ljungdahl *et al.*, 1978a; Cuello and Kanazawa, 1978) confirm the pattern of distribution of SPLI found by radioimmunoassay. At the light microscopic level in the rat, cell bodies with SPLI have been observed in the neostriatum, globus pallidus, nucleus habenulae medialis, nucleus interpeduncularis, septal complex, nucleus intertitialis striae, and in numerous subdivisions of the mesencephalon, pons, and medulla oblongata. In the hypothalamus, the preoptic suprachiasmatic nucleus, periventricular and paraventricular regions, ventromedial and dorsomedial nuclei, arcuate nucleus, posterior region, and the mammillary complex all contain cell bodies labeled with SPLI. Positively stained somata have also been found in the dorsal root ganglia and the dorsal horn of the spinal cord. Fiber staining is most abundant in the substantia nigra (by fluorescence), the medial segment of the globus pallidus in the primate (Haber and Elde, 1981), the dorsal horn of the spinal cord, and trigeminal nucleus of the medulla. In our experience, the quantitation of SPLI by immunohistochemistry is unreliable. Perhaps because of variability in the penetration by antibodies, areas with known high concentrations of immunoreactivity by radioimmunoassay, such as the substantia nigra, are frequently difficult to label with the peroxidase–antiperoxidase method. Furthermore, some antisera adequate for radioimmunoassay prove to be unsatisfactory for labeling neuronal elements. Nonetheless, immunohistochemistry at the light microscopic level offers the possibility of localizing SPLI within cell bodies and fibers. With use of the peroxidase–antiperoxidase technique (Sternberger, 1974), the ultrastructural features and the synaptic connections of SPLI neuronal elements can be studied.

A. SUBSTANTIA NIGRA

High levels of SPLI are measurable by radioimmunoassay within both the pars reticulata and the pars compacta. Data from several laboratories (Brownstein *et al.*, 1976; Kanazawa *et al.*, 1977a) have shown that the pars reticulata has higher concentrations of SPLI. The fibers containing SPLI in the pars reticulata originate mainly from the neostriatum (Mroz *et al.*, 1977; Kanazawa *et al.*, 1977b; Gale *et al.*, 1977) and perhaps the globus pallidus (Jessell *et al.*, 1978). In the pars compacta, by immunofluorescence, the processes with SPLI appear to be associated with dopamine-containing somata (Ljungdahl *et al.*, 1978b). Since dendrites of pars compacta penetrate the pars reticulata (Schwyn and Fox, 1974), it is possible that SPLI in both regions of the substantia nigra may interact with dopamine-containing elements.

Recent ultrastructural evidence with the peroxidase–antiperoxidase method in monkey shows that the fibers with SPLI include both my-elinated and unmyelinated axons and enter the substantia nigra via the cere-bral peduncle (DiFiglia *et al.*, 1981a). The SPLI axon terminals contain both large granular vesicles (80–120 nm) which have reaction product and clear small vesicles (40 nm) and form predominately axo-dendritic synapses (Fig. 3). Although chemical identification of the elements post-synaptic to SPLI boutons has not been shown, it is probable that many of these dendrites contain dopamine because of (1) the proximity of SPLI and dopamine labeling at the light microscopic level and (2) the finding that substance P microiontophoresis in the substantia nigra results in dopamine release in the caudate (Glowinski *et al.*, 1980).

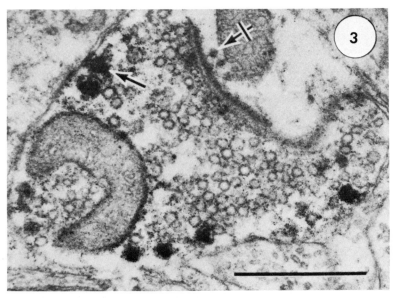

FIG. 3.   Axon terminal labeled with SPLI in the monkey substantia nigra. This terminal contains small clear vesicles (approximately 40 nm) and large granular vesicles (80–120 nm) which have a dense concentration of reaction product. The axo-dendritic synapse is asym-metric and has postjunctional bodies (crossed arrow). Scale: 0.5 μm. From DiFiglia *et al.* (1981a).

B. RELEASE OF SUBSTANCE P FROM RAT BRAINSTEM

Substance P has been demonstrated to be released from a synaptosomal preparation of rat brainstem tissue upon depolarization with high K^+ in a Ca^{2+}-dependent manner (Schenker *et al.*, 1976). Evidence that at least part of this releasable pool is contained within a synaptic vesicle fraction has been provided by some experiments in which a depletion of vesicular substance P was measured after depolarization of synaptosomes by veratridine (Floor and Leeman, 1980). Synaptosomes from rat brainstem were lysed by osmotic shock and centrifuged to remove debris. The resulting crude vesicle supernatant was then fractionated according to particle size on a glass bead column with an average pore size of 290 nm. Acid extractable, radioimmunoassayable SPLI eluted in a major peak of material of 117 nm apparent diameter (Floor *et al.*, 1982). This size is consistent with the range identified at the ultrastructural level (Pickel *et al.*, 1977; DiFiglia *et al.*, 1982b). In the peak fractions from the glass bead column, SPLI was enriched 75-fold (per mg protein) over the initial homogenate. Vesicular SPLI in the crude vesicle supernatant was not attacked by endogenous proteases at 0 or 37°C, although added synthetic substance P was degraded at both temperatures.

If the vesicle population purified in this way were active in transmitter release, strong depolarization of synaptosomes might be expected to reduce its content of SPLI. Veratridine (VA) has been shown to depolarize rat brain synaptosomes and to induce a tetrodotoxin (TTX)-sensitive, calcium-dependent release of transmitters (Blaustein, 1975). Recoveries of SPLI in the vesicle peak after treatments with VA (75 μM) or TTX (1 μM) were as follows (percentage of control ± SEM): VA, 63 ± 2 ($n = 5$); TTX + VA, 100 ± 4 ($n = 4$); and VA in calcium-free buffer, 104 ± 8 ($n = 3$). These results, summarized in Fig. 4, show that veratridine induces a substantial TTX-sensitive, calcium-dependent depletion of SPLI in the vesicle fraction.

C. SPINAL CORD

The dorsal horn is of particular interest because it is the area where the role of SPLI has been most studied as a putative transmitter in nociceptive pathways (see Nicoll *et al.*, 1980). As described previously, high concentrations of SPLI are found there by bioassay (Takahashi and Otsuka, 1975) and radioimmunoassay (Kanazawa and Jessell, 1976). By immunohistochemistry, most of the peptide is located in laminae I and II (Barber *et al.*, 1979; DiFiglia *et al.*, 1981b; Hökfelt *et al.*, 1975; Cuello and Kanazawa, 1978) and, to a somewhat lesser extent, in lamina V (DiFiglia

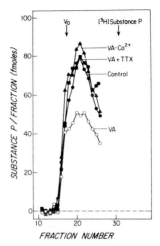

FIG. 4. Vesicular SP from VA treated synaptosomes. Results of a representative experiment performed with brainstem from 10 rats are shown. Synaptosomal lysates (~3 ml) from treated synaptosomes (see text) were run on a 34 cm³ column of CPG-3000. Fraction volume was 1 ml. Substance P values are means of two assays of acid extracted fractions and were corrected for vesicular SP degradation at $t_{1/2}$ = 430 minutes with a total chromatography time per sample of 50 minutes. Tritiated SP was run separately. From Floor *et al.* (1982).

et al., 1981b), areas (Figs. 5 and 6) which are known to be involved in the relay of nociceptive information. Cells in the dorsal root ganglia contain SPLI by fluorescence (Hökfelt *et al.*, 1975; Chan-Palay and Palay, 1977) and a marked reduction in assayable SPLI (Takahashi and Otsuka, 1975; Jessell *et al.*, 1979b) and fibers labeled with SPLI (Hökfelt *et al.*, 1977a; Barber *et al.*, 1979) follows primary afferent interruption. Application of substance P onto the dorsal aspect of the spinal cord excites some dorsal horn neurons that are likely to be involved in the pain pathway (Henry, 1976; Radić and Miletić, 1977). Administration of capsaicin, a homovanyllic acid analog, releases SPLI from primary afferent axons in the spinal cord (Yaksh *et al.*, 1980). After administration in the newborn rat over an extended period of time, capsaicin depletes SPLI from the dorsal spinal cord in association with analgesia to some noxious stimuli (Hayes and Tyers, 1980; Gamse *et al.*, 1981b). In addition, SPLI is released into the cerebrospinal fluid after stimulation of C- and A-delta fibers (Jessell *et al.*, 1979a; Fig. 7), which are the classes of axons that convey nociception to the dorsal horn (Kerr, 1975). Together, these data suggest a major role of substance P in the transmission of pain at the level of the spinal cord.

The opioid peptides, particularly the enkephalins, are thought to modulate nociception in part through interactions with primary afferent fibers

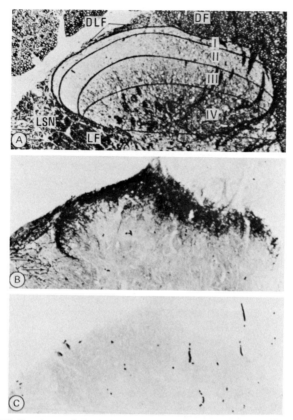

FIG. 5. (A) Laminae of the lumbar rat dorsal horn. Toluidine blue stain. Numerals
denote laminae. DLF, dorsolateral funiculus; DF, dorsal funiculus; LSN, lateral spinal nucleus; LF, lateral funiculus. ×40. (B) Localization of SPLI in the lumbar dorsal horn of the
rat. Labeling of SPLI is distributed mainly in the superficial dorsal horn, the DLF and the
LSN (arrows). ×40. (C) Preabsorption control of substance P antiserum prior to immunocytochemistry. Following incubation of substance P antiserum with excess substance
P, staining for SPLI was eliminated in this section of rat lumbar spinal cord. Erythrocytes,
which contain endogenous peroxidase-like activity, are still able to form reaction product.
×40. From Barber *et al.* (1979).

containing SPLI (LaMotte *et al.*, 1976; Jessell and Iverson, 1977; Mudge
et al., 1979; Zieglgänsberger and Tulloch, 1979). By immunohistochemistry at the light microscopic level, met-enkephalin (Elde *et al.*, 1976; Sar *et
al.*, 1978) and leu-enkephalin (Aronin *et al.*, 1981) are distributed mainly in
the superficial dorsal horn and laminae IV, V, and VI overlapping with
SPLI. Primary deafferentation in the monkey (LaMotte *et al.*, 1976) and
rat (Jessell *et al.*, 1979b) results in a decline in the opiate receptor concen-

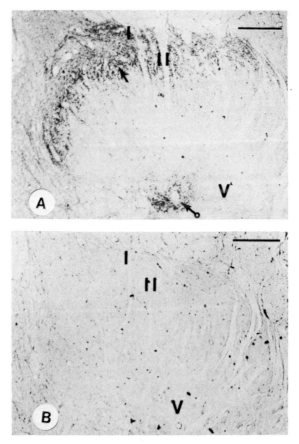

FIG. 6. (A) A cervical section of the monkey dorsal horn labeled with SPLI. Dense staining is found in lamina I (I) and the outer aspect of lamina II (II). Intense labeling is also present in the lateral portion of lamina V (V). Scale: 200 μm. (B) Preabsorbed control of monkey spinal cord. Immunoreactivity for substance P is eliminated following preabsorption of substance P antiserum (1 : 500 dilution) with substance P (10 μg/ml). From DiFiglia *et al.* (1981b).

tration in the dorsal spinal cord. The autoradiographic localization of opiate receptors overlies the substantia gelatinosa (lamina II; Atweh and Kuhar, 1977). The reported inhibitory action by morphine and enkephalin of potassium-induced SPLI release from the trigeminal nucleus tissue was reversed by naloxone (Jessell and Iverson, 1977). In cultured dorsal root ganglia containing only sensory neurons, enkephalin inhibits SPLI release (Mudge *et al.*, 1979; Fig. 8). From these data, it has been suggested that the opioid peptides modulate SPLI activity (and presumably pain trans-

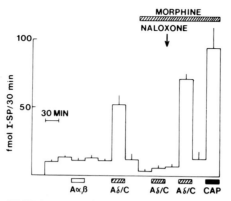

FIG. 7. Release of I-SP from superfused cat spinal cord in response to sciatic nerve stimulation and capsaicin (CAP). Superfusate in all experiments consisted of NaCl, 151.1 mM; KCl, 2.6 mM; Mg$_2$SO$_4$, 0.9 mM; CaCl$_2$, 1.3 mM; NaHCO$_3$, 21.0 mM; K$_2$HPO$_4$, 2.5 mM; and gassed with 95% O$_2$ and 5% CO$_2$ before perfusion. Three milliliter perfusion samples were collected in glacial acetic and (final concentration of 2 N) immediately frozen and lyophilized. Samples were reconstituted in 1.0 ml phosphate buffered saline (pH 7.4) containing 0.1% gelatin and aliquots of each fraction were used to determine the content of substance P by radioimmunoassay using antibody R6P with a sensitivity of 2 fmol/sample. Serial dilutions of synthetic substance P and immunoreactivity in superfusate samples produced parallel dilution curves. Each value is the mean ± SEM from four separate experiments. From Yaksh *et al.* (1980).

mission) by preventing directly the release of SPLI from primary afferent axons. This process has been postulated by several investigators to occur via axo-axonic synapses (LaMotte *et al.*, 1976; Jessell and Iverson, 1977).

There is recent evidence to suggest that the main influence of enkephalin occurs after the initial synapse of primary afferent axons in the superfi-

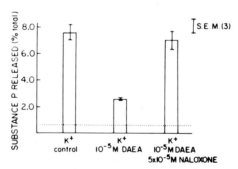

FIG. 8. Inhibition of substance P release by D-Ala$_2$-enkephalin amide (DAEA). Release of substance P from sibling cultures during depolarization for 5 minutes. All three groups were depolarized by 30 mM potassium; the second group was depolarized in the presence of 10^{-5} M DAEA; the third group was depolarized in the presence of 10^{-5} M DAEA plus 5 × 10^{-5} M naloxone. From Mudge *et al.* (1979).

cial laminae of the dorsal horn (postsynaptic effect). Glutamate-induced excitation of neurons in the laminae I and II is inhibited by enkephalin (Zieglgänsberger and Tulloch, 1979). Since glutamate is thought to act mainly on perikarya and dendrites, the modulating effect of enkephalin has been interpreted to occur on a postsynaptic site, rather than presynaptically (directly onto the incoming afferents). Furthermore, ultrastructural studies from several laboratories, including our own, show that enkephalin (Hunt et al., 1981; Aronin et al., 1981) and SPLI (Figs. 9 and 10; Barber et al., 1979; DiFiglia et al., 1982b) labeled neuronal elements only rarely participate in axo-axonic synapses. This finding is consistent with electron microscopic studies in the monkey superficial dorsal horn, where axo-axonic synapses are very infrequent (Ralston and Ralston, 1979). It now appears that the enkephalin and SPLI terminals may converge onto a common neuron (Aronin et al., 1981; DiFiglia et al., 1982b) perhaps a cell of origin of the spinothalamic tract. In sum, the morphologic evidence to

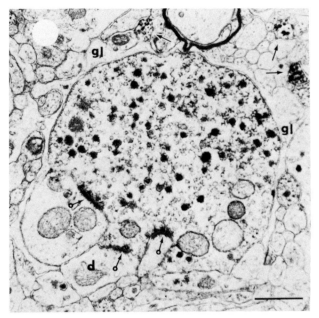

FIG. 9.   SPLI in the central axon of a synaptic glomerulus in the monkey dorsal horn. The terminal with SPLI forms the central element of a synaptic glomerulus, which is characterized by multiple axo-dendritic synapses (ringed arrows) and glial process (gl) which surrounds the axon and one of the dendrites. This synaptic arrangement is typical of primary afferent axons in the superficial monkey dorsal spinal cord (Ralston and Ralston, 1979). Unmyelinated small diameter axons are also observed (arrows). d, dendrites. Scale: 0.5 μm. From DiFiglia et al. (1981b).

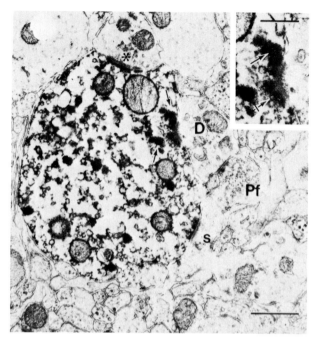

FIG. 10. Terminal with SPLI in the monkey dorsal horn. The positively labeled bouton is the central element of a synaptic glomerulus and forms multiple contacts, including a punctum adhaerens (*) with one dendrite and synapses with a dendritic spine (s) and dendrite (D). Dendrite, D, is contacted by profile PF, a terminal which contains flattened vesicles, and is likely to receive convergent information from both the SPLI axon and PF. Large granular vesicles appear near to the axodendritic synapse (arrows). Scale: 0.5 μm. Inset: The axodendritic synapse at a higher magnification shows multiple presynaptic densities, some of which are contiguous with small vesicles (crossed arrow) and one large granular vesicle (arrow). Scale: 0.2 μm. From DiFiglia *et al.* (1982b).

date mainly supports postsynaptic modulation of substance P mediated nociception by enkephalin at the level of the dorsal horn.

IV. Substance P in the Sympathetic Nervous System and the Adrenal Medulla

In addition to its possible role as a transmitter in the central nervous system (for review, see Nicoll *et al.,* 1980), substance P is also widely distributed throughout the autonomic nervous system (Pernow, 1953; Hökfelt *et al.,* 1977b; Gamse *et al.,* 1980a). In the autonomic nervous system, at least some of the substance P is associated with sensory neurons. Evidence has been provided that it is an excitatory transmitter in mesenteric sympathetic ganglia in the guinea pig (Konishi *et al.,* 1979).

However, substance P inhibits the firing induced by acetylcholine in Renshaw cells (Krnjević and Lekić, 1977; Belcher and Ryall, 1977; Ryall and Belcher, 1977) and the nicotinic activation of catecholamine secretion in adrenal paraneurons in culture (Livett *et al.*, 1979; Mitzobe *et al.*, 1979). In that system, substance P inhibits the acetylcholine or nicotine-induced calcium-dependent release of [^{3}H]norepinephrine, but is ineffective in inhibiting the release of [^{3}H]norepinephrine in response to high potassium. Because these cells do not respond to muscarinic agonists, the results indicate an inhibitory interaction of substance P on the nicotinic–receptor channel complex.

In a further delineation of this substance P inhibition of catecholamine secretion, Role *et al.* (1981) studied freshly isolated guinea pig adrenal medullary cells. Guinea pig adrenal tissue contains immunoreactive substance P that chromatographs with synthetic substance P on gel permeation chromatography. Adrenal medullary cells were shown to respond to both nicotinic and muscarinic agonists and in confirmation of the finding of Livett *et al.* (1979), substance P was found to inhibit nicotine-induced catecholamine secretion but not the secretion induced by pilocarpine (Table IV). Role *et al.* (1981) also found that substance P did not alter the catecholamine secretion induced by veratridine or high [K$^+$] and that the inhibition is noncompetitive with respect to acetylcholine, sodium or cal-

TABLE IV

Substance P Inhibits Nicotinic but Not Muscarinic Stimulation of Catecholamine Secretion[a]

Agonist	Catecholamine secretion (dpm μg protein)	
	Control	10 μM substance P
None	396	
Acetylcholine (200 μM)	2119	1353
Nicotine (50 μM)	865	387
Pilocarpine (500 μM)	888	840

[a] Aliquots of cells were incubated for 10 minutes at 37°C under the specified conditions. Catecholamine secretion was measured as release of ^{3}H-labeled catecholamine from cells previously labeled with [^{3}H]norepinephrine. Data presented here are means of duplicate or triplicate tests of a given condition from two separate experiments.

cium. Thus it seems that substance P acts somehow to inhibit the binding of acetylcholine to its receptor or interacts (independently or dependently) on the receptor–channel complex. The precise mechanism has not yet been determined.

V. Neurotensin: Discovery, Isolation, and Chemical Characterization

While screening column eluates for sialogogic activity, which led to the purification of substance P, another material recovered in the same fractions as substance P by gel permeation chromatography but with a less basic charge by ion-exchange chromatography (Fig. 11) was observed to cause a visible vasodilation in the exposed cutaneous regions of anesthesized rats. This response occurred within seconds after intravenous injection, was not accompanied by the secretion of saliva, was associated with a transient hypotension and was susceptible to degradation by proteolytic enzymes. Using this biological property to monitor purification procedures, the peptide was isolated (Carraway and Leeman, 1973) and named neurotensin because of its presence in neural tissue and its hypotensive activity. A summary of the purification steps followed is given in Table V.

The best evidence for the purity of this peptide was that the molar ratios of the constituent amino acids were integral and remained constant after reelectrophoresis at several different pH values (Table VI). The specific

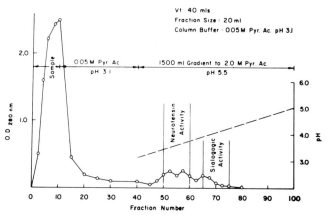

FIG. 11.   Ion-exchange chromatography of a bovine hypothalamic extract on sulfoethyl Sephadex. Neurotensin and substance P (sialogogic activity) were detected using bioassay; protein concentration was monitored at 280 nm. Pyr Ac, pyridine acetate. From Carraway and Leeman (1973).

TABLE V

Summary of Purification of Neurotensin from 45 kg of Bovine Hypothalami

Purification step	Total protein (mg)	Total sialogogic doses recovered	Total neurotensin doses recovered	Neurotensin yield	Neurotensin specific activity (doses[a]/mg)
80% acetone extraction	270,000[b]	40,000	15,000[c]	100	0.06
First gel chromatography on Sephadex G-25	10,000[b]	33,000			
Second gel chromatography on Sephadex G-25	1,500[b]	30,000	11,000	75	7.0
First chromatography on SE-Sephadex	250[b]	20,000	7,500	50	30.0
Second chromatography on SE-Sephadex	10[d]		6,000	40	600.0
Paper electrophoresis pH 3.5	0.3[d]	3,100	21	10,300.0	

[a] Material was tested for hypotensive activity in anesthetized rats weighing 250–300 g. Systemic arterial pressure was measured with a Hewlett-Packard recorder and pressure transducer after cannulation of the carotid artery. A dose was defined as the amount of material per 100 g body weight which caused a fall in systemic blood pressure of approximately 35 mm Hg when injected intravenously.

[b] Protein is expressed as absorbance units at 280 nm.

[c] Calculated by assuming a 75% yield of neurotensin through the two initial gel chromatography stages.

[d] Protein was calculated from quantitative amino acid analyses.

biological activity also remained constant. Spectrophotometric analysis confirmed the presence of two tyrosine residues and the lack of tryptophan. The apparent molecular weight estimated by gel permeation chromatography was in good agreement with that calculated by its amino acid composition.

Shortly afterward the amino acid sequence of this tridecapeptide was determined to be < Glu-Leu-Tyr-Glu-Asn-Lys-Pro-Arg-Arg-Pro-Tyr-Ile-Leu-OH (Carraway and Leeman, 1975a) by a combination of Edman degradation and carboxypeptidase treatment of papain-generated fragments (Fig. 12).

Synthetic material was prepared by solid phase synthesis (Carraway and Leeman, 1975b) and found to be indistinguishable by multiple biochemical criteria from native material. Synthetic material was used to generate radioimmunoassays (Carraway and Leeman, 1976a). Several immunogens were prepared by coupling neurotensin to different carrier

TABLE VI

Molar Ratios of Amino Acids in Neurotensin after Electrophoresis[a]

Amino acid	Electrophoresis at pH 3.5		Electrophoresis at pH 3.5 then pH 6.5		Electrophoresis at pH 3.5 then pH 8.9		Assumed residues per mole peptide
	13[b]	9[b]	25[b]	6[b]	7[b]	7[b]	
Lysine	1.0	1.0	1.2	1.0	1.1	1.1	1
Arginine	1.9	2.1	1.9	1.9	2.0	2.0	2
Aspartic acid	1.1	1.2	1.1	1.2	1.1	1.2	1
Glutamic acid	2.1	1.8	2.1	2.1	2.0	2.1	2
Proline	1.9	2.1	1.9	2.1	1.8	1.8	2
Isoleucine	0.9	1.0	1.0	1.0	1.0	1.0	1
Leucine	1.9	2.0	1.9	2.0	2.0	2.1	2
Tyrosine	2.2	2.1	2.0	2.0	1.8	1.9	2
	(2.5)[c]	(2.2)[c]	(2.0)[c]	(2.1)[c]			
Total							13
Specific activity (doses/mg)	10,000	10,500	10,000	10,500	10,500	11,000	

[a] Each column represents a separate preparation.

[b] Amount of peptide per analysis (nmoles).

[c] The value in parentheses is that of tyrosine determined spectrophotometrically assuming a molar extinction coefficient of 274 nm = 1.4×10^3.

proteins and three different antisera with well defined specificities (Fig. 13) were obtained and used to provide further information on the distribution and characteristics of neurotensin-like immunoreactivity (NTLI) (Carraway and Leeman, 1976b; Carraway *et al.*, 1980).

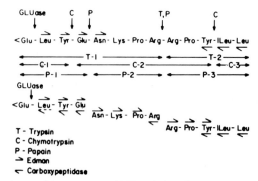

FIG. 12.   Complete amino sequence of NT and the alignment of the fragments obtained by enzymic cleavage < GLUase, Pyrrolidonecarboxylyl peptidase; T-1,2, tryptic peptides; C-1-3, chymotryptic peptides; P-1-2, papain peptides. From Carraway and Leeman (1975a).

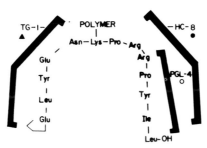

FIG. 13. Orientation of NT in immunogens used and average binding sites determined for three of the antisera obtained. Polymer refers to carrier; PGL, antisera obtained with NT-poly(Glu^{60}, Lys^{40}) conjugate; HC, antisera obtained with NT-succinylated hemocyanin conjugate; TG, antisera obtained with NT-bovine thyroglobulin conjugate. Courtesy Dr. Robert Carraway; from Leeman and Hammer (1981).

VI. Neurotensin: Distribution in the Central Nervous System (CNS)

The CNS distribution of NTLI has been mapped by radioimmunoassay in the rat (Carraway and Leeman, 1976b; Kobayashi *et al.*, 1977), calf (Uhl and Snyder, 1976), monkey (Kataoka *et al.*, 1979), and human (Cooper *et al.*, 1981), as shown in Table VII. In the rat, the highest concentrations of NTLI are found within the limbic system, particularly the median eminence and preoptic nuclei of the hypothalamus, the septum, nucleus accumbens, and amygdaloid nuclei. In postmortem human tissue, the highest levels of NTLI have been found in the hypothalamus and median eminence, the substantia nigra, periquaductal grey, and locus coeruleus. Considerable variation exists in the NTLI content in the several mammalian species. These differences may result not only from actual species variations, but also from loss of immunoreactivity in postmortem human tissue extracted several hours after death, different methods of tissue extraction, or from different cross-reactivities in the antisera for radioimmunoassay.

From immunohistochemical studies in the rat, NTLI has been observed within cell bodies of the hypothalamus, interstitial nucleus of the stria terminalis, amygdala, midbrain tegmentum, and many subdivisions of the brain stem (Uhl *et al.*, 1977, 1979). A more detailed investigation of the rat hypothalamus shows numerous somata with NTLI in the medial preoptic area, the periventricular region, the parvocellular aspect of the paraventricular nucleus (Figs. 14 and 15), the arcuate nucleus, and the lateral hypothalamus (Kahn *et al.*, 1980). Labeled fibers are identified in these same areas, and additionally in the lateral part of the zona external of the median eminence and the posterior mammillary nucleus (Kahn *et al.*, 1980).

TABLE VII

Regional Distribution of NTLI in the Central Nervous System of Several Mammalian Species

Region	Carraway and Leeman (rat) (pmol/g wet weight)	Kobayashi et al. (rat) (pmol/mg protein)	Uhl and Snyder (calf) (pmol/g wet weight)	Kataoka et al. (monkey) (pmol/g wet weight)	Cooper et al. (human) (pmol/g wet weight)
Cerebral cortex					
Area 3-1-2	2.0 ± 0.6			4.1 ± 4.1	
Area 4				10.3 ± 3.8	
Area 5				6.1 ± 0.46	
Area 6				2.5 ± 5.1	
Area 7				3.6 ± 0.63	
Area 17				2.3 ± 0.86	
Supplementary motor area				4.7, 6.1	
Frontal			1.80 ± 0.11		0.8 ± 0.1
Parietal			2.36 ± 0.07		0.8 ± 0.1
Uncal					4.9 ± 1.2
Entorhinal		0.03 ± 0.1			2.3 ± 0.7
Hippocampal formation		<0.01	2.99 ± 0.39		4.4 ± 0.6
Cingulate		<0.01	3.84 ± 0.24		2.1 ± 0.4
Striate					0.7 ± 0.1
Occipital pole			2.53 ± 0.30		
Precentoal gyrus			2.44 ± 0.15		
Parahippocampal gyrus			6.56 ± 0.67		
Basal ganglia					
Caudate (head)		0.017 ± 0.001	11.05 ± 0.13	4.86 ± 0.5	2.9 ± 0.4
Putamen				7.5 ± 3.1	2.5 ± 0.3

Region				
Globus pallidus				
Internal	9.8 ± 1.1			
External	9.7 ± 1.3			
Subthalamic nucleus	9.7 ± 3.7	9.34 ± 0.66		
Substantia nigra	23.4 ± 2.0	5.9 ± 1.6	0.18 ± 0.05	
Pars compacta		3.5 ± 1.4		
Pars reticulata	20.5 ± 2.7	9.3 ± 2.9		
Locus coeruleus	12.8 ± 1.7	14.5		
Raphe nucleus	11.7 ± 2.4			
Area postrema	2.6 ± 0.2	27.3, 18.5		
Inferior olive		8.74, 7.37		
Reticular formation of medulla		3.3		
Cerebellum				
Cortex	0.8 ± 0.1		<0.32	0.82 ± 0.26
Dentate n.	0.6 ± 0.1			<0.011
Cortex of hemisphere		2.6 ± 0.5		
Cortex of vermis		4.6, 8.7		
Fatigeal n.		13.4, 10.2		
Interpostus n.		15.3 ± 2.1		
Dentate n.		15.5 ± 2.1		
Hypothalamus				60.0 ± 14.0
Preoptic area				0.97 ± 0.25
Anterior hypothalamus	33.4 ± 5.0		17.32 ± 3.33	0.21 ± 0.086
Medial basal hypothalamus	31.2 ± 5.0		19.14 ± 3.12	0.53 ± 0.69
Posterior hypothalamus				0.19 ± 0.09
Median eminence		48.9, 52.5		1.93 ± 0.27
Arcuate n.		40.5 ± 4.1		0.56 ± 0.18
Ventromedial n.		48.4 ± 7.1		0.99 ± 0.18
Retrochiasmatic area				0.47 ± 0.13
Suprachiasmatic PO				0.73 ± 0.45

(Continued)

TABLE VII (Continued)

Region	Carraway and Leeman (rat) (pmol/g wet weight)	Kobayashi et al. (rat) (pmol/mg protein)	Uhl and Snyder (calf) (pmol/g wet weight)	Kataoka et al. (monkey) (pmol/g wet weight)	Cooper et al. (human) (pmol/g wet weight)
Periventricular PO					
Medial PO		0.96 ± 0.19			
Lateral PO		1.33 ± 0.13		29.4 ± 6.5	
Dorsomedial n.		1.46 ± 0.13		25.4 ± 9.2	
Lateral area				48.5 ± 5.2	
Mammillary body				32.6 ± 3.9	
Cervical cord			11.11 ± 0.88	14.9 ± 12.6	23.6 ± 2.6
Anterior column		0.080 ± 0.04	1.06 ± 0.008	15.0 ± 2.3	
Posterior/lateral				10.21 ± 1.5/2.9, 6.3	
Gray matter					
Amygdala					
Medial		0.37 ± 0.03	1.94 ± 0.38	10.7 ± 3.0	5.4 ± 1.1
Central				11.0 ± 3.2	

Region					
Thalamus	16.1 ± 5.8				
Anterior n.			4.32 ± 0.66	16.0 ± 2.7	
Ventral n.			1.27 ± 0.22	9.0 ± 1.3	
Dorsomedial n.			2.47 ± 0.09	15.7 ± 3.7	6.0 ± 1.4
Midline n.				26.7 ± 3.6	
Pulvinar complex			1.42 ± 0.03	14.6 ± 1.1	
Centre median				16.3 ± 20.0	
Lateral dorsal					3.1 ± 0.5
Lateral posterior					2.7 ± 0.6
Lateral geniculate				4.6 ± 1.1	1.9 ± 0.3
Medial geniculate				4.86	
Zona incerta		0.78 ± 0.15		24.8, 16.9	
N. accumbens		0.39 ± 0.05			
Septal area					
Brainstem	12.9 ± 3.3				
Interpeduncular n.		0.46 ± 0.08		45.1 ± 9.9	
Mesencephalon		0.08 ± 0.05			
Central grey of mesencephalon			0.42 ± 0.05	42.3	
Pons		0.057 ± 0.03	1.25 ± 0.23	2.2 ± 1.1	
Medulla		0.10	1.62 ± 0.05		
Ventral tegmental area				27.8	
Red nucleus			2.74 ± 0.27	16.7 ± 2.8	
Colliculi					
Colliculus superior				3.2, 5.6	
Colliculus inferior				8.6 ± 3.3	

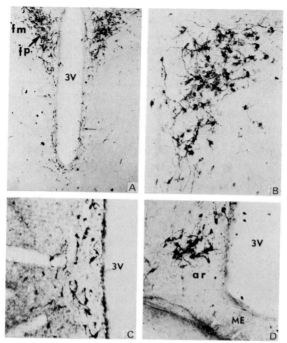

FIG. 14. Neurons with NTLI in frontal sections of the rat hypothalamus. Animals were pretreated with intraventricular colchicine. (A) Region of the paraventricular nucleus. Immunoreactive cells are found in the parovcellular (fp) and, to a lesser extent, in the magnocellular (fm) aspect of the paraventricular nucleus. Labeled neurons are also found in the periventricular region (arrows). 3V, Third ventricle. ×30. (B) Higher magnification of the right paraventricular nucleus in A. Stained cell bodies and fibers. ×75. (C) Neurons in the paraventricular nucleus rostral to A. ×75. (D) Cell in the arcuate nucleus (ar) caudal and ventral to A, at the level of the median eminence (ME). The colchicine pretreatment eliminated fibers with NTLI in the ME. ×60. From Kahn *et al.* (1980).

Few pathways involving NTLI have been identified, but a projection containing this neuropeptide originates from the amygdala and enters the stria terminalis (Uhl and Snyder, 1979). To date, these ultrastructural localizations of NTLI are limited to the dorsal horn of the rat and monkey spinal cord, where NTLI is found in large granular vesicles in axon terminals which participate in axodendritic synapses (Leeman *et al.*, 1980) (Fig. 16).

VII. Neurotensin in Plasma

Multiple forms of NTLI have been found to be present in acid/acetone extracts of bovine, rat, rabbit, and human plasma (Carraway *et al.*, 1980).

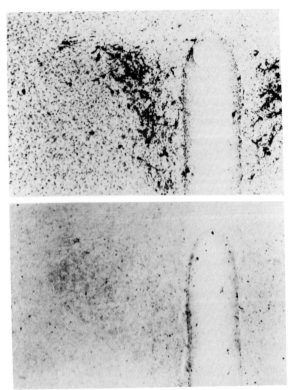

FIG. 15. Preabsorption control of NTLI in the rat hypothalamus. NTLI in cells in the rat paraventricular nucleus (above) is markedly reduced following preincubation of neurotensin antiserum (1 : 1000 dilution) with synthetic neurotensin (5 μg/ml; Beckman Instruments, Palo Alto, CA). ×60. From Kahn *et al.* (1980).

Approximately 30–50% of the NTLI measured in radioimmunoassay by an antiserum directed against the COOH-terminus of neurotensin has physicochemical properties of neurotensin, while the remainder of the NTLI is smaller on gel permeation chromatography in Sephadex G-25 and may contain several substances sharing COOH-terminal homologies with neurotensin (Fig. 17). Measurable concentrations of NTLI are present in plasma by radioimmunoassay with an antiserum against the NH_2-terminal end of neurotensin. However, smaller NTLI substances measured by this assay which lack COOH-terminal cross-reactivity are found on gel permeation chromatography on Sephadex G-25 (Fig. 17). It is likely that neurotensin is present in the circulation of a variety of mammalian

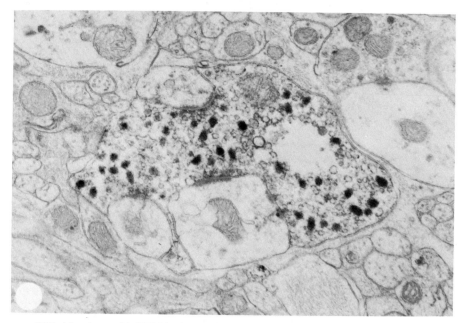

FIG. 16.   Axon with NTLI in the monkey outer dorsal horn. This labeled terminal forms several axo-dendritic synapses and has large granular vesicles with deposits of reaction product. Uranyl acetate counterstain only. ×20,000. Courtesy of Dr. DiFiglia.

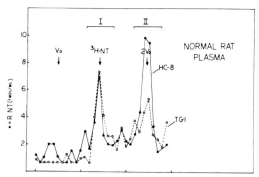

FIG. 17.   Gel chromatography on Sephadex G-25 of rat plasma extracts. An acid/acetone extract of 160 ml of normal rat plasma was submitted to a gel permeation chromatography with 0.2 M acetic acid solvent. Recovery was 40%. Peak I coeluted with [^{3}H]neurotensin while peak II contained smaller, presumably COOH- and NH$_2$-terminal, NTLI. HC-8 denotes the code for the COOH-terminal directed antiserum; TG-1 for the NH$_2$-terminal directed antiserum. V_0, void volume. From Carraway et al. (1980).

species, along with other circulating substances which have NH_2- or COOH-terminal immunoreactive similarities with neurotensin.

To elucidate the stability of neurotensin in the circulation, studies in our laboratory have been undertaken to describe the pharmacokinetics of neurotensin and related peptides in the circulation of the rat (Aronin *et al.*, in preparation). Neurotensin administered intravenously has a half-life of less than 2 minutes and is degraded rapidly into NH_2-terminal peptides with chromatographic and immunochemical properties of NT_{1-12}, NT_{1-11}, and NT_{1-8}. These latter fragments have a much slower half-life of disappearance and are more likely to persist in the circulation after the stimulation of neurotensin than is neurotensin itself.

It appears that for accurate interpretation of studies that involve measurement of plasma neurotensin levels one needs to account for (1) the presence of multiple forms of NTLI, which are dependent on cross-reaction with NH_2- and COOH-terminal directed antisera and (2) the more rapid disappearance of circulating neurotensin relative to its probable metabolic products. To this end, reports that show changes in concentrations of plasma NTLI are likely to be describing in part altered levels of substances other than neurotensin. Companion investigations to identify more precisely NTLI become essential in experiments designed to measure neurotensin responses to possible physiologic stimuli.

VIII. Neurotensin in the Gastrointestinal Tract

A. ISOLATION AND CHEMICAL CHARACTERIZATION

Studies on mapping the distribution of NTLI in various tissues suggested the presence of neurotensin in gastrointestinal tract (Carraway and Leeman, 1976b). From a large scale preparation of bovine intestine, a tridecapeptide was isolated which had the same amino acid composition and specific hypotensive activity as neurotensin (Kitabgi *et al.*, 1976). The amino acid sequence of this peptide was determined (Carraway *et al.*, 1978) and also found to be identical to neurotensin.

In collaboration with the late Dr. Robert Williams, immunoreactive neurotensin was also isolated from fresh postmortem scrapings of human intestinal tissue (Hammer *et al.*, 1980). Although insufficient pure material was obtained for a complete characterization, this peptide had the same chromatographic and hypotensive properties of neurotensin and the same amino acid composition as neurotensin. After papain digestion, the fragments generated had the same composition as fragments generated from synthetic neurotensin. Thus, its identity to neurotensin was considered to be established.

B. DISTRIBUTION AND CELLULAR LOCALIZATION

Using radioimmunoassay, Carraway and Leeman (1976b) demonstrated the differential distribution of NTLI in the gastrointestinal tract of the rat. Small amounts of NTLI are present in the esophagus, stomach, large intestine, and pancreas, while the greatest concentration is found in the intestinal epithelium lining of the jejunoileum (130 pmol/g). Similar studies in other mammalian species, including humans (Hammer *et al.*, 1980), have corroborated and extended these findings (Orci *et al.*, 1976; Helmstaedter *et al.*, 1977a; Polak *et al.*, 1977).

Immunohistochemical studies have identified neurotensin cells, called N cells, which are most numerous in the distal ileum but are scattered throughout the mucosa of the small intestine (Helmstaedter *et al.*, 1977a; Fig. 18). Ultrastructural immunocytochemistry has shown that neurotensin-containing granules are present primarily near the base of N cells, in the direction of the lamina propria (Helmstaedter *et al.*, 1977b; Fig. 19).

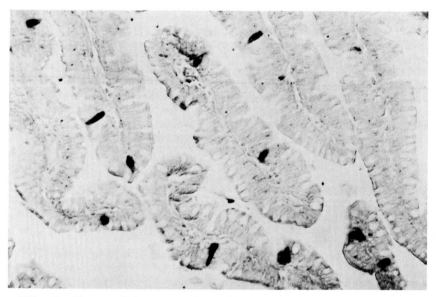

FIG. 18. Neurotensin-immunoreactive cells in the human ileum visible after peroxidase–antiperoxidase staining. Note the pyramidal shape of the cells, with the apex reaching the intestinal lumen. ×50. From Helmstaedter *et al.* (1977a).

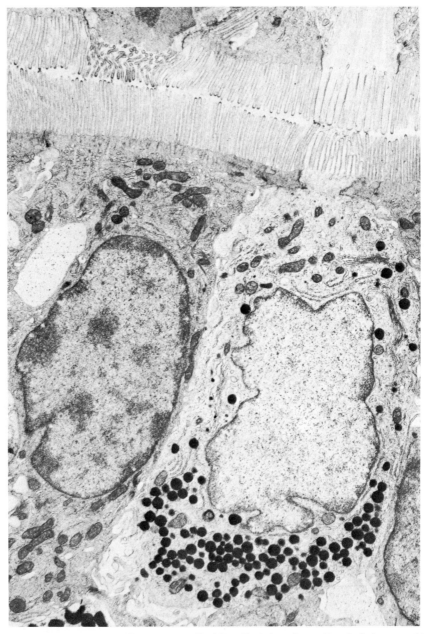

FIG. 19. Low magnification of the ileal N-cell of the primate *Tupaia belangeri* which stained in the adjacent semithin section with anti-neurotensin. The secretory granules (Sg) are clustered mostly at the basal region. From Helmstatedter *et al.* (1977b).

C. ELEVATION OF CIRCULATING NTLI FOLLOWING LIPID PERFUSION

Recent studies in our laboratory suggest that the neurotensin rises after lipid ingestion. Ferris *et al.* (1981) measured an elevation in plasma NTLI in blood collected from a superior mesenteric vein during the perfusion of rat small intestine with lipid (Fig. 20). Similar perfusion of amino acids, glucose, hyperosmotic saline, acidified saline, bile salt, and diluted rat bile had no effect on plasma NTLI levels. In addition, extracts from plasma samples collected from superior mesenteric vein during control and lipid perfusion of the small intestine were submitted to high-pressure liquid chromatography to identify more precisely the forms of NTLI. A 2-fold

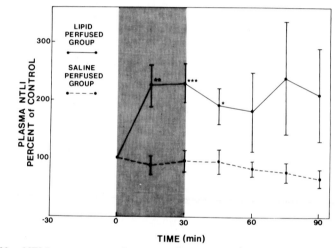

FIG. 20.   NTLI measurements in extracted plasma during saline and lipid perfusion of the rat small intestine. The small intestine was cannulated at the pylorus and ileocecal junction and the common bile duct ligated. A needle was inserted into the superior mesenteric vein near its entrance to the portal vein allowing for intermittant blood sampling without occlusion of mesenteric flood flow. Blood samples (1.5 ml) were collected at 15-minute intervals, spun immediately, and the plasma extracted and radioimmunoassayed with a carboxy-terminal directed neurotensin antiserum. NTLI levels were calculated as percentage changes with each animal serving as its own control. The mean and SEM (vertical bars) of these values are presented. The levels in samples obtained at −15 and 0 minutes were averaged and used as the control values. The NTLI (mean ± SEM) in the control period for the saline perfused rats ($n = 4$) was 47 ± 5 fmol/ml and for the lipid perfused rats ($n = 10$) was 53 ± 9 fmol/ml. The shaded area denotes the duration of the lipid perfusion in the experimental group. Values obtained at 15, 30, and 45 minutes in the lipid perfused group were significantly greater than their control. The NTLI levels (mean ± SEM) at these times were 116 ± 28, 117 ± 22, and 98 ± 25 fmol/ml, respectively. *$p < 0.025$; **$p < 0.01$; ***$p < 0.005$. From Ferris *et al.* (1981).

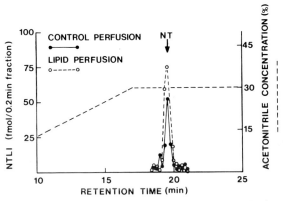

FIG. 21. High-pressure liquid chromatographic analysis of NTLI in plasma collected during control and lipid perfusion of the small intestine. Samples from superior mesenteric vein plasma were pooled, extracted, lyophilized, and dissolved in 1.8 ml distilled water. Samples were injected onto a 3.9 × 300 mm μBondapak C-18 column running at 2 ml/minute in 0.01 M KH$_2$PO$_4$ pH 4.0. Five minutes after sample application a 12 minute long gradient was run to 30% acetonitrile in 0.01 M KH$_2$PO$_4$. The arrow denotes the retention time of a synthetic preparation of neurotensin (NT). The chromatograms were obtained using pooled extracts of 17 ml of plasma from nine animals during control perfusion and 16 ml of plasma obtained during lipid perfusion. Immunoreactive material which eluted at the position of neurotensin was calculated to have been present in extracted plasma during the control perfusion at a concentration of 10 fmol/ml, while the estimated concentration obtained during lipid perfusion was 18 fmol/ml. From Ferris *et al.* (1981).

increase in immunoreactive material that eluted at the same position as synthetic neurotensin was found during lipid stimulation as compared to the saline control (Fig. 21). These results demonstrate that intraintestinal lipid is an effective and specific stimulus for the release of neurotensin from the small intestine into the portal circulation.

It has been proposed by Rosell and colleagues (1980) that neurotensin or an immunoreactive metabolite is an enterogastrone, a small circulating intestinal hormone that inhibits gastric motility and acid secretion in response to the ingestion of lipid. In support of this notion, NTLI has been detected in plasma extracts of several mammalian species (see above). It has been reported that the intravenous administration of synthetic neurotensin can inhibit gastric acid secretion (Andersson *et al.*, 1976), suppress gastric motility (Andersson *et al.*, 1977), and increase intestinal blood flow (Rosell *et al.*, 1976). In addition, Mashford *et al.* (1978) have shown a venous–arterial gradient of NTLI across the distal small intestine in anesthetized dogs. Following the ingestion in humans of various nutrients (Blackburn and Bloom, 1979), particularly fats (Rosell and Rokaeus, 1979), plasma NTLI levels are reported to increase. In these aforementioned studies, the contribution of neurotensin to the NTLI was not identified. Increases in plasma NTLI concentrations after meal ingestion may result from elevation of several substances that cross-react with neurotensin in radioimmunoassay. A recent study from our laboratory (Hammer *et al.*, 1981) has provided evidence that neurotensin is secreted into the circulation of volunteers in response to ingestion of a high fat meal, by identifying chromatographically metabolites of neurotensin that appear in the circulation 45 minutes later. In summary, these results indicate a close relationship between lipid ingestion and the secretion of neurotensin. The precise role of neurotensin in digestion or absorption and its mode of action as a hormone or paracrine agent are still unsettled.

IX. Conclusion

Substance P and neurotensin are two peptides that were isolated as a result of chance findings of a sialogogic substance and a separate hypotensive substance in hypothalamic extracts. Their structures were determined and synthetic material prepared, greatly facilitating the many biochemical, physiological, and pharmacological studies that have subsequently been carried out in many different laboratories. This widespread, uneven distribution throughout the central nervous system, peripheral nervous system (including the autonomic nervous system), and other scattered cells in other tissues, particularly the gastrointestinal tract, indicates that both these peptides subserve multiple physiological functions. The precise mechanism of action of either peptide in a given system is still unknown. Although considerable evidence supports a transmitter role for these substances, there are compelling reasons to consider hormonal, paracrine, and modulatory roles for these peptides. The alteration of nicotinic-induced secretion of catecholamines from adrenal chromaffin cells by substance P suggests an important interaction of substance P with receptor complexes of another neurotransmitter that may point the way to many important interrelationships between the peptide constituents of neurons and classical transmitters.

ACKNOWLEDGMENTS

The original work in this article was supported in part by NIH grants 5 R01 AM1650 (Susan E. Leeman) and 5 F32 AM06143-02 (Neil Aronin). We wish to thank Drs. Robert Carraway, Eric Floor, and Ernst Singer in our laboratory for their kind assistance in the preparation of the manuscript and Ms. Debra George for her excellent technical help. We are also grateful to Dr. Marian DiFiglia, Departments of Neurology and Anatomy, Harvard Medical School, Boston, MA, for the copies of the ultrastructural prints.

REFERENCES

Andersson, S., Chang, D., Folkers, K., and Rosell, S. (1976). *Life Sci.* **19**, 367.

Andersson, S., Rosell, S., Hjelmquist, U., Chang, D., and Folkers, K. (1977). *Acta Physiol. Scand.* **100**, 231.

Aronin, N., DiFiglia, M., Liotta, A. S., and Martin, J. B. (1981). *J. Neurosci.* **1**, 561.

Atweh, S. F., and Kuhar, M. J. (1977). *Brain Res.* **124**, 53.

Barber, R. P., Vaughn, J. E., Slemmon, J. R., Salvaterra, P. M., Roberts, E., and Leeman, S. E. (1979). *J. Comp. Neurol.* **184**, 331.

Belcher, G., and Ryall, W. W. (1977). *J. Physiol. (London)* **272**, 105.

Blackburn, A. M., and Bloom, S. R. (1979). *J. Endocrinol.* **83**, 75.

Blaustein, M. P. (1975). *J. Physiol. (London)* **247**, 617.

Brownstein, M. J., Mroz, E. A., Kizer, J. S., Palkovits, M., and Leeman, S. E. (1976). *Brain Res.* **116**, 299.

Carraway, R. E., and Leeman, S. E. (1973). *J. Biol. Chem.* **248**, 6854.

Carraway, R. E., and Leeman, S. E. (1975a). *J. Biol. Chem.* **250**, 1907.

Carraway, R. E., and Leeman, S. E. (1975b). *J. Biol. Chem.* **250**, 1912.

Carraway, R. E., and Leeman, S. E. (1976a). *J. Biol. Chem.* **251**, 7035.

Carraway, R. E., and Leeman, S. E. (1976b). *J. Biol. Chem.* **251**, 7045.

Carraway, R. E., and Leeman, S. E. (1979). *J. Biol. Chem.* **254**, 2944.

Carraway, R. E., Kitabgi, P., and Leeman, S. E. (1978). *J. Biol. Chem.* **253**, 7996.

Carraway, R. E., Hammer, R. A., and Leeman, S. E. (1980). *Endocrinology* **107**, 400.

Chan-Palay, V., and Palay, S. L. (1977). *Proc. Natl. Acad. Sci. U.S.A.* **74**, 4050.

Chang, M. M., and Leeman, S. E. (1970). *J. Biol. Chem.* **245**, 4784.

Chang, M. M., Leeman, S. E., and Niall, H. D. (1971). *Nature (London) New Biol.* **232**, 86.

Cooper, P. E., Fernstrom, M. H., Rorstad, O. P., Leeman, S. E., and Martin, J. B. (1981). *Brain Res.* **218**, 219.

Cuello, A. C., and Kanazawa, I. (1978). *J. Comp. Neurol.* **178**, 129.

DiFiglia, M., Aronin, N., and Leeman, S. E. (1982a). *Brain Res.* **233**, 381.

DiFiglia, M., Aronin, N., and Leeman, S. E. (1982b). *Neuroscience* (in press).

Elde, R., Hokfelt, T., Johansson, O., and Terenius, L. (1976). *Neuroscience* **1**, 349.

Emson, P. C., Arrequi, A., Clemont-Jones, V., Sandberg, B. E. B., and Rosser, M. (1980). *Brain Res.* **199**, 147.

Ferris, C., Hammer, R., and Leeman, S. E. (1981). *Peptides* **2** (Suppl. 2) (in press).

Floor, E., and Leeman, S. E. (1980). *Soc. Neurosci. Abstr.* **6**, 573.

Floor, E., Grad, O., and Leeman, S. E. (1982). *Neuroscience* (in press).

Gaddum, J. H., and Schild, H. (1934). *J. Physiol. (London)* **82**, 1.

Gale, J. S., Bird, E. D., Spokes, E. G., Iverson, L. L., and Jessell, T. M. (1978). *J. Neurochem.* **30**, 633.

Gale, K., Hong, J. S., and Guidotti, A. (1977). *Brain Res.* **136**, 371.

Gamse, R., Wax, A., Zigmond, R. E., and Leeman, S. E. (1981a). *Neuroscience* **6**, 437.

Gamse, R., Leeman, S. E., Holzer, P., and Lembeck, F. (1981b). *Arch. Pharmacol.* **317**, 140.

Glowinski, J., Michelot, R., and Cheramy, A. (1980). *Adv. Biochem. Psychopharmacol.* **22**, 51.

Haber, S., and Elde, R. (1981). *Neuroscience* **6**, 1291.

Hammer, R. A., Leeman, S. E., Carraway, R. E., and Williams, R. H. (1980). *J. Biol. Chem.* **255**, 2576.

Hammer, R. A., Carraway, R. E., and Leeman, S. E. (1981). *J. Clin. Invest.* (in press).

Hayes, A. G., and Tyers, M. B. (1980). *Brain Res.* **114**, 439.

Helmstaedter, V., Taugner, C., Feurle, G. E., and Forssmann, W. G. (1977a). *Histochemistry* **53**, 35.

Helmstaedter, V., Feurle, G. E., and Forssmann, W. G. (1977b). *Cell Tissue Res.* **184**, 445.

Henry, J. L. (1976). *Brain Res.* **114**, 439.

Hökfelt, T., Kellerth, J.-O., Nilsson, G., and Pernow, B. (1975). *Brain Res.* **100**, 235.

Hökfelt, T., Johansson, O., Kellerth, J. O., Ljungdahl, Å., Nilsson, G., Nygards, A., and Pernow, B. (1977a). *In* "Substance P" (U. S. von Euler and B. Pernow, eds.), pp. 117–145. Raven, New York.

Hökfelt, T., Elfvin, L.-G., Schultzberg, M., Goldstein, M., and Nilsson, G. (1977b). *Brain Res.* **132**, 29.

Hunt, S. P., Kelly, J. S., and Emson, P. C. (1980). *Neuroscience* **5**, 1871.

Jessell, T. M., and Iverson, L. L. (1977). *Nature (London)* **268**, 549.

Jessell, T. M., Iverson, L. L., and Cuello, A. C. (1978). *Brain Res.* **152**, 183.

Jessell, T. M., Mudge, A. W., Leeman, S. E., and Yaksh, T. L. (1979a). *Soc. Neurosci. Abstr.* **5**, 611.

Jessell, T., Tsunoo, A., Kanazawa, I., and Otsuka, M. (1979b). *Brain Res.* **168**, 247.

Kahn, D., Abrams, G. M., Zimmerman, E. A., Carraway, R., and Leeman, S. E. (1980). *Endocrinology* **107**, 47.

Kanazawa, I., and Jessell, T. (1976). *Brain Res.* **117**, 362.

Kanazawa, I., Bird, E., O'Connell, R., and Powell, D. (1977a). *Brain Res.* **120**, 387.

Kanazawa, I., Emson, P. C., and Cuello, A. C. (1977b). *Brain Res.* **119**, 442.

Kataoka, K., Mizuno, N., and Frohman, L. A. (1979). *Brain Res. Bull.* **4**, 57.

Kerr, F. W. L. (1975). *Pain* **1**, 325.

Kitabgi, P., Carraway, R. E., and Leeman, S. E. (1976). *J. Biol. Chem.* **251**, 7053.

Kobayashi, R. M., Brown, M., and Vale, W. (1977). *Brain Res. Bull.* **126**, 584.

Konishi, S., Tsunoo, A., and Otsuka, M. (1979). *Proc. Jpn. Acad.* **55**(B), 525.

Krnjevic, K., and Lekić, D. (1977). *Can. J. Physiol. Pharmacol.* **55**, 958.

LaMotte, C., Pert, C. B., and Snyder, S. H. (1976). *Brain Res.* **112**, 407.

Leeman, S. E., and Hammer, R. A. (1981). *In* "Cellular Basis of Chemical Messengers in the Digestive System" pp. 139–150. Academic Press, New York.

Leeman, S. E., and Hammerschlag, R. (1967). *Endocrinology* **81**, 803.

Leeman, S. E., DiFiglia, M., and Aronin, N. (1980). *Soc. Neurosci. Abstr.* **6**, 354.

Lembeck, F., and Starke, K. (1968). *Naunyn-Schmiedebergs Arch. Pharmakol. Exp. Pathol.* **259**, 375.

Livett, B. G., Kozousek, V., Mitzobe, F., and Dean, D. M. (1979). *Nature (London)* **278**, 256.

Ljungdahl, Å., Hökfelt, T., and Nilsson, G. (1978a). *Neuroscience* **3**, 861.

Ljungdahl, Å, Hökfelt, T., Nilsson, G., and Goldstein, M. (1978b). *Neuroscience* **3**, 945.

Lowry, O. H., Rosebrough, N. J., Farr, A. L., and Randall, R. J. (1951). *J. Biol. Chem.* **193**, 265.

Mashford, M. L., Nilsson, G., Rokaeus, A., and Rosell, S. (1978). *Acta Physiol. Scand.* **104**, 244.

Mitzobe, F., Kozousek, V., Dean, D. M., and Livett, B. G. (1979). *Brain Res.* **178**, 555.

Mroz, E., and Leeman, S. E. (1979). *In* "Methods of Hormone Radioimmunoassay" (B. M. Jaffe and H. R. Behrman, eds.), pp. 121–137. Academic Press, New York.

Mroz, E. A., Brownstein, M. J., and Leeman, S. E. (1977). *Brain Res.* **125**, 305.

Mudge, A. W., Leeman, S. E., and Fischbach, G. D. (1979). *Proc. Natl. Acad. Sci. U.S.A.* **76**, 526.

Nicoll, R. A., Schenker, C., and Leeman, S. E. (1980). *Annu. Rev. Neurosci.* **3**, 227.

Orci, L., Baetens, O., Rufener, C., Brown, M., Vale, W., and Guillemin, R. (1976). *Life Sci.* **19**, 559.

Pernow, B. (1953). *Acta Physiol. Scand. Suppl.* **105**, 1.

Pickel, V. M., Reis, D. J., and Leeman, S. E. (1977). *Brain Res.* **122**, 534.

Polak, J. M., Sullivan, S. N., Bloom, S. R., Buchan, A. M. J., Facer, P., Brown, M. R., and Pearse, A. G. E. (1977). *Nature (London)* **262**, 92.

Powell, D., Leeman, S. E., Tregear, G. W., Niall, H. D., and Potts, J. T., Jr. (1973). *Nature (London) New Biol.* **241**, 252.

Ralston, H. J., III, and Ralston, D. D. (1979). *J. Comp. Neurol.* **184**, 643.

Randić, M., and Miletić, V. (1977). *Brain Res.* **128**, 164.

Role, L. W., Leeman, S. E., and Perlman, R. L. (1981). *Neuroscience* **6**, 1813.

Rosell, S., and Rokaeus, A. (1979). *Acta Physiol. Scand.* **107**, 263.

Rosell, S., Burcher, E., Chang, D., and Folkers, K. (1976). *Acta Physiol. Scand.* **98**, 484.

Rosell, S., Rokaeus, A., Mashford, M. L., Thor, K., Chang, D., and Folkers, K. (1980). *In* "Neuropeptides and Neural Transmission" (C. A. Marson and W. Z. Farzyk, eds.), pp. 181–189. Raven, New York.

Ryall, R. W., and Belcher, G. (1977). *Brain Res.* **137**, 376.

Sar, M., Stumpf, W. E., Miller, R. V., Chang, K.-J., and Cuatrecasas, P. (1978). *J. Comp. Neurol.* **181**, 17.

Schenker, C., Mroz, E. A., and Leeman, S. E. (1976). *Nature (London)* **264**, 790.

Schwyn, R. C., and Fox, C. A. (1974). *J. Hirnforsch.* **15**, 95.

Sternberger, L. A. (1974). "Immunocytochemistry." Prentice-Hall, New York.

Studer, R. O., Trzeciak, H., and Lergier, W. (1973). *Helv. Chim. Acta.* **56**, 860.

Takahashi, T., and Otsuka, M. (1975). *Brain Res.* **87**, 1.

Treger, G. W., Niall, H. D., Potts, J. T., Jr., Leeman, S. E., and Chang, M. M. (1971). *Nature (London) New Biol.* **232**, 87.

Uhl, G. R., and Snyder, S. H. (1976). *Life Sci.* **19**, 1827.

Uhl, G. R., and Snyder, S. H. (1979). *Brain Res.* **161**, 522.

Uhl, G. R., Kuhar, M. J., and Snyder, S. H. (1977). *Proc. Natl. Acad. Sci. U.S.A.* **74**, 4059.

Uhl, G. R., Goodman, R. R., and Snyder, S. H. (1979). *Brain Res.* **167**, 77.

von Euler, U. S., and Gaddum, J. H. (1931). *J. Physiol. (London)* **72**, 74.

von Euler, U. S., and Pernow, B. (1977). "Substance P." Raven, New York.

Yaksh, T. L., Jessell, T. M., Gamse, R., Mudge, A. W., and Leeman, S. E. (1980). *Nature (London)* **286**, 155.

Zieglgänsberger, W., and Tulloch, I. F. (1979). *Brain Res.* **167**, 53.

DISCUSSION

L. J. Dorflinger: Does enkephalin block the synthesis of substance P from primary neuronal cultures in addition to inhibiting its release from these cells?

S. Leeman: Since we have only done acute experiments we have no information as to whether enkephalin affects the synthesis of substance P.

L. J. Dorflinger: In neuronal cultures where somatostatin production is increased, can you demonstrate an enkephalin-induced inhibition of somatostatin release?

S. Leeman: We have not done that.

E. Peck: I would like your response to a comment. It seems to me that you don't need to find an axo-axonic synapse in the dorsal horn at all if you presume that interneurons which contain enkephalin are really neurosecretory elements which control a whole field of analgesia, not point by point communication. In that manner you can turn off calcium channels via the elevation of adenylate cyclase and protein phosphorylation, etc. and reduce synaptic efficacy of the entire system. Is this reasonable? Why spend a lot of time searching for synapses everywhere.

S. Leeman: Yes, that is certainly a possibility. Another likely alternative, still in the genre of chemical synaptic interactions, is that terminals containing SP and enkephalin coverage into a common neuron. Some of these may be in the spinothalamic tract.

J. K. Findlay: Chubb and Hodgson (I. W. Chubb and A. D.Smith, *Proc. R. Soc. B.* **191,** 245–261, 1975) have demonstrated that there is a soluble form of acetylcholinesterase present between the nerve terminals. Is it possible that substance P might be modulating the activity of that soluble enzyme and thereby regulating the amount of acetylcholine which is being transmitted across the synapse. Is substance P antiproteolytic? It could act like leupeptin if enough of it was around. I think you have to have fairly large amounts of leupeptin in the test tube, but then within the environment of the nerve terminal, the concentration of substance P might also be high.

B. S. McEwen: I wonder if you could elaborate a little bit on this matter of the coassociation of various putative transmitters in the same neurons, because it seems to be an emerging story which is one of the most remarkable features of the peptide field.

S. Leeman: In a recent review (T. Hökfelt *et al., Nature (London)* **284,** 515, 1980) Hökfelt has a nice list which seems to be growing all the time of coexistence of peptides with a classical transmitter.

B. S. McEwen: Yes, that is the beginning, but a further aspect of this coassociation is that there may be a reciprocal relationship between the presence of two substances. Certainly there are neurons that have both, but many of them seem to have either more of the one substance or the other as if they made a choice between producing one or the other or under certain circumstances. Perhaps they are even in transition between expressing one or expressing the other. I was wondering if from your reading of the literature whether that was a very real possibility or whether I am just misreading the data.

B. S. McEwen: From the standpoint of neural regulation you would expect that a nerve impulse arriving at the presynaptic ending would trigger the release of almost anything that the nerve ending was prepared to release. Thus the presence of two, rather than only one, releasable substances might create problems for the postsynaptic cell.

S. Leeman: There has been evidence presented that acetylcholine and vasoactive intestinal peptide are released from the same sympathetic terminals and act on two different cell types in the sweat glands of cats (Lundberg *et al., Proc. Natl. Acad. Sci. U.S.A.* **77,** 1651, 1980). The VIP causes vasodilatation while the acetylcholine causes secretion.

G. T. Campbell: I would like to ask a question about the effects of substance P and acetylcholine on the release of catecholamines from cultured adrenal medullary cells. I think I caught the statement that, in culture, the medullary cells assume a neuronal shape. We have had an opportunity to transplant medullary cells into an area in which the vascular bed is remarkably devoid of catecholaminergic innervation. We have noticed that several weeks after transplantation the medullary cells do assume a neuronal shape and within this time period they look like they are going to innervate the vessels in this area. What we want to do is to cotransplant the cholinergic system along with them to see whether that would prevent the change in shape. In those studies you mentioned, did you happen to notice whether substance P or acetylcholine not only affected the release of catecholamines but also caused shrinkage of those processes.

S. Leeman: No, but your observation is really very exciting.

H. Papkoff: Could you say anything about the biosynthesis of both substance P and neurotensin in terms of possible precursor forms and second, how prevalent are these peptides in nonmammalian species?

S. Leeman: To date, the identification of a precursor of substance P has remained elusive. There is, however, recent *in vitro* evidence in the dorsal root ganglia that the incorporation of [^{35}S]methionine into substance P is blocked by cyclohexamide which suggests involvement of ribosomal-dependent synthesis of this peptide (A. Harmar *et al., Nature (London)* **284**, 267, 1980). In addition, the *in vivo* incorporation of [^{35}S]methionine into substance P has been demonstrated following the stereotaxic injection of the labeled amino acid into the corpus striatum of the rat (Spark and Singer, in press). Furthermore, the detection of labeled substance P in the substantia nigra, which is colchicine-sensitive, is consistent with lesion studies which show a striatal-nigral substance P pathway.

I am unaware of any work on the biosynthesis of neurotensin. Recently a cell line derived from a calcitonin-producing medullary thyroid carcinoma has been shown to synthesize and secrete neurotensin (F. Zeztenogler *et al., Proc. Natl. Acad. Sci. U.S.A.* **77**, 3741, 1980). These cells may provide a good system in which to investigate the biosynthesis of neurotensin.

In regard to nonmammalian forms of substance P, physalaemin, from the skin of a South American amphibian (PCA-Ala-Asp-Pro-Asn-Lys-Phe-Tyr-Gly-Leu-Met-NH$_2$), and eledoisin, from the salivary glands of a cephalopod (PCA-Pro-Ser-Lys-Asp-Ala-Phe-Ile-Gly-Leu-Met-NH$_2$), are analogs of substance P. Xenopsin (<Glu-Gly-Lys-Arg-Pro-Trp-Ile-Leu-OH) is a neurotensin analog.

E. A. Zimmerman: A propos of your last point, a photomicrograph of a cultured dorsal root ganglion cell (DRG) immunoreacted with your antiserum to substance P (the cells were grown in Dr. Phil Nelson's lab at NIH and the immunocytochemistry was performed by Dr. Elizabeth Mathew from my lab) shows that substance P is present in cultured DRGs and their processes. I would also like to introduce just briefly some new data performed again by immunoperoxidase technique using another antiserum to substance P very similar to Dr. Leeman's that was raised in our laboratory by Dr. Nilaver. These studies were performed in collaboration with Dr. Richard Defendini in our Department of Neuropathology at Columbia University. Dr. Defendini has been looking in human autopsy tissue at nerve terminals reactive for substance P in different parts of the nervous system. In the internal segment of the globus pallidus and substantia nigra substance P is present in nerve terminals on distal dendrites. In the spinal cord we see different kinds of innervation patterns: distal dendritic and proximal axodenditric and axosomatic endings, depending where you are in the spinal cord. We postulate that the endings in basal ganglia are excitatory, while those in spinal cord are inhibitory or stimulatory. There are very different kinds of specialized substance P terminals, and I'm not yet ready to throw away nerve endings as being important for substance P.

M. Saffran: May I return to the coexistence of peptides in the same cell. Is it possible that in analogy with the pro-opiocortin story there is a common precursor to two or more of these peptides?

S. Leeman: Yes.

T. H. Wise: I'd like to lead up to my question with the fact that at Florida the work of Barron and Caton showed that the estrogens can increase uterine blood flow and my cooperative work with them revealed that estrogen decreases ovarian blood flow. Now, this takes about 15–20 minutes for this effect and the phenomena of how this is complexed together, the mechanism, has never been known. But today, I just had a staggering thought, that accompanied with this bolus of estrogen given to either increase uterine blood flow or decrease ovarian blood flow is always a phenomenal amount of salivation from the cattle. Have you looked at uterine substance P levels or does substance P get out into the circulation where this would be a possibility (possible vasomechanism induced by the estrogen).

S. Leeman: The concentration of substance P in the circulation is very low and I don't know if there are going to be any targets which are sensitive to circulating levels of substance P. Substance P also stimulates the release of histamine from mast cells. I don't know whether that could in any way be involved with the control of ovarian blood vessels.

T. H. Wise: A number of neurotransmitters will directly or indirectly increase the blood flow or decrease the flow; the problem is that none of them fits this salivation produced by substance P.

K. Sterling: With regard to the enkephalin suppression by substance P secretion and its reversal by naloxone, I wanted to know first whether this is duplicated by the pharmacologic opiates, and second, whether you conceive this is suggesting an important role of substance P as a pain mediator?

S. Leeman: Considerable evidence points to an important role for substance P as a mediator of painful stimuli. Opioid peptides can inhibit substance P release.

E. A. Zimmerman: Your two peptides may talk to each other. There was some enthusiasm about a year or two ago for neurotensin as a pain inhibitor.

S. Leeman: There is neurotensin in the dorsal horn of the spinal cord. It is possible that it mediates some release or action of substance P.

Biological Properties of the Nuclear Matrix: Steroid Hormone Binding

EVELYN R. BARRACK AND DONALD S. COFFEY

*The James Buchanan Brady Urological Institute of the Department of Urology,
The Johns Hopkins Oncology Center and the Department of Pharmacology and
Experimental Therapeutics,
The Johns Hopkins University School of Medicine,
Baltimore, Maryland*

I. Introduction

A. OVERVIEW

The importance of cellular structural elements in the regulation of biological function is becoming increasingly apparent (see reviews by Shaper *et al.*, 1979; Porter and Tucker, 1981; Isaacs *et al.*, 1981). One of these structural components is the nuclear matrix, which is an insoluble, skeletal framework of the nucleus. The nuclear matrix may be defined as a residual nuclear scaffolding system with dynamic properties that provides functional organization for the DNA. The nuclear matrix may provide a direct passageway from the interior of the nucleus to the pore complexes. During mitosis, the peripheral lamina components of the matrix depolymerize, and the matrix proteins at the points of attachment of the DNA loops appear to condense to form the core scaffolding of the metaphase chromosomes.

We will review briefly some aspects of the isolation and characterization of the nuclear matrix, as well as some of the observations that have been made in this and other laboratories which support the concept that the nuclear matrix plays a functional and dynamic role in many important biological processes, such as DNA synthesis, RNA synthesis, processing and transport, and hormone action. We will focus primarily on our studies on the interaction of sex steroid hormones with the nuclear matrix (Barrack *et al.*, 1977, 1979; Barrack and Coffey, 1980).

B. THE CYTOSKELETON

A major change in the understanding of cellular structure was obtained in the 1970s with the identification of an elaborate structural network

133

within the cytoplasm or ground substance of the cell that has been termed the cytoskeleton or microtrabecular lattice. These earlier observations of intracellular structural proteins (see early reviews of Goldman and Knipe, 1972; and Pollard and Weihing, 1973) were confirmed when fluorescent actin antibodies revealed directly an elaborate actin network within a variety of nonmuscle cells (Lazarides and Weber, 1974). It now appears that an even more elaborate and dynamic protein cytoskeleton is formed from several components including actin filaments, microtubules, and intermediate filaments (Lazarides, 1981; Schliwa and Van Blerkom, 1981). This cytoskeleton system appears to form a microtrabecular lattice or network in whole cells when viewed in stereophotography utilizing high-voltage electron microscopy (Porter and Tucker, 1981; Henderson and Weber, 1979). This cytoskeleton system had also been observed earlier in detergent-washed cells after extraction of the plasma membrane phospholipid as well as many of the soluble cellular proteins (Osborn and Weber, 1977; Lenk *et al.*, 1977). This elaborate network had essentially escaped previous notice by microscopists using standard fixing and embedding techniques with thin sections and low-voltage electron microscopy.

Many investigators now believe that most of the soluble proteins comprising the cytosol may not in fact be soluble in the cell but are actually associated with the microtrabecular lattice and are extracted by the specific buffers and salts in the homogenizing medium and in the wash solutions; it will remain to be proven what proteins, if any, are actually soluble in the cytoplasm (Porter and Tucker, 1981). As will be discussed later, this may have important implications with regard to our concepts of soluble steroid hormone receptors.

In summary, the old concept of defining the cytoplasm as a sol-gel state is slowly being replaced by the more modern concept of a dynamic filamentous and trabecular system that orders and directs the function of the cytoplasmic compartment (Table I). The older concept that macromolecules, such as proteins, RNA, and receptor molecules, freely diffuse toward a random collision with an acceptor site, appears now to require some reevaluation.

C. THE NUCLEAR MATRIX

As the cytoplasm was being redefined in terms of residual structural elements, so were the nucleus and its nucleoplasm and chromatin fractions undergoing conceptual revision. Studies of the nuclear matrix (nuclear skeleton) (Berezney and Coffey, 1974, 1976, 1977) actually preceded those of the cytoskeleton, but the full acceptance of the nuclear matrix has

TABLE I
Concepts of the Ground Substance of the Cell

	Nomenclature	Intracellular macromolecular transport	Determination of cell shape and motility
Sol-gel concept	Protoplasm Cytoplasm Nucleoplasm	Primarily by diffusion	Interconversion of sol to gel states
Fibrillar-trabecular concept	Cytoskeleton Microtrabecular- lattice Nuclear matrix	Directed by filaments and microtrabeculae	Polymerization or chemomechanical interaction of fibrillar components

been slower because of the difficulties in developing specific fluorescent antibodies to the nuclear matrix, and the very insoluble nature of these proteins which have been most difficult to characterize. Such insoluble proteins raise justified questions concerning denaturation artifacts. Our studies have concentrated not on circumventing this issue, but rather on determining if the nuclear matrix is associated with important biological properties that would indicate whether it was worthy of additional study. Since the isolated nuclear matrix contains approximately 10% of the original nuclear proteins and is essentially devoid of histones and phospholipids, it represents only a fraction of the original nuclear mass. In contrast, the nuclear matrix structure is very highly enriched (>90% of the total) with newly synthesized DNA, as well as heterogeneous nuclear RNA. These and many other important biological functions reported to be associated with the nuclear matrix are summarized in Table II. Additional details regarding the properties of the nuclear matrix are also presented in several reviews (Berezney and Coffey, 1976; Shaper *et al.*, 1979; Berezney, 1979; Agutter and Richardson, 1980; Isaacs *et al.*, 1981). These summaries would indicate that the nuclear matrix may be involved directly in many fundamental nuclear processes such as DNA replication, RNA synthesis, processing and transport, as well as hormone action. The possibility that these observations are the results of nonspecific adsorption, macromolecular aggregation, and denaturation must be considered as alternative explanations. However, although these arguments cannot be eliminated completely, many attempts to assess these difficult problems by a variety of mixing experiments have all tended to diminish this possibility. In summary, the increasing evidence for an important role for the nuclear matrix in biological processes reported by numerous investigators over the past 7 years (Table II) indicates that this matrix system merits continued study.

TABLE II

Biological Functions Associated with the Nuclear Matrix (1974–1981)

1. The nuclear matrix contains structural elements of the pore complex, lamina, internal network and nucleolus (Berezney and Coffey, 1974, 1976, 1977; Comings and Okada, 1976; Wunderlich and Herlan, 1977; Hodge *et al.*, 1977)
2. DNA binding proteins in the nuclear matrix
   a. DNA is tightly attached to the nuclear matrix (Berezney and Coffey, 1975, 1976, 1977)
   b. Tenacious binding of HeLa DNA to specific matrix proteins of HeLa cell nuclei (Bowen *et al.*, 1980)
   c. Mouse liver nuclear matrix proteins have a high affinity for DNA and show a preference for binding single-stranded DNA, AT-rich DNA and poly(dT) (Comings and Wallack, 1978)
3. Role in DNA organization
   DNA is organized in the nucleus in the form of supercoiled loops, each containing 60,000–100,000 base pairs per loop. These loops are anchored at their base to the nuclear matrix (Vogelstein *et al.*, 1980; Georgiev *et al.*, 1978; Cook *et al.*, 1976; Razin *et al.*, 1979)
4. Role in DNA replication
   a. Newly replicated DNA is associated preferentially with the nuclear matrix (Berezney and Coffey, 1975, 1976; Dvorkin and Vanyushin, 1978; Dijkwel *et al.*, 1979; Pardoll *et al.*, 1980; Vogelstein *et al.*, 1980; McCready *et al.*, 1980; Hunt and Vogelstein, 1981; Berezney and Buchholtz, 1981a,b)
   b. The nuclear matrix contains fixed sites of DNA replication (Pardoll *et al.*, 1980; Vogelstein *et al.*, 1980; Berezney and Buchholtz, 1981a)
   c. DNA polymerase α is tightly bound to the nuclear matrix of actively replicating liver, but not of normal liver (Smith and Berezney, 1980)
5. Enrichment of certain actively transcribed genes with the nuclear matrix
   a. Ribosomal RNA genes are enriched at least 6-fold in the residual DNA associated with liver nuclear matrix (Pardoll and Vogelstein, 1980)
   b. SV40 sequences are enriched 4- to 7-fold in nuclear matrix-associated DNA of SV40 transformed 3T3 cells (Nelkin *et al.*, 1980)
6. Association of hnRNA with the nuclear matrix
   a. RNP particles are a component of the internal network of the nuclear matrix (Berezney and Coffey, 1974, 1976, 1977; Miller *et al.*, 1978a; Berezney, 1979, 1980; Steele and Busch, 1966)
   b. Essentially all of the hnRNA and snRNA are associated exclusively with the nuclear matrix (Miller *et al.*, 1978a,b; Herman *et al.*, 1978; Long *et al.*, 1979; van Eekelen and van Venrooij, 1981; Jackson *et al.*, 1981)
   c. Globin RNA, containing introns, is tightly associated with the nuclear matrix of chicken erythroblasts (Ross, 1980). Precursor mRNAs for ovomucoid and ovalbumin are on the nuclear matrix of hen oviduct (Ciejek *et al.*, 1981)
   d. hnRNA is attached to the nuclear matrix via two of the major hnRNP proteins (van Eekelen and van Venrooij, 1981)
   e. RNA is synthesized at fixed transcription complexes on the nuclear matrix (Jackson *et al.*, 1981)
   f. Nascent RNA is attached at the 5′ cap, and perhaps also at the 3′ end, to the nuclear matrix (Jackson *et al.*, 1981)

TABLE II (*continued*)

7. Interaction with viruses
   a. Certain SV40 specific proteins are associated exclusively with the nuclear matrix of infected HeLa cells (Deppert, 1978)
   b. Significant amounts of polyoma T-antigen and intact viral genomes are associated with the nuclear matrix of lytically infected 3T6 cells; implication of the nuclear matrix as a site of viral DNA replication (Buckler-White *et al.*, 1980)
8. Phosphorylation of matrix and lamina proteins
   a. Increased phosphorylation of specific rat liver nuclear matrix proteins occurs just prior to the onset of DNA synthesis in regenerating rat liver (Allen *et al.*, 1977)
   b. Phosphorylation of specific proteins of clam nuclear lamina-pore complex fraction by endogenous nuclear envelope-associated enzymes (Maul and Avdalović, 1980)
   c. Protein phosphokinase activity in the pore complex-lamina fraction of rat liver phosphorylates endogenous pore complex-lamina proteins (Steer *et al.*, 1980; Lam and Kasper, 1979a)
   d. The three major nuclear lamina proteins of the matrix are phosphoproteins and are phosphorylated to a greater extent prior to or during mitosis than in interphase. Phosphorylation of the major lamina proteins is probably involved in the reversible depolymerization of the lamina during cell division (Gerace and Blobel, 1980)
   e. Phosphorylation of nuclear matrix proteins of sea urchin embryos by endogenous matrix kinase activity *in vitro;* more phosphorylation in blastula than pluteus stage (Sevaljević *et al.*, 1981)
9. Reversible contraction of the matrix
   The nuclear matrix isolated from Tetrahymena macronuclei reversibly contracts when Ca^{2+} and Mg^{2+} concentration is decreased to 5 mM or increased to 125 mM (Wunderlich and Herlan, 1977)
10. Modulation of nuclear membrane lipid fluidity by internal components of the nuclear matrix
    Lipid fluidity is higher in isolated nuclear membrane ghosts than in intact nuclei (Giese and Wunderlich, 1980; Wunderlich *et al.*, 1978)
11. Contains binding sites for steroid hormones, EGF[a], lectins, and polyribonucleotides
    a. Specific, high-affinity, tissue and steroid-specific binding sites for androgens and estrogens on the nuclear matrix of target tissues (rat uterus, chicken liver, rat prostate) (Barrack *et al.*, 1977, 1979; Barrack and Coffey, 1980; Agutter and Birchall, 1979)
    b. Lentil binding sites on nuclear matrix of sea urchin embryos (Sevaljević *et al.*, 1981)
    c. Binding of WGA to the internal structure and binding of Con A to the periphery of HeLa cell nuclear scaffolds (Hozier and Furcht, 1980)
    d. Binding of poly(A) to lamina (McDonald and Agutter, 1980)
    e. Binding sites for EGF in chromatin-depleted nuclei (Johnson *et al.*, 1980)
12. Preferential binding of carcinogens to the nuclear matrix
    a. Benzo(*a*)pyrene binding to nuclear matrix of rat lung, rat liver, and thymocytes (Hemminki and Vainio, 1979; Blazsek *et al.*, 1979)
    b. Retinol markedly inhibits binding of benzo(*a*)pyrene to DNA and protein of the rat liver nuclear matrix but has little or no effect on binding of benzo(*a*)pyrene to bulk DNA and protein in chromatin (Nomi *et al.*, 1981)

[a] EGF, epidermal growth factor; WGA, wheat germ agglutinin; Con A, concanavalin A.

II. Isolation and Characterization of the Nuclear Matrix

A. THE RESIDUAL NUCLEUS

Several investigators have reported the isolation of residual nuclear protein fractions and their appearance by light and electron microscopy. Mirsky and Ris (1951) treated isolated nuclei with high concentrations of salt and nucleases and found residual chromosomal proteins. The laboratories of Zbarsky and Georgiev reported that after extraction of nuclei with 1 to 2 M NaCl solutions, residual nuclear structures were still observed (Zbarsky and Georgiev, 1959; Georgiev and Chentsov, 1962; Zbarsky et al., 1962). Although the majority of the DNA, RNA, and protein had been extracted, histochemical staining revealed residual nucleoli closely associated with residual chromosome structures. Electron microscopy of this material, which was referred to as a nucleonemata, showed a nuclear membrane surrounding fibrillar structures and ribonucleoprotein (RNP) particles. Following these earlier studies, Busch and his colleagues reported a more detailed electron microscopic study of this type of structure which they termed the nuclear ribonucleoprotein network. This network was observed to extend from an intact nuclear envelope to the nucleolus (Smetana et al., 1963; Shankar Narayan et al., 1967). A comprehensive study was made by Steele and Busch (1966) of the RNA associated with this residual nucleus.

B. THE NUCLEAR MATRIX

The residual nuclear structures referred to above were complex structures composed of intact nuclear envelopes, residual nucleoli, and considerable amounts of ribonucleoprotein (RNP) particles. Based on these previous observations, experiments were carried out in this laboratory to determine whether a fundamental constitutive framework structure was present in the cell nucleus. Our approach was to remove as many of the nuclear components as possible, including the lipid of the membrane, without destroying nuclear spheres, and thereby isolate the minimal residual components required for maintaining the basic structure of the nucleus. The progressive removal of various nuclear components was monitored biochemically (Table III), and light and electron microscopic observations were made to monitor the integrity of nuclear structure. We succeeded in removing 98% of both the phospholipid and RNA of the rat liver nucleus as well as 99.9% of the DNA and 90% of the total nuclear proteins, thus yielding what appears to be the fundamental structural framework of the nucleus (Berezney and Coffey, 1974, 1976, 1977). The resulting constitutive structure, which we termed the nuclear protein matrix, is composed primarily of protein. The four major steps in the procedure for the isolation of the matrix involve sequential extractions of isolated nuclei with buffers of low ionic strength and high ionic strength, nonionic detergent and nuclease treatment. These are shown in Table III, along with the cumulative percentages of total nuclear constituents remaining after each step.

A detailed electron microscopic analysis of the nuclear protein matrix has been described by Berezney and Coffey (1974, 1976, 1977). Three major structural components of the nuclear matrix can be resolved (e.g., see Fig. 1):

1. The residual elements of the nuclear envelope and nuclear lamina that form a continuous structure surrounding the nuclear sphere. Tangen-

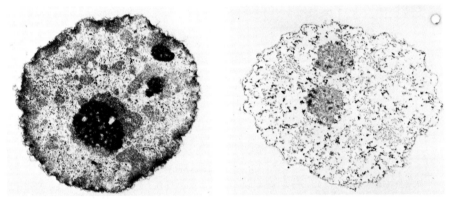

FIG. 1.   Electron micrographs of thin sections of an isolated rat liver nucleus (left panel) and of an isolated rat liver nuclear matrix (right panel). The nuclear matrix is isolated from highly purified nuclei, by a modification of the original method of Berezney and Coffey (1977). Freshly prepared nuclei are extracted sequentially with 1% Triton X-100 [4°C, 10 minutes, in 0.25 M sucrose containing TM buffer (10 mM Tris, pH 7.4, 5 mM MgCl$_2$)]; pancreatic DNase I (electrophoretically purified by Worthington, Freehold, N.J.; 10 to 20 μg/ml in TM buffer, 4°C, 30 minutes); 0.2 mM MgCl$_2$, 10 mM Tris, pH 7.4 (LM buffer), 4°C, 15 minutes; 2 M NaCl in LM buffer, obtained by increasing gradually the concentration of NaCl from 0 to 2 M (two extractions, 4°C, 30 minutes); and finally washed and resuspended in 0.2 mM MgCl$_2$, 10 mM Tris, pH 7.4. Phenylmethylsulfonyl fluoride (PMSF), at a final concentration of 1 mM, is generally added to all buffers used in the isolation and extraction of nuclei. Centrifugation of samples is carried out at 750 g for 15 minutes (following Triton X-100 and DNase I treatments) or 1500 g for 30 to 40 minutes (following subsequent extractions). Recoveries of nuclear matrix spheres are routinely greater than 70%, based on counts in a hemocytometer chamber. Fixation, embedding, and staining for electron microscopy are carried out using standard procedures (see Berezney and Coffey, 1977; Kaufmann et al., 1981). Magnification, ×9280.

TABLE III

Steps in the Original Procedure for Isolation of the Nuclear Matrix from Rat Liver Nuclei[a,b]

Step	Consecutive extractions	Resultant nuclear sphere	Extraction medium (0°C)	Number of extractions	Centrifugation time at 770 g (minutes)	Percentage recovery from starting nuclei			
						Protein	DNA	RNA	Phospholipid
0	Untreated control nuclei	Intact nucleus (N)	Isolated through 2.2 M sucrose, 5 mM MgCl$_2$, 10 mM Tris, pH 7.4	—	—	100	100	100	100
1	Low magnesium treatment (0.2 mM MgCl$_2$)	Low Mg^{2+} sphere (LM)	0.2 mM MgCl$_2$, 10 mM Tris, pH 7.4	3	30	48.0 ± 1.23	24.2 ± 2.78	80.3 ± 1.83	97.5 ± 2.13
2	High salt treatment (2 M NaCl)	High salt sphere (HS)	2 M NaCl, 0.2 mM MgCl$_2$, 10 mM Tris, pH 7.4	3	60	16.3 ± 1.17	2.4 ± 0.21	34.0 ± 1.64	93.6 ± 1.65
3	Detergent treatment (1% Triton X-100)	Nuclear matrix (NM)	1% (w/v) Triton X-100, 5 mM MgCl$_2$, 10 mM Tris, pH 7.4	1	30	10.0 ± 0.57	2.3 ± 0.21	29.0 ± 1.68	2.2 ± 0.51
4	Nuclease treatment (DNase, RNase)	Nuclear protein matrix (NPM)	200 µg DNase I/ml plus 200 µg RNase A/ml in 5 mM MgCl$_2$, 10 mM Tris, pH 7.4, 1 hour at 22°C	1	30	9.8 ± 0.55	<0.01	3.0 ± 0.12	2.0 ± 0.47

[a] See method of Berezney and Coffey (1977).

[b] See text for special considerations. This general procedure has been modified, as described in the text and in the legend to Fig. 1.

tial sections through this residual nuclear envelope reveal the presence of annular structures characteristic of the nuclear pore complex which forms an integral part of the intact nuclear envelope.

2. Highly condensed residual nucleoli.

3. An extensive granular and fibrous interchromatinic matrix structure which extends throughout the interior of the nuclear sphere.

The nuclear matrix appears to be a universal feature of eukaryotic nuclei. Such residual structures have now been isolated from a wide variety of mammalian and nonmammalian sources (Table IV), and there appear to be numerous similarities in their protein constituents.

One should distinguish between the *nuclear matrix* and the *nuclear protein matrix* (Table III). The nuclear matrix, as originally defined, represents a DNase-, Triton-, and 2 M NaCl-resistant structure that retains the

TABLE IV

Eukaryotic Systems from Which a Residual Nuclear Matrix Structure Has Been Isolated

Source of nuclei	References
Rat liver	Berezney and Coffey (1974, 1977); Miller *et al.* (1978a,b); Agutter and Birchall (1979); Berezney (1980); Kaufmann *et al.* (1981); Zbarsky (1981)
Mouse liver	Comings and Okada (1976)
Rat uterus	Barrack *et al.* (1977); Agutter and Birchall (1979)
Rat lung	Hemminki and Vainio (1979); Agutter and Birchall (1979)
Rat ventral prostate	Barrack and Coffey (1980)
HeLa cells	Riley *et al.* (1975); Riley and Keller (1976); Hodge *et al.* (1977); Herman *et al.* (1978); Adolph (1980); Bouvier *et al.* (1980); van Eekelen and van Venrooij (1981)
SV40-infected HeLa cells	Deppert (1978)
Human lymphocytes and granulocytes	Shaper *et al.* (1979)
Erythroleukemia cells	Long *et al.* (1979)
3T6 fibroblasts	Buckler-White *et al.* (1980)
Hepatoma	Berezney *et al.* (1979); Kuz'mina *et al.* (1980); Zbarsky (1981)
Rabbit granulocytes	Eastment *et al.* (1981)
Tetrahymena pyriformis	Wunderlich and Herlan (1977); Herlan *et al.* (1979); Wolfe (1980)
Physarum polycephalum	Mitchelson *et al.* (1979); Hunt and Vogelstein (1981)
Xenopus laevis liver	Snead *et al.* (1979)
Sea urchin embryos	Poznanović and Sevaljević (1980); Sevaljević *et al.* (1980)

spherical integrity of the nucleus, but which contains only 10% of the protein, 2% of the DNA, 30% of the RNA, and 2% of the phospholipid of the nucleus (see Table III). Since the original objective had been to describe the minimal residual components of the nucleus responsible for maintaining nuclear spherical integrity (Berezney and Coffey, 1974, 1976, 1977), additional attempts were made to fully digest the remaining nucleic acid constituents, using high concentrations of DNase I and RNase A (Table III); the resultant structure was called the *nuclear protein matrix*.

C. CONSIDERATIONS IN THE ISOLATION OF THE NUCLEAR MATRIX

Many factors are important in the nuclear matrix isolation process which can affect the nature of the final product (Table V). Although most investigators use a similar approach to obtain the nuclear matrix, in that they employ detergent, hypotonic, and high salt extractions, and nuclease treatments, the specific details are frequently different (Table V; see also Shaper *et al.*, 1979). For example, rat liver nuclei contain an endogenous

TABLE V

Variations in Extraction Procedures Reported for Isolating Nuclear Matrix Preparations[a]

General Scheme
    1. Detergents
    2. Hypotonic solutions
    3. Hypertonic solutions
    4. Nuclease treatment

Variables
    1. Source and purity of nuclei
    2. Nature and purity of detergent (Triton X-100; NP-40; peroxide contaminants)
    3. High salt (0.4–2.0 M; NaCl, KCl, or ammonium sulfate)
    4. Magnesium concentration (0–0.2 mM–5 mM–0.5 M)
    5. Chelating agents (EDTA; citric acid)
    6. Inhibitors of proteolysis (PMSF; sodium tetrathionate)
    7. Sulfhydryl reagents (β-mercaptoethanol, dithiothreitol)
    8. State of sulfhydryl oxidation
    9. DNase (type, amount, time, temperature; protease and RNase contaminants)
    10. RNase A, RNase T_1
    11. Endogenous nuclease activity
    12. Protease activity (endogenous; contaminants)
    13. Extraction temperature (−20 to +37°C), pH (7.2–8.5)
    14. Order of extractions (also number, duration)
    15. Centrifugation conditions (g force, duration)
    16. Fixatives and method of observing (thin section; whole mounts)

[a] See Shaper *et al.* (1979).

magnesium-activated DNase, the activity of which facilitates the extraction of DNA at low magnesium ion concentrations (0.2 mM) and high ionic strength (2 M NaCl) (see Table III, steps 1 and 2). Without the endogenous DNase activity, these extractions may yield large gelatinous aggregates that interfere with the subsequent isolation of the nuclear matrix. Since nuclei from different tissues contain varying amounts of endogenous DNase activity, the problem of gel formation can be circumvented by carrying out an initial brief digestion of the nuclei with low concentrations of DNase I, followed by the hypotonic and hypertonic extraction steps as described in the legend to Fig. 1. (Compare these modifications with the original procedure described in Table III.)

Other important factors that can affect the isolation of the nuclear matrix include endogenous protease activities, the state of oxidation of the nuclear protein sulfhydryl groups, and the order of the extraction steps (also see Table V). Matrix structures of varying morphology and that retain variable amounts of the internal network material and residual nucleolus can be obtained by manipulating these variables. Specific details of these effects have been reported for rat liver nuclei (Shaper et al., 1979; Kaufmann et al., 1981). Of particular interest is the observation that if DNase and RNase treatments are applied after the salt extraction, an extensive internal fibrogranular network is retained (Table III), whereas digestion of nuclei with both DNase I and RNase A prior to extraction with 2 M NaCl often leads to the disruption of the internal network structure of rat liver nuclear matrix spheres (Kaufmann et al., 1981). Other factors may contribute to these observations, however, since the internal network of the nuclear matrix is not universally found to be sensitive to this latter treatment regimen (Wunderlich and Herlan, 1977; Miller et al., 1978a; Wolfe, 1980).

D. THE PROTEINS OF THE NUCLEAR MATRIX

The nuclear matrix represents about 10–20% of the total nuclear protein mass and is composed of nonhistone proteins. The matrix proteins are primarily, but not exclusively, in the molecular weight range of 55,000 to 75,000 (Berezney and Coffey, 1974, 1977; Comings and Okada, 1976; Riley et al., 1975; Hodge et al., 1977; Cobbs and Shelton, 1978; Peters and Comings, 1980). Three of the major polypeptide fractions of 62,000–70,000 MW appear to be associated with the pore complex-lamina component of the matrix (Aaronson and Blobel, 1975; Dwyer and Blobel, 1976; Gerace et al., 1978). Some of these matrix proteins appear, by tryptic peptide mapping analysis, to be related in sequence (Shaper et al., 1979; Cochran et al., 1979; Shelton et al., 1980) and may form oligomers by

disulfide bridge cross-linking (Cobbs and Shelton, 1978; Shelton and Cochran, 1978; Lam and Kasper, 1979b; S. H. Kaufmann and J. H. Shaper, in
preparation). These three lamina protein fractions have recently been
termed lamin A, lamin B, and lamin C and appear to be phosphorylated at
the time of disassembly of the nuclear envelope during mitosis (Gerace
and Blobel, 1980).

Peters and Comings (1980) have made a detailed analysis by two-
dimensional polyacrylamide gel electrophoresis of the rat liver nuclear
proteins, and conclude that 80% of the mass of the nonhistone
chromosomal proteins of unextracted nuclei are contained in the nuclear
matrix and hnRNP fractions. They point out that the three lamin protein
bands (A, B, C) of 60,000 to 75,000 MW are themselves composed of three
distinct subsets comprising a group of several isomers. They also conclude that approximately one-third of the nuclear matrix proteins consist
of hnRNP proteins and that actin is also present in the matrix. Peters and
Comings (1980) point out that the residual nucleolar matrix is made up of
proteins that are different from those of the lamina or intranuclear network of the nuclear matrix (see also Todorov and Hadjiolov, 1979; Franke
et al., 1981).

At present, antibodies have been made only against the matrix proteins
of 62,000–70,000 MW that are associated with the lamina (Krohne *et al.*,
1978; Gerace *et al.*, 1978; Stick and Hausen, 1980; Jost and Johnson,
1981).

III. DNA Synthesis on the Nuclear Matrix

Work in this laboratory has demonstrated the possible role of the nuclear matrix in DNA replication (see also Table II). Berezney and Coffey
(1975, 1976) reported that newly synthesized DNA is tightly associated
with the nuclear matrix. At the earliest time intervals after injecting
[³H]thymidine into the hepatic portal vein of partially hepatectomized
rats, nuclear matrix fractions were obtained which contained tightly attached DNA that was highly enriched in label. At later times after the
injection, the specific activity of the matrix-associated DNA decreased,
while that of the easily extracted bulk DNA increased (Berezney and
Coffey, 1975, 1976). They concluded that the newly synthesized DNA is
associated with the nuclear matrix and is subsequently transported off of
the matrix (Berezney and Coffey, 1975, 1976). Further insight into nuclear
matrix-associated DNA replication was obtained from studies carried out
by Pardoll *et al.* (1980), using 3T3 cells in culture. From a detailed analysis
of the kinetics of pulse-chase labeling studies, Pardoll *et al.* (1980) proposed a fixed site model of DNA replication in which DNA replication
complexes are anchored to the nuclear matrix, and that loops of DNA are

reeled through these fixed complexes as they are replicated. Autoradiograms of pulse-labeled, matrix-associated DNA indicate that the replication sites are distributed throughout the interior network of the nuclear
matrix (Pardoll *et al.*, 1980). Experiments using synchronized *Physarum
polycephalum* provide additional evidence that is consistent with this
model of DNA synthesis (Hunt and Vogelstein, 1981).

According to the model proposed by Pardoll *et al.* (1980) (see Fig. 2),
multiple loops (approximately 20,000/cell) of DNA are attached at their
base to the nuclear matrix. The two sites of attachment for each loop
contain a fixed site for DNA replication. During replication, each DNA
loop moves downward, through each of the two fixed replicating complexes. As the parent DNA loop passes through the fixed replication sites,
two new loops are formed and the old loop disappears. Each of the new
loops contains one single strand of the parent DNA combined with a
single strand of newly synthesized DNA (see Fig. 2). This model fulfills
many of the earlier experimental observations related to DNA synthesis;
these are summarized in Table VI. The aspect of the new model of Pardoll
et al. (1980) that fits each observation is given within parentheses following each of the earlier observations (Table VI).

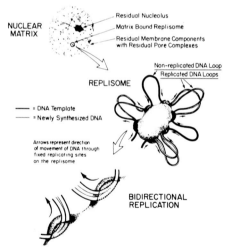

FIG. 2.   Proposed model for fixed sites of DNA replication on the nuclear matrix. The top
drawing in the figure represents a nuclear matrix. The middle drawing shows a cluster of
fixed replication complexes forming a replisome. DNA is bound via the replication complexes in alternating replicated and nonreplicated loops. The bottom drawing shows one
fixed replication complex with the DNA being reeled through as it is replicated. The process
shown would result in a bidirectionally replicated section of DNA with the origin of replication at the center of the replicated loop. (For details of evidence for this model consult
Pardoll *et al.*, 1980; Vogelstein *et al.*, 1980.)

TABLE VI

Previous Observations of DNA Synthesis That Are Satisfied by the Proposed Model of Fixed Replication Sites[a]

---

1. Loop domains of DNA are often observed in interphase nuclei and may be maintained even in metaphase chromosomes. (These loops are attached at their base to the nuclear matrix)

2. A replicating point moves outward forming two replicating forks moving in opposite directions. An "eye" pattern of newly synthesized DNA is formed (Pattern also consistent with fixed site model)

3. DNA is synthesized in replication units. (A replicon = one DNA loop)

4. Replicons are approximately 50,000 to 100,000 base pairs in length. (Corresponds to the length of a loop of DNA attached to the matrix at its base)

5. An individual replicon is synthesized in approximately 30 minutes. (Time of loop synthesis derived from kinetic analyses)

6. Replicons are often synthesized in tandem. (Coupled loop movements on replisome)

7. Origin of DNA synthesis is never next to a terminus of DNA synthesis. (Origin starts at bottom of loop, and after DNA replication, is found at top of new loop next to another origin)

8. Many enzymes are required for DNA synthesis and they may be combined into a large complex at the replicating fork. (Size more compatible with fixed site of DNA synthesis)

9. New and old strands of DNA are combined following DNA replication

10. The vast amount of DNA must be ordered so that there is no entanglement during or following DNA replication. (DNA ordered by loop attachment to matrix)

---

[a] See Pardoll *et al.* (1980).

Recently it has become possible to directly visualize the loops of supercoiled DNA attached to the matrix, and to monitor the movement of newly synthesized DNA within these loops (Vogelstein *et al.*, 1980).

There have been several additional recent studies of DNA synthesis associated with the nuclear matrix (Dijkwel *et al.*, 1979; McCready *et al.*, 1980; Berezney and Buchholtz, 1981a,b). Models have been proposed which are essentially similar in nature to the one described above, but which differ with respect to the questions of whether the origin of DNA replication remains attached to the nuclear matrix throughout DNA replication (Dijkwel *et al.*, 1979), and whether the matrix-bound replication complexes slide along the DNA (Berezney and Buchholtz, 1981a) or remain fixed with respect to the movement of the DNA loops through these sites (Pardoll *et al.*, 1980; see Fig. 2).

Many more studies will be required to resolve the many complex aspects of DNA synthesis, and to test and resolve the fine features of the loop model and the fixed site model of DNA replication. Nevertheless, the proposal that the DNA of the eukaryotic nucleus is organized in the form of supercoiled loops which are attached to the nuclear matrix, and that during DNA replication these loops of DNA are reeled through fixed replication sites on the nuclear matrix (Pardoll *et al.*, 1980; Vogelstein *et al.*, 1980) provides an attractive explanation for the mechanism by which an enormous length of DNA must be ordered spatially during replication such that the daughter strands remain untangled yet coupled in a precise fashion for later entry into mitosis.

IV. The Association of RNA with the Nuclear Matrix

Earlier studies had recognized that RNA was an important component of the residual nucleus (Georgiev and Chentsov, 1962; Zbarsky *et al.*, 1962; Steele and Busch, 1966; Shankar Narayan *et al.*, 1967; Busch and Smetana, 1970). Early studies by Busch and his colleagues (Steele and Busch, 1966; Busch and Smetana, 1970) analyzed the specific RNAs associated with the ribonucleoprotein network of the nucleus, and found that following a 20-minute pulse of [^{32}P]orthophosphate to rats, the specific activity of the residual liver nuclear RNA was 3-fold higher than that of the RNA associated with the chromatin. The highest specific activity was with the high molecular weight RNA >45 S. These observations were confirmed and extended by Faiferman and Pogo (1975). In addition, several investigators have observed that nuclear RNP particles are associated with the nuclear matrix (Berezney and Coffey, 1974, 1976, 1977; Miller *et al.*, 1978a; Berezney, 1979, 1980). Since the nuclear matrix provides a continuous structure directly linking residual nuclear components with the nuclear pore complexes, it was suggested by Berezney and Coffey (1976) that the nuclear matrix might provide a structural passageway for RNA transport. This concept may be feasible since essentially all of the hnRNA and snRNA molecules are associated with the nuclear matrix (Miller *et al.*, 1978a,b; Herman *et al.*, 1978; Long *et al.*, 1979; van Eekelen and van Venrooij, 1981; Jackson *et al.*, 1981). Recently it has been reported that the pre-mRNA for globin, containing the introns, is tightly associated with the nuclear matrix isolated from chicken erythroblasts (Ross, 1980). Similarly, when chicken oviduct nuclei were fractionated into matrix and nonmatrix components, virtually all of the precursor to ovomucoid and ovalbumin mRNA were observed to be bound to 7% of the total nuclear protein that represented the nuclear matrix fraction (Ciejek *et al.*, 1981). They suggested that following synthesis, the precursor to mRNA is integrated into the structure of the nuclear matrix. Several investigators have proposed that the matrix is either the site for RNA processing or is involved in a structural sense with the processing of RNA precursors (Herman *et al.*, 1978; Ross, 1980; van Eekelen and van Venrooij, 1981; Jackson *et al.*, 1981; Ciejek *et al.*, 1981). Recently insight has been gained into the site of attachment of the hnRNP particles to the nuclear matrix (van Eekelen and van Venrooij, 1981). These investigators demonstrated that ultraviolet irradiation resulted in the cross-linking of two of the major hnRNP proteins of 41,500 and 43,000 MW to the hnRNA. These same proteins became cross-linked to the hnRNA when either intact cells (HeLa S3) or the isolated nuclear matrix were irradiated. Since these proteins were found to be components of the nuclear matrix, it was suggested that the hnRNA is bound to the matrix via these proteins (van Eekelen and van Venrooij, 1981). In addition, there are a wide variety of stable small-molecular-weight RNAs associated with the nuclear matrix that may provide attachment sites for hnRNA (Miller *et al.*, 1978b).

In the previous section related to DNA synthesis on the nuclear matrix evidence was presented that DNA loops are reeled through fixed replication sites that are attached to the nuclear matrix (Pardoll *et al.*, 1980). Recently, a similar mechanism has been proposed that transcription also occurs as DNA passes through transcription complexes that are fixed to the nuclear matrix (Jackson *et al.*, 1981). In addition, these authors report that the nascent RNA is attached to the matrix at the 5' cap and perhaps also at the 3' end.

All of the models of DNA moving through fixed sites attached to the matrix will require special considerations related to topological problems arising from the supercoiling of DNA that can be relieved by topoisomerase-like activities (B. Vogelstein and D. M. Pardoll, unpublished results). Recently, it has been reported that chicken oviduct progesterone receptor subunit A binds preferentially to single-stranded DNA, providing a possible mechanism for DNA helix destabilization (Hughes *et al.*, 1981).

Several investigators have proposed that active genes may be in relatively close proximity to the nuclear matrix (Pardoll and Vogelstein, 1980; Nelkin *et al.*, 1980; Bekhor and Mirell, 1979; Gates and Bekhor, 1980; Norman and Bekhor, 1981). Studies cited by Bekhor and his colleagues were related to salt-resistant components of chromatin that appear to be related to the nuclear matrix proteins but as yet this has not been proven.

In summary, there is increasing evidence that the nuclear matrix may have an important role in the transcription, processing, and transport of nuclear RNA. Elements of the nuclear matrix may order the DNA both in the interphase nucleus and become part of the core scaffold of the metaphase chromosomes (Basler *et al.*, 1981). If the nuclear matrix possesses chemomechanical properties such as those observed in the condensation of chromosomes, similar properties may also be utilized in the transport of macromolecules within the interphase nucleus.

The control of DNA replication, gene expression, and RNA processing and transport remain at the frontier of our knowledge in cell biology. It is of interest that each of these biological processes appears to be related to the nuclear matrix. Since hormones initiate these functions it seemed only logical to determine how hormones might interact in a specific manner with the nuclear matrix.

V. The Interaction of Steroid Hormones with the Nuclear Matrix

A. INTRODUCTION

The interaction of steroid hormones and their specific receptor proteins with the nucleus of target tissues is an essential step in the mechanism by which these hormones modulate nuclear events such as gene expression (see reviews by Gorski and Gannon, 1976; Thrall et al., 1978; Jensen, 1979; Liao et al., 1979). The hormone–receptor complex is presumed to bind to specific regulatory sites near the genes they regulate, but the identification of these binding sites and the mechanism for specific recognition of these sites remain an enigma. Numerous efforts to identify and localize these nuclear "acceptor" sites to which the steroid–receptor complex binds have attributed this property to basic nuclear proteins (Puca et al., 1975), DNA (Yamamoto and Alberts, 1976), ribonucleoprotein particles (Liao et al., 1973), chromatin (Thrall et al., 1978; Jensen, 1979), nucleosomes (Senior and Frankel, 1978; Rennie, 1979), nonhistone proteins (Thrall et al., 1978), nuclear membrane (Jackson and Chalkley, 1974; Lefebvre and Novosad, 1980; Smith and von Holt, 1981), or salt-insoluble nuclear fractions (see following section). We have focused our attention on the identification of specific steroid binding sites associated with the nuclear matrix. While it might appear that this only adds to the apparently confusing array of potential nuclear targets for steroid hormone action, there is increasing evidence that the nuclear matrix provides an organizational and structural framework on which nuclear events are regulated (see Table II).

B. HORMONE BINDING TO SALT-RESISTANT NUCLEAR COMPONENTS

Nuclear steroid receptors are frequently characterized by extraction from nuclei with 0.3–0.6 M KCl or NaCl (Jensen et al., 1968; Puca and Bresciani, 1968; Bruchovsky and Wilson, 1968). However, in many different target tissue systems a significant amount of steroid binding activity remains resistant to solubilization by salt (Fang et al., 1969; DeHertogh et al., 1973; Lebeau et al., 1973; Mester and Baulieu, 1975; Klyzsejko-

Stefanowicz *et al.*, 1976; Nyberg and Wang, 1976; Clark and Peck, 1976; Barrack *et al.*, 1977, 1979; Boesel *et al.*, 1977; Davies *et al.*, 1977; Ruh and Baudendistel, 1977; Snow *et al.*, 1978; Gschwendt and Schneider, 1978; Danzo and Eller, 1978; Kaufman *et al.*, 1978; Wang, 1978; Franceschi and Kim, 1979; Sanborn *et al.*, 1979; Sato *et al.*, 1979; Barrack and Coffey, 1980; Tsai *et al.*, 1980). A number of attempts have been made to characterize these salt-resistant steroid binding sites further. DeHertogh *et al.* (1973) proposed, on the basis of *in vivo* infusion studies of [³H]estradiol labeling of rat uterine nuclei, that the salt-resistant nuclear fraction represented the ultimate site of hormone localization in the nucleus. Using an *in vitro* [³H]estradiol exchange assay (Anderson *et al.*, 1972a) to quantitate the amount of hormone that had become bound to these sites as a result of *in vivo* processes of hormone–receptor complex translocation, Clark and Peck (1976) observed that the number of salt-resistant nuclear estradiol receptors was identical with the number of receptors required for maximal uterine growth, and they proposed that these binding sites represented specific nuclear acceptor sites. Similar observations were made by Ruh and Baudendistel (1977), who concluded from studies that compared the growth responses of rat uteri to estrogens and antiestrogens that these salt-resistant nuclear estradiol binding sites may be involved primarily in events that result in the replenishment of cytoplasmic receptors (Ruh and Baudendistel, 1978). In cell-free binding assays, high affinity, tissue-specific nuclear acceptor sites for isolated steroid hormone–receptor complexes have been described in residual fractions of chromatin that resist dissociation by $0.5–2\,M$ NaCl or $4–5\,M$ GuHCl. These salt-resistant acceptor sites have been characterized for androgen receptors in the rat prostate (Wang, 1978), testis (Klyzsejko-Stefanowicz *et al.*, 1976), and Sertoli cell (Tsai *et al.*, 1980), and for progesterone receptors in the chick oviduct (Thrall *et al.*, 1978). Thus, by three different experimental approaches—labeling *in vivo*, exchange *in vitro*, and cell-free reconstitution—biological functions have been ascribed to nuclear salt-resistant hormone binding activities.

Some have questioned the evidence for a salt-resistant class of nuclear receptors (Juliano and Stancel, 1976; Traish *et al.*, 1977; Müller *et al.*, 1977). Following the incubation of rat uteri *in vitro* in the presence of 10 nM [³H]estradiol (Müller *et al.*, 1977), approximately 100 fmol/uterus, or 10%, of the nuclear bound radioactivity is resistant to repeated extractions with $0.6\,M$ KCl. Wotiz and his colleagues concluded that this is an insignificant number and probably represents nuclear receptors entrapped in the gelatinous DNA pellet that results when uterine nuclei are exposed to high concentrations of salt (Traish *et al.*, 1977). It is important to recognize, however, that only about 10–20% of the maximum number of estrogen receptors that can be translocated to the nucleus following treatment of rats with pharmacological doses (1–2.5 μg) of estradiol exhibit long-term retention in the nucleus, which is a requirement for the stimulation of true uterine growth (Anderson et al., 1972b, 1975; Clark and Peck, 1976). Moreover, this limited number of nuclear estradiol binding sites is salt-resistant (Clark and Peck, 1976). It is important to note that although the *percentage* of nuclear receptors which are salt-resistant varies with the dose of estradiol given *in vivo* (20% following 2.5 μg estradiol vs 60% following 0.1 μg estradiol), maximal uterine growth is obtained with both doses, and the *number* of salt-resistant receptors is the same (Clark and Peck, 1976).

Therefore, although Wotiz and colleagues (Traish et al., 1977; Müller et al., 1977) measured steroid binding directly (via 1 μg [³H]estradiol *in vivo* or 10 nM [³H]estradiol *in vitro* with intact uteri), while Clark and co-workers (Anderson et al., 1972b, 1975; Clark and Peck, 1976) measured receptors by an *in vitro* exchange assay (following 0.1–2.5 μg unlabeled estradiol *in vivo*), a significant number of salt-resistant estradiol receptors (1500–3000 molecules/nucleus) can be detected by these three different approaches. Conflicting results, however, have been obtained by Juliano and Stancel (1976), who injected a physiological dose (0.1 μg) of [³H]estradiol into rats and found essentially no salt-resistant nuclear radioactivity.

Additional insight into this problem has been obtained from experiments carried out in this laboratory (Barrack et al., 1977, 1979). Our analysis of several different protocols has revealed that methodological differences may account, in large part, for the divergent interpretations related to the measurement of nuclear salt-resistant steroid receptors. Some of these experiments are summarized in Table VII. Studies *in vivo* were carried out in which immature female rats were given a physiological dose (0.1 μg) of estradiol, either unlabeled or radiolabeled. One hour later, uterine nuclei were isolated and estradiol binding to the total, salt-extractable and salt-resistant nuclear fractions was quantitated. Following the administration of unlabeled steroid, specific estradiol binding sites were quantitated by the *in vitro* [³H]estradiol exchange assay method described by Anderson et al. (1972a). Approximately 50% (220 fmol/uterus) of the total nuclear estradiol binding capacity was resistant to solubilization by 0.6 M KCl (Table VII, part I,A), in agreement with the findings of Clark and Peck (1976). Comparable results were obtained whether binding was measured before or after salt extraction.

In contrast, when the same dose of *radiolabeled* estradiol (0.1 μg) was administered *in vivo* and bound estradiol was quantitated by direct counting of the nuclear fractions before and after salt extraction, 22 fmol/uterus

TABLE VII

Comparison of Different Methods Used to Study Subnuclear Distribution of Estradiol Binding Sites in Immature Rat Uteri[a]

	Specific estradiol binding (fmol/uterus)		
	Total nuclei	Salt-extractable	Salt-resistant
I. *In vivo* studies[b]			
A. Unlabeled E₂ (0.1 μg)			
1. *In vitro* exchange, then extract	483 ± 19	269 ± 33	220 ± 10
2. Extract, then exchange	—	181 ± 20	210 ± 17
B. ³H-E₂ (0.1 μg)			
1. Count fractions directly	210 ± 15	214 ± 18	22 ± 4
2. *In vitro* exchange assay	—	—	199 ± 20
II. *In vitro* studies[c]			
A. Unlabeled E₂ (20 nM)			
1. *In vitro* exchange, then extract	826 ± 179	551 ± 139	233 ± 63
B. ³H-E₂ (20 nM)			
1. Count fractions directly	1137 ± 131	865 ± 179	204 ± 55

[a] Data taken from Barrack *et al.* (1977, 1979).

[b] Immature female Sprague–Dawley rats (21–25 days old) were given a single subcutaneous injection of either 0.1 μg [³H]17β-estradiol (90–102 Ci/mmol) (I,B) or 0.1 μg unlabeled 17β-estradiol (I, A), in 0.5 ml of 0.9% NaCl. One hour later, the uteri were homogenized in 10 mM Tris, pH 7.4, 1.5 mM EDTA, and a crude nuclear myofibrillar pellet was prepared, as described by Anderson *et al.* (1972a). Where indicated, the *in vitro* exchange assay (Anderson *et al.*, 1972a) was carried out at 37°C, 30 minutes in the presence of 14 nM [³H]estradiol without (to measure total binding) or with excess unlabeled estradiol (1.4 μM; to measure nonspecific binding). Only specific binding data (total minus nonspecific binding) are shown (mean ± SD). Samples were pelleted at 4°C, washed 3 times with Tris–EDTA buffer to remove unbound steroid, and then either dissolved in tissue solubilizer or extracted with ethanol and counted, or extracted with 0.6 M KCl and 10 mM Tris, pH 8.0 before counting. Where extraction with KCl preceded the exchange assay, the binding reactions for the soluble salt extracts were terminated by the addition of hydroxylapatite, washing, and extraction of bound radioactivity with ethanol.

[c] Uteri obtained from untreated immature female rats were placed into Eagle's HeLa medium containing 20 nM of ³H-labeled or unlabeled estradiol and incubated at 37°C for 1 hour under an atmosphere of 95% O₂–5% CO₂. Nuclei were isolated and extracted with KCl as described above.

or less than 10% of the total nuclear label was salt-resistant (Table VII, part I,B,1). A similar observation was made by Juliano and Stancel (1976). However, if we further subjected this salt-resistant pellet to an *in vitro* binding assay in the presence of [³H]estradiol, 200 fmol of specific estradiol binding was detected (Table VII, part I,B,2). Thus, labeled estradiol (0.1 μg) injected *in vivo* is not recovered with the salt-resistant sites, though these binding sites can be revealed when the isolated fractions are subjected to an exchange assay *in vitro*.

Total nuclear estradiol binding sites measured by the exchange assay were 2.3-fold more numerous than those found following injection of label *in vivo* (Table VII, part I,A vs I,B). This increase is accounted for by the ability of the exchange assay to detect salt-resistant sites *in vitro* which are not labeled by the *in vivo* approach (Table VII, part I,B). In contrast, labeling of the salt-extractable receptors is equally efficient by both methods (Table VII, parts I,A and I,B).

The results of incubating intact uteri *in vitro* at 37°C for 1 hour in the presence of labeled or unlabeled estradiol (20 n*M*) are also shown in Table VII. Incubation with unlabeled estradiol, followed by quantitation of nuclear estradiol receptors by the *in vitro* exchange assay, results in higher levels of total nuclear and salt-extractable receptors than are obtained 1 hour after the injection of 0.1 μg unlabeled estradiol *in vivo* (Table VII, part I,A vs II,A). This is probably due to a dose-dependent translocation of cytoplasmic receptors into the nucleus, since the level of estradiol to which the uteri are continuously exposed during an *in vitro* incubation is likely to be greater than that which follows a single injection of 0.1 μg estradiol *in vivo*. Evidence for dose-related translocation is the observation by Clark and Peck (1976) of much greater levels of nuclear estradiol receptors 1 hour following the administration of a pharmacological dose (2.5 μg) of estradiol than a physiological dose (0.1 μg).

As shown in Table VII (parts II,A and I,A), the number of nuclear salt-resistant estradiol binding sites is the same following incubation of intact uteri *in vitro* or the injection of unlabeled estradiol *in vivo*. This is in agreement with the observation by Clark and Peck (1976) of similar numbers of nuclear salt-resistant estradiol binding sites following either low (0.1 μg) or high (2.5 μg) doses of estradiol.

Table VII also shows that whereas only about 5–10% of the nuclear salt-resistant sites can be labeled by injecting 0.1 μg [³H]estradiol *in vivo* (Table VII, part I,B,1), virtually all of these sites can be labeled by incubating intact uteri *in vitro* with [³H]estradiol, despite the fact that this salt-resistant binding represents less than 20% of the total nuclear binding measured under these conditions (Table VII, part II,B). Similar results were obtained whether the uteri were homogenized in the presence or absence of a 100-fold excess (2 μ*M*) of unlabeled estradiol, indicating that the binding did not merely occur during cell disruption. Coincubation of uteri with [³H]estradiol and 2 μ*M* unlabeled estradiol greatly diminished the amount of [³H]estradiol bound to all fractions. We conclude that nuclear salt-resistant sites in the intact cell are accessible to estradiol, though the degree of occupancy of these sites may be dose related.

It is important to account for the observation that 0.1 μg [^{3}H]estradiol *in vivo* does not appear to label nuclear salt-resistant binding sites (Table VII), yet this dose is capable of stimulating true uterine growth (Anderson *et al.*, 1972b, 1975). Several possible explanations might be considered. (a) If nuclear salt-resistant binding sites can be demonstrated only by subjecting isolated nuclei to an *in vitro* labeling method, one might question whether the *in vitro* exchange assay conditions are measuring or exposing binding sites that do not bind estradiol under *in vivo* conditions. However, salt-resistant sites can become occupied by steroid when intact uteri are incubated with [^{3}H]estradiol *in vitro* (Table VII, part II,B). (b) Alternatively, one might infer that the *in vitro* exchange reaction is capable of detecting both occupied and unoccupied sites, whereas the *in vivo* labeling method measures only unoccupied sites. This would imply that the salt-resistant sites were already occupied by endogenous estrogen *in vivo;* however, if this were the case, one would have to explain why the immature uterus is not already maximally stimulated. (c) The inability to recover label with the nuclear salt-resistant sites following an *in vivo* pulse may be due to a more rapid dissociation of [^{3}H]estradiol from salt-resistant sites than from salt-extractable sites during the nuclear isolation procedure. Yet, when salt-resistant sites are labeled by the exchange assay *in vitro,* the [^{3}H]estradiol remains bound throughout extensive washing procedures to remove unbound steroid. However, there is no way of knowing whether subtle changes in binding parameters might be induced during *in vitro* manipulations. (d) Another explanation is that partial occupancy of salt-resistant sites by estradiol *in vivo,* following the administration of 0.1 μg estradiol, may be all that is required for maximal growth stimulation. Thus, estradiol may induce an increase in the number of salt-resistant sites to a level of approximately 200 fmol/uterus, but most of these may represent spare receptors. Alternatively, the mechanism by which salt-resistant sites may be related to growth may not necessarily involve or require bound estradiol, at least during the time frame of these experiments.

C. HORMONE BINDING SITES ON THE NUCLEAR MATRIX: RAT UTERUS

We set out to determine whether the nuclear salt-resistant estradiol receptors of the rat uterus were in fact associated with the nuclear matrix, since the salt-resistant nuclear fraction still contained the nuclear envelope and most of the nuclear DNA and RNA. One hour after the injection of 0.1 μg unlabeled estradiol into immature female rats, uterine nuclei were isolated and extracted sequentially with 1% Triton X-100, DNase I, low magnesium hypotonic buffer, 2 M NaCl, and Tris–EDTA buffer. The residual nuclear matrix fraction contained only 1% of the total nuclear DNA. Specific estradiol binding sites on the nuclear matrix were quantitated *in vitro,* as follows. Saturation analysis, as described by Anderson *et al.* (1972a), was carried out at 37°C for 30 minutes in the presence of increasing concentrations of [³H]estradiol (70 pM to 14 nM) without (to measure total binding) or with a 100-fold excess of unlabeled estradiol (to measure nonspecific binding). Specific binding was calculated by subtracting nonspecific from total binding and plotted according to the method of Scatchard (1949), as shown in Fig. 3. Thus the nuclear matrix contains saturable, high-affinity, specific estradiol binding sites. Quantitation of specific, high-affinity estradiol binding to unextracted uterine nuclei is shown for comparison in Fig. 4. The nuclear matrix, which remains after the removal of most of the nuclear phospholipid, DNA, RNA, and protein, retains 22% of the total nuclear specific estradiol binding capacity, a significant enrichment. It is important to note that these calculations underestimate binding recovery since they do not take into account the less than quantitative recovery of matrix spheres from the starting nuclear spheres.

Several additional points are worth noting. It had been argued by Traish *et al.* (1977) that salt-resistant binding merely represents incomplete extraction of nuclear salt-extractable receptors which have become entrap-

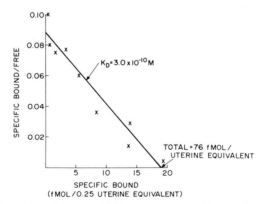

FIG. 3.   Binding of estradiol to rat uterine nuclear matrix. Nuclei were isolated from uteri of 23-day-old female rats, 1 hour after the injection of 0.1 μg unlabeled estradiol. The nuclear matrix fraction was isolated as described in Fig. 1, but in the absence of protease inhibitors. The final nuclear matrix pellet was washed in 10 mM Tris, pH 7.4, 1.5 mM EDTA; estradiol binding was measured *in vitro* by saturation analysis in the presence of increasing concentrations of [³H]estradiol (70 pM to 14 nM) without (total binding) or with a 100-fold excess of unlabeled estradiol (nonspecific binding). Specific binding was calculated by subtracting nonspecific from total binding; a Scatchard plot of the specific binding data is shown.

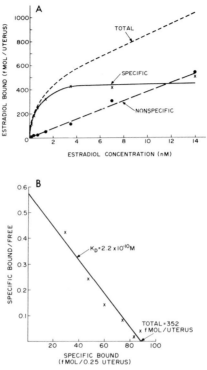

FIG. 4.   Binding of estradiol to isolated rat uterine nuclei. Nuclei were isolated from uteri of estradiol-treated rats, and were subjected to saturation analysis *in vitro* as described in the legend to Fig. 3. (A) Total, nonspecific and specific binding are plotted. (B) Scatchard plot of specific binding.

ped in the gelatinous DNA pellet that is obtained when nuclei are incubated in concentrated salt solutions. This is not the case, however, since we can demonstrate significant amounts of specific steroid binding activity in the nuclear matrix fraction, which routinely contains much less than 5% of the total nuclear DNA. In addition, the isolation of nuclear matrix spheres involves an initial brief digestion of the nuclei with DNase I, which allows the subsequent solubilization of chromatin by low magnesium and 2 M NaCl solutions and prevents the formation of a gelatinous pellet.

Other important features of the estradiol binding sites associated with the uterine nuclear matrix are their steroid specificity and tissue specificity. In competitive binding assays carried out *in vitro*, only estrogens are capable of inhibiting the binding of [^{3}H]estradiol to specific, high-affinity binding sites (Table VIII). With regard to tissue specificity, nuclear matrix spheres isolated from livers of immature female rats that had received 0.1 μg estradiol *in vivo* contained no detectable high-affinity, saturable estradiol binding activity (Barrack *et al.*, 1977). It is important to note, however, that rat liver is an estrogen-responsive tissue, but the translocation of cytoplasmic estradiol receptors to the liver nucleus occurs only following treatment of animals with very large doses of estrogens (Aten *et al.*, 1978). It appears that the requirement for a high dose of estrogen to affect liver responsiveness is due to rapid metabolism by the liver which greatly reduces the concentration of estradiol in the cell that is available for binding to receptors and translocation into the nucleus (Dickson *et al.*, 1980; Dickson and Eisenfeld, 1981). Recently, Agutter and Birchall (1979) have confirmed that the rat uterine nuclear matrix contains specific estradiol binding sites and have shown in addition that the rat lung nuclear matrix contains none.

Clark and his colleagues have recently demonstrated that rat uterine nuclei contain, in addition to the well known high affinity (Type I, $K_d \sim 1$ nM) estradiol receptors, low affinity (Type II, $K_d \sim 30$ nM) specific estradiol binding sites (Markaverich *et al.*, 1980; Clark *et al.*, 1980). They find that, under certain conditions, the sum of the number of Type II sites measured independently in the salt-extractable and salt-resistant fractions

TABLE VIII

Steroid-Specific Inhibition of [³H] Estradiol Binding to Rat Uterine Nuclear Matrix[a]

	Relative binding affinity (%)
Estradiol	100
Estrone	51
Estriol	32
Testosterone	4
Dihydrotestosterone	9
Progesterone	23
Cortisol	18

[a] The nuclear matrix fraction from uteri of immature female rats, given 0.1 μg unlabeled estradiol 1 hour prior to sacrifice, was incubated *in vitro* in the presence of [³H]estradiol (12 nM) with or without increasing concentrations of unlabeled steroids (120 to 1200 nM). The relative binding affinity equals (the concentration of unlabeled estradiol required to inhibit [³H]estradiol binding to specific sites by 50%) divided by (the concentration of other competitors required to produce the same amount of inhibition), multiplied by 100%.

is much greater than the number of Type II sites detected in unextracted isolated nuclei. In other words, extraction of rat uterine nuclei with KCl exposes estradiol binding sites in the salt-resistant fraction that were not originally accessible to estradiol in the intact nucleus (Markaverich et al., 1980; Clark et al., 1980). This is in marked contrast to the situation we observe for the high-affinity ($K_d \sim$ 1 nM, equivalent to the Type I sites, according to Clark's terminology) estradiol binding sites that are associated with the nuclear matrix. As shown in Table VII and Fig. 3, high-affinity binding in the salt-extractable and salt-resistant nuclear fractions account for essentially all of the binding that is observed in unextracted nuclei. It is important to keep in mind, however, that the experiments described in Table VII and Figs. 3 and 4 were carried out under conditions in which *only* high-affinity (Type I) steroid–receptor interactions would be detected. In order to measure low-affinity binders, saturation analysis must be performed over a wide range of [^{3}H]estradiol concentrations, up to 80 nM (Eriksson et al., 1978; Markaverich et al., 1980; Clark et al., 1980). It remains to be seen whether the salt-resistant low-affinity Type II nuclear estradiol binding sites are also associated with the uterine nuclear matrix.

D. HORMONE BINDING SITES ON THE NUCLEAR MATRIX: AVIAN LIVER

The uterine nuclear matrix fractions used for the estradiol binding studies discussed in the previous section were not purified, since it is difficult to isolate uterine nuclei free of myofibrillar components. Thus, we could not be certain whether the salt-resistant estradiol binding sites were associated with the nuclear matrix or with the contaminating nonnuclear structures.

To circumvent this problem, we chose to study hormone interactions in a target tissue from which nuclei can be isolated in good yield and with a high degree of purity. For this purpose, the estrogen-sensitive avian liver offers many advantages.

The estrogen-dependent regulation of vitellogenin synthesis in the liver of hens and estrogen-treated immature chicks or roosters is a well-characterized model for studying the modulation of specific gene expression by steroid hormones (Deeley et al., 1977; Tata, 1978). Increased nuclear binding of estradiol has been correlated with the stimulation of the biological response (Snow et al., 1978; Lazier, 1975), and, in addition, it has been reported that a large proportion (40–80%) of the estrogen receptors in these liver nuclei is resistant to salt extraction (Lebeau et al., 1973; Snow et al., 1978; Gschwendt and Schneider, 1978).

The nuclear matrix fraction was isolated from purified liver nuclei of diethylstilbestrol-treated chicks. Extraction of these nuclei with Triton X-100, DNase I, low magnesium, and high salt buffers results in the removal of most of the total nuclear DNA, protein, phospholipid, and RNA. Examination of the residual pellet of nuclear matrix by phase contrast microscopy reveals intact spheres of low refractivity that have retained the major nuclear landmarks: a distinct peripheral boundary (lamina), and residual nucleoli. Electron microscopy reveals, in addition, remnants of an internal fibrogranular network. Saturation analysis of the binding of [³H]estradiol to this isolated liver nuclear matrix was determined by an exchange assay *in vitro*, and the results are shown in Fig. 5. Specific binding of estradiol to the matrix is saturable and high affinity, with an apparent equilibrium dissociation constant, K_d, of 0.5 nM (Fig. 5). Furthermore, there appears to be only a single class of high-affinity estradiol

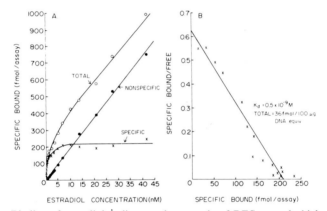

FIG. 5. Binding of estradiol to liver nuclear matrix of DES-treated chicks. Immature White Leghorn chicks (3- to 5-week-old males and females) were given a single subcutaneous injection of 5 mg diethylstilbestrol (25 mg/kg; dissolved in 1 ml of sesame oil) and were killed 20 to 24 hours later. Livers were perfused with ice-cold saline (0.9%), and purified nuclei were isolated by centrifugation through 2.2 M sucrose, 10 mM Tris, pH 7.4, 5 mM MgCl₂, as described by Berezney and Coffey (1977). Nucleated erythrocytes were a minor contaminant (1 to 2%); however, erythrocytes do not bind significant amounts of estradiol (Gschwendt and Kittstein, 1973). The nuclear matrix was isolated from these purified liver nuclei as described in Fig. 1, and estradiol binding was quantitated by an *in vitro* assay (4°C, 20–24 hours) as described by Snow *et al.* (1978). Each assay tube contained 165 μg nuclear matrix protein which was derived from an amount of nuclei equivalent to 580 μg of starting nuclear DNA. (A) Total binding (O——O) was measured in the presence of [³H]estradiol alone (70 pM to 42 nM). Nonspecific binding (●——●) was measured in the presence of [³H]estradiol plus unlabeled estradiol (0.7 μM). Specific binding (×——×) is the difference between total and nonspecific binding. (B) Scatchard plot of specific binding (×——×) in A. Total binding capacity of the nuclear matrix was 210 fmol/assay (from Barrack and Coffey, 1980).

binding sites associated with the nuclear matrix. In an assay that contained 165 μg of nuclear matrix protein the total number of specific estradiol binding sites was 210 fmol, or 127 fmol/100 μg matrix protein (Table IX). Since 165 μg of matrix protein was obtained from a starting amount of nuclei equivalent to 580 μg of DNA, we can also express the binding data as 36 fmol/100 μg starting nuclear DNA equivalents. This corresponds to approximately 520 sites/nucleus, based on a value of 2.4 pg DNA per intact nucleus, and on the assumption that all nuclei have the same binding capacity. For comparison, the specific binding of estradiol to intact liver nuclei from DES-treated chicks is 24.2 fmol/100 μg total nuclear protein, or 59.2 fmol/100 μg nuclear DNA (Table IX). Therefore, the recovery of estradiol binding sites with the nuclear matrix constitutes 61% of the total specific estradiol binding to unextracted nuclei (Table IX). In contrast, only 7% of the total nuclear protein and 2% of the DNA were recovered with the nuclear matrix. Thus there is a 5-fold enrichment of nuclear estradiol binding sites on the nuclear matrix, when expressed per unit amount of protein (Table IX).

The high-affinity binding sites on the liver nuclear matrix of estrogen treated chicks are specific for estrogens (Fig. 6). In a competitive binding assay, the binding of [³H]estradiol can be inhibited equally efficiently by the simultaneous addition of unlabeled estradiol or diethylstilbestrol, and less well by estriol. In contrast, the binding of [³H]estradiol is virtually

TABLE IX

Comparison of Specific Estradiol Binding in Chick Liver Nuclei and Nuclear Matrix[a]

	Recovery		Specific binding of estradiol			
	Protein (% of total nuclear)	DNA	fmol/100 μg protein in fraction	fmol/100 μg starting DNA equivalents	Binding sites per nucleus	K_d (nM)
Total nuclei[b]	100	100	24.2(1.0)[d]	59.2(1.0)	850[e]	0.9
Nuclear matrix[c]	7	2	127.3(5.3)	36.2(0.61)	520	0.5

[a] Liver nuclei and nuclear matrix were isolated from immature chicks 20 hours following a single injection of DES, as described earlier (Barrack and Coffey, 1980). Specific estradiol binding capacities and dissociation constants were derived from Scatchard analyses.

[b] Aliquots of nuclei containing 255 μg DNA and 625 μg total nuclear protein were assayed for estradiol binding by saturation analysis. Total specific binding, derived from a Scatchard plot, was 151 fmol/assay.

[c] Estradiol binding to liver nuclear matrix is described in the legend to Fig. 5.

[d] Numbers in parentheses indicate values relative to intact nuclei.

[e] Based on a value of 2.4 pg DNA per nucleus (Lebeau et al., 1973) and on the assumption that all nuclei have the same binding capacity.

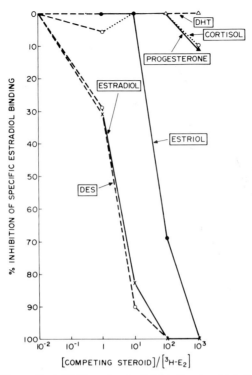

FIG. 6. Steroid specific inhibition of estradiol binding to chick liver nuclear matrix. Liver nuclear matrix, isolated from the liver nuclei of DES-treated chicks, was incubated *in vitro* (4°C, 24 hours) in the presence of [³H]estradiol (7 nM) alone (total binding) or with increasing concentrations of unlabeled steroids (7 nM to 7 μM; nondisplaceable binding). Specific binding of [³H]estradiol measured in the presence and absence of a 100-fold excess of unlabeled estradiol (0.7 μM) was set equal to 100%. DHT, 5α-dihydrotestosterone. DES, diethylstilbestrol (from Barrack and Coffey, 1980).

unaffected by the addition of even very high concentrations of unlabeled dihydrotestosterone, cortisol, or progesterone (Fig. 6).

To determine whether the levels of nuclear matrix-associated estradiol binding reflected the hormonal status of the animal, we examined the binding of estradiol to the liver nuclear matrix of egg-laying hens and of adult roosters. The binding of estradiol to the liver nuclear matrix of hens is shown in Fig. 7. Since untreated roosters are not under estrogen stimulation and do not produce vitellogenin, they represent a control situation that offers an ideal opportunity to investigate the relationship between steroid binding sites and biological responsiveness. The liver nuclear matrix of hens and roosters were subjected individually to saturation analysis under exchange conditions *in vitro*, and a composite of the Scatchard plots

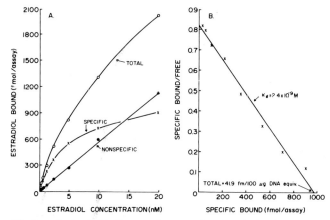

FIG. 7.   Binding of estradiol to liver nuclear matrix of egg-laying hens. The liver nuclear matrix was isolated from egg-laying hens and assayed *in vitro* for specific [³H]estradiol binding activity, as described in the legend to Fig. 5.

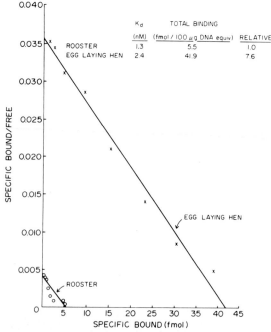

	K_d (nM)	TOTAL BINDING (fmol / 100 μg DNA equiv)	RELATIVE
ROOSTER	1.3	5.5	1.0
EGG LAYING HEN	2.4	41.9	7.6

FIG. 8.   Specific binding of estradiol to liver nuclear matrix of adult roosters and egg-laying hens. Scatchard plots are presented of specific binding of [³H]estradiol to the liver nuclear matrix fractions isolated from purified liver nuclei of untreated roosters and hens. Saturation analyses were carried out in the presence of 0.15 to 20 nM [³H]estradiol alone or together with 1 μM unlabeled estradiol. Specific binding results have been normalized to fmol per 100 μg starting nuclear DNA equivalents (from Barrack and Coffey, 1980).

of specific estradiol binding is presented in Fig. 8. The liver nuclear matrix of the vitellogenin-producing hen can bind approximately 42 fmol of estradiol/100 μg starting nuclear DNA equivalents, or 600 molecules/ nucleus. In contrast, the liver nuclear matrix of untreated roosters, which do not produce yolk proteins, contains only one-eighth as many specific binding sites for estradiol (5.5 fmol/100 μg nuclear DNA equivalents) as that of the laying hen (Fig. 8). However, the administration of pharmacological doses of estrogen (diethylstilbestrol, 25 mg/kg) to roosters results in a stimulation of vitellogenin mRNA synthesis (Deeley *et al.*, 1977) and a marked increase (12-fold) in the number of nuclear matrix-associated specific estradiol binding sites (65 fmol/100 μg nuclear DNA equivalents; Fig. 9). The recoveries of matrix spheres (>70%) and nuclear protein (8–12%) from all groups of animals were approximately similar,

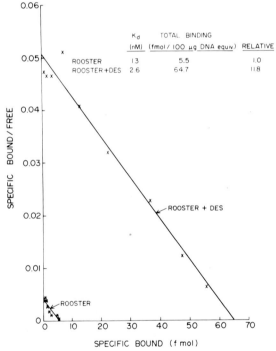

FIG. 9.   Specific binding of estradiol to liver nuclear matrix of untreated and estrogenized roosters. Scatchard plots are presented of specific binding of estradiol to liver nuclear matrix fractions isolated from adult untreated roosters (*———*), and roosters given two daily injections of DES (25 mg/kg; dissolved in propylene glycol) (×———×). Saturation analyses were carried out over a concentration range of 0.15 to 20 n*M* [³H]estradiol alone and together with 1 μ*M* unlabeled estradiol. Specific binding data have been normalized to fmol/100 μg starting nuclear DNA equivalents. PMSF was added at each step of the isolation and assay procedures (from Barrack and Coffey, 1980).

and therefore indicate that the different binding capacities observed in
Figs. 8 and 9 are not the result of variable recoveries of nuclear matrix.
Thus, the appearance of specific estradiol binding sites on the liver nuclear matrix occurs in response to an appropriate hormonal stimulus, not
indiscriminately.

E. HORMONE BINDING SITES ON THE NUCLEAR MATRIX: RAT PROSTATE

The binding of steroids to the nuclear matrix appears to be a general
property of the interactions of both estrogens and androgens with their
respective target tissues. As a model of androgen target tissue interactions
we have studied the rat ventral prostate, the growth and functions of
which are androgen-dependent. Since 5α-dihydrotestosterone (DHT) is
the major active androgen metabolite in the nucleus of the prostate
(Bruchovsky and Wilson, 1968; Fang *et al.*, 1969), we use [³H]DHT to
measure specific androgen binding sites on the nuclear matrix of the adult

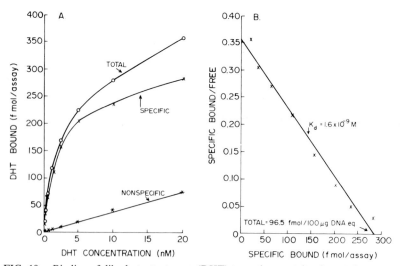

FIG. 10.   Binding of dihydrotestosterone (DHT) to nuclear matrix of ventral prostates of
intact adult rats. The nuclear matrix was isolated (see Figs. 1 and 14) from ventral prostate
nuclei that had been purified by the method of Chung and Coffey (1971). [³H]DHT binding to
the nuclear matrix was assayed *in vitro* as described for estradiol binding in Fig. 5. Each
assay tube contained nuclear matrix derived from nuclei equivalent to 295 μg starting nuclear DNA. PMSF was added at all steps. (A) O——O, total binding in the presence of
[³H]DHT only. *——*, nonspecific binding in the presence of [³H]DHT with unlabeled DHT.
×——×, specific binding represents the difference between total and nonspecific binding.
(B) Scatchard plot of specific binding (×——×) in A (from Barrack and Coffey, 1980).

TABLE X

Specific Binding of Dihydrotestosterone in Rat Ventral Prostates of Intact Adult Rats:
Subnuclear Distribution

	Specific binding of DHT[a]			
	fmol/100 μg starting DNA equiv.	Binding sites/ nucleus	Relative	Number of experiments
Total nuclei[b]	286 ± 35[e]	20,600[f] ± 2,520	1.00	8
Salt-extractable[c]	130 ± 25	9,360 ± 1,800	0.45	10
Nuclear matrix[d]	128 ± 23	9,220 ± 1,660	0.45	13

[a] Binding assays were carried out in the presence of 20 nM [³H]DHT with and without 2 μM unlabeled DHT. Specific binding was calculated by subtracting nonspecific from total binding. PMSF was added at all steps. From Barrack and Coffey (1980).

[b] Binding assays were carried out with purified ventral prostate nuclei. Nuclear pellets were washed, solubilized, and counted.

[c] Salt extracts were obtained by incubating nuclei with DNase I and extracting once with 2 M NaCl in buffer. Extracts obtained following an exchange assay of nuclei were counted directly. Alternatively, nuclei were first extracted and binding activity of the salt extract was assayed. Assays were terminated by the addition of either dextran-coated charcoal (an aliquot of the supernatant was then counted), or hydroxylapatite (the precipitate was washed and an ethanol extract was counted). Results were similar for the different methods.

[d] Binding assays were carried out with isolated nuclear matrix.

[e] Mean ± standard deviation.

[f] Based on a value of 12 pg DNA per nucleus (DeKlerk *et al.*, 1976; Van Doorn *et al.*, 1976).

male rat ventral prostate. Specific binding of [³H]DHT to the ventral prostate nuclear matrix (Fig. 10), quantitated by an *in vitro* exchange assay, is saturable and high affinity (K_d = 1.6 nM). The total specific binding capacity of the matrix for DHT is approximately 100 fmol/100 μg starting nuclear DNA equivalents, or 7200 molecules of DHT/nucleus. We have looked, in addition, for low-affinity ($K_d \sim$ 30 nM; Type II) binding of [³H]DHT to the nuclear matrix of these prostates by carrying out the saturation analysis in the presence of concentrations of [³H]DHT ranging from 0.1 to 80 nM but find only a single class of specific, high-affinity (K_d = 2–3 nM) DHT binding sites which become saturated by 10–20 nM [³H]DHT.

Table X shows the subnuclear distribution of specific DHT binding in the ventral prostates of intact adult rats. Only about 50% of the total nuclear binding can be extracted with salt. Salt-resistant nuclear matrix binding sites comprise approximately 50% of the total nuclear binding; yet the nuclear matrix contains only 10–15% of the total nuclear protein and about 1–2% of the DNA. The sum of the binding activities in these two fractions accounts for almost all (90%) of the binding to unextracted nuclei.

It is essential to add inhibitors of proteolysis such as phenylmethylsulfonyl fluoride (PMSF), at a final concentration of 1 mM, to all buffers used in the isolation of prostate nuclei and nuclear matrix. In the absence of such protease inhibitors, the amount of specific DHT binding to the nuclear matrix is 20 to 50 times lower (Table XI). The specific binding of DHT to whole nuclei also is lower when PMSF is omitted from the homogenization buffer, although the yield of nuclei from prostate tissue is not affected. The amount of binding in the salt-extractable nuclear fraction is the same in the presence or absence of PMSF; in contrast, the salt-resistant DHT binding activity is markedly reduced in the absence of the inhibitor (Table XI). The greatly lowered binding of DHT to the nuclear matrix in the absence of PMSF is accompanied by a severely reduced recovery of matrix spheres and matrix protein from nuclei. The structural protein components of the rat ventral prostate nuclear matrix are highly sensitive to proteolytic degradation, an observation that has been reported as well for the nuclear matrix of the rat liver (Shaper et al., 1979). It is important to note, however, that the level of specific binding of estradiol to the nuclear matrix of chicken liver is not found to be affected significantly by the presence or absence of PMSF. The greater lability of androgen binding sites on the nuclear matrix of the ventral prostate is probably a reflection of the high concentrations of hydrolytic and proteolytic enzymes that are normally present in the prostatic secretions within the acinar lumina and in the intracellular lysosomes (Paris and Brandes, 1974). In addition, many investigators have noted the greater thermal lability of androgen receptors than estrogen receptors; this may relate to

TABLE XI

Effect of a Protease Inhibitor on Nuclear Androgen Binding Capacity[a]

	Specific binding of [³H]DHT (fmol/100 μg starting DNA equivalents)		
	Total nuclei	Salt extract	Nuclear matrix
+PMSF	286 ± 35	130 ± 25	128 ± 23
−PMSF	102 ± 4	119 ± 51	6 ± 4

[a] Specific [³H]DHT binding was quantitated as described in the footnote to Table X. In experiments noted +PMSF, all buffers used in the isolation of nuclei and nuclear matrix contained 1 mM PMSF, which was added from a stock solution (0.1 M PMSF in anhydrous *n*-propanol) immediately before use. In experiments noted −PMSF, the inhibitor of proteolysis, PMSF, was omitted from all buffers. PMSF, phenylmethylsulfonyl fluoride.

the presence of proteolytic enzymes in the fraction being studied. PMSF is used, therefore, in all experiments on the rat prostate.

Similar levels of [³H]DHT binding are observed whether samples are dissolved in tissue solubilizer or the radioactivity is extracted into ethanol. This indicates that the nuclease-, detergent-, and salt-resistant binding of steroid to the nuclear matrix is not the result of a covalent interaction. In addition, no significant metabolism of [³H]dihydrotestosterone occurs during the time interval of the binding assay *in vitro* (4°C, 20–24 hours), since greater than 95% of the radioactivity that is recovered from prostate nuclei, salt extracts, or nuclear matrix can be identified as DHT, using thin layer chromatography techniques that separate DHT, testosterone, 5α-androstane-3α,17β-diol and 5α-androstane-3β,17β-diol, androstenedione, androstanedione, and polar metabolites. Dihydrotestosterone is also the predominant androgen in the nucleus *in vivo* (Bruchovsky and Wilson, 1968; Fang *et al.*, 1969). In contrast, however, it is of interest to note that salt-resistant nuclear glucocorticoid receptors in the rat mammary gland are associated predominantly with an acylated form of corticosterone, whereas the precursor, corticosterone, is found associated primarily with salt-extractable glucucorticoid receptors (Hampel *et al.*, 1978).

With the rat ventral prostate system we have been able to demonstrate a physiological basis for the binding of DHT to the ventral prostate nuclear matrix. It is well known that the rat ventral prostate, as well as the other male sex accessory tissues, involutes following castration of the animal. The cells decrease in size from tall columnar to cuboidal, secretory functions diminish, and by 7 days after castration there is a loss of about 80% of the cells. Cell number and secretory activities can be restored to normal following the administration of androgens to the animal (Coffey *et al.*, 1968; Brandes, 1974; DeKlerk *et al.*, 1976).

Figure 11 compares the number of specific binding sites for DHT on the ventral prostate nuclear matrix of intact and castrated rats. By 20–24 hours after castration there is minimal cell loss; however, the amount of specific DHT binding activity on the nuclear matrix has decreased to 2% of intact control levels. The time course of the disappearance of DHT binding activity associated with the nuclear matrix following castration is shown in Fig. 12. When DHT injections are initiated 40 hours after castration, the level of matrix-associated DHT binding is restored to normal values within 1 hour (Fig. 12). In contrast, treatment of castrates with 5 mg of estradiol or cyproterone acetate does not increase the level of matrix-associated androgen binding sites above the castrate control value. Therefore the presence of specific binding sites for DHT on the ventral prostate nuclear matrix is related to the response of the tissue to androgen.

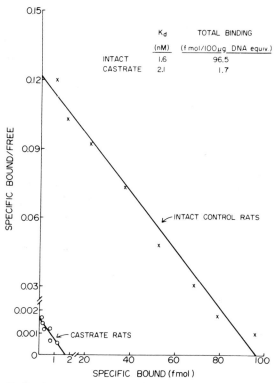

FIG. 11.   Specific binding of DHT to ventral prostate nuclear matrix of intact and castrate rats. Specific binding of DHT to the nuclear matrix of intact adult rat ventral prostates (×——×) was obtained from data of Fig. 10B. Specific binding of DHT to the ventral prostate nuclear matrix of adult rats 20 hours after castration (O——O) was determined by saturation and Scatchard analysis. Specific binding data have been normalized to fmol per 100 μg starting nuclear DNA equivalents (from Barrack and Coffey, 1980).

The androgen-specific nature of the binding sites on the ventral prostate nuclear matrix is demonstrated in Fig. 13. In competitive binding assays, the concentration of unlabeled DHT required to inhibit specific binding of [3H]DHT by 50%, relative to the concentration of other unlabeled steroids required to produce the same inhibition, provides an indication of the relative binding affinity of these steroids for binding sites on the nuclear matrix. Unlabeled methyltrienolone (R 1881), a potent synthetic androgen, is as effective as dihydrotestosterone (relative binding affinity, 100%) in inhibiting specific binding of [3H]DHT. Testosterone has a relative binding affinity of 20%. The relative binding affinities of progesterone, estradiol, cyproterone acetate (an antiandrogen), and cortisol are 1.0, 0.9, 0.6, and <0.1%, respectively. Steroid specificity patterns similar to those shown in Fig. 13 have been observed for other androgen receptor proteins (Wilson and French, 1976), and are in contrast to the more stringent steroid specificity of estrogen receptors for estrogens (Fig. 6).

The DHT binding component associated with the prostate nuclear matrix appears to be protein in nature, since binding activity is destroyed by proteolytic digestion with Pronase (1 mg/ml; 37°C, 30 minutes) or by heat denaturation (100°C, 30 minutes).

F. LOCALIZATION OF MATRIX-ASSOCIATED STEROID HORMONE BINDING SITES

The nuclear matrix preparations used in the studies described in the preceding sections consist of a peripheral lamina, residual nucleoli, and an internal ribonucleoprotein network (e.g., Figs. 1 and 14). We and others have noted that the presence of an internal network-like structure within the isolated nuclear matrix appears to be dependent on the methods used

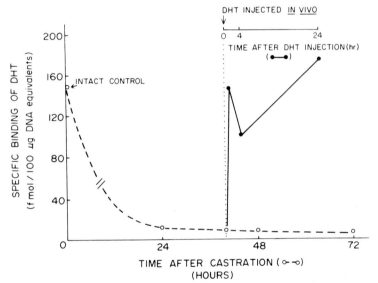

FIG. 12.   Ventral prostate nuclear matrix DHT binding sites: Time course of disappearance following castration and of reappearance following androgen treatment *in vivo*. Rats were castrated and sacrificed at various times thereafter (O----O). Another group of animals was castrated and 40 hours later received a single subcutaneous injection of 5 mg DHT (●——●). These rats were sacrificed at various times after DHT treatment. Ventral prostate nuclei and nuclear matrix fractions were isolated and the binding of DHT to nuclear matrix was assayed in the presence of 20 nM [³H]DHT with and without 2 μM unlabeled DHT. Specific binding data are expressed as fmol per 100 μg starting nuclear DNA equivalents (from Barrack and Coffey, 1980).

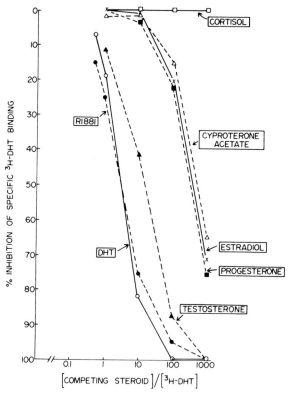

FIG. 13. Steroid specific inhibition of DHT binding to rat ventral prostate nuclear matrix. Ventral prostate nuclear matrix from intact adult rats was incubated *in vitro* in the presence of [³H]DHT (20 n*M*) with or without increasing concentrations of unlabeled steroids (10 n*M* to 20 μ*M*). Specific binding of [³H]DHT measured in the presence and absence of a 100-fold excess of unlabeled DHT (2 μ*M*) was set equal to 100%. R 1881, methyltrienolone (from Barrack and Coffey, 1980).

to extract the nuclei (Shaper *et al.*, 1979; Kaufmann *et al.*, 1981). For example, conditions that promote endogenous protease activity (Shaper *et al.*, 1979), the use of high concentrations of MgCl₂ (Aaronson and Blobel, 1975; Dwyer and Blobel, 1976), the use of alkaline (pH 8.5) conditions (Aaronson and Blobel, 1975; Dwyer and Blobel, 1976; Cobbs and Shelton, 1978), or the use of RNase (Herman *et al.*, 1978; Giese and Wunderlich, 1979; Adolph, 1980; Kaufmann *et al.*, 1981) have been noted to contribute to the isolation of nuclear matrix fractions that lack nucleoli and the majority of the internal fibrogranular network. Whether or not the internal network structure withstands the rigors of the extraction procedures, a reasonable body of evidence indicates that it is derived from ribonucleoprotein-containing structures of the nucleus (Berezney and Coffey, 1974; Berezney, 1979; Herman *et al.*, 1978; Miller *et al.*, 1978a; Faiferman and Pogo, 1975; Shankar Narayan *et al.*, 1967; Monneron and Bernhard, 1969; Bouteille *et al.*, 1974; Ghosh *et al.*, 1978). Under certain conditions, the RNA components can be extracted, leaving a residual internal protein network (Berezney and Coffey, 1974, 1976, 1977; Comings and Okada, 1976; Wunderlich and Herlan, 1977; Miller *et al.*, 1978a; Mitchelson *et al.*, 1979; van Eekelen and van Venrooij, 1981). Within the nuclear matrix the RNA and protein-containing network appears to be

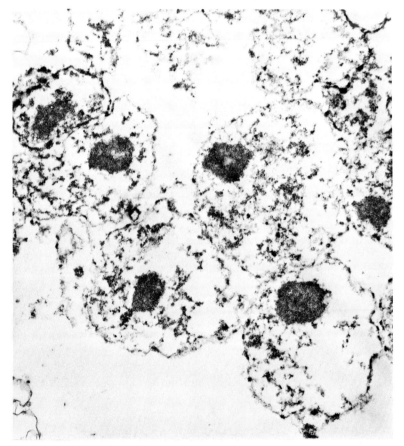

FIG. 14.   Thin section electron micrograph of intact nuclear matrix spheres. Nuclear matrix spheres were isolated from hen liver nuclei as described in the legend to Fig. 1. Structures similar to those shown here are obtained from rat ventral prostate nuclei, using the procedure outlined in the legend to Fig. 1. Magnification, ×16,640.

intimately associated with the peripheral pore complex-lamina (Berezney and Coffey, 1976, 1977; Comings and Okada, 1976; Hodge *et al.*, 1977; Herman *et al.*, 1978; Miller *et al.*, 1978a; Berezney *et al.*, 1979; Wunderlich and Herlan, 1977). The important observations that newly replicated DNA (Berezney and Coffey, 1975, 1976; Dijkwel *et al.*, 1979; Pardoll *et al.*, 1980; McCready *et al.*, 1980; Berezney and Buchholtz, 1981a,b) and rapidly labeled heterogeneous nuclear RNA (Herman *et al.*, 1978; Miller *et al.*, 1978a; van Eekelen and van Venrooij, 1981; Jackson *et al.*, 1981) are tightly associated with the nuclear matrix indicate the significance of this structure. Appropriate controls carried out by these investigators indicate that these associations are probably not the result of adventitious adsorption of RNA or DNA to these structures (Faiferman and Pogo, 1975; Herman *et al.*, 1978; Miller *et al.*, 1978a; Pardoll *et al.*, 1980; Jackson *et al.*, 1981; van Eekelen and van Venrooij, 1981; Berezney and Buchholtz, 1981a,b). Moreover, electron autoradiographic studies have demonstrated that the DNA replication sites (Pardoll *et al.*, 1980) and the newly labeled heterogeneous nuclear RNA (Fakan *et al.*, 1976; Herman *et al.*, 1978) are associated with the internal network structure, and indicate the potential biological importance of this internal component of the nuclear matrix.

It was of considerable interest, therefore, to determine whether the hormone binding sites are distributed uniformly throughout the matrix structure, or are enriched in a specific morphological component of the matrix. To investigate this further, we have taken advantage of the observation that under certain conditions the internal RNA–protein network of the matrix is sensitive to RNase. For example, treatment of some types of nuclei with both DNase I and RNase A, followed by extraction of these nuclei with low and high ionic strength salt solutions, leads to the isolation of a nuclear matrix fraction that lacks nucleoli and the majority of the internal fibrogranular network (Herman *et al.*, 1978; Giese and Wunderlich, 1979; Adolph, 1980; Kaufmann *et al.*, 1981). If the hormone binding sites were localized exclusively to the peripheral lamina, these empty nuclear matrix structures would contain as many binding sites as intact nuclear matrix spheres that contain internal network material. Moreover, as a result of extracting protein that had been a component of the internal network, these "lamina-associated" steroid binding sites would exhibit a higher specific activity per unit amount of protein than that in the intact nuclear matrix. In contrast, if the hormone binding sites were extensively enriched on the internal RNA–protein network of the nuclear matrix, then the number and specific activity of binding sites associated with the empty peripheral lamina fraction would be greatly diminished. In this latter situation, the hormone binding sites would be rendered salt-extractable, and the specific activity of this soluble fraction would be increased. A third possibility would be that the hormone binding sites are distributed uniformly throughout all components of the nuclear matrix; in this case, the specific activity of binding for both intact nuclear matrix and empty spheres would be similar.

We used the nuclear matrix of the ventral prostate of intact adult rats to test this approach (Table XII). Purified ventral prostate nuclei were treated with either DNase (control method) or both DNase and RNase, and then extracted with 2 M NaCl. It is important to note that nuclease treatment alone solubilizes *no* binding activity. The amount of protein and specific DHT binding activity in the salt extract and nuclear matrix pellet fractions were determined. Compared to control matrix preparations (e.g., Figs. 1 and 14) that were prepared by pretreatment of the nuclei with DNase (Table XII, experiment A, control), pretreatment with DNase and RNase (Table XII, experiment B) leads to the isolation of nuclear matrix spheres that contain less RNA and internal structure and that have lost 20% of the total matrix protein and 52% of the specific DHT binding sites. The specific activity of these residual matrix-associated DHT binding sites is only 62% of control. Unfortunately, however, the loss of binding sites from the matrix pellet cannot be accounted for in the salt extract, nor any other fraction. The use of DNase plus RNase results in the loss of 29% of the total nuclear DHT binding activity (150 vs 106 fmol/100 μg DNA equivalents); this effect cannot be prevented by boiling the RNase to inactivate possible protease contaminants. RNase effects were similar at three concentrations tested (20, 40, or 200 μg/ml). When the RNase was inhibited by pretreatment with diethylpyrocarbonate, the distribution, recovery and specific activity of DHT binding were similar to control (Table XII, A) values (data not shown).

When nuclei are treated with DNase and RNase in the presence of 1 mM dithiothreitol (DTT), and then extracted with 2 M NaCl, no destruction of total nuclear binding sites is observed (Table XII, experiment D). As a result of this treatment, matrix spheres are obtained that are totally devoid of internal structure (e.g., Fig. 15), and contain only 60% as much protein as control matrix preparations. In addition, the recovery of specific DHT binding sites with these empty matrix spheres (consisting only of a peripheral lamina) represents only 17% of the total matrix DHT binding activity associated with intact nuclear matrix structures that contain internal network material (17 vs 101 fmol/100 μg starting nuclear DNA equivalents). If this loss of binding activity and protein had simply been due to a loss of spheres, the specific activity of binding in the residual fraction would have been unchanged. We find, however, that the specific activity of the DHT binding sites that remain associated with these empty matrix spheres (52 fmol/100 μg protein) is only 27% of that of intact

TABLE XII

Effect of Various Treatments on the Subnuclear Distribution of DHT Binding Sites in the Rat Ventral Prostate

		Protein distribution			Specific binding of DHT[f]				
					Distribution			Specific activity	
Pretreatment of nuclei[a]	N[b]	Nuclear matrix[c]	Salt extract[d]	Total[e]	Nuclear matrix	Salt extract	Total	Nuclear matrix	Salt extract
		(μg protein/100 μg starting DNA equivalents)			(fmol DHT/100 μg starting DNA equivalents)			(fmol DHT/100 μg protein)	
A. DNase (Control)	6	55 ± 14 (100%)	254 ± 16	304 ± 21	101 ± 8 (100%)	49 ± 14	150 ± 17 (100%)	194 ± 48 (100%)	19 ± 6 (100%)
B. DNase + RNase	8	44 ± 9 (80%)	259 ± 11	300 ± 15	48 ± 10 (48%)	57 ± 13	106 ± 11 (71%)	121 ± 19 (62%)	21 ± 6 (111%)
C. DNase + DTT	2	41 ± 2 (75%)	285 ± 8	325 ± 6	29 ± 6 (29%)	129 ± 8	157 ± 1 (105%)	71 ± 19 (37%)	45 ± 4 (237%)
D. DNase + RNase + DTT	2	33 ± 4 (60%)	310 ± 32	343 ± 28	17 ± 4 (17%)	136 ± 3	153 ± 2 (102%)	52 ± 20 (27%)	44 ± 6 (232%)

[a] Preatreatments with nucleases alone extract no binding activity. Highly purified ventral prostate nuclei were obtained from intact, untreated rats. The protein/DNA ratio of these Triton washed nuclei was 3.55 ± 0.33 (mean ± SD for 6 experiments) and the RNA/DNA ratio was 0.18 ± 0.06. Nuclei were incubated in 10 mM Tris, pH 7.4, 5 mM MgCl$_2$ with nucleases (4°C, 30 minutes) and pelleted prior to extraction with 2 M NaCl. PMSF (1 mM) was added at all steps. In all experiments, nuclei were pretreated with DNase I at a final concentration of 20 μg/ml. RNase A, where indicated, was added at 40 μg/ml; the RNase had been pretreated by heating at 100°C, 15 minutes. Dithiothreitol (DTT), where indicated, was at 1 mM; the DTT was present only during the nuclease incubation. From Barrack and Coffey (1980).

[b] N, number of individual experiments. Results are expressed as mean ± standard deviation.

[c] The nuclear matrix fraction represents the insoluble pellet following 2 M NaCl extraction of the nuclease-treated nuclei, and washing in 10 mM Tris, pH 7.4, 1.5 mM EDTA.

[d] Supernatant obtained from extraction of nuclease-treated nuclei with 1 M NaCl.

[e] Total represents the sum of values for the nuclear matrix pellet and salt extract of each individual experiment.

[f] Binding assays were carried out in triplicate in the presence of 20 nM [³H]DHT with and without 2 μM unlabeled DHT. Specific DHT binding was calculated by subtracting nonspecific from total binding. Binding of DHT to nuclear matrix fractions was terminated by washing on Whatman GF/B glass fiber filters. Binding activity in soluble salt extracts was assayed following dilution to 1.2 M NaCl, and terminated by further dilution to 0.4 M NaCl prior to the addition of a slurry of hydroxylapatite to 12.5% (v/v). After 15 minutes at 4°C, the hydroxylapatite was pelleted, washed three times, and then extracted with ethanol.

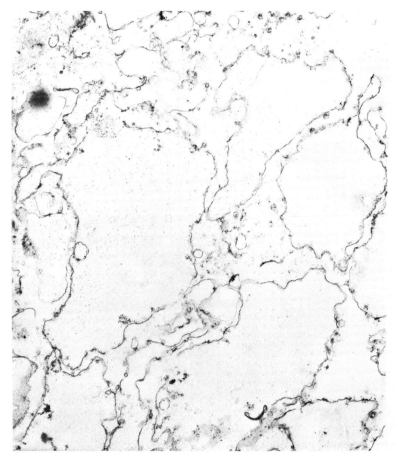

FIG. 15. Thin section electron micrograph of empty nuclear matrix spheres. Nuclear matrix spheres lacking internal network material and residual nucleoli were obtained from hen liver nuclei. When Triton X-100 washed nuclei are digested with low concentrations of DNase I, RNase A, and 1 mM dithiothreitol, and then sequentially extracted with low magnesium and 2 M NaCl buffers, as described in more detail in the text and in the footnotes to Table XII, empty spheres like those shown here can be prepared from liver nuclei and prostate nuclei (also see text for discussion of considerations, and Kaufmann et al., 1981). Magnification, ×16,640.

nuclear matrix structures (194 fmol/100 μg protein). The DHT binding sites that are extracted from the nuclear matrix as a result of this treatment are recovered in the salt extract. The specific activity of the DHT binding sites in the total salt extract is thereby increased 2.3-fold (19 vs 44 fmol/100 μg salt-extractable protein). The specific activity of the binding sites that become salt-extractable as a result of the additional treatment with RNase and DTT (i.e., the difference between the amount of salt-resistant matrix binding and protein in experiments A vs D) can be calculated to be approximately 400 fmol/100 μg of protein extracted from the matrix; if one assumes that these DHT binding sites had been associated with the internal ribonucleoprotein network of the nuclear matrix, then the specific activity of these internal sites is about 7-fold greater than that of the sites remaining with the peripheral lamina fraction (52 fmol/100 μg protein). This distribution is not altered if the nuclei have not been extracted with Triton X-100.

Treatment of nuclei with DNase and DTT (Table XII, experiment C) is almost as effective as DNase, RNase, and DTT (experiment D) in allowing the subsequent solubilization by 2 M NaCl of specific DHT binding sites (71 and 83%, respectively) from the nuclear matrix. In contrast, DNase and DTT pretreatment results in the removal of some but not all of the internal RNA–protein network material of the matrix, as determined by protein and RNA analyses and microscopy. The specific activity of the salt-resistant DHT binding sites is reduced to 37% of control (experiment A) values, and that of the total salt extract increases 2.4-fold. The difference between the amount of matrix DHT binding in experiments A and C is calculated to have a specific activity of about 620 fmol/100 μg of protein extracted from the matrix, or about 7-fold that of the sites remaining insoluble (71 fmol/100 μg protein).

With regard to the observed effects of dithiothreitol, it is important to note that DTT treatment alone does not extract steroid binding sites; it only renders them capable of being solubilized by subsequent or simultaneous treatment with salt. Thus, even if DTT is added only to the tissue homogenization buffer, extraction of the isolated nuclei with NaCl will result in the solubilization of most of the nuclear receptors. Indeed, this may explain why some investigators do not find significant amounts of salt-resistant binding (Traish et al., 1977; Müller et al., 1977; Chamness et al., 1978).

A similar effect of DTT is observed with hen liver nuclear estradiol binding sites (Table XIII). When detergent-washed hen liver nuclei are digested with DNase I plus RNase A in the presence of 1 mM DTT, and then extracted with 2 M NaCl, only 18% of the total nuclear specific estradiol binding sites remain in the residual nuclear matrix fraction (Table XIII, C; 10/54). From nuclei that are digested with only DNase I and then extracted with salt, 55% of total nuclear binding is recovered with the nuclear matrix (Fig. 14; Table XIII, A; 28/51). In addition, the nuclear matrix fraction obtained following salt extraction of DNase-, RNase-, and DTT-treated nuclei (Fig. 15) contains only 36% as many specific estradiol binding sites as nuclear matrix obtained following salt extraction of

TABLE XIII

Effect of Various Treatments on the Subnuclear Distribution of Estradiol Binding Sites in the Hen Liver[a]

Pretreatment of nuclei	Protein distribution (μg protein/100 μg starting DNA equivalents)			Specific binding of estradiol					
				Distribution (fmol E$_2$[b]/100 μg starting DNA equivalents)			Specific activity (fmol E$_2$/100 μg protein)		
	Nuclear matrix	Salt extract	Total	Nuclear matrix	Salt extract	Total	Nuclear matrix	Salt extract	
A. DNase (control)	28 (100%)	188	216	28 (100%)	23	51 (100%)	99 (100%)	12 (100%)	
B. DNase + RNase	25 (89%)	197	222	25 (89%)	26	51 (100%)	97 (98%)	13 (108%)	
C. DNase + RNase + DTT	21 (75%)	194	215	10 (36%)	44	54 (106%)	45 (45%)	23 (192%)	

[a] See footnotes to Table XII for explanation of pretreatment protocols and nuclear fractions.
[b] E$_2$, estradiol.

DNase-pretreated nuclei, and only 75% as much protein (Table XIII, A vs C). As calculated for the ventral prostate, the hen liver matrix binding sites for estradiol that are released by the additional RNase and DTT pretreatment are calculated to have a specific activity of 300 fmol/100 μg of protein extracted from the matrix.

In contrast to the effects of DNase and RNase on androgen binding sites in rat ventral prostate nuclei (Table XII), estrogen binding sites in hen liver nuclei appear to be inert (Table XIII, B). Thus, not only does treatment of liver nuclei with DNase plus RNase not destroy any of the total nuclear binding activity, it also does not render any of the nuclear matrix protein *or* matrix-associated estradiol binding sites susceptible to salt extraction (Table XIII, B vs A). These observations are consistent with the findings of others that conditions that lead to the extraction of internal network components of the nuclear matrix from nuclei of some tissues (e.g., Shaper *et al.*, 1979; Kaufmann *et al.*, 1981) may not be applicable to all cell types (e.g., Wunderlich and Herlan, 1977; Miller *et al.*, 1978a; Wolfe, 1980) (also see Section II,C).

The distribution and specific activity of DHT binding sites associated with various subfractions of the nucleus and nuclear matrix of the ventral prostate are summarized in Table XIV. The solubilization of internal ribonucleoprotein network material from the nuclear matrix is associated with the extraction of up to 83% of the total matrix-specific DHT binding sites. Matrix spheres can be isolated that are totally devoid of internal structure, and consist only of a peripheral lamina. These empty spheres still contain a limited number of DHT binding sites (11% of total nuclear). DHT binding sites do not appear to be localized exclusively to the peripheral lamina of the matrix, nor distributed uniformly on all matrix components. Rather, our data suggest that there is an enrichment of binding sites with internal matrix structures. Similarly, Agutter and Birchall (1979) find that whereas the nuclear matrix of rat uterine nuclei contains estradiol binding sites, the pore complex-lamina fraction contains virtually none of these sites.

In this regard, it is interesting to note that Liao *et al.* (1973) have reported the ability of prostate cytosol DHT–receptor complexes to bind to isolated nuclear RNP particles that were resistant to solubilization from nuclei by 1 *M* KCl and DNase I but could be released by deoxycholate treatment. That these RNP-associated binding sites (Liao *et al.*, 1973) may have been a component of the internal RNA–protein network that is observed in the isolated nuclear matrix (Herman *et al.*, 1978; Miller *et al.*, 1978a; Faiferman and Pogo, 1975) is supported by the observation of Miller *et al.* (1978a) that the RNP complexes of this RNP network are highly susceptible to disruption by deoxycholate treatment.

TABLE XIV

Distribution and Specific Activity of DHT Binding Sites in Subfractions of the Nucleus and Nuclear Matrix of the Rat Ventral Prostate

| | Specific binding of DHT | | | |
| | Distribution | | Specific activity | |
	fmol/100 μg starting DNA equivalents	Percentage of total binding	fmol/100 μg protein	Relative
Total[a]	152 ± 13	100	49 ± 6	1.0
Salt extract[b]	49 ± 14	33	19 ± 6	0.4
Total nuclear matrix[c]	101 ± 8	67	194 ± 48	4.0
Peripheral lamina[d]	17 ± 4	11	52 ± 20	1.1
Internal RNP network[e]	76 ± 9	50	395 ± 101	8.1

[a] Represents the sum of binding activities in the salt extract and total nuclear matrix fractions.

[b] Supernatant obtained from 2 M NaCl extraction of nuclei that had been pretreated with only DNase I (Table XII, control, Experiment A).

[c] Control nuclear matrix preparations that contain an internal RNA–protein network; obtained following 2 M NaCl extraction of nuclei that had been pretreated with only DNase I (Table XII, control, Experiment A).

[d] Residual nuclear matrix preparations that consist only of a preipheral lamina (empty spheres); obtained following 2 M NaCl extraction of nuclei that had been pretreated with DNase I, RNase A, and 1 mM DTT (Table XII, Experiment D).

[e] This fraction is calculated from the difference between insoluble nuclear matrix preparations that contain an internal network (total nuclear matrix) and empty spheres that consist only of a peripheral lamina. The DHT binding activity in this fraction represents an average of 75% of the binding associated with total nuclear matrix (76/101). From Barrack and Coffey (1980).

We have also observed that a small percentage of the total matrix DHT binding sites remains associated with the lamina of empty matrix spheres; it is not known whether these sites derive from incomplete extraction of internal network components, or whether the conditions that result in solubilization of the internal RNP network also extract certain components from the peripheral lamina. Thus the possibility cannot be ruled out that these binding sites in fact also derive from components of the peripheral lamina of the matrix. The pore complex-lamina fraction itself represents residual components of the nuclear envelope. When isolated nuclear membrane fractions are extracted by procedures similar to those used to prepare the matrix, a residual pore complex-lamina is obtained that contains many of the same polypeptides as those of the entire nuclear matrix fraction (Aaronson and Blobel, 1975; Dwyer and Blobel, 1976; Jackson, 1976a; Cobbs and Shelton, 1978; Peters and Comings, 1980).

In this regard, it is interesting to note that nuclear envelopes isolated from rat ventral prostate contain approximately 10% as many DHT binding sites as intact nuclei, and this binding is relatively resistant to Triton X-100 treatment (Lefebvre and Novosad, 1980) (compare with data in Table XIV). In addition, Jackson and Chalkley (1974) found specific, high-affinity binding sites for estradiol in a nuclear membrane fraction isolated from bovine endometrial tissue. These binding sites were also resistant to solubilization by 0.4 M KCl and appeared to have properties distinct from those of cytoplasmic receptors (Jackson and Chalkley, 1974). High-affinity binding of purified glucocorticoid–receptor complexes to isolated rat liver nuclear envelopes has also been observed; this binding, which represents 20% of total nuclear receptor binding capacity, is dissociated by 0.3 M KCl (Smith and von Holt, 1981). These authors further suggest that chromatin-associated receptors reflect binding to nuclear envelope fragments that are contaminants of chromatin preparations (Smith and von Holt, 1981).

G. ADDITIONAL COMMENTS ON THE NATURE OF NUCLEAR MATRIX-ASSOCIATED STEROID BINDING SITES

1. Criteria for Steroid Hormone Receptors

The specific binding of estradiol and dihydrotestosterone to the nuclear matrix of rat uterus and chicken liver, and rat ventral prostate, respectively, satisfies the criteria that are commonly used to characterize steroid hormone receptors. The binding of these steroids is saturable, high affinity, and heat and Pronase sensitive. In addition, the steroid specificity of estradiol binding to the nuclear matrix of estrogen-responsive tissues (rat uterus and chicken liver) and of dihydrotestosterone binding to the nuclear matrix of an androgen-dependent tissue (rat ventral prostate) are characteristic of target tissue hormone receptor systems. In these tissues, the appearance of specific steroid binding sites with the nuclear matrix occurs in response to an appropriate hormonal stimulus. Thus, the nuclear matrix of the liver of untreated roosters contains very few estradiol binding sites; following administration of a dose of estrogen to the rooster that stimulates synthesis of vitellogenin in the liver (Deeley et al., 1977), there is a 12-fold increase in the number of specific estradiol binding sites associated with the nuclear matrix. The liver of the egg-laying hen, which is actively producing large quantities of vitellogenin, contains similarly high levels of nuclear matrix-associated specific estradiol binding sites. Likewise, in the rat ventral prostate the presence of specific dihydrotestosterone binding sites on the nuclear matrix is associated with androgen stimulation of this gland. These binding sites are present in the ventral prostate nuclear matrix of an intact adult male rat. Following withdrawal of androgen (castration), there is a rapid loss (within 24 hours) of these nuclear matrix binding sites that precedes the involution of the gland. Androgen administration restores these sites to normal levels within 1 hour. Thus the appearance of nuclear matrix-associated steroid binding sites correlates with the stimulation of biological response.

2. Steroid–Receptor–Acceptor Interactions

An important aspect of the nature of these specific steroid hormone binding sites associated with the nuclear matrix concerns the question of whether these sites represent a native steroid–receptor–acceptor interaction. The first point relates to whether these sites are occupied by steroid *in vivo*. The measurement of steroid binding sites on the nuclear matrix involves *in vitro* incubation of the isolated nuclear matrix fraction with labeled steroid. The underlying assumption of this approach is that the addition of labeled steroid will, under equilibrium conditions, exchange with unlabeled steroid that had become bound to these sites as a result of the *in vivo* processes of steroid hormone–receptor complex translocation following administration of the hormone (Anderson *et al.*, 1972a). However, the state of occupancy of these binding sites in the isolated nuclear matrix is not known. Thus, indirect binding studies such as those we have used do not distinguish between the binding of the labeled steroid to receptors previously occupied by endogenous unlabeled steroid (i.e., exchange), and direct binding to unoccupied sites. Unoccupied binding sites might represent receptor from which steroid has dissociated during the time it takes to isolate the nuclear matrix, or a form of unoccupied receptor that is bound to the nuclear matrix *in vivo* without steroid attached.

As to whether labeled steroid binds to the nuclear matrix via receptor proteins that had been translocated to the nucleus remains to be established with certainty. Although we find that the equilibrium dissociation constant for the interaction of steroids with the nuclear matrix is similar to that of the cytoplasmic and nuclear salt-extractable steroid receptors, this is consistent with, but does not prove that the binding site on the matrix is the same receptor moiety. In this regard, however, soluble macromolecule-associated estradiol binding, which on sucrose density gradient analysis had a sedimentation coefficient of 7 S, somewhat larger than that of the nuclear salt-extractable estradiol receptor (Snow *et al.*, 1978), has been obtained by extracting the chicken liver nuclear matrix with 2 M LiCl and 4 M urea (Hardin and Clark, 1979). In addition, when the nuclear matrix-associated androgen binding sites of the rat ventral prostate are rendered salt-soluble following NaCl extraction of nuclei that had been digested with DNase I plus RNase A and dithiothreitol (see Table XII), sucrose density gradient analysis reveals that the bound steroid is macromolecule-associated (E. R. Barrack, unpublished observations).

Additional evidence that (steroid)–receptor complexes are associated with the nuclear matrix is the observation that in the hormone-withdrawn state (roosters or castrate rats) there are virtually no high-affinity, specific steroid binding sites in the nucleus, whereas shortly after appropriate hormonal treatment (within less than an hour in the androgen-treated castrate rat) significant levels of specific steroid binding activity are found associated with the nuclear matrix (Fig. 12). These data are consistent with the types of observations that formed the basis for the well-established model of steroid hormone-mediated translocation of cytoplasmic receptors into the nucleus (Gorski and Gannon, 1976; Jensen, 1979; Liao et al., 1979).

Of course, the possibility that these matrix-associated steroid binding sites do not reflect the native state, but rather merely result from adventitious adsorption of receptors must always be considered. The adsorption of uncharged cytosol receptors to the nuclear matrix, however, can be ruled out, since in the prostate of the castrate one finds large amounts of androgen receptor in the cytosol (Bruchovsky and Wilson, 1968; Fang et al., 1969; E. R. Barrack, unpublished observations), but under these conditions only very few binding sites are found associated with the matrix (Fig. 11). Nevertheless, one must still consider the possibility that during the isolation of nuclei and nuclear matrix some activated cytoplasmic steroid–receptor complexes or salt-extractable nuclear receptors may become associated with the nuclear matrix in a nonphysiological interaction that remains resistant to disruption and solubilization by high ionic strength.

On the other hand, however, since the precise mechanism by which steroid hormone–receptor complexes act in the nucleus to modulate gene expression by affecting the synthesis of premessenger heterogeneous nuclear RNA is still unresolved, the possibility that salt-resistant interactions of receptors with the nuclear matrix in fact reflect a meaningful association should not be discounted (see also Clark and Peck, 1976; Honma et al., 1977; Ruh and Baudendistel, 1978; Sato et al., 1979).

Moreover, the apparent existence of two forms of steroid-receptor–acceptor complexes in the nucleus, one which is easily disrupted by high salt conditions, and the other which is resistant, raises some interesting questions. For example, one possibility is that the acceptors are the same, but that the cytoplasm-derived nuclear receptors themselves are heterogeneous. Though there may be little evidence to support this notion, the methods that are currently used for characterizing receptors may not be sufficiently sensitive to detect such heterogeneity. Additionally, one must keep in mind that salt-extractable and salt-resistant receptors are operationally defined, and may not reflect in a precise manner the *in vivo* interaction of receptors with the nucleus. For example, alterations in the conditions for extracting nuclear receptors, such as the inclusion of reducing agents (see Tables XII and XIII), can alter the relative proportions of nuclear receptor that are salt-extractable and salt-resistant. Thus, the extent to which, for example, oxidation of protein sulfhydryl groups may be involved in the *in vivo* interaction of receptors with the nucleus remains to be elucidated. Another example is that the inclusion of inhibitors of proteolysis can affect the amount of nuclear receptor found to be salt-resistant (see Table XI). In addition, inclusion of sodium molybdate in the homogenizing buffer appears to result in redistribution of a large proportion of the nuclear receptors to the cytosol (Trachtenberg *et al.*, 1981).

3. Relationship to Chromatin-Associated Receptors

The role of hormone binding components of chromatin, and subfractions thereof, in the mechanism of steroid hormone action has been investigated extensively (see review by Thrall *et al.*, 1978). Unfortunately however, chromatin is operationally defined and a variety of different methods are used to prepare and subfractionate chromatin. Hence individual preparations may represent functionally variable components of the nucleus. In addition, chromatin preparations often contain fragments of the nuclear envelope (Jackson, 1976b; Smith and von Holt, 1981) and of the nuclear matrix (Berezney, 1979). Thus the concept of "chromatin" is undergoing a redefinition in terms of modern concepts of the nucleus (Busch, 1978).

Since all the DNA in the nucleus is organized into supercoiled loop domains which are tightly attached to the nuclear matrix (see Table II), it should not be surprising to find that isolated chromatin would contain components of the nuclear matrix, particularly if chromatin is prepared by simply washing nuclei with a low ionic strength buffer to extract the soluble nuclear proteins (Spelsberg *et al.*, 1971; Thrall and Spelsberg, 1980), or by sonicating nuclei to disrupt nuclear (and nuclear matrix) structure (e.g., Pederson, 1974; de Boer *et al.*, 1978; Rennie, 1979; Berezney, 1980; van Eekelen and van Venrooij, 1981). In this regard, it is important to note that nuclear acceptor sites for steroid hormone–receptor complexes have been found in chromatin fractions that resist solubilization by both low and high ionic strength (Klyzsejko-Stefanowicz *et al.*, 1976; Wang, 1978; Thrall *et al.*, 1978; Tsai *et al.*, 1980), and in chromatin subfractions obtained by sonicating nuclei (de Boer *et al.*, 1978).

Localization of hormone receptor binding sites has also been probed by DNase or micrococcal nuclease digestion of nuclei or chromatin. Many of the receptors that are solubilized by nuclease digestion are associated with nucleosomes (Senior and Frankel, 1978; Scott and Frankel, 1980) or internucleosomal DNA (Rennie, 1979). On the other hand, Schoenberg and Clark (1981) find no such association. Only 5 to 70% of nuclear steroid receptors are released by nuclease digestion (Senior and Frankel, 1978; Alberga et al., 1979; Scott and Frankel, 1980; Schoenberg and Clark, 1981), and these receptors can be dissociated from nuclease-sensitive sites by 0.4 M KCl or 0.6 M NaCl (Senior and Frankel, 1978; Rennie, 1979). These nuclease-sensitive hormone binding sites therefore appear to be distinct from the nuclease-resistant sites associated with the nuclear matrix.

Template-active regions of chromatin are known to be preferentially sensitive to nuclease digestion (Garel and Axel, 1976; Weintraub and Groudine, 1976; Bloom and Anderson, 1978), yet hormone receptors have been found in association with both template-active and -inactive fractions (Alberga et al., 1979; Scott and Frankel, 1980; Davies et al., 1980). In MCF-7 cells, estradiol–receptor complexes were enriched in the transcriptionally active fraction of chromatin (Scott and Frankel, 1980). In contrast, the template-inactive fraction of the ventral prostate appears to contain about 3 times as many acceptor sites as the transcriptionally active chromatin (Davies et al., 1980). In this regard, it is important to consider that certain actively transcribed genes have been shown to be associated preferentially with the nuclear matrix (Pardoll and Vogelstein, 1980; Nelkin et al., 1980) and with specific nonhistone chromosomal proteins that are very tightly bound to DNA (Norman and Bekhor, 1981). In addition, all of the nascent heterogeneous nuclear RNA is associated with the nuclear matrix (Miller et al., 1978a; Herman et al., 1978; Long et al., 1979; van Eekelen and van Venrooij, 1981; Jackson et al., 1981). Moreover, the precursor mRNAs for globin in chicken erythroblasts (Ross, 1980), and ovomucoid and ovalbumin in hen oviduct (Ciejek et al., 1981) are associated with the nuclear matrix. Therefore, the ability of nuclease digestion to release transcriptionally active regions from chromatin belies the fact that their native localization is in association with a discrete, nuclease-resistant structure, the nuclear matrix. Whether a similar situation applies to the preferential release of nuclear steroid hormone–receptor complexes by nucleases or salt remains to be determined.

ACKNOWLEDGMENTS

We would like to thank Ms. Ruth Middleton and Ms. Mary Buedel for their assistance in the preparation of this manuscript.

This work was supported by Grant AM 22000, USPHS, NIAMDD.

REFERENCES

Aaronson, R. P., and Blobel, G. (1975). *Proc. Natl. Acad. Sci. U.S.A.* **72**, 1007–1011.

Adolph, K. W. (1980). *J. Cell Sci.* **42**, 291–304.

Agutter, P. S., and Birchall, K. (1979). *Exp. Cell Res.* **124**, 453–460.

Agutter, P. S., and Richardson, J. C. W. (1980). *J. Cell Sci.* **44**, 395–435.

Alberga, A., Tran, A., and Baulieu, E. E. (1979). *Nucleic Acids Res.* **7**, 2031–2044.

Allen, S. L., Berezney, R., and Coffey, D. S. (1977). *Biochem. Biophys. Res. Commun.* **75**, 111–116.

Anderson, J., Clark, J. H., and Peck, E. J., Jr. (1972a). *Biochem. J.* **126**, 561–567.

Anderson, J. N., Clark, J. H., and Peck, E. J., Jr. (1972b). *Biochem. Biophys. Res. Commun.* **48**, 1460–1468.

Anderson, J. N., Clark, J. H., and Peck, E. J., Jr. (1975). *Endocrinology* **96**, 160–167.

Aten, R. F., Weinberger, M. J., and Eisenfeld, A. J. (1978). *Endocrinology* **102**, 433–442.

Barrack, E. R., and Coffey, D. S. (1980). *J. Biol. Chem.* **255**, 7265–7275.

Barrack, E. R., Hawkins, E. F., Allen, S. L., Hicks, L. L., and Coffey, D. S. (1977). *Biochem. Biophys. Res. Commun.* **79**, 829–836.

Barrack, E. R., Hawkins, E. F., and Coffey, D. S. (1979). *In* "Steroid Hormone Receptor Systems" (W. W. Leavitt and J. H. Clark, eds.), pp. 47–70. Plenum, New York.

Basler, J., Berezney, R., and Sandberg, A. A. (1981). *J. Cell Biol.* **91**, 60a.

Bekhor, I., and Mirell, C. J. (1979). *Biochemistry* **18**, 609–616.

Berezney, R. (1979). *In* "The Cell Nucleus" (H. Busch, ed.), Vol. 7, pp. 413–456. Academic Press, New York.

Berezney, R. (1980). *J. Cell Biol.* **85**, 641–650.

Berezney, R., and Buchholtz, L. A. (1981a). *Exp. Cell Res.* **132**, 1–13.

Berezney, R., and Buchholtz, L. A. (1981b). *Biochemistry* **20**, 4995–5002.

Berezney, R., and Coffey, D. S. (1974). *Biochem. Biophys. Res. Commun.* **60**, 1410–1417.

Berezney, R., and Coffey, D. S. (1975). *Science* **189**, 291–293.

Berezney, R., and Coffey, D. S. (1976). *Adv. Enzyme Regul.* **14**, 63–100.

Berezney, R., and Coffey, D. S. (1977). *J. Cell Biol.* **73**, 616–637.

Berezney, R., Basler, J., Hughes, B. B., and Kaplan, S. C. (1979). *Cancer Res.* **39**, 3031–3039.

Blazsek, I., Vaukhonen, M., and Hemminki, K. (1979). *Res. Commun. Chem. Pathol. Pharmacol.* **23**, 611–626.

Bloom, K. S., and Anderson, J. N. (1978). *Cell* **15**, 141–150.

Boesel, R. W., Klipper, R. W., and Shain, S. A. (1977). *Endocr. Res. Commun.* **4**, 71–84.

Bouteille, M., Laval, M., and Dupuy-Coin, A. M. (1974). *In* "The Cell Nucleus" (H. Busch, ed.), Vol. 1, pp. 3–71. Academic Press, New York.

Bouvier, D., Hubert, J., and Bouteille, M. (1980). *J. Ultrastruct. Res.* **73**, 288–298.

Bowen, B., Steinberg, J., Laemmli, U. K., and Weintraub, H. (1980). *Nucleic Acids Res.* **8**, 1–20.

Brandes, D. (1974). *In* "Male Accessory Sex Organs: Structure and Function in Mammals" (D. Brandes, ed.), pp. 183–222. Academic Press, New York.

Bruchovsky, N., and Wilson, J. D. (1968). *J. Biol. Chem.* **243**, 2012–2021.

Buckler-White, A. J., Humphrey, G. W., and Pigiet, V. (1980). *Cell* **22**, 37–46.

Busch, H. (1978). *In* "The Cell Nucleus" (H. Busch, ed.), Vol. 6, pp. xxiii–xxvii. Academic Press, New York.

Busch, H., and Smetana, K. (1970). "The Nucleolus," pp. 361–381. Academic Press, New York.

Chamness, G. C., Zava, D. T., and McGuire, W. L. (1978). *In* "Methods in Cell Biology"

(G. Stein, J. Stein, and L. J. Kleinsmith, eds.), Vol. 17, pp. 325–333. Academic Press, New York.

Chung, L. W. K., and Coffey, D. S. (1971). *Biochim. Biophys. Acta* **247**, 570–583.

Ciejek, E. M., Nordstrom, J. L., Tsai, M.-J., and O'Malley, B. W. (1981). *J. Cell Biol.* **91**, 132a.

Clark, J. H., and Peck, E. J., Jr. (1976). *Nature (London)* **260**, 635–637.

Clark, J. II., Markaverich, B., Upchurch, S., Eriksson, H., Hardin, J. W., and Peck, E. J., Jr. (1980). *Recent Prog. Horm. Res.* **36**, 89–134.

Cobbs, C. S., Jr., and Shelton, K. R. (1978). *Arch. Biochem. Biophys.* **189**, 323–335.

Cochran, D. L., Yeoman, L. C., Egle, P. M., and Shelton, K. R. (1979). *J. Supramol. Struct.* **10**, 405–418.

Coffey, D. S., Shimazaki, J., and Williams-Ashman, H. G. (1968). *Arch. Biochem. Biophys.* **124**, 184–198.

Comings, D. E., and Okada, T. A. (1976). *Exp. Cell Res.* **103**, 341–360.

Comings, D. E., and Wallack, A. S. (1978). *J. Cell Sci.* **34**, 233–246.

Cook, P. R., Brazell, I. A., and Jost, E. (1976). *J. Cell Sci.* **22**, 303–324.

Danzo, B. J., and Eller, B. C. (1978). *J. Steroid Biochem.* **9**, 477–483.

Davies, P., Thomas, P., and Griffiths, K. (1977). *J. Endocrinol.* **74**, 393–404.

Davies, P., Thomas, P., Borthwick, N. M., and Giles, M. G. (1980). *J. Endocrinol.* **87**, 225–240.

de Boer, W., deVries, J., Mulder, E., and van der Molen, H. J. (1978). *Nucleic Acids Res.* **5**, 87–103.

Deeley, R. G., Gordon, J. I., Burns, A. T. H., Mullinix, K. P., BinaStein, M., and Goldberger, R. F. (1977). *J. Biol. Chem.* **252**, 8310–8319.

DeHertogh, R., Ekka, E., Vanderheyden, I., and Hoet, J. J. (1973). *J. Steroid Biochem.* **4**, 313–320.

DeKlerk, D. P., Heston, W. D. W., and Coffey, D. S. (1976). *In* "Benign Prostatic Hyperplasia" (J. T. Grayhack, J. D. Wilson, and M. J. Scherbenske, eds.), pp. 43–54. U.S. Govt. Printing Office, Washington, D.C.

Deppert, W. (1978). *J. Virol.* **26**, 165–178.

Dickson, R. B., and Eisenfeld, A. J. (1981). *Endocrinology* **108**, 1511–1518.

Dickson, R. B., Aten, R. F., and Eisenfeld, A. J. (1980). *Mol. Pharmacol.* **18**, 215–233.

Dijkwel, P. A., Mullenders, L. H. F., and Wanka, F. (1979). *Nucleic Acids Res.* **6**, 219–230.

Dvorkin, V. M., and Vanyushin, B. F. (1978). *Biochemistry (USSR)* **43**, 1297–1301.

Dwyer, N., and Blobel, G. (1976). *J. Cell Biol.* **70**, 581–591.

Eastment, C. E., Scott, R. B., Shelton, K. R., and Haar, J. L. (1981). *Blood* **57**, 747–757.

Eriksson, H., Upchurch, S., Hardin, J. W., Peck, E. J., Jr., and Clark, J. H. (1978). *Biochem. Biophys. Res. Commun.* **81**, 1–7.

Faiferman, I., and Pogo, A. O. (1975). *Biochemistry* **14**, 3808–3816.

Fakan, S., Puvion, E., and Spohr, G. (1976). *Exp. Cell Res.* **99**, 155–164.

Fang, S., Anderson, K. M., and Liao, S. (1969). *J. Biol. Chem.* **244**, 6584–6595.

Franceschi, R. T., and Kim, K. H. (1979). *J. Biol. Chem.* **254**, 3637–3646.

Franke, W. W., Kleinschmidt, J. A., Spring, H., Krohne, G., Grund, C., Trendelenburg, M. F., Stoehr, M., and Scheer, U. (1981). *J. Cell Biol.* **90**, 289–299.

Garel, A., and Axel, R. (1976). *Proc. Natl. Acad. Sci. U.S.A.* **73**, 3966–3970.

Gates, D. M., and Bekhor, I. (1980). *Science* **207**, 661–662.

Georgiev, G. P., and Chentsov, J. S. (1962). *Exp. Cell Res.* **27**, 570–572.

Georgiev, G. P., Nedospasov, S. A., and Bakayev, V. V. (1978). *In* "The Cell Nucleus" (H. Busch, ed.), Vol. 6, pp. 3–34. Academic Press, New York.

Gerace, L., and Blobel, G. (1980). *Cell* **19**, 277–287.

Gerace, L., Blum, A., and Blobel, G. (1978). *J. Cell Biol.* **79**, 546–566.

Ghosh, S., Paweletz, N., and Ghosh, I. (1978). *Exp. Cell Res.* **111**, 363–371.

Giese, G., and Wunderlich, F. (1979). *Anal. Biochem.* **100**, 282–288.

Giese, G., and Wunderlich, F. (1980). *J. Biol. Chem.* **255**, 1716–1721.

Goldman, R. D., and Knipe, D. M. (1972). *Cold Spring Harbor Symp. Quant. Biol.* **37**, 523–534.

Gorski, J., and Gannon, F. (1976). *Annu. Rev. Physiol.* **38**, 425–450.

Gschwendt, M., and Kittstein, W. (1973). *Hoppe Seylers Z. Physiol. Chem.* **354**, 1642–1644.

Gschwendt, M., and Schneider, W. (1978). *Eur. J. Biochem.* **91**, 139–149.

Hampel, M. R., Peng, L.-H., Pearlman, M. R. J., and Pearlman, W. H. (1978). *J. Biol. Chem.* **253**, 8545–8553.

Hardin, J. W., and Clark, J. H. (1979). *J. Cell Biol.* **83**, 252a.

Hemminki, K., and Vainio, H. (1979). *Cancer Lett.* **6**, 167–173.

Henderson, D., and Weber, K. (1979). *Exp. Cell Res.* **124**, 301–316.

Herlan, G., Eckert, W. A., Kaffenberger, W., and Wunderlich, F. (1979). *Biochemistry* **18**, 1782–1788.

Herman, R., Weymouth, L., and Penman, S. (1978). *J. Cell Biol.* **78**, 663–674.

Hodge, L. D., Mancini, P., Davis, F. M., and Heywood, P. (1977). *J. Cell Biol.* **72**, 194–208.

Honma, Y., Kasukabe, T., Okabe, J., and Hozumi, M. (1977). *J. Cell. Physiol.* **93**, 227–236.

Hozier, J., and Furcht, L. T. (1980). *Cell Biol. Int. Rep.* **4**, 1091–1099.

Hughes, M. R., Compton, J. G., Schrader, W. T., and O'Malley, B. W. (1981). *Biochemistry* **20**, 2481–2491.

Hunt, B. F., and Vogelstein, B. (1981). *Nucleic Acids Res.* **9**, 349–363.

Isaacs, J. T., Barrack, E. R., Isaacs, W. B., and Coffey, D. S. (1981). In "The Prostatic Cell: Structure and Function" (G. P. Murphy, A. A. Sandberg, and J. P. Karr, eds.). Part A, pp. 1–24. Liss, New York.

Jackson, R. C. (1976a). *Biochemistry* **15**, 5641–5651.

Jackson, R. C. (1976b). *Biochemistry* **15**, 5652–5656.

Jackson, V., and Chalkley, R. (1974). *J. Biol. Chem.* **249**, 1615–1626.

Jackson, D. A., McCready, S. J., and Cook, P. R. (1981). *Nature (London)* **292**, 552–555.

Jensen, E. V. (1979). *Pharmacol. Rev.* **30**, 477–491.

Jensen, E. V., Suzuki, T., Kawashima, T., Stumpf, W. E., Jungblut, P. W., and De Sombre, E. R. (1968). *Proc. Natl. Acad. Sci. U.S.A.* **59**, 632–638.

Johnson, L. K., Vlodavsky, I., Baxter, J. D., and Gospodarowicz, D. (1980). *Nature (London)* **287**, 340–343.

Jost, E., and Johnson, R. T. (1981). *J. Cell Sci.* **47**, 25–53.

Juliano, J. V., and Stancel, G. M. (1976). *Biochemistry* **15**, 916–920.

Kaufman, M., Pinsky, L., Kubski, A., Straisfeld, C., Dobrenis, K., Shiroky, J., Chan, T., and MacGibbon, B. (1978). *J. Clin. Endocrinol. Metab.* **47**, 738–745.

Kaufmann, S. H., Coffey, D. S., and Shaper, J. H. (1981). *Exp. Cell Res.* **132**, 105–123.

Klyzsejko-Stefanowicz, L., Chiu, J.-F., Tsai, Y.-H., and Hnilica, L. S. (1976). *Proc. Natl. Acad. Sci. U.S.A.* **73**, 1954–1958.

Krohne, G., Franke, W. W., Ely, S., D'Arcy, A., and Jost, E. (1978). *Cytobiologie* **18**, 22–38.

Kuz'mina, S. N., Bul'dyaeva, T. V., and Zbarskii, I. B. (1980). *Biochemistry (USSR)* **45**, 1071–1077.

Lam, K. S., and Kasper, C. B. (1979a). *Biochemistry* **18**, 307–311.

Lam, K. S., and Kasper, C. B. (1979b). *J. Biol. Chem.* **254**, 11713–11720.

Lazarides, E. (1981). *Cell* **23**, 649–650.

Lazarides, E., and Weber, K. (1974). *Proc. Natl. Acad. Sci. U.S.A.* **71**, 2268–2272.

Lazier, C. (1975). *Steroids* **26**, 281–298.
Lebeau, M. C., Massol, N., and Baulieu, E. E. (1973). *Eur. J. Biochem.* **36**, 294–300.
Lefebvre, Y. A., and Novosad, Z. (1980). *Biochem. J.* **186**, 641–647.
Lenk, R., Ransom, L., Kaufmann, Y., and Penman, S. (1977). *Cell* **10**, 67–78.
Liao, S., Liang, T., and Tymoczko, J. K. (1973). *Nature (London) New Biol.* **241**, 211–213.
Liao, S., Mezzetti, G., and Chen, C. (1979). In ''The Cell Nucleus'' (H. Busch, ed.), Vol. 7, pp. 201–227. Academic Press, New York.
Long, B. H., Huang, C.-Y., and Pogo, A. O. (1979). *Cell* **18**, 1079–1090.
McCready, S. J., Godwin, J., Mason, D. W., Brazell, I. A., and Cook, P. R. (1980). *J. Cell Sci.* **46**, 365–386.
McDonald, J. R., and Agutter, P. S. (1980). *FEBS Lett.* **116**, 145–148.
Markaverich, B. M., Upchurch, S., and Clark, J. H. (1980). *J. Receptor Res.* **1**, 415–438.
Maul, G. G., and Avdalović, N. (1980). *Exp. Cell Res.* **130**, 229–240.
Mester, J., and Baulieu, E. E. (1975). *Biochem. J.* **146**, 617–623.
Miller, T. E., Huang, C.-Y., and Pogo, A. O. (1978a). *J. Cell Biol.* **76**, 675–691.
Miller, T. E., Huang, C.-Y., and Pogo, A. O. (1978b). *J. Cell Biol.* **76**, 692–704.
Mirsky, A. E., and Ris, H. (1951). *J. Gen. Physiol.* **34**, 475–492.
Mitchelson, K. R., Bekers, A. G. M., and Wanka, F. (1979). *J. Cell Sci.* **39**, 247–256.
Monneron, A., and Bernhard, W. (1969). *J. Ultrastruct. Res.* **27**, 266–288.
Müller, R. E., Traish, A. M., and Wotiz, H. H. (1977). *J. Biol. Chem.* **252**, 8206–8211.
Nelkin, B. D., Pardoll, D. M., and Vogelstein, B. (1980). *Nucleic Acids Res.* **8**, 5623–5634.
Nomi, S., Matsuura, T., Ueyama, H., and Ueda, K. (1981). *J. Nutr. Sci. Vitaminol.* **27**, 33–41.
Norman, G. L., and Bekhor, I. (1981). *Biochemistry* **20**, 3568–3578.
Nyberg, L. M., and Wang, T. Y. (1976). *J. Steroid Biochem.* **7**, 267–273.
Osborn, M., and Weber, K. (1977). *Exp. Cell Res.* **106**, 339–349.
Pardoll, D. M., and Vogelstein, B. (1980). *Exp. Cell Res.* **128**, 466–470.
Pardoll, D. M., Vogelstein, B., and Coffey, D. S. (1980). *Cell* **19**, 527–536.
Paris, J. E., and Brandes, D. (1974). In ''Male Accessory Sex Organs: Structure and Function in Mammals'' (D. Brandes, ed.), pp. 223–233. Academic Press, New York.
Pederson, T. (1974). *J. Mol. Biol.* **83**, 163–183.
Peters, K. E., and Comings, D. E. (1980). *J. Cell Biol.* **86**, 135–155.
Pollard, T. D., and Weihing, R. R. (1973). *Crit. Rev. Biochem.* **2**, 1–65.
Porter, K. R., and Tucker, J. B. (1981). *Sci. Am.* **244**, 56–67.
Poznanović, G., and Sevaljević, L. (1980). *Cell Biol. Int. Rep.* **4**, 701–709.
Puca, G. A., and Bresciani, F. (1968). *Nature (London)* **218**, 967–969.
Puca, G. A., Nola, E., Hibner, U., Cicala, G., and Sica, V. (1975). *J. Biol. Chem.* **250**, 6452–6459.
Razin, S. V., Mantieva, V. L., and Georgiev, G. P. (1979). *Nucleic Acids Res.* **7**, 1713–1735.
Rennie, P. S. (1979). *J. Biol. Chem.* **254**, 3947–3952.
Riley, D. E., and Keller, J. M. (1976). *Biochim. Biophys. Acta* **444**, 899–911.
Riley, D. E., Keller, J. M., and Byers, B. (1975). *Biochemistry* **14**, 3005–3013.
Ross, D. A. (1980). *Fed. Proc. Fed. Am. Soc. Exp. Biol.* **39**, 2196.
Ruh, T. S., and Baudendistel, L. J. (1977). *Endocrinology* **100**, 420–426.
Ruh, T. S., and Baudendistel, L. J. (1978). *Endocrinology* **102**, 1838–1846.
Sanborn, B. M., Steinberger, A., and Tcholakian, R. K. (1979). *Steroids* **34**, 401–412.
Sato, B., Spomer, W., Huseby, R. A., and Samuels, L. T. (1979). *Endocrinology* **104**, 822–831.
Scatchard, G. (1949). *Ann. N. Y. Acad. Sci.* **51**, 660–672.
Schliwa, M., and Van Blerkom, J. (1981). *J. Cell Biol.* **90**, 222–235.

Schoenberg, D. R., and Clark, J. H. (1981). *Biochem. J.* **196**, 423–432.

Scott, R. W., and Frankel, F. R. (1980). *Proc. Natl. Acad. Sci. U.S.A.* **77**, 1291–1295.

Senior, M. B., and Frankel, F. R. (1978). *Cell* **14**, 857–863.

Sevaljević, L., Poznanović, G., Petrović, M., Konstantinović, M., and Ratković, M. (1980). *Period. Biol.* **82**, 325–330.

Sevaljević, L., Poznanović, G., Petrović, M., and Krtolica, K. (1981). *Biochem. Int.* **2**, 77–84.

Shankar Narayan, K., Steele, W. J., Smetana, K., and Busch, H. (1967). *Exp. Cell Res.* **46**, 65–77.

Shaper, J. H., Pardoll, D. M., Kaufmann, S. H., Barrack, E. R., Vogelstein, B., and Coffey, D. S. (1979). *Adv. Enzyme Regul.* **17**, 213–248.

Shelton, K. R., and Cochran, D. L. (1978). *Biochemistry* **17**, 1212–1216.

Shelton, K. R., Higgins, L. L., Cochran, D. L., Ruffolo, J. J., Jr., and Egle, P. M. (1980). *J. Biol. Chem.* **255**, 10978–10983.

Smetana, K., Steele, W. J., and Busch, H. (1963). *Exp. Cell Res.* **31**, 198–201.

Smith, H. C., and Berezney, R. (1980). *Biochem. Biophys. Res. Commun.* **97**, 1541–1547.

Smith, P., and von Holt, C. (1981). *Biochemistry* **20**, 2900–2908.

Snead, H. W., McDonald, T. F., Baker, M. D., and Lanclos, K. D. (1979). *J. Supramol. Struct.* **12**, 471–479.

Snow, L. D., Eriksson, H., Hardin, J. W., Chan, L., Jackson, R. L., Clark, J. H., and Means, A. R. (1978). *J. Steroid Biochem.* **9**, 1017–1026.

Spelsberg, T. C., Steggles, A. W., and O'Malley, B. W. (1971). *J. Biol. Chem.* **246**, 4188–4197.

Steele, W. J., and Busch, H. (1966). *Biochim. Biophys. Acta* **129**, 54–67.

Steer, R. C., Goueli, S. A., Wilson, M. J., and Ahmed, K. (1980). *Biochem. Biophys. Res. Commun.* **92**, 919–925.

Stick, R., and Hausen, P. (1980). *Chromosoma* **80**, 219–236.

Tata, J. R. (1978). *In* "Biochemical Actions of Hormones" (G. Litwack, ed.), Vol. 5, pp. 397–431. Academic Press, New York.

Thrall, C. L., and Spelsberg, T. C. (1980). *Biochemistry* **19**, 4130–4138.

Thrall, C. L., Webster, R. A., and Spelsberg, T. C. (1978). *In* "The Cell Nucleus" (H. Busch, ed.), Vol. 6, pp. 461–529. Academic Press, New York.

Todorov, I. T., and Hadjiolov, A. A. (1979). *Cell Biol. Int. Rep.* **3**, 753–757.

Trachtenberg, J., Hicks, L. L., and Walsh, P. C. (1981). *Invest. Urol.* **18**, 349–354.

Traish, A., Müller, R. E., and Wotiz, H. H. (1977). *J. Biol. Chem.* **252**, 6823–6830.

Tsai, Y.-H., Sanborn, B. M., Steinberger, A., and Steinberger, E. (1980). *J. Steroid Biochem.* **13**, 711–718.

Van Doorn, E., Craven, S., and Bruchovsky, N. (1976). *Biochem. J.* **160**, 11–21.

van Eekelen, C. A. G., and van Venrooij, W. J. (1981). *J. Cell Biol.* **88**, 554–563.

Vogelstein, B., Pardoll, D. M., and Coffey, D. S. (1980). *Cell* **22**, 79–85.

Wang, T. Y. (1978). *Biochim. Biophys. Acta* **518**, 81–88.

Weintraub, H., and Groudine, M. (1976). *Science* **193**, 848–856.

Wilson, E. M., and French, F. S. (1976). *J. Biol. Chem.* **251**, 5620–5629.

Wolfe, J. (1980). *J. Cell Biol.* **84**, 160–171.

Wunderlich, F., and Herlan, G. (1977). *J. Cell Biol.* **73**, 271–278.

Wunderlich, F., Giese, G., and Bucherer, C. (1978). *J. Cell Biol.* **79**, 479–490.

Yamamoto, K. R., and Alberts, B. M. (1976). *Annu. Rev. Biochem.* **45**, 721–746.

Zbarsky, I. B. (1981). *Mol. Biol. Rep.* **7**, 139–148.

Zbarsky, I. B., and Georgiev, G. P. (1959). *Biochim. Biophys. Acta* **32**, 301–302.

Zbarsky, I. B., Dmitrieva, N. P., and Yermolayeva, L. P. (1962). *Exp. Cell Res.* **27**, 573–576.

DISCUSSION

E. J. Peck: Recently we examined the estrogen receptor system in brain, that is, in the adult brain which does not grow in response to steroids. In that system there are no salt inextractable sites. This fits very well with the idea that salt inextractable sites are bound to nuclear matrix, since the adult neuron does not replicate. In fact, we relate these sites to long-term retention and growth systems, not to the overall stimulation of polymerases in the nuclear fraction. Do you wish to comment on this.

D. S. Coffey: That sounds very interesting.

W. Moyle: Testosterone and 5α-dihydrotestosterone appear to act differently in the prostate, since men with 5α-reductase deficiency have abnormal prostate development even though their testosterone level is normal. Testosterone and 5α-dihydrotestosterone appear to bind to prostatic androgen receptors and would be expected to elicit identical actions. Have you been able to find differences in the way testosterone and dihydrotestosterone receptor complexes bind to the matrix?

D. S. Coffey: Others have shown quite clearly that the major androgen metabolite in the prostate nucleus is DHT. In competitive binding assays *in vitro*, we have shown that testosterone appears to have a lower binding affinity to the matrix of the prostate than does DHT.

E. Jensen: Your finding of there being hormone binding sites on the matrix that are inextractable with salt is very very interesting. There is one thing I am not quite clear on when you say these are estradiol binding sites. Are you implying that there is receptor there or that this is estradiol binding to the matrix without the presence of the receptor protein? And do you have major observations that the estrogen receptor complex is binding to the matrix not extractable with salt?

D. S. Coffey: The working hypothesis is that the steroid binds via receptor but we don't have definitive proof for this. The only one who has made any comments on that is Dr. Clark who reported, at least in an abstract, that the salt resistant estradiol binding sites could be solubilized by using 4 M urea and 2 M LiCl and they had the size of the estrogen receptor. Is this correct?

J. H. Clark: Did we do that?

D. S. Coffey: Yes, this was reported at the Endocrine Meeting in 1978 (Abstract No. 448) and at the Cell Biology meeting in 1979 (Abstract No. 1265) and I have not seen any follow-up.

J. H. Clark: We might have done that.

D. S. Coffey: We have not tried to resolubilize these estradiol binding sites. However, in the ventral prostate, we can solubilize the DHT binding sites from the nuclear matrix with DNase, RNase, DTT, and 2 M NaCl.

E. Jensen: As a follow-up to this can you in an *in vitro* system bind estradiol to the matrix in isolated purified nuclei without the presence of the cytosol receptor. Do you get the same nonextractable bound hormone on the matrix?

D. S. Coffey: Yes, if the nuclei or matrix have been isolated from animals exposed to the hormone *in vivo*, because these are exchange reactions.

E. Jensen: I was going to say, we can take purified uterine nuclei, or fairly purified, using 2.2 M sucrose, treat these with estradiol, and with no soluble receptor, no extra nuclear receptor present, you certainly do get significant binding of estradiol to purified nuclei that is nonextractable by salt and of course our interpretation of this before the days of the matrix was that here you have estradiol that is nonspecific and you can do this not only with uterine nuclei, you can do this with nuclei of nontarget tissues as well. Here you have a nonspecific solubilization of the hormone in the lipid component which of course is not extractable with salt and in our opinion had very little physiologic relevance and because it did not involve the receptor and was not tissue specific for the hormone dependent tissue. So I had a little reservation about your hypothesis interesting though it is, until you can show either that there is receptor there or you have evidence that estradiol is acting on the matrix in the absence of receptor which would be an additional type of mechanism to that which we have been talking about.

D. S. Coffey: First of all let me say that when you look at the rooster, the matrix does not have the specific estrogen binding sites until the rooster has been treated with estrogen, and the prostate matrix of the rat doesn't bind DHT specifically unless the rat has been treated *in vivo* with androgen. So that is the first thing, it is not just an indiscriminate type of binding, it's very specific. Second, you mentioned quite correctly that you can do an exchange assay with nuclei and get a lot of nonspecific binding, and this may, as you say, be with the lipid. However, the matrix is a delipidated system. Remember we are only looking at 10% of the nuclear proteins; no lipids are left in this system since over 98.8% of the lipid has been removed during the matrix isolation process. Our exchange assays are done on this lipid-depleted structure. I agree with you that if you have a lot of lipid you can get many things going on. In addition, our system does have the right specificity for the steroids too.

J. H. Clark: I think the answer is that you have demonstrated that the sites satisfy the criteria for estrogen receptors. That is, these sites have the binding parameters and hormonal specificity which are identical to those of the estrogen receptor. In addition, these sites appear on the matrix after an injection of estradiol probably through the process of nuclear translocation.

E. Jensen: Yes, I would only add though that I have not seen any evidence for involvement in the physiologic or biological response.

D. S. Coffey: One of the things that has always been missing from the story of steroid hormone action is what you are asking now, that is, a correlation of these sites with biological activity. When you see in all the reviews that are written what is required to prove that this is a receptor, who has really shown that the biological response, i.e., growth, is really related to one of these receptors. That I think is what Dr. Clark did when he showed that true uterine growth, with various doses of estradiol, seemed to correlate with one of these sites, the salt-resistant ones, and that the ones that we usually look at, the salt-extractable sites, could go up and down according to the estrogen treatment and were not directly related to growth. This is what caught our attention. Now I know that this is a long way from cause and effect, but at least it was in the right direction, which sort of excited us.

E. Jensen: You are giving an answer but I guess I am asking for experimental evidence that has not yet been produced, so maybe next year I'll ask the same question again.

D. S. Coffey: No, absolutely, we have not shown that and I would not want anybody in this audience to think that we have done an experiment that in our own minds definitively proves that the salt-resistant binding is related to true uterine growth and is not just going along for the ride.

E. Jensen: I would certainly agree with that.

A. K. Roy: Just to follow up Dr. Jensen's question, did you chew up the DNA with the nuclease and then see whether the receptor or the hormone is still there in the matrix?

D. S. Coffey: Yes, you can digest with DNase I and the steroid binding sites on the matrix are unaltered.

A. K. Roy: So the receptor is not binding to chromatin?

D. S. Coffey: That is right.

L. E. Faber: As a corollary to Dr. Jensen's question, do you have data from nontarget tissues where you could show that there was not an increase in the number of binding sites after hormone treatment. Negative evidence might strengthen your case for the importance of the binding sites.

D. S. Coffey: That is right. We have looked at the immature female rat liver nuclear matrix and there is no specific estrogen binding there. Also, there is none on the rooster liver nuclear matrix until the animal is treated with DES. Those are the types of controls that we have used. It is always hard to say what is not a target tissue and I know I don't have to go through those arguments for this group, but at least that was a reason we moved to the liver system where we could turn it on and off and see if the hormone binding sites responded to the manipulations. That is not a perfect control, by any means. Another control where there was no binding to the matrix was the castrate rat prostate, as you might expect. The other reason we went to these systems instead of the uterus is because it is really rather shocking to see what has been reported as nuclear receptor in the past. If you go to the literature about 90% of the papers use an 800 g pellet as their nuclear pellet. If you look under the microscope at an 800 g pellet less than 10% of that mass is nuclei, and then to start talking about that as a nuclear receptor really worried us. We could get highly purified liver nuclei and that is the reason we moved to it. Widnell and Tata and others have reported the purification of uterine nuclei without the myofibrillar components. When we tried this, we got about a 4% recovery of nuclei.

P. K. Siiteri: I don't recall what the occasion was when we talked about the location of the nuclear estrogen receptor, but I was delighted to see that you followed up on it. We did some work on nuclear estrogen receptors in the guinea pig, which happens to have a very nice uterus because it has a very thick fluffy sort of endometrium which you can scrape off and leave the muscle behind. If you do experiments as a good cell biologist does, you can get about 60% recovery of very pure nuclei. It is virtually impossible to extract any receptor from these nuclei with high salt buffers. So my question to you is, is it possible that all of the nuclear receptor is in fact matrix associated number one, and two if it isn't where do you think it comes from?

D. S. Coffey: It certainly sounds like in your system, virtually all of the nuclear binding may be matrix-associated. I would be surprised if all nuclear receptors were matrix-associated because I believe steroid receptors are heterogeneous, and furthermore there may be several sites of action within the cell. We do not know the origin of the nuclear matrix hormone binding sites, nor do we know how many of these sites may have been extracted during the isolation procedure. If they all turned out to be on the matrix, I would be surprised, but they might be. Now there is the argument, how do you know you are not just precipitating the receptor on the matrix. That is a good question. We would like to think that it is important that there could be hormone binding sites on the matrix because heterogeneous nuclear RNA and newly synthesized DNA are associated with the matrix, and hormones turn on these processes. But we are a long way from understanding all this. Let me say this—the cytoplasmic matrix, the cytoskeleton, is a beautiful network that exists throughout the cell, and for years it was not seen in EM because the density of the structure was the same as that of the embedding medium. Then when antibodies against actin were used we found this ubiquitous beautiful network in the cell. I cannot help but believe that the inside of the nucleus also has a nice network. We come along and extract the nucleus with 2 M NaCl—this is like bombing the building and looking at the remains inside. This amorphous looking nuclear matrix structure is probably a very well designed system. That is easy to say and hard to prove. We are still in the dark ages.

E. J. Peck: Once again, it seems to me that the way to answer the question which Elwood and others are asking here is to select a nondividing target, as neuronal systems which do not undergo mitosis and to compare these with the uterus or any other proliferative system. Since adult neurons do not divide, ask whether the matrix of adult neurons possess ER. If Elwood will give you his antibody, you can establish whether, with or without estrogen treatment, you have receptors bound to matrix in a growing target, but no receptors bound to matrix in a nongrowing, nonproliferating target.

D. S. Coffey: Let me first of all say that we don't believe that the hormone binding to the matrix has to be involved in DNA synthesis, because if it was just DNA synthesis, then when you treat the rooster with DES, you wouldn't expect to find estrogen binding sites on the liver nuclear matrix. DES doesn't massively increase the liver size, it stimulates vitellogenin synthesis. Talwar had reported earlier that there is DNA synthesis in the liver; I'm not sure how much there is, or whether it is in the Kupfer cells, but anyway that is not a gland that gets big. But your question is still a very good one; we should look at other tissues that do not grow and see if hormones bind to the matrix in those systems.

D. Moore: Lasky and co-workers have described a rather unsettling set of data suggesting that there is no such thing as origins in eukaryotic DNA. You seemed to suggest that you had reason to believe that there are DNA sequence-specific origins in eukaryotic chromosomes. Would you care to comment on this?

D. S. Coffey: I am aware of that work where they inject DNA and it looks like it doesn't need an origin to start. We don't know how that works. All I can tell you is that viral DNA in infected cells attaches to this matrix and makes the replicative forms. Dr. Pigiet and others have shown that very clearly. How it gets onto that machinery and whether it needs an origin is beyond me. The other question is very important, whether genes move on and off the matrix when they are activated. There are published reports that there are certain types of genes associated with the matrix and some believe that they are put on while they are activated and it would be important to see what can move in relation on and off this system. I cannot answer your question, but I am aware of those experiments.

D. Moore: But, do you think that the DNA that remains associated with the matrix is origin DNA?

D. S. Coffey: It is not fair to talk about papers in press, but I am aware of two papers that claim that the matrix has origin DNA associated with it, but that is for those workers to report. It is not my work.

S. R. Glasser: While it is valid to criticize the nuclear matrix work on the basis of its failure, at this time, to relate these changes to biological responses, I think it is improper to use an argument about the work done to date on receptors and response. Much of those data are ambivalent. We still wait to establish some direct relationships based perhaps on better biophysical data which will relate receptor to response. So although the level of indirection may be somewhat more secure with the classical receptor data, it is still not beyond suspicion. I would now like to ask one question about the matrix which plays off the comment that Dr. Peck made. What accommodation is made during coiling and uncoiling in those cells which are nondividing but undergoing polyploid and/or endoreduplication.

D. S. Coffey: I do not know. Let me come back to your first statement. We cannot hide ever in science, at least I do not want to hide behind the type of argument that if you didn't prove it I don't have to prove it. If you are going to make these statements you better prove it ultimately. So we certainly would like to find some way to answer that question. The critical question here is Dr. Jensen's question and it is a critical question for all receptor work. We cannot get away from it and we should stand up to the heat of it. How the receptor works in the nucleus is still a mystery. One of the things that impressed us in going in this direction was something that Jim Watson used to say. Jim Watson said when biochemistry fails you, you better study structure. People worked very hard on trying to figure out how proteins were made, but until we knew about messenger RNA and ribosomes we were a long long way from understanding about this. We hope that structure will be the next step in the story of hormone action. As Dr. Jensen said, the steroid goes into the nucleus and something happens. We hope the matrix is related to that; now that may not be, but only time will tell that. But at least we think it is something to be looking at.

J. H. Clark: We all study correlations and can only make probability statements about the truth.

J. E. Rall: As you of course well know, actively transcribed genes are more sensitive to DNase I and probably also to micrococcal nuclease than is bulk DNA. How do you correlate that with your findings about the relative susceptibility of DNA on the nuclear matrix. Do you use DNase I and how do you treat with it.

D. S. Coffey: Yes, DNase I is what we use and we vary the DNase I according to how much DNA we want to remove from the nucleus as we digest the loops back toward the matrix. Now about the organization of the loops, there is a big difference between what you think and what you know so I will tell you what I believe. We believe that each chromosome which has about 2.5 cm of DNA is looped from one part of the membrane to the other in a gigantic loop. And off that are the smaller loops, attached to the matrix, that I was telling you about; there are about 20,000 of these in the cell. Each of these loops contains about 100,000 base pairs and can contain 5 or 10 genes even with their introns. Each of these 100,000 base pair-loops may be arranged in little loops, and the introns may be arranged as loops within these loops. These are all part of the way the system is moved and processed; now how it moves remains to be seen. I think that you are going to have lots of systems to uncoil the DNA in various regions and to release its template restriction so it can be transcribed or replicated.

J. E. Rall: I don't think you answered my question. The point is that when you treat chromatin with small concentrations of DNase I for a short period of time at low temperatures you preferentially solubilize active genes. Now how does that fit in with your matrix looping because there is nothing a priori if I understand it about the matrix looping which makes active genes more susceptible to DNase I.

D. S. Coffey: That is correct. What I am trying to say is that the loops that I am talking about that are anchored to the matrix are large loops that contain many genes. What is happening to each one of those loops in terms of which genes are active or inactive is unrelated as far as we have been talking about or measuring here. How that fits with the model we are showing you, we do not know. And that is what I may not have made too clear.

J. E. Rall: It does not fit.

D. S. Coffey: But it doesn't not fit. We are not trying to explain gene activation. Now we have theories on that but I am not going to try to do miracles if I don't have any data to back them up.

J. Kallos: In relation to the problem of why the receptor can sometimes be easily extracted with KCl from the nuclei and at other times it remains insoluble. We tried to develop a simple *in vitro* system in which we have looked at nucleosomes or DNA–histone complexes and whether or not we could mimic some of the receptor which can be easily extracted or retained and, very briefly, one can produce such a system. In other words, if we expose estrogen receptor or androgen receptor to DNA and histone H2B complexes, the receptor sticks very strongly and is very difficult to extract. In other words if the receptor would see DNA and H1 histone then the receptor became very loose and easily removed from this complex. Obviously I do not know any necessary physiological meanings, but one could speculate that if in some instances the receptor would be more exposed on the nucleosome to H2B complex, somehow it would be more retained; on the other hand, if it turned around and saw H1 it could be very easily kicked out from the nuclear system. I'm not really sure how this would relate in any sense to the nuclear matrix system but somehow in these *in vitro* experiments it was very easy to manipulate the system and might be correlated.

D. S. Coffey: I don't know how to interpret that either, but it is certainly interesting. The linker DNA has been proposed by Paul Rennie to be involved with the binding of androgen receptors (*J. Biol. Chem.* **254,** 3947, 1979). How that would fit I'm not sure.

E. R. Barrack: I would like to make a comment related to Dr. Rall's question about the DNase sensitivity of active genes and how that relates to the finding that certain actively transcribed genes are found associated with the nuclear matrix following the removal of the bulk of the DNA. A point of clarification is that the nuclease digestion studies that were done to look at the association of specific genes with the matrix (Nelkin *et al., Nucleic Acids. Res.* **8**, 5623, 1980) were done following the removal of histones from the nuclei by 2 *M* NaCl. The removal of all histones and most of the nonhistone nuclear proteins allows for the random, indiscriminate clipping of DNA by nucleases (Pardoll, Vogelstein, and Coffey, *Cell* **19**, 527, 1980). Therefore, in order to be able to determine whether or not active genes really are enriched on the matrix, one has to obtain naked DNA associated with the nuclei, so that one can eliminate the possibility that one is preferentially chopping off active or inactive genes.

D. S. Coffey: Along those lines, newly synthesized DNA itself is also preferentially degraded by DNase I and this was one of the problems we had to overcome in carrying out kinetic studies on DNA synthesis in association with the nuclear matrix, where we digested the DNA loops to study the location of the newly synthesized DNA. You have to remove the histones first, and then there is no preference for digestion of newly synthesized DNA.

A. R. Means: If the sites that you see by autoradiography represent replicative DNA synthesis, then there should be some correlation between either the number of active genes in the cell or in the number of chromosomes per nucleus with the number of sites. Have you attempted to make such calculations?

D. S. Coffey: Such calculations have been made, but they are very crude estimates.

A. R. Means: This obviously has to be a dynamic structure. If you are correct that it interacts with the microskeleton of the cytoplasm, then it is going to have to change during different morphological transitions in the cell. Do you know what happens to the nuclear matrix when growing cells are plateaued into G_0?

D. S. Coffey: We don't know that; all we know is that if you look, for example, at the castrate prostate, the volume of the nucleus is down, and after you treat the animal with androgen, the volume increases. It looks like there's a tremendous decondensation of the DNA occurring in the nucleus that is far more than the amount of DNA that could be involved in gene activation. These types of changes have been seen with other systems, of course, and they have been quantitated by morphometry. How that relates to some unwinding or uncoiling of some specific regions of the chromatin is unknown. But there appears to be a phase shift occurring, not a minor little puffing, but a big response.

J. H. Oppenheimer: Have you had the opportunity to analyze the stochiometrics of increase of extractable and nonextractable sites with increasing hormone doses? What would be the proportion of matrix and nonmatrix associated sites as a function of dose?

D. S. Coffey: We have not studied that in great detail, but when matrix-associated steroid binding sites increase following hormone treatment, the salt-extractable receptors also increase.

V. C. Jordan: Your results with salt-resistant sites on the matrix of estrogen-treated roosters are very interesting. As you may be aware, the nonsteroidal antiestrogens exhibit a lot of species differences but in the chick liver they tend to be completely antiestrogenic. To link this fact with some observations on salt-resistant sites in the rat uterus, there have been reports (T. S. Ruh and L. J. Baudendistel, *Endocrinology* **100**, 420, 1977; V. C. Jordan *et al., Mol. Cell Endocrinol.* **7**, 177, 1977) that show that after nonsteroidal antiestrogens translocate receptor to the nucleus, these can all be extracted with salt. Could I suggest that you try the effects of antiestrogens in your roosters to see if (unlike estrogen) they can all be extracted from the nuclear matrix with high salt.

D. S. Coffey: Yes, we thought about doing that. We would like to use antiandrogens and antiestrogens as a tool.

Structure, Expression, and Evolution of Growth Hormone Genes

David D. Moore,* Michael D. Walker,† Don J. Diamond,*
Mark A. Conkling,* and Howard M. Goodman*

* Department of Molecular Biology, Massachusetts General Hospital,
Boston, Massachusetts, and
† Department of Biochemistry and Biophysics, University of California,
San Francisco, California

I. Introduction

Growth hormone is a member of a family of polypeptide hormones which share both sequence homology and some biological activities. In humans, growth hormone, which is synthesized by the somatotrophs of the anterior pituitary, is very homologous to chorionic somatomammotropin, which is synthesized by the syncitio-trophoblast layer of the placenta (Goodman *et al.*, 1980). These two are much more distantly related to the third member of the family, prolactin, which is synthesized by the mammotrophs of the anterior pituitary (Niall *et al.*, 1971).

The synthesis and release of these peptide hormones is regulated by a variety of factors. For example, release of growth hormone is stimulated by increased levels of arginine in the blood, and by an unidentified hypothalamic releasing factor (Daughaday *et al.*, 1975). Synthesis of growth hormone is stimulated by steroid hormones and thyroid hormones. This regulation has been most thoroughly studied in a series of tissue culture cell lines (collectively called "GH" cells) derived from rat pituitary tumors. In these cells, growth hormone messenger RNA levels may be increased 50- to 100-fold following stimulation by the synthetic glucocorticoid hormone, dexamethasone (dex), and the thyroid hormone, triiodothyronine (T_3) (Ivarie *et al.*, 1981). This induction is synergistic, i.e., the induction observed when both hormones are present is greater than the sum of inductions of each of the two hormones individually.

We are interested in the ways in which the expression of this family of genes is regulated. In particular, we would like to understand both the mechanisms which lead to tissue-specific expression of the various members of the family and the ways in which external factors modulate such expression. To this end we and our colleagues have spent the last several

197

years isolating and characterizing the genes themselves. More recently, we have begun to use these cloned DNAs as probes of the state of the genes in various tissues. We will review here some of the conclusions from the structural studies of the unique rat growth hormone gene and the surprisingly large family of genes closely related to human growth hormone, and present some more recent results on the characterization and expression of the rat growth hormone gene in several tissues and cell lines.

II. Rat Growth Hormone Gene Structure

The rat growth hormone (rGH) gene has been isolated from two different rat strains, Hooded (Page *et al.*, 1981a) and Sprague–Dawley (Chien and Thompson, 1981; Barta *et al.*, 1981), and the nucleotide sequence of both genes has been determined. Figure 1 diagrams the structure of the gene isolated from Hooded rats. Comparison of the cDNA sequence to the gene sequence shows that the gene is interrupted by four intervening sequences (introns), all of which occur within the protein coding region rather than the 5' or 3' untranslated regions of the sequence. Three of these intervening sequences lie between a series of four partially homologous internally repeated sequences originally noted in the rGH protein by Niall *et al.* (1971). This led Barta *et al.* (1981) to propose that the growth hormone gene arose by multiplication of a single coding region, or exon, to four exons, followed by insertion of a fifth nonhomologous exon between the first and second repeats. However, this scheme predicts that the repeated unit should be an entire exon rather than the small internal portion which seems to be repeated. In fact, the intervening sequences appear to be randomly located between the repeated segments.

A surprising feature was found in the second intervening sequence (intron B) of both the Hooded (Page *et al.*, 1981a) and Sprague–Dawley (Barta *et al.*, 1981) genes. A sequence of 180 nucleotides, which has been termed RU (repeat unit), is present in two nearly perfect direct repeats in the Hooded rat gene and two and a half repeats in the Sprague–Dawley gene. Additional RU sequences are present just beyond the 3' end of the rGH gene (Page *et al.*, 1981b) and several kilobases (kb) further downstream (G. S. Page, personal communication). The RU sequences in and near the gene are indicated by arrows in Fig. 1.

The RU sequences share a number of characteristics with a class of DNA sequences termed transposable elements, or transposons, DNA elements which are able to move from one place in the genome to another (see Calos and Miller, 1980, for review). Like transposons, the RU sequences are repeated sequences, present many times in the rat genome. At least the RUs in intron B are flanked by short direct repeats, an important

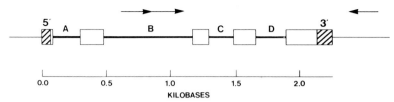

FIG. 1. Structure of the rat growth hormone gene. Boxes indicate the five rGH mRNA coding regions (exons). Untranslated regions are cross-hatched; thicker lines signify intervening sequences. Thin lines signify flanking sequences. Arrows indicate positions and relative orientations of repeated sequences termed RU within and around the rGH gene. 5' and 3' ends of the transcript are indicated.

feature of both prokaryotic and eukaryotic transposable elements. However, there is currently no direct evidence that any RU sequences can actually transpose. In fact, there is no currently good evidence that any of the potential transposable elements in vertebrate genomes can transpose.

The RUs in intron B may comprise an *in vitro* transcription unit which is independent of the rGH transcription unit. Studies by Page *et al.* (1981b) have shown that these sequences can direct the *in vitro* transcription of two RNAs of approximately 180 and 360 bases. The two RNAs are transcribed by RNA polymerase III, which transcribes the 5 S RNA and the tRNA genes both *in vivo* and *in vitro*. This enzyme is distinct from RNA polymerase II, which transcribes the messenger RNA for peptide encoding genes, presumably including the GH gene (Roeder, 1976). RU-derived RNA species of the same size as those produced *in vitro* have been identified *in vivo* by Cordell, Smith, and Goodman (in preparation). However, since there are so many nearly identical RU sequences in the rat genome it is not possible to determine whether the rGH RUs are actually transcribed *in vivo*. The function of these small RNAs, if any, is not known, but the two intron B RUs could encode two slightly different 40 amino acid peptides.

III. Analysis of the rGH Gene in Tissues and Cell Lines

The extensive structural characterization of the rGH gene described above has permitted a direct analysis of the state of the gene in various tissues and cell lines. In this regard, we have examined the state of methylation of the gene and its accessibility to digestion by DNase I in isolated nuclei. Both of these aspects of chromatin structure have been correlated with gene expression in other systems.

Ninety percent of all cytidines adjacent to guanines are methylated in a large variety of eukaryotic tissues and cell lines (see Ehrlich and Wang,

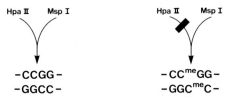

FIG. 2. Detection of methylated CG sequences with restriction enzymes. *Msp*I and *Hpa*II are isoschizomers which both recognize and cleave at the tetranucleotide sequence indicated, but only *Msp*I will cleave the 5-methyl cytosine containing derivative.

1981). However, several authors have demonstrated that such CG dinucleotides within and near a gene are not methylated in tissues in which that gene is expressed. Direct evidence that such hypomethylation may be an important facet of regulation of gene expression was provided by the finding that azacytidine, which inhibits methylation, can activate some previously silent genes (Groudine *et al.*, 1981; Compero and Palmiter, 1981). For example, metallothionein gene expression is stimulated by dex in some cells but is unresponsive to the hormone in others. Treatment of the unresponsive cells with azacytidine resulted in a stable change of a large fraction of the cells to a hormone responsive state (Compero and Palmiter, 1981).

The methylation pattern of genes can be studied by use of restriction enzymes which are sensitive to base methylation. A pair of enzymes which both cleave at the tetranucleotide recognition cite CCGG has been exploited in many previous examples (Waalwijk and Flavell, 1978). As diagrammed in Fig. 2, *Msp*I cleaves regardless of the state of methylation of the recognition site, but *Hpa*II only cleaves at the unmethylated site. The *Msp*I restriction map of the rGH gene is shown in Fig. 3.

Since dex and T_3 stimulate growth hormone expression in GH_3 cells, we compared the state of methylation of the rGH gene in GH_3 cells induced with both hormones, GH_3 cells deinduced by withdrawal of hormones for 7 days, and a liver cell line (HTC) which does not express rGH. As shown

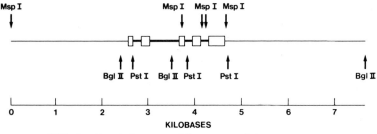

FIG. 3. Restriction map of the rat growth hormone gene.

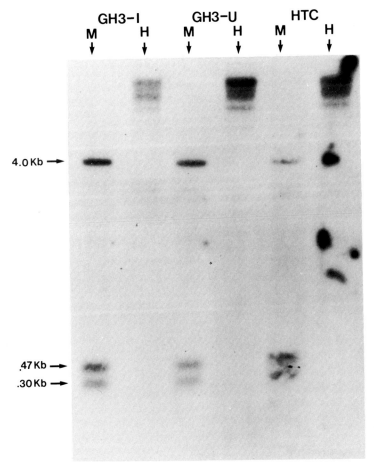

FIG. 4.   Methylation of the rGH gene cell lines. Rat genomic DNA was prepared from tissue culture cells. The DNA was restricted using either the enzyme *Msp*I or *Hpa*II. An aliquot from each digest was removed, and it was incubated together with a plasmid DNA that was known to be restricted by either enzyme. If the digest went to completion, the main digest was processed and electrophoresed on a 1.5% agarose gel transferred to nitrocellulose paper (Southern, 1975) and hybridized to a nick translated (Rigby *et al.*, 1977) cDNA probe under the conditions of Wahl *et al.* (1979). H, *Hpa*II digests; M, *Msp*I digests. GH3-I, DNA prepared from induced GH₃ cells; GH3-U, DNA prepared from uninduced GH₃ cells; HTC, DNA prepared from HTC cells.

in Fig. 4, there were no differences in the methylation pattern around the growth hormone gene in GH cells and HTC cells.

We also examined a number of rat tissues, some of which expressed growth hormone. As shown in Fig. 5, both pituitary and brain exhibit

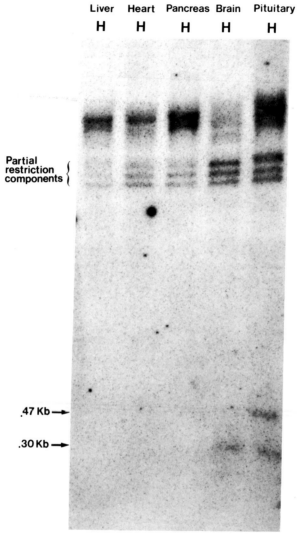

FIG. 5.   Methylation of the rGH gene in tissues. DNA prepared from the indicated tissues was digested with *Hpa*II and processed as described (see Fig. 4).

hypomethylation of the growth hormone gene, while the gene is completely methylated in liver and pancreas. The pituitary hypomethylation is particularly interesting since it shows that there are sites within the growth hormone gene which vary in level of methylation and which are detectable by the *Msp*I/*Hpa*II system. Thus, the lack of hypomethylation observed in the GH₃ cells is not simply due to the fact that the small fraction of CG sites probed by this system are not subject to changes in methylation. The hypomethylation observed in the brain was unexpected and remains unexplained.

IV. DNase I Sensitivity of the rGH Gene

Since the pioneering work of Weintraub (Weintraub and Groudine, 1976), many groups have used the enzyme DNase I as a probe of gene activity. These studies have revealed a correlation between expression of a gene and sensitivity of that gene to digestion by DNase I added to isolated nuclei. In fact, in some systems the potential for further expres-

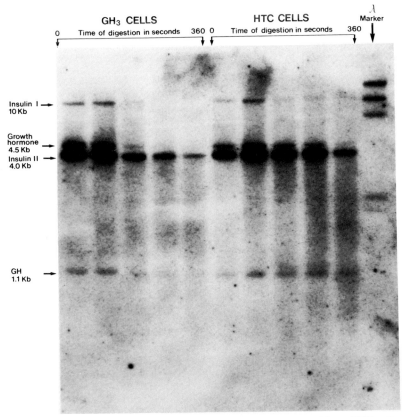

FIG. 6. DNase I sensitivity of the rGH gene. Nuclei were isolated from HTC cells and from GH₃ cells induced with dex and T₃ and treated with DNase I as described (Yamamoto *et al.*, 1981) for the times indicated. DNA was purified, digested with *Bgl*II, and blotted and probed as described (see Fig. 4) with rGH and rat insulin probes. Bands from the rGH and insulin genes are indicated.

sion is sufficient for the chromatin to remain in a DNase I sensitive conformation after gene expression is terminated (Weintraub and Groudine,
1976; Garel and Axel, 1976).

We examined DNase I sensitivity of the rGH gene in the GH₃ and HTC
cell lines. The two rat insulin genes which are not expressed in either line
served as a control. Figure 6 shows the pattern of bands after DNase I
treatment of nuclei and subsequent restriction endonuclease cutting of the
naked DNA. Densitometer tracings show that the 4.5 kb rGH BglII fragment is slightly more sensitive to digestion in the GH₃ than the HTC cells.
The insulin control 4.0 kb fragment appears relatively resistant to nuclease cutting in both cell lines. In contrast to this small difference in
sensitivity of the rGH gene, expressed or repressed proviral MMTV genes
in different HTC sublines show a much larger difference in sensitivity to
DNase I (Yamamoto et $al.$, 1981).

Thus, the rGH gene in hormonally induced GH₃ cells displays neither
the hypomethylation nor the high level of DNase I sensitivity characteristic of expressed genes in other systems. The reason for this discrepancy is
not clear. It is possible that the GH₃ system is different in some general
manner from other systems. Alternatively, the discrepancy may be
specific to the rGH gene. Such a specific effect on the rGH gene might
explain the fact that the GH₃ cells make much less rGH than the pituitary
cells. It is possible that for a pituitary cell to change from a generally
nonproliferative secretory cell to a stable cell line, the very high level of
expression of the rGH gene must be decreased. Perhaps the observed
patterns of methylation and DNase I sensitivity of the rGH gene are a
result of a specific suppression of rGH synthesis. Certainly, further studies are needed to better understand expression of the rGH gene in pituitary cells and in cell lines.

V. Gene Transfer Experiments

One way to obtain definitive mapping of regions of genes which have
regulatory functions is to reintroduce the gene or an in $vitro$ generated
variant into a live eukaryotic cell in such a way as to preserve regulated
expression of the gene. A convenient procedure for introducing DNA into
cultured cells is by exposing the cells to a DNA-CaPO₄ coprecipitate
(Graham and van der Eb, 1973). Under such conditions a small subpopulation of cells appears to take up the DNA. Use of appropriate selection
conditions enables isolation of cells transformed in this manner, as initially described by Wigler et $al.$ (1977) using the Herpes thymidine kinase
(TK) DNA and mutant mouse L cells deficient in TK. Selection for TK⁺
colonies was accomplished by culture in medium containing aminopterin,

hypoxanthine, and thymidine (HAT) (Littlefield, 1964). Aminopterin blocks *de novo* purine synthesis, forcing cells to use salvage pathways, and thus selecting for the TK$^+$ phenotype. A further significant advance made by Wigler *et al.* (1979) was the finding that exposing L TK$^-$ cells to a mixture of Herpes TK DNA and another gene and selecting for TK leads to isolation of transformed cells containing both the TK gene and the nonselected gene (see Fig. 7). Thus, this procedure provides a simple method for introducing genes for which no selective criteria are available into mammalian cells.

With a view to defining the regions of the rGH gene which are responsible for stimulation of rGH synthesis by hormones, mouse L cells were transformed by M. C. Nguyen-Huu with a mixture of TK DNA and a purified 11 kb fragment containing the entire rGH gene. The suitability of L cells for such an approach was indicated by the well-documented

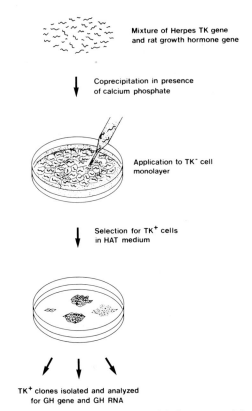

Mixture of Herpes TK gene and rat growth hormone gene

Coprecipitation in presence of calcium phosphate

Application to TK$^-$ cell monolayer

Selection for TK$^+$ cells in HAT medium

TK$^+$ clones isolated and analyzed for GH gene and GH RNA

FIG. 7. Cotransformation of TK$^-$ mouse cells with the rat growth hormone gene and the TK gene.

glucocorticoid responsiveness exhibited by these cells (Lippman and Thompson, 1974).

Following exposure of L cells to a mixture of TK DNA and the 11 kb rGH gene, TK$^+$ colonies were isolated, grown in mass culture, and DNA was prepared from each. The DNA was digested with restriction enzymes and analyzed using blotting procedures. The autoradiogram shown in Fig. 8 reveals the presence of rGH sequences as evidenced by the 0.85 and 1.1 kb hybridizing fragments characteristic of rGH (Fig. 3). The 6 kb band probably represents the mouse growth hormone gene, since it also appears in DNA from nontransformed L cells, but not in DNA from rats. From the intensity of the hybridizing 0.85 and 1.1 kb bands in the transformed cell DNA relative to the rat DNA, we estimate that the cell lines examined contain from 1 to 5 copies of the rGH gene.

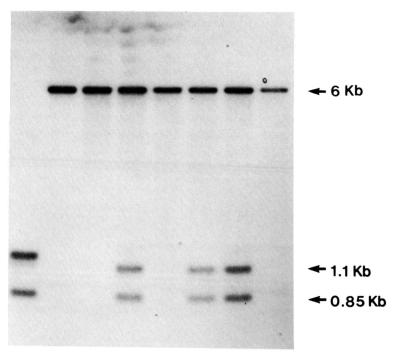

FIG. 8.   DNA blot analysis of transformed cells. DNA was prepared from transformed L cells, digested with *Pst*I, electrophoresed on a 1% agarose gel, transferred to nitrocellulose (Southern, 1975), and hybridized to a ^{32}P probe prepared by nick translation (Rigby *et al.*, 1977) rGH cDNA fragment. R, DNA from rat liver; L, DNA from untransformed LTK cells. Numbers refer to independent transformed clones.

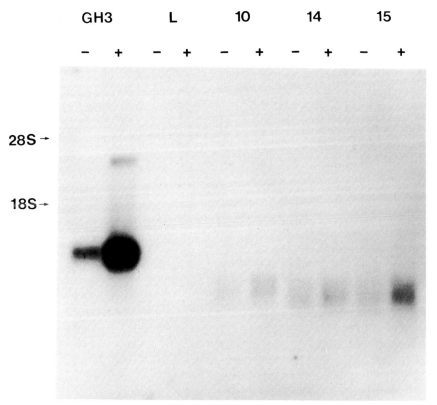

FIG. 9. RNA blot analysis of transformed cells. RNA was prepared from transformed L cells following incubation for 48 hours in the presence or absence of dexamethasone ($10^{-6} M$) and T_3 ($10^{-8} M$). mRNA was isolated by affinity chromatography on oligo(dT) cellulose (Aviv and Leder, 1972). Samples were electrophoresed on 1.5% agarose gels in the presence of 2.2 M formaldehyde, transferred to nitrocellulose (Thomas, 1980), and hybridized with nick-translated rGH cDNA. GH$_3$, rat pituitary cell line, 1 μg total RNA per slot. L, untransformed LTK$^-$ cells, 5 μg mRNA per slot. Numbers refer to independent transformed clones. +, The presence of T_3 and dex; −, absence of these.

Three of the cell lines which contained the rGH gene were selected for analysis of RNA. RNA was prepared from these cell lines following exposure for 48 hours to medium containing 10% fetal calf serum with or without dex plus T_3. Poly(A)-containing RNA was isolated and samples were analyzed by blotting procedures (Fig. 9). In the case of all the transformed clones examined, transcripts hybridizing to the probe were detected. These transcripts appeared to be rather heterogeneous in size, and were approximately 200 nucleotides shorter than the GH$_3$ cell transcript. Such transcripts were absent in nontransformed L cells. Comparison of the intensity of the hybridization signal from cells exposed to hormone treatment with untreated cells indicates that hormone treatment leads to a 2- to 4-fold increase in concentration of rGH transcripts. When total RNA from these cells was examined in a similar manner, a qualitatively similar pattern was observed (results not shown).

This stimulation is unlikely to represent a nonspecific effect of the hormone on general L cell metabolism, since it is opposite to the general inhibitory action of dex on L cell metabolism (Pratt and Aranow, 1966). As a direct test of this possibility we used α-tubulin as a model for a protein whose expression would not be expected to be increased specifically following hormone treatment. We therefore analyzed the content of α-tubulin transcripts on the same blots of the RNA prepared from the transformed cells. Both untransformed and transformed L cells showed either no change or a moderate decrease in the relative content of tubulin RNA after hormone treatment (results not shown).

It is currently believed that steroid hormones exert their actions on gene expression mainly by influencing the rate of mRNA transcription (McKnight and Palmiter, 1979; Swaneck et al., 1979). The mechanism whereby these effects are mediated remains obscure. One plausible explanation is that the nuclear steroid receptor complex binds at specific sites at or near the regulated gene, leading to a conformational change in chromatin structure which in turn leads to an increased rate of gene transcription. Direct evidence for this hypothesis has been very difficult to obtain. Recently, however, Payvar et al. (1981) have demonstrated specific binding of purified glucocorticoid receptor to a cloned DNA fragment of the glucocorticoid responsive mouse mammary tumor virus (MMTV) genome.

An essential complement to such in vitro studies are experiments demonstrating that DNA fragments believed to contain a steroid receptor binding site do indeed show hormone regulated expression when introduced into cultured cells. Such regulated expression has been reported for the mouse mammary tumor virus (Buetti and Diggelman, 1981; Hynes et al., 1981) and the $\alpha_{2\mu}$-globulin gene (Kurtz, 1981). In both cases insertion of sequences into recipient L cells was accomplished by cotransformation with the TK gene. Our finding of hormone-regulated expression of rGH RNA suggests that this approach may be applicable to a wide variety of hormone-regulatable genes. Furthermore, these results imply that the DNA element responsible for hormonal regulation resides on the 11 kb fragment used in the initial transformation and hence in relatively close proximity to the rGH gene.

There are a number of approaches for localizing such elements. A simple method would involve in vitro mutagenesis of the gene followed by analysis of loss of hormone responsiveness. More elegantly, one could construct hybrid genes containing the putative regulatory element joined to the structural sequences of a constitutively expressed gene. If such hybrids exhibited hormonal responsiveness, this would permit a direct dissection of such regulatory elements.

VI. Human Growth Hormone

Two groups have used mRNA populations prepared from human pituitary tumors to clone cDNA copies of the human growth hormone (hGH) mRNA (Martial *et al.*, 1979; Roskam and Rougeon, 1979). In addition to their use as scientific tools, such clones have already had practical, clinical use. Derivatives of the original clones led to the first example of efficient synthesis of an authentic mammalian polypeptide by bacteria (Goeddel *et al.*, 1979). Such bacterially produced hGH is already being tested for biological potency and safety in human patients. Since there is a shortage of hGH for children with various pituitary deficiencies, this is a particularly good example of the enormous potentials of the techniques of recombinant DNA to solve clinical as well as scientific problems.

There are several hGH-related genes in the human genome, in contrast to the rat genome, which contains only a single rGH gene. This was first suggested by restriction analysis of human genomic DNA using an hGH cDNA probe (Fiddes *et al.*, 1978). In order to study these sequences directly, we isolated several hGH-related sequences from two different libraries of human DNA. Six fragments hybridizing to an hGH cDNA probe were obtained from a library constructed from DNA purified from a single placenta. Initial characterization of two of these clones has been described (Fiddes *et al.*, 1978). The five different restriction maps obtained for these cloned fragments are shown in Fig. 10.

Screening of a complete library of larger fragments of DNA prepared from human fetal liver from a different individual (Lawn *et al.*, 1978) yielded four more clones containing six different segments hybridizing to the hGH cDNA probe. The restriction maps of these clones are shown in Fig. 11. Comparison of restriction maps of the sequences cloned from the two libraries suggests that several of the sequences isolated from the placental library are present in the liver library.

Thus, at least seven different fragments containing sequences which hybridize to hGH have been isolated from the genomes of two different individuals. It is possible that some of the members of this set could simply be different alleles of single genes. However, the extensive differences seen in the sequences flanking the members of the set isolated from fetal liver DNA show that this cannot substantially lower the number of

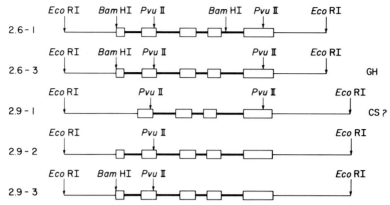

FIG. 10. Restriction maps of *Eco* RI fragments containing hGH-related sequences. Restriction sites differentiating five cloned *Eco* RI fragments containing sequences related to hGH are shown. Boxes signify sequences present in hGH or hCS mRNA (exons), thick lines signify intervening sequences (introns). The positions of the coding regions and intervening sequences have been determined completely for the 2.6–3 fragment and partially for all others except 2.9–2, in which case they are placed by analogy to 2.6–3. 2.6–3 encodes hGH, and 2.6–1 encodes an extremely closely related peptide. 2.9–1 encodes most of the hCS mRNA but is missing the first exon, as indicated. 2.9–3 encodes a hybrid gene in which the first exon is GH-like and the second, third, and fourth are hCS-like.

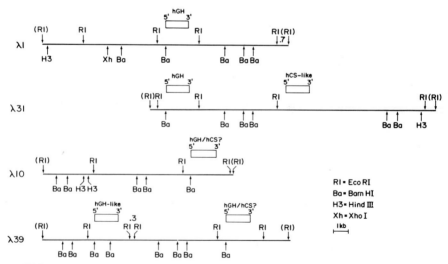

FIG. 11. Restriction maps of cloned genomic segments carrying hGH-related sequences. Restrictions sites in four human genomic clones are shown. The human DNA segments cloned in λ1 and λ31 overlap partially as indicated. Boxes denote hGH-related segments. Both λ1 and λ31 contain the hGH gene, which is identical to the gene on the 2.6–3 fragment. λ31 also contains a 9.3 kb *Eco* RI fragment which is hCS-like. λ39 contains an hGH-like gene similar or identical to the gene encoded by the 2.6–1 fragment and a fragment which is similar to the 2.9–3 fragment which encodes the GH/CS hybrid gene. λ10 also contains a fragment similar to 2.9–3.

genes represented by these fragments. Comparisons of the restriction maps of the cloned fragments with restriction maps of genomic DNA suggest that the set of cloned genes is nearly a complete representation of the total set of hGH-related sequences. Thus, we estimate that the haploid human genome contains approximately seven different sequences very closely related to hGH.

This set of sequences is only known to encode two proteins: growth hormone and the very closely related placental hormone, chorionic somatomammotropin (hCS, also termed placental lactogen). The sequences of the hGH and hCS cDNAs are 92% homologous in the protein coding region (Goodman *et al.*, 1980) although the proteins themselves are only 85% homologous (Niall *et al.*, 1971). This level of homology is easily high enough to lead to nearly complete cross-hybridization of these two sequences under the conditions used. Thus, this set of sequences should include the genes encoding both hGH and hCS.

Comparison of restriction maps of the cloned genes and cDNAs first led to the suggestion that the 2.6 kb *Eco*RI fragments contained hGH-like genes and the 2.9 kb fragments contained hCS-like genes (Fiddes *et al.*, 1978). This original prediction has been confirmed and extended by quantitative hybridization experiments and complete or partial DNA sequence determinations. In particular, the 2.6–3 fragment contains the authentic hGH gene, as demonstrated by the complete match of the sequences of the cDNA and the gene (De Noto *et al.*, 1981). Partial sequence information shows that the 2.9–1 fragment contains sequences which could encode nearly all of the hCS protein, but is missing the first amino acids of the signal peptide (D. D. Moore and M. A. Conkling, unpublished).

The structure of the hGH gene is diagrammed in Fig. 12. The hGH gene, like the rGH gene, is interrupted by four intervening sequences. Comparison of the sequences of the two genes showed that the intervening sequences are located in the same positions in the two genes. This corrobo-

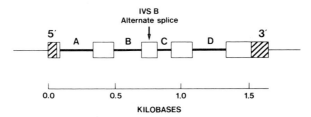

FIG. 12. Structure of the human growth hormone gene. Boxes indicate the five hGH mRNA coding regions (exons); untranslated segments are cross-hatched. Thicker lines signify intervening sequences (introns). Thinner lines signify flanking regions. B denotes the position of an alternative 3′ end for intron B. 5′ and 3′ ends of the transcript are indicated.

rates the assumption that these two genes arose from a single common ancestor, since the positions of intervening sequences are generally invariant even over the longest evolutionary separations which have been examined. For example, α- and β-globin genes, which have been separated for approximately 500 million years, have two intervening sequences located in homologous positions (Efstradiatis et al., 1980).

The intervening sequences themselves are not subject to stringent sequence conservation, however. A striking example of this variability is provided by the fact that intron B in the hGH gene does not contain repeated sequences such as are found within intron B of the rGH gene. If a function exists for these interesting inhabitants of the genome, it clearly is not required for the expression of the growth hormone genes.

Recent experiments with other eukaryotic genes have suggested that at least some essential elements involved in the various levels of transcriptional control of gene expression are located just before the transcriptional start site (see, for example, Hentschel and Birnstiel, 1981; Myers et al., 1981; McKnight et al., 1981). Any such control signals would be expected to be strongly conserved. A detailed comparison of various portions of the sequences of the rat and human growth hormone genes should highlight functionally important conserved sequences. Figure 13 shows such a comparison of the sequences 250 nucleotides upstream from the first intervening sequence. It can be seen that there are two regions of especially strong homology in this region. One of them, from position -34 to -19 relative to the start of transcription, is in a previously identified conserved

```
Human GH   -210 AACCCTCACA ACACTGGTTG ACGGTGGGAA GGGAAAGATG ACAAGCCAGG GGCATGATCC
                    *              *    * *   *         ** * *       *      **  *  **
Rat GH     -210 TGGCAAAGGC GGCGGTGGAA AGGTAAGATC AGGGACGTCA CCGCAGGAGA GCAGTGGGGA

           -150 CAGCATGTGT GGGAGGAGCT TCTAAATTAT CCATTAGCAC AAGCCCGTCA GTGGCC::::
                    *  ****** ********** ********** **** ***** ****   **** *****
           -150 CGCGATGTGT GGGAGGAGCT TCTAAATTAT CCATCAGCAC AAGCT:GTCA GTGGCTCCAG

            -90 CCATGCATAA ATGTACACAG AAACAGGTGG GGGC:AACAG TGGGAGAGAA GGGGCCAGGG
                   ***** **** ***** *    * *** *** * * **      *     *** **    * ****
            -90 CCATGAATAA ATGTATAGGG AAAAAGGCAG GAGCCTTGGG GTCGAGGAAA ACAGGTAGGG
                                                     1
            -30 TATAAAAAGG GCCCACAAGA GACCGGCTCA AGGATCCCAA GGCCCAACTC CCCGAACCAG
                   ********** **  ****  ****  **  ** * **     ***** *   ** *** *
            -30 TATAAAAAGG GCATGCAAGG GACCAAATCC AGCACCCTCG AGCCCAGATT :CCAAACTAC

             31 TCAGGGTCCT GTGGAC:GCT CACCTAGCTG CAATGGCTAG AG
                   ***** **** ****** * * *** ** * * ****** **
             31 TCAGG:TCCT GTGGACAGAT CACTGAGTGG CGATGGCTGC AG
```

FIG. 13. Comparison of the DNA sequences flanking the 5' ends of the rGH and hGH genes. Homologous nucleotides are indicated by asterisks. Gaps introduced to maximize homology are indicated by colons. The start site for transcription of each gene is nucleotide 1. The first exon of each gene is denoted by boldface print. The conserved "TATA" or Goldberg–Hogness box upstream of the 5' end of each gene is underlined in both sequences.

region very close to the transcriptional start site (Goldberg, 1979; Benoist *et al.*, 1980). This segment contains the so-called TATA or Goldberg–Hogness box which is required for transcription of eukaryotic genes by RNA polymerase II, at least *in vitro* (Wasylyk *et al.*, 1980). The other segment from −154 to −193 further upstream from the transcription start is in a region which is not generally conserved in other eukaryotic genes. This segment is thus a candidate for a growth hormone-specific control signal.

VII. Alternative Patterns for Removal of Intervening Sequences from the hGH Nuclear RNA Precursor

If any of the other sequences related to hGH and hCS encoded proteins which were expressed at high level, amino acid sequence variations in preparations of hGH or hCS could have been detected. The only such variant clearly documented to date is a smaller, 20,000 (20K) molecular weight hGH peptide present in normal pituitaries at up to 20% of the level of the major 22K peptide. However, we have shown that this smaller peptide probably results from an alternative pattern of removal of one of the intervening sequences from the nuclear precursor to the hGH messenger RNA (De Noto *et al.*, 1981).

The 20K variant differs from the major 22K polypeptide by an internal deletion of 15 amino acids (Lewis *et al.*, 1980), which begins precisely at the position of intron B. Furthermore, the sequence 45 nucleotides beyond the 3' end of intron B corresponds very well with consensus sequences for 3' or acceptor sites for removal of intervening sequences (Seif *et al.*, 1979; Lerner *et al.*, 1980; Rodgers and Wall, 1980). It seemed possible, therefore, that the 45 nucleotides past the normal 3' end of intron B could be removed from the RNA along with the rest of intron B by splicing at this alternative site, resulting in the deletion of 15 amino acids. This hypothesis was testable since it predicted that the mRNA for the 20K hGH mRNA would be identical to the 22K mRNA except for this simple 45 nucleotide deletion.

This prediction was borne out by the experiment diagrammed in Fig. 14. An end-labeled fragment containing about one-half the 22K hGH cDNA sequence was prepared. This cDNA fragment was denatured and mixed with total pituitary mRNA under conditions in which RNA–DNA but not DNA–DNA duplexes are stable (Kaback *et al.*, 1979). The resulting hybrids were then treated with nuclease S1, which digests single-stranded DNA but does not digest double-stranded DNA or RNA–DNA duplexes (Weaver and Weissman, 1979). The 45 nucleotides present in the 22K cDNA but deleted in the 20K mRNA would form a single-stranded loop in

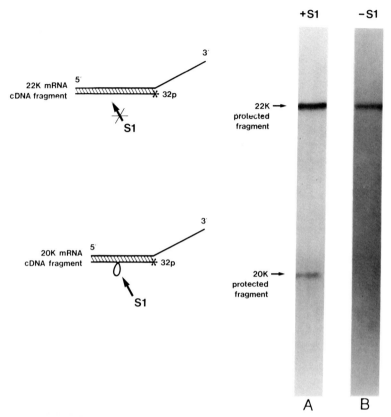

FIG. 14.   Mapping the hGH messenger RNA species with nuclease S1. Hybrids between restriction fragments from hGH cDNA at the 5' end and messenger RNA for the major 22K hGH or the minor 20K hGH are diagrammed. The entire cDNA fragment is protected from cleavage with the single-strand-specific nuclease S1 by the 22K mRNA. The 20K mRNA hybrid has a 45 nucleotide single strand loop which is cleaved by S1. In each case arrows point to the resulting protected fragments in lane A, which were resolved by electrophoresis through acrylamide gels. Lane B shows the labeled cDNA fragment not treated with S1 and resolved on the same gel.

such a hybrid which would be subject to clevage by the nuclease. However, any other differences between 22K cDNA and the 20K mRNA should also generate sites sensitive to S1 cleavage. Thus, a fragment resistant to S1 cleavage extending from the end-label to the deleted 45 nucleotides would be observed only if the 20K mRNA was otherwise identical to the 22K mRNA in this region. As shown in Fig. 14, such a fragment was, in fact, observed. Since all the other hGH-related genes examined contain at least a few changes from hGH in this region, we concluded that the 20K peptide arises by alternate splicing of the hGH nuclear RNA precursor rather than by expression of a different hGH-related gene.

VIII. An hGH/hCS Hybrid Gene

All of the hGH-related genes form quite stable hybrids with radioactive probes prepared from both hGH and hCS cDNA. However, more quantitative analysis of melting temperatures using the two probes separates the group into three classes (D. D. Moore, unpublished). Both the 2.6–3 fragment and the 2.6–1 *Eco*RI fragments (see Fig. 10) form hybrids with the hGH cDNA probe which have melting temperatures approximately two degrees higher than hybrids of those fragments with a similar hCS cDNA probe. Conversely, both the 2.9–1 *Eco*RI fragment and the 9.3 kb *Eco*RI fragment from λ31 (see Fig. 11) form more stable hybrids with the hCS probe. The 2.9–2 and 2.9–3 *Eco*RI fragments (Fig. 10) appear intermediate by this criterion, i.e., they hybridize approximately equally well to both probes. Thus, hybridization analysis shows that of the six genes examined, two are most like hGH, two are most like hCS, and two seem to be intermediate between hCS and hGH.

Of the two hGH-like fragments, 2.6–3 contains the hGH gene and 2.6–1 contains sequences nearly identical to hGH (R. A. Hallewell, personal communication). In fact, Hamer and co-workers (personal communication) have shown that the 2.6–1 fragment encodes a peptide which cross-reacts strongly with authentic hGH in radioreceptor assays. There is currently no evidence that such a peptide is expressed in pituitaries. However, it seems possible that it could be expressed only at restricted developmental stages, or at low levels in some tissue other than the pituitary. Alternatively, it could be a pseudogene (a nonexpressable analog of an expressed gene).

The two hCS-like fragments may present a similar situation. The 2.9–1 fragment, as noted above, contains sequences which could encode most of hCS, although it does not contain the amino terminal exon. Differences between the restriction maps of the hCS cDNA and the 9.3 kb *Eco*RI fragment from λ31 show that this larger fragment could not encode hCS. However, these changes do not rule out the possibility that this fragment could encode an hCS-like protein analogous to the potential hGH-like protein encoded by the 2.6–1 fragment.

The two apparently intermediate genes are interesting from an evolutionary standpoint. They could either have large blocks of homology with hGH and hCS, suggesting evolution by large scale recombinational processes such as exon shuffling as described by Gilbert (1978), or they could have multiple smaller interspersed segments, suggesting evolution by smaller scale processes such as the accumulation of point mutations. As diagrammed in Fig. 15, nucleotide sequence analysis shows that the former is the case for the 2.9–3 fragment. This fragment encodes a hybrid gene in which the first exon is hGH-like and the next two are identical to hCS. (Further sequence results show that the fourth exon is also hCS-like.)

The first GH-like exon encodes the 5' untranslated region of the hGH mRNA plus the first three and one-third codons of the signal peptide. Since the signal peptide is cleaved as part of the process of secretion, the protein encoded by the 2.9–3 gene should be identical to hCS for at least the first 126 amino acids. It might be expected that the hGH-like potential controlling sequences which flank the gene at least on the 5' side could direct pituitary cells to synthesize this protein under the normal program of hGH control. However, no evidence is available for expression of such an hCS-like product in pituitary cells.

There is enormous potential for exchange of sequences by various types of recombination events between members of any highly homologous multigene family. The hybrid nature of the 2.9–3 gene is direct proof that such processes are acting on the hGH family. Furthermore, the fact that the sequences of the second and third exons of the 2.9–3 gene are identical to hCS means that this hybrid gene has undergone an exchange of information so recently that the sequences have not even begun to diverge. The hGH family, therefore, is likely to be plastic with regard to both the number and sequence organization of the genes.

This predicts that there should be changes in gene number and sequence organization in the GH gene families of our close primate relatives. Preliminary analysis of the growth hormone gene families of the great apes confirms this prediction. Our closest relatives, chimpanzees and gorillas, are very similar to humans, but orangutangs and gibbons, which are only slightly more distantly related to humans, have fewer growth hormone-

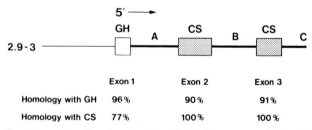

FIG. 15.   Structure of the 5' end of the GH/CS hybrid gene encoded on the 2.9–3 fragment. Boxes indicate sequences homologous with hGH or hCS mRNA. Percentage homology of each potential exon with the corresponding segment of the hGH and hCS cDNA is given. As indicated, the first exon is hGH-like and the second and third are identical to hCS.

like genes (D. D. Moore and Barbara Chapman, unpublished observations).

The plasticity of the hGH family might also be manifested by genetic abnormalities affecting synthesis of hGH or hCS. It is clear that there are several types of genetically determined dwarfism (see for example Rimoin *et al.*, 1968). The nature of the genetic lesion in such patients is not known, although there are preliminary reports that at least one deletion of the hGH gene has been detected.

IX. Evolution of a Gene Family: The CS Paradox

It is striking that the hCS gene is detected by an hGH probe, even under stringent conditions, but the putative rCS gene(s) is not detected by an rGH probe under any conditions. In fact, the two growth hormone genes are more different from each other than are the genes encoding the different two human hormones. It is possible to estimate the time elapsed since these genes have diverged using empirically determined values for the amount of time necessary to accumulate given numbers of sequence changes. Such calculations suggest that the rGH and hGH genes diverged about 85 million years ago (MYA) (Martial and Cooke, 1980). This is in very good agreement with the estimated time for the divergence of rodents and primates approximately 80 MYA (Romero-Herrera *et al.*, 1973). Similar comparisons indicate that the hGH and hCS genes diverged only 56 MYA. This figure may even be an overestimate, because these two different hormones should be acted on by slightly different selections, and would thus be expected to accumulate changes relatively rapidly after their divergence.

This estimate places the divergence of hGH and hCS well after the origin of placental mammals at about 100 MYA (Dickerson and Geis, 1980). Thus, the evolution of CS in rodents and primates is paradoxical in two ways. First, because the two products differ so greatly in their homology to the growth hormone of the same species, and second, because the human gene for this major placental protein seems to have arisen well after the origin of placental mammals.

Since the sequence of rat CS is not known, very little can be said about its origin and evolution. The greater divergence from rGH is consistent with an origin by a relatively ancient duplication of the growth hormone precursor. Alternatively, rCS could have arisen by duplication of another related gene, such as that encoding prolactin. This has been proposed for the generation of the sheep CS gene, based on structural similarities between sheep CS and prolactin (Hurley *et al.*, 1977). These two pathways are diagrammed in Fig. 16.

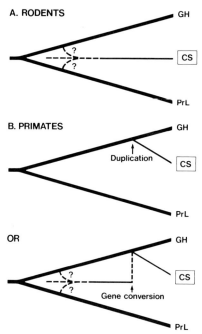

FIG. 16. Different pathways for evolution of CS in rodents and primates. Hypothetical evolutionary trees are shown for development of rat and human growth hormone (GH), chorionic somatomammotropin (CS), and prolactin (PrL). GH and PrL diverged approximately 400 million years ago (MYA). rCS could have evolved by duplication of the precursor of rGH or rPrL sometime greater than 56 MYA. hCS arose approximately 56 MYA after either duplication of the GH precursor or gene conversion of a preexisting CS precursor by GH sequences.

The greater amount of information allows somewhat more definite hypotheses regarding the generation of hCS. Two basically different models are diagrammed in Fig. 16. First, hCS could have arisen by duplication of the GH precursor at some relatively recent time, after the divergence of rodents and primates. In this case the difference between the rat and human CS genes would be a reflection of their independent generation. This would be an example of convergent evolution at the molecular level. Second, the hCS gene could have arisen from a much more ancient precursor which was changed to the current GH-like sequence by a simple recombination event, or a more complex gene conversion-type event. Gene conversion, which is similar to two independent, closely spaced recombination events, but is nonreciprocal, is diagrammed in Fig. 17.

It is not presently possible to choose between these two hypotheses. The first mechanism is perhaps less appealing since it demands that CS function be generated by independent events in the several mammalian

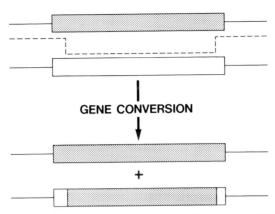

FIG. 17.   Gene conversion. A given conversion event between two partially homologous genes, denoted by boxes, is diagrammed. Dotted lines indicate the positions of crossovers between the two genes. Note that the products of the gene conversion event are not reciprocal as would have been the case for two independent homologous recombination events.

lines, apparently after the origin of the first placental mammal. However, it could be corroborated if the characterization of the rat or other nonprimate CS genes revealed strong homology to prolactin, as is already suspected for ovine CS (Hurley *et al.*, 1977). Alternatively, if the CS genes of primate species such as lemurs, which are separated from humans by 50 million years or more, were demonstrated to be much more divergent from the GH gene of the same species like the rCS and rGH genes, then the second mechanism would be corroborated. Clearly, an extensive characterization of CS genes will be necessary to resolve this question.

X. Summary

The rat and human growth hormone genes have been isolated and their nucleotide sequences have been determined. The rGH gene is unique in the haploid rat genome, but there are approximately seven hGH related genes in the haploid human genome. Only two protein products, hGH and hCS, are known to be encoded by these multiple human genes. Perhaps surprisingly in the face of such potential diversity the hGH gene gives rise to two different protein products, the 22K major hGH polypeptide and the smaller 20K minor hGH, by two alternative splicing pathways for removal of one of the four intervening sequences present in the nuclear messenger RNA precursor.

The rGH gene has been examined in various functional states. In both the pituitary and the brain, the gene shows a lowered level of methylated cytosine residues, a state which has been correlated with active transcription in other gene systems. However, the gene is highly methylated in the GH_3 rat pituitary cell line which makes and secretes significant amounts of rGH.

The rGH gene and several kb of flanking DNA sequences have been introduced into a mouse cell line. Synthesis of rGH RNA is detectable in three different rGH-containing clones, and in all of them the level of rGH RNA is increased by the addition of dexamethasone plus triiodothyronine. This indicates that at least some of the signals which cause the gene to respond to hormones are very close to the gene itself.

Nucleic acid hybridization analysis shows that the hCS gene is very homologous to the hGH gene, but the putative rCS gene is not strongly homologous to the rGH gene. Two different hypotheses for the evolutionary origin of the hCS gene have been offered to explain this paradox. According to the first, the hCS gene arose by duplication of the hGH precursor after rodents and primates diverged. Alternatively, a more ancient hCS precursor could have been changed to the observed hGH-like sequence by a recent recombination or gene conversion event involving the hGH precursor.

ACKNOWLEDGMENTS

We would like to thank M. C. Nguyen-Huu for providing transformed L cell lines, D. Cleveland for the α-tubulin probe, R. A. Hallewell for unpublished sequence information, and S. Bock for preparation of this manuscript. MDW is the recipient of a fellowship from the Anna Fuller Fund. MAC is the recipient of a fellowship from the Helen Hay Whitney Foundation. HMG was an investigator of the Howard Hughes Medical Institute. This work was supported by grant CA14206 from NIH.

REFERENCES

Aviv, H., and Leder, P. (1972). *Proc. Natl. Acad. Sci. U.S.A.* **69**, 1408.

Barta, A., Richards, R. I., Baxter, J. D., and Shine, J. (1981). *Proc. Natl. Acad. Sci. U.S.A.* **78**, 4867.

Benoist, C., O'Hare, K., and Chambon, P. (1980). *Nucleic Acids Res.* **8**, 127.

Buetti, E., and Diggelman, H. (1981). *Cell* **23**, 335.

Calos, M. P., and Miller, J. H. (1980). *Cell* **20**, 579.

Chien, Y. H., and Thompson, E. B. (1981). *Proc. Natl. Acad. Sci. U.S.A.* **77**, 4583.

Compero, S. J., and Palmiter, R. D. (1981). *Cell* **25**, 233.

Daughaday, W. H., Harrington, A. C., and Phillips, L. S. (1975). *Annu. Rev. Physiol.* **35**, 211.

De Noto, F., Moore, D. D., and Goodman, H. M. (1981). *Nucleic Acids Res.* **9**, 3719.

Dickerson, R. E., and Geis, I. (1980). "Proteins: Structure, Function and Evolution." Cummings, Menlo Park, California, in press.

Efstradiatis, A., Posakony, J. W., Maniatis, T., Lawn, R. M., O'Connell, C., Spritz, R. A., DeRiel, J. K., Forget, B. G., Weissman, S., Slightom, J. L., Blechl, A. E., Smithies, O., Baralle, F. E., Shoulders, C. C., and Proudfoot, N. J. (1980). *Cell* **21**, 653.

Erlich, M., and Wang, R. Y. H. (1981). *Science* **212**, 1350.

Fiddes, J. C., Seeburg, P. H., DeNoto, F. M., Hallewell, R. A., Baxter, J. D., and Goodman, H. M. (1978). *Proc. Natl. Acad. Sci. U.S.A.* **76**, 4294.

Garel, A., and Axel, R. (1976). *Proc. Natl. Acad. Sci. U.S.A.* **73**, 3966.

Gilbert, W. (1978). *Nature (London)* **271**, 501.

Goeddel, D. V., Heyneker, H. L., Hozumi, T., Arntzen, R., Itakura, R., Jansura, D. G., Ross, M. J., Miozani, G., Crea, R., and Seeburg, P. H. (1979). *Nature (London)* **281**, 544.

Goldberg, M. (1979). Ph.D. Thesis, Stanford University.

Goodman, H. M., DeNoto, F., Fiddes, J. C., Hallewell, R. A., Page, G. S., Smith, S., and Tischer, E. (1980). *Miami Winter Symp.* **17**, 155.

Graham, F. L., and van der Eb, A. J. (1973). *Virology* **52**, 456.

Groudine, W., Eisenman, R., and Weintraub, H. (1981). *Nature (London)* **292**, 311.

Hentschel, C. C., and Birnstiel, M. L. (1981). *Cell* **25**, 301.

Hurley, T., Handwerger, S., and Fellows, R. E. (1977). *Biochemistry* **16**, 5598.

Hynes, N. E., Kennedy, N., Rahmsdorf, V., and Groney, B. (1981). *Proc. Natl. Acad. Sci. U.S.A.* **78**, 2038.

Ivarie, R. D., Baxer, J. D., and Morris, J. A. (1981). *J. Biol. Chem.* **256**, 4520.

Kaback, D. B., Angerer, L. M., and Davidson, N. (1979). *Nucleic Acids Res.* **66**, 2499.

Kuo, M. T., Mandel, J. L., and Chambon, P. (1979). *Nucleic Acids Res.* **9**, 2105.

Kurtz, D. T. (1981). *Nature (London)* **291**, 629.

Lawn, R. M. Fritsch, E. F., Parker, R. C., Blake, G., and Maniatis, T. (1978). *Cell* **15**, 1157.

Lerner, M., Boyle, J., Mount, S., Wolin, S., and Steitz, J. (1980). *Nature (London)* **283**, 220.

Lewis, V. J., Bonewald, I. F., and Lewis, L. J. (1980). *Biochem. Biophys. Res. Commun.* **92**, 511.

Lippman, M. E., and Thompson, E. B. (1974). *J. Biol. Chem.* **249**, 2483.

Littlefield, J. W. (1964). *Science* **145**, 709.

McKnight, G. S., and Palmiter, R. D. (1979). *J. Biol. Chem.* **254**, 9050.

McKnight, S. L., Gavis, E. R., Kingsbury, R., and Axel, R. (1981). *Cell* **25**, 385.

Martial, J. A., and Cooke, N. E. (1980). *In* "Central and Peripheral Regulation of Prolactin Function" (R. M. MacLeod and V. Scapagini, eds.), p. 115. Raven, New York.

Martial, J. A., Hallewell, R. A., Baxter, J. D., and Goodman, H. M. (1979). *Science* **205**, 602.

Myers, R. M., Rio, D. C., Robbins, A. K., and Tjian, R. (1981). *Cell* **25**, 373.

Niall, H. D., Hogan, M. L., Sauer, R., Rosenblum, I. Y., and Greenwood, F. C. (1971). *Proc. Natl. Acad. Sci. U.S.A.* **68**, 866.

Page, G. S., Smith, S., and Goodman, H. M. (1981a). *Nucleic Acids Res.* **9**, 2087.

Page, G. S., Salvato, M., and Goodman, H. M. (1981b). In preparation.

Payvar, F., Wrange, O., Carlstedt-Duke, J., Okret, S., Gustaffson, J-A., and Yamamoto, K. R. (1981). *Proc. Natl. Acad. Sci. U.S.A.* **78**, 6628.

Phillips, J. A., Hjelle, B. L., Seeburg, P. H., Plotnick, L. P., Migeon, C. J., and Zachman, M. (1981). Abstract, American Society of Human Genetics.

Pratt, W. B., and Aranow, L. (1966). *J. Biol. Chem.* **241**, 5244.

Rigby, P. W. J., Dieckmann, M., Rhodes, C., and Berg, P. (1977). *J. Mol. Biol.* **113**, 237.

Rimoin, D. L., Merimee, T. J., Rabinowitz, D., and McKusick, V. A. (1968). *Recent Prog. Horm. Res.* **24**, 365.

Rodgers, J., and Wall, R. (1980). *Proc. Natl. Acad. Sci. U.S.A.* **77**, 1877.

Roeder, R. G. (1976). *In* "RNA Polymerase" (R. Losick and M. Chamberlin, eds.), p. 285. Cold Spring Harbor Lab., Cold Spring Harbor, New York.

Romero-Herrera, A. E., Lehman, H., Joysey, K. A., and Friday, A. E. (1973). *Nature (London)* **246**, 389.

Roskam, W. G., and Rougeon, F. (1979). *Nucleic Acids Res.* **7**, 305.

Seif, J. D., Khoury, G., and Dhar, R. (1979). *Nucleic Acids Res.* **6**, 3387.
Southern, E. M. (1975). *J. Mol. Biol.* **98**, 503.
Swaneck, G. E., Nordstrom, J. L., Kreuzaler, F., Tsai, M.-J., and O'Malley, B. W. (1979). *Proc. Natl. Acad. Sci. U.S.A.* **76**, 1049.
Thomas, P. (1980). *Proc. Natl. Acad. Sci. U.S.A.* **77**, 5201.
Waalwijk, C., and Flavell, R. A. (1978). *Nucleic Acids Res.* **9**, 3231.
Wahl, G. M., Stern, M., and Stark, G. R. (1979). *Proc. Natl. Acad. Sci. U.S.A.* **76**, 3683.
Wasylyk, B., Derbyshire, R., Guy, A., Molko, D., Roget, A., Teoule, R., and Chambon, P. (1980). *Proc. Natl. Acad. Sci. U.S.A.* **77**, 7024.
Weaver, R. F., and Weissman, C. (1979). *Nucleic Acids Res.* **7**, 1145.
Weintraub, H., and Groudine, M. (1976). *Science* **93**, 848.
Weintraub, H., Larsen, A., and Groudine, M. (1981). *Cell* **24**, 333.
Wigler, M., Silverstein, S., Lee, L.-S., Pellicer, A., Cheng, Y.-C., and Axel, R. (1977). *Cell* **11**, 223.
Wigler, M., Sweet, R., Sim, G. K., Wold, B., Pellicer, A., Lacy, E., Maniatis, T., Silverstein, S., and Axel, R. (1979). *Cell* **16**, 777.
Yamamoto, K. R., Chandler, V. L., Ross, S. R., Ucker, D. S., Ring, J. C., and Feinstein, S. C. (1981). *Cold Srping Harbor Symp. Quant. Biol.* **45**, 687.

DISCUSSION

C. S. Nicoll: If the rat or another mammalian species had multiple growth hormone genes but only one was expressed, would your technology allow you to detect the repressed genes?

D. Moore: Absolutely. For example, if two such genes were as similar as the two genes encoding human growth hormone and human chorionic somatomammatropin, that would have been picked up right away. If there was an analogous cryptic rat growth hormone gene, it should have been found by the hybridization conditions that were used. I don't think you could pick the rat growth hormone gene with the human probe but, for example, the human growth hormone probe is able to detect genes in species as far apart as humans and orangs and so I think that these technologies allow you to pick a reasonably divergent gene and should, in fact, have been able to tell us if there was more than one rat growth hormone gene or cryptic gene.

H. H. Samuels: Does the rat hormone probe react with mouse growth hormone mRNA?

D. Moore: Yes it does, at least if one tries to count the number of genes that have been introduced into the L cells using the rat growth hormone probe one finds pretty reasonaly hybridization with a mouse growth hormone gene.

H. H. Samuels: The question I am getting to is that you may be introducing not only the growth hormone gene but some regulatory components which allows the mouse growth hormone gene to be expressed. Do you know whether what you have identified represents rat growth hormone sequences or is it mouse growth hormone sequences?

D. Moore: As I was saying this is all rather preliminary. We hope to characterize the L cell message more to figure out why it is smaller, for example. However, one possibility is that it is from the mouse growth hormone gene, although this would not exactly be my first guess. Not all of the cell lines containing reintroduced rat growth hormone DNA make RNA that hybridizes to growth hormone and of course the parental L cells don't. But you are perfectly right that it could be a result of the introduction of some sort of regulatory sites. If you introduce large number of copies of the β-galactosidase regulatory region into *E. coli* that turns on the chromosomal β-galactosidase genes.

J. E. Rall: These CpG results are interesting and unexpected. Have you looked, with those two different restriction enzymes, at a clone of one of the growth hormone genes which has maybe 1000 nucleotides upstream of where you start initiation, because presumably the methyl C would probably act somewhere in the promoter region rather than in the gene itself.

D. Moore: You are right. The $MspI/HpaII$ system cannot detect all of the methylation sites and in fact could miss potential points of regulation. The only probe that we have used so far is the rat growth hormone cDNA. It is possible that sites upstream could be totally unmethylated and we would not know that at all. I should say, however, that the DNA prepared from pituitaries does show under methylation of the growth hormone gene in this assay using this probe, and surprisingly enough there is actually some under methylation in brain DNA as well.

H. G. Friesen: In the rat, there are two forms of placental lactogen secreted. In the first phase day 10–13 of gestation the principal form has a larger molecular weight $\simeq$60,000. In the later period of gestation from perhaps day 14 onward, the smaller molecular weight form $\simeq$20,000 is the major species. Only the smaller molecular weight form cross-reacts with antibodies to ovine prolactin. Therefore, I wondered if in your studies you had ever hybridized with a cDNA probe of prolactin rather than cDNA growth hormone to search for a rat placental lactogen gene.

D. Moore: We don't have a prolactin probe in our laboratory at the moment, so we haven't done that experiment. I believe that similar experiments have been done in John Baxter's laboratory, but I can't describe the results that they got with it.

J. Roberts: I was curious as to the growth hormone induction in the L cells. There has been a controversy as to whether this is specific induction or transcription or stabilization of the mRNA. Would you care to comment?

D. Moore: There are certainly two explanations to an increase in the amount of mRNA present, one is an increase in the rate of synthesis and another is a decrease in the rate of degradation. There has been a lot of controversy I think about the relative contributions of these two effects in the dexamethasone induction and there has been some argument that a lot of the effects are the result of stabilization. All I can say for the L cell experiment right now is that we're just measuring a mass of mRNA, using the rather semiquantitative approach of these Northern-type gels, and I would certainly be willing to believe that the induction seen is due to stabilization. It's true that if you start dissecting genes and reinserting them into cells, an effect on mRNA stability could confuse you in looking for regulatory signals; that's undoubtedly true and we will keep that in mind.

B. G. Forget: Given the presence of multiple copi s of growth hormone-related genes, can you rule out the possibility that the minor 20K varia nt of growth hormone derives from a low abundance transcript of one of these other related genes, rather than resulting from an alternate of splice of the RNA precursor from the one authentic expressed gene?

D. Moore: It's possible, of course, that the 20K variant is a transcript of another gene. However, the S1 technique used should be able to detect a single base mismatch between the DNA and the RNA and I tried to push the S1 digest as hard as possible because of just this objection. The distance from the end label to the point of divergence, that is, the alternative splice site, contains several differences between the growth hormone gene and the most closely related alternative gene. I think, but I can't swear, that if the 20K variant arose by expression of that gene, the observed band would not have been found. This is the sort of objection that can never be totally dispensed with, but the fact that the sequenced portion of the 20K variant peptide is identical in sequence to authentic growth hormone at least tends to support the prediction that it results from different sort of splicing rather than the expression of a different gene.

B. G. Forget: With respect to the "variant growth hormone gene" that you mentioned, how different is the predicted protein sequence of its gene product, compared to that of authentic growth hormone? Is it one of the other related genes that are found in all individuals or is it a particular mutant isolated from a given individual?

D. Moore: The growth hormone-like variant gene is found in every individual I have looked at. I have examined 20 or more individuals from all over the world using DNAs prepared by people in Allan Wilson's lab in Berkeley, and I didn't find any differences in gene number. So, the growth hormone-like variant is present in every individual, but is only known to be expressed when cloned in SV40 as shown by Dean Hamer and co-workers. The homology numbers I don't have right at the tip of my tongue, that sequence was finished at Genetech, and I don't have it at the moment.

B. G. Forget: Roughly, how many amino acid differences are there?

D. Moore: I believe it is something like 3 or 4 out of 191.

B. G. Forget: And it is not expressed *in vivo?*

D. Moore: It is certainly not expressed at high levels in normal pituitaries because this would have confused the sequence analysis of growth hormone. How many other places can you think of? It could be expressed at various times in development. It could be expressed in other tissues. It could be almost anything, but at the moment I just can't say.

K. Sterling: I have a question unrelated to growth hormone or endocrinology that arises from your speculative mechanisms at the end of the talk; it's a question about convergent evolution seen throughout the animal kingdom, and I'm sure you can't do more than speculate.

D. Moore: I've already done that too much, but maybe I'll try a little more.

K. Sterling: I'd like a little more as to which of these—knowing that there is such conservation of genes throughout biological history and yet we see all these instances of convergent evolution in totally different orders of mammals and others, even between mammals and reptiles and fish—I wonder which of these two models that you showed, the gene conversion or the convergent evolution or perhaps some other mechanism may allow it to occur.

D. Moore: I think that it's certainly true that genes are shuffling around relative to each other by transposition and gene conversion type events, and this is undoubtedly a major part of the process of evolution. The extent to which so-called convergent evolution occurs is something that I just can't say, but it's undoubtedly true that there are basic requirements for getting along in the world which have to be fulfilled, and sometimes there will be alternative approaches to similar ends. I certainly would like to emphasize that I think that more and more examples of these gene conversion events are going to be found, but whether that's the explanation to the CS paradox I described, I can't really say.

H. H. Samuels: You stated that glucocorticoids acted by stabilizing mRNA. Were you referring to this precisely for the L cell system or also for the GH3 cell system? Have you looked at the nuclear precursors of growth hormone mRNA in cells incubated with T3. For example, in GH1 cells we can identify a 5.7 and a 2.3 kb nuclear precursor to growth hormone mRNA. If you look at the relative abundance of those precursors compared to the abundance of cytoplasmic mRNA it appears that they increase in parallel, in cells incubated with T3, glucocorticoid alone, or T3 plus glucocorticoid, indicating that all of the response to glucocorticoid cannot be due to mRNA stabilization.

D. Moore: You have more to say about this than I do. I believe the people in John Baxter's lab have reached somewhat similar conclusions doing similar sorts of experiments looking at precursors. The RNA metabolism has been something that frankly we've stayed away from to some extent and tried to concentrate more on the DNA up to now. So yes, stabilization is certainly possible, but I think that it can't explain the entire effect. Is that what you were suggesting as well?

H. H. Samuels: Yes.

J. H. Oppenheimer: Do you have any information on the situation in Laron dwarfism which is characterized by biologically inactive growth hormone?

D. Moore: This is a very interesting question. One could imagine two quite clear mechanisms to explain this sort of phenomenon: it could be due to a mutation in the growth hormone gene itself, or it could be a failure to produce normal growth hormone resulting, for some reason, in synthesis of a peptide encoded by one of the other variant genes. At the moment I have no reason to pick one or the other. I hear a rumor that there has been a description of an individual who has a deletion of the growth hormone gene, but that wouldn't be the sort of thing that would explain this result.

H. Friesen: My question was related to the last question, namely, have you had any experience in looking at individuals with growth hormone deficiency clinically to see whether any have a gene deletion or gene mutation?

D. Moore: This is certainly a very exciting group of experiments to do. I hope that at the Massachusetts General Hospital, I will be able to do a lot of them. One can imagine a number of sorts of mutations of the growth hormone gene and its relatives that would result in quite clear phenotypes that would be quite simply detected. We'll hear more of these sorts of things from Dr. Forget, with regard to the globin genes, but I think that the growth hormone gene family provides a case where a number of interesting mutants should be detectable.

M. Saffran: Has enough of the variant growth hormone been gathered to see whether it is biologically active?

D. Moore: This is the approach that Dean Hamer's group is taking. I understand that they're trying to make monoclonal antibodies to it to detect it that way. I presume that they would be able to do various sorts of more biological assays than they have reported to date. I think the answer is yes, it will be possible, but no, I don't know what the answer is right now.

Glucocorticoid Regulation of Proopiomelanocortin Gene Expression in Rodent Pituitary

JAMES L. ROBERTS, CHING-LING C. CHEN, JAMES H. EBERWINE,
MARIAN J. Q. EVINGER, CONNIE GEE, EDWARD HERBERT,
AND BETH S. SCHACHTER

*Department of Biochemistry, Columbia University,
New York, New York*

I. Introduction

The pituitary peptide hormones, adrenocorticotropin (ACTH), endorphin, and melanocyte stimulating hormone (MSH), are derived from a larger precursor protein designated as proopiomelanocortin (POMC), whose structure is shown in Fig. 1. The three MSH peptides contained within POMC, α, β, and γ are each located in a different region of the precursor. This structure was originally deduced by classical peptide chemical analysis of proteins isolated from tissue (Mains *et al.*, 1977) and by analysis of cell-free translation products (Roberts and Herbert, 1977; Nakanishi *et al.*, 1977b). Subsequently, the amino acid sequence of POMC from several species has been determined from the nucleotide sequence of the POMC mRNA and its gene (Nakanishi *et al.*, 1978; Chang *et al.*, 1980; Roberts *et al.*, 1979b; Drouin and Goodman, 1980).

POMC is produced in many different tissues particularly the anterior and intermediate lobes of the pituitary, which are the major sites of its synthesis. Additionally, the synthesis of POMC outside the pituitary has been documented for bovine hypothalamus (Liotta *et al.*, 1979) and human placenta (Liotta *et al.*, 1977) by *in vitro* biosynthesis experiments. Radioimmunoassay and immunohistochemical evidence have identified POMC related peptides in central nervous system tissue (reviewed in Krieger and Liotta, 1979), intestinal tissue (Larson, 1977), and in certain ectopic tumors (Bertagna *et al.*, 1978; Miller *et al.*, 1980). Recently, Herbert and colleagues (1981) have reported the presence of POMC mRNA in specific regions of the brain (hypothalamus and amygdala) and in the liver, suggesting that POMC may be synthesized in these tissues also. The functional significance of POMC production by nonpituitary tissues is not clear at this time. Furthermore, it has not been determined whether the

227

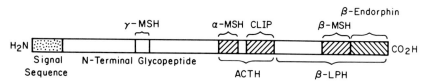

FIG. 1. Protein structure of proopiomelanocortin. Hormonal units of the precursor are separated by pairs of basic amino acids. ACTH, Adrenocorticotropin; MSH, melanocyte stimulating hormone; CLIP, corticotropin-like intermediate lobe peptide; LPH, lipotropin.

POMC proteins expressed in the different tissues are derived from the same POMC gene, an issue which will be discussed later.

POMC is processed to its end product hormones by several posttranslational events, some of which are tissue specific. Differential processing of the POMC precursor is best characterized in the anterior and intermediate lobes of the pituitary. Although the POMC protein appears to be the same in the two lobes (Rosa *et al.*, 1980; Schachter *et al.*, 1982), proteolytical processing results in distinctly different final peptide products (for review, Eipper and Mains, 1980). The anterior lobe of the pituitary is the source of the bioactive ACTH which is secreted into the blood stream. In this lobe, POMC is processed to ACTH and to β-LPH, which is further cleaved to generate β-endorphin. In contrast, the intermediate lobe cleaves ACTH to MSH and corticotropin-like intermediate lobe peptide (CLIP); only β-endorphin (essentially no β-LPH) is produced. Although bioactive ACTH has been identified in the rat intermediate lobe (Moriarity and Moriarity, 1975) the presence of extremely small quantities of ACTH relative to MSH is more consistent with its role as a processing intermediate in this tissue. The processing of the amino-terminal region of POMC in the different lobes currently awaits further analysis. Thus, only one region of the pituitary, the anterior lobe, produces bioactive ACTH as a secretory product.

Glucocorticoids regulate the expression of POMC-derived peptides, as shown in Fig. 2. Initially, ACTH is released from the pituitary in response to hypothalamic factors, including corticotropin releasing hormone (CRF) (Gillies and Lowry, 1978; Vale *et al.*, 1981). This ACTH then stimulates the synthesis and secretion of glucocorticoids by the adrenal gland. In a classical example of a feedback inhibitory loop, glucocorticoids exert a negative effect on ACTH production by the pituitary. Although glucocorticoids may affect this inhibition by action at the hypothalamic level, evidence now suggests that glucocorticoids may also act directly on the corticotrophs of the pituitary to inhibit ACTH synthesis and secretion. (Gillies and Lowry, 1978; Rosa *et al.*, 1980; Roberts *et al.*, 1978; Nakamura *et al.*, 1978). The inhibitory effects of glucocorticoids on the synthe-

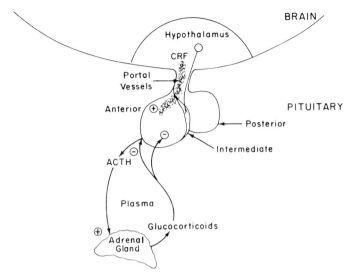

FIG. 2.   Hypothalamic/pituitary/adrenal axis. ACTH is released into the bloodstream from the anterior pituitary in response to hypothalamic factors (CRF, vasopressin) which travel down the portal vessles. ACTH then causes an increase in glucocorticoid production by the adrenal gland. The glucocorticoids, in turn, elicit a negative (feedback inhibitory) effect on both ACTH production and secretion from the anterior pituitary. POMC production in the intermediate lobe, in contrast, is regulated by direct neural innervation.

sis of ACTH are manifested as changes in the pituitary content of ACTH over a period of hours to days, a response consistent with a glucocorticoid effect at the transcriptional or translational level (Herbert *et al.*, 1981; Rees *et al.*, 1971). In contrast, adrenalectomy has no effect on rat intermediate lobe POMC protein content (Moriarity and Moriarity, 1975). The release of ACTH is rapidly (within minutes) suppressed by glucocorticoids in both intact animals and in isolated pituitary cultures, probably via inhibition of the CRF-mediated release at the pituitary level (Gillies and Lowry, 1978; Rosa *et al.*, 1980). Glucocorticoids have also failed to affect POMC protein release either positively or negatively in primary cultures of rat intermediate lobes (Rosa *et al.*, 1980). Thus the responses of these two lobes of the pituitary to glucocorticoids are quite different to glucocorticoids with respect to POMC peptide content and secretion.

II. POMC Is a Model for Small Secretory Peptide Biosynthesis

The peptides that comprise the POMC protein belong to a larger class of small peptide hormones. These small peptides range in size from 3 to 100 amino acids with many experiencing posttranslational modifications such

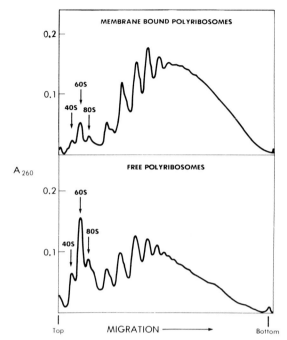

FIG. 3.   AtT20 polysome profiles. Membrane bound ribosomes (MBR) and free ribosomes (FR) were isolated from AtT20 cells by a differential centrifugation scheme previously
described (Roberts and Herbert, 1977). Five hundred micrograms of each was layered on a
linear 15–30% sucrose gradient in buffer and centrifuged at 40,000 rpm in an SW-41 rotor for
18 hours. Gradients were eluted using a direct flow Gilford gradient fractionator coupled to a
Gilford UV spectrophotometer monitoring at 260 nm. Both FR and MBR show a high
percentage of large polyribosomes, suggesting that they are intact.

as glycosylation and carboxy and amino terminal modifications. In accordance with their endocrine functions, these peptide hormones may also be
described as secretory proteins. They are packaged into secretory
granules to await the proper environmental stimuli necessary for their
release into the bloodstream. The intracellular pathway of secreted proteins has been described in detail by Palade and colleagues using the
pancreatic zymogen producing cell as a model (Palade, 1975). Briefly, the
secretory proteins are translated from mRNAs located in membrane
bound polyribosomes (MBR) on the rough endoplasmic reticulum (RER).
It appears that the secretory protein mRNA becomes associated with the
RER by an interaction between a highly hydrophobic protein sequence
(signal sequence) at the amino terminus of the nascent chain and the
surface of the RER. The newly synthesized protein is sequestered co-
translationally into the cisternae of the RER and is subsequently trans-

ferred to a smooth membrane organelle, the Golgi apparatus. After passing through the Golgi apparatus, the secretory proteins are packaged into secretory granules to await their exit from the cell.

The biosynthetic scheme described above predicts that a secretory protein should be present only within membrane organelles and not found free in the cellular cytosol. Indeed, this is what is observed in the POMC system. Subcellular fractionation studies have shown that greater than 98% of the ACTH radioimmunoactivity may be isolated with the particulate fraction of the cell (Roberts and Herbert, 1977).

Another prediction of this model for secretory proteins is that POMC mRNA should be located exclusively in the MBR and not in association with free ribosomes (FR). Polyribosomes prepared from both MBR and FR of AtT20 mouse tumor cells (see Fig. 3) were allowed to complete their nascent chains in a cell-free protein-synthesizing system. ACTH-containing proteins synthesized in this system were isolated by immunoprecipitation and analyzed by SDS–PAGE. The results of this experiment (Fig. 4) show that POMC is synthesized exclusively on MBR. These data, along with the subcellular fractionation studies described above, demonstrate that POMC behaves as a model secretory peptide as evidenced by

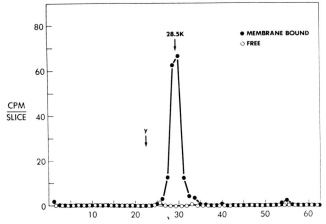

FIG. 4. Polysome runoff experiment. Five micrograms of both FR and MBR was added to a reticulocyte cell-free protein synthesizing system containing radioactive amino acids and 10^{-4} M aurintricarborylic acid, a protein synthesis initiation inhibitor (Roberts and Herbert, 1977). Both types of polysomes were equally active in protein synthesis. Radioactive POMC protein was immunoprecipitated with an ACTH affinity purified antisera and the immunoprecipitate analyzed by 12.5% acrylamide SDS gel electrophoresis system. The gel was sliced, protein eluted, and counted in a triton containing fluor as previously described (Roberts and Herbert, 1977). The profile of the FR "runoff" proteins showed no label over background in the 28,500 MW POMC peak, whereas the MBR runoff proteins had 3–4% of their label in POMC.

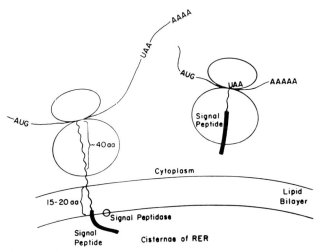

FIG. 5. Cotranslation vectorial discharge of secretory proteins. This diagram illustrates the difficulty that would occur in the efficient sequestering in RER of small peptide hormones if they were not initially synthesized as a large precursor. A detailed description of this concept is discussed elsewhere (Roberts, 1982).

the fact that all of its mRNA and related peptides remain associated with the membrane organelles of the cytoplasm.

Several studies have indicated that newly synthesized proteins are co-translationally and vectorially discharged into the lumen of the RER where they are sequestered until secretion. Based on the physical constraints of this system (see Fig. 5 for a visualization of this process), it is estimated that a nascent peptide chain must be at least 60 to 80 amino acids in length before it may enter the lumen of the RER. If small peptide hormones were synthesized with only an amino terminal signal sequence (20–25 amino acids), the nascent peptide chain would be terminated before it could reach the RER lumen (right side, Fig. 5). In reality, this problem is circumvented by synthesizing the small peptide hormones as portions of larger precursor proteins. Indeed, no small peptide hormone whose biosynthesis has been thoroughly studied has been shown to be derived from a primary translation product of less than 100 amino acids.

III. Glucocorticoids Specifically Affect POMC Synthesis

There are three basic mechanisms by which glucocorticoids could specifically decrease anterior pituitary content of POMC-related peptides in conjunction with a decrease in secretory rate: (1) increase the rate of intracellular degradation, (2) block the processing pathway, or (3) decrease the rate of synthesis. Pulse labeling experiments with POMC-producing cell cultures permits us to distinguish among the different mechanisms described above. An increased rate of degradation would be manifested experimentally as a rapid disappearance of labeled POMC peptide or portion thereof from a particular size class of proteins during a peptide pulse-chase experiment. A block in the processing pathway would result in a redistribution of labeled POMC proteins, favoring the higher molecular weight forms, in a continuous labeling experiment. Finally, a decrease in the rate of synthesis would be seen as a reduced level of amino acid incorporation into POMC during very short labeling times.

In order to determine by which mechanism glucocorticoids elicit their responses, we analyzed the long-term effects of glucocorticoids on POMC production in AtT20 tumor cells (Roberts *et al.*, 1978) and intact rat pituitaries (Schachter *et al.*, 1982). AtT20 cell cultures were treated with saturating levels ($10^{-6}\,M$) of the synthetic glucocorticoid, dexamethasone (dex) for 2 days to obtain a maximal inhibition of the POMC protein. These cultures and corresponding untreated cultures were then used for a continuous and pulse-chase labeling experiments with both radioactive amino acids and sugars. After labeling, the cellular proteins were extracted, and the POMC-related peptides isolated by specific immunoprecipitation and analyzed by SDS–PAGE. An example of a 2 hour continuous label experiment is shown in Fig. 6. In this experiment, the only difference between the two profiles is that the dex-treated cultures contain approximately one-half as much label in each of the different molecular forms of ACTH. Similar results were obtained in other experiments in which cells were labeled for different lengths of time and analysis was performed by two-dimensional PAGE. Pulse-chase studies showed no differences in the biosynthetic pathway other than an approximate 2-fold decrease in the amount of label occurring in the 29K precursor (the first POMC protein synthesized in the biosynthetic scheme) after a 10-minute labeling period. It should be noted that glucocorticoids have no general effect on total cellular protein synthesis. The conclusion of these observations for the AtT20 cells indicates that glucocorticoids decrease the intracellular levels of POMC-related peptides by a decrease in the rate of synthesis of POMC, not affecting POMC peptide processing or degradation.

In intact rat pituitaries a similar mechanism appears to be responsible for the decreased intracellular levels of anterior lobe POMC peptides. In these experiments rats were either adrenalectomized to remove endogenous glucocorticoids or administered large, maximally effective (10 μg/ml) doses of dexamethasone in their drinking water. After 7 days of treatment, the animals were sacrificed and the pituitary dissected into the anterior

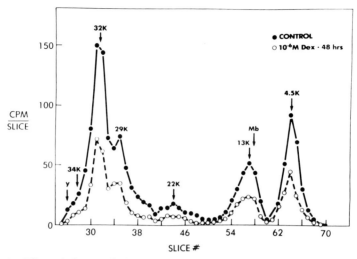

FIG. 6. Effect of glucocorticoids continuous labeling of AtT20 cells: ACTH immuno-precipitate. Microwell cultures of AtT20 cells, both control and 10^{-6} M dexamethasone treated, were labeled for 2 hours with [^{3}H]lysine in a lysine-free minimal media (Roberts *et al.*, 1978). Protein was extracted from the cells and analyzed as in Fig. 4. The 29K to 34K peaks of label represent different molecular forms of POMC, 22K to 27K are the ACTH/N-terminal intermediate, 13K is glycosylated ACTH, and 4.5K is (1–39) ACTH. Y refers to the position of yeast alcohol dehydrogenase, an internal MW marker. Note that prior treatment of the AtT20 cells with dexamethasone causes an approximate 2-fold reduction in the amount of label in all forms of ACTH.

and neurointermediate lobes. These tissues were then cultured in media with radioactive amino acids for varying periods of time from 10 minutes to 6 hours. Within this time frame, a linear rate of incorporation of amino acid into protein was observed, suggesting that the cultures were not abnormal. After incubation, radioactive protein was extracted and ana-lyzed in the two-dimensional gel electrophoresis system of O'Farrell *et al.* (1977). If labeling periods are short (1 hour) relative to the time required for mRNA level changes (8–24 hours), then the amount of radioactivity incorporated into the POMC protein should be a measure of its rate of synthesis in the animal. Thus, if equal amounts of total radioactivity from the different hormonal treatments are analyzed on the 2D gels, the relative amounts of label in POMC between treatments should be a measure of the relative rates of synthesis.

An example of these studies (1 hour labeling) is shown in Fig. 7. In the anterior lobe, adrenalectomy caused a 5- to 10-fold increase relative to control in POMC synthesis (arrows labeled "POMC" point to 2 forms of POMC precursor) whereas dexamethasone caused a decrease in synthesis

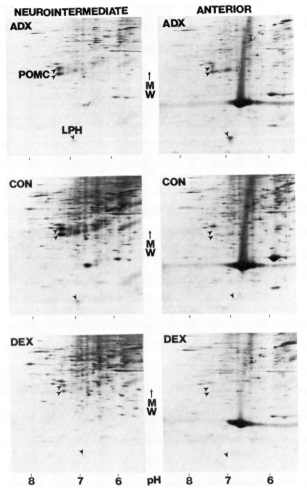

FIG. 7. Two-dimensional gel electrophoresis of S-met labeled pituitary organ cultures. Anterior and neurointermediate lobes dissected from adrenalectomized (ADX) (7 day), control (CON), or dexamethasone (DEX) (2 μg/ml, drinking water, 7 days) treated Sprague–Dawley rats were incubated for 1 hour in [^{35}S]methionine containing methionine-free media (Schachter *et al.*, 1982). Tissues were extracted and 100,000 cpm of labeled protein fractionated by two-dimensional nonequilibrium isoelectric focusing gel electrophoresis, using a pH gradient of 4.5 to 9 (O'Farrell *et al.*, 1977). Dried slab gels were autoradiographed for 7 days. Three radioactive proteins (arrows) relating to the POMC system have been identified: 29,000 MW (lower) POMC and 32,000 MW (higher) POMC and β-LPH.

below the level of detection (at least 5-fold). In contrast, adrenalectomy shows no effect on POMC synthesis in intermediate lobe while dexamethasone treatment caused only a 2-fold decrease in POMC synthesis. Similar observations were made with only a 20-minute labeling period, however, the lower level of radioactive incorporation made it more difficult to quantitate the effects. Although it is not possible to say that glucocorticoids acted directly on the corticotrophs to alter POMC synthesis, the magnitudes and directions of change seen in POMC synthesis parallel those changes seen after long-term (greater than 3 days) treatment in POMC-related peptide content in anterior and intermediate lobe. The conclusion from this is that the changes seen in pituitary POMC protein content after long-term treatment of rats with or without glucocorticoids is most likely caused by a parallel change in POMC mRNA levels.

IV. Glucocorticoids Modulate POMC mRNA Levels

We have also considered three possible mechanisms by which the synthesis of POMC might be inhibited by glucocorticoids: (1) the translational efficiency of the cytoplasmic POMC mRNA may be decreased, (2) a portion of the POMC mRNA may be removed from the actively translated pool of mRNAs, and (3) the amount of POMC mRNA in the cytoplasm may be reduced. The mechanism of glucocorticoid inhibition of POMC synthesis in the AtT20 tumor cells (Roberts *et al.*, 1979a) has been identified using a coupled cell-free translation/POMC immunoprecipitation system. In this study, three types of RNA was isolated from AtT20 cells treated with varying doses of dexamethasone (10^{-11} to $10^{-6} M$) for varying periods of time (8 to 72 hours). Total RNA was prepared by phenol extraction of the whole cytoplasm. Polysomes (representing RNA actively involved in protein synthesis) were isolated by a differential centrifugation scheme. Polysomal RNA was isolated by phenol extraction of the polysomes. Total and polysomal RNA were then translated *de novo* in a modified reticulocyte cell-free protein synthesizing system whereas the polysomes were allowed to complete their nascent chains without any reinitiation of protein synthesis ("runoff synthesis"). Following immunoprecipitation of POMC from the radioactive cell-free synthesized proteins, the amount of POMC translatable mRNA was estimated by determining the ratio of immunoprecipitable to total radioactivity. If glucocorticoids decrease the level of cytoplasmic mRNA, a decrease should be observed in all three fractions of RNA. Removal of POMC mRNA from the translatable pool by glucocorticoids would be evidenced as a decrease in the polysomes or polysomal POMC RNA, but no change would be observed in total cytoplasmic POMC mRNA. Finally, a decrease in the translational efficiency of POMC mRNA would be detectable only in the polysome runoff system. Because this fraction best represents the active state of the mRNA in the cytoplasm, it is predicted that there would be no change in the polysome-associated POMC mRNA levels, just a decrease in the number of ribosomes associated with each POMC mRNA. We (Roberts *et al.*, 1979a) observed a parallel decrease in all three classes of mRNA in response to varying glucocorticoid doses and time of administration. The conclusion of these experiments is that POMC synthesis decreases in AtT20 cells as a direct result of a decrease in cytoplasmic POMC mRNA levels.

This knowledge of glucocorticoid action in AtT20 cells permitted us to determine similarly how glucocorticoids decrease the rate of POMC synthesis in the pituitary of the intact animal. Molecular hybridization of cDNAs complementary to POMC mRNA (Roberts *et al.*, 1979b) provides a direct measurement of POMC mRNA levels in contrast to the indirect translation/immunoprecipitation assay. The protocol used for quantitation of POMC mRNA is described in Fig. 8. With this assay, differences (as small as 15%) of the POMC mRNA levels may be resolved in total RNA samples; additionally, these filters may be reused in other hybridization reactions.

Glucocorticoid levels in the intact animal were depleted by adrenalectomy or raised to saturating levels by addition of 2 μg/ml dexamethasone in the drinking water of adrenalectomized rats (Schachter *et al.*, 1982). After 7 days, the animals were sacrificed, the pituitaries dissected into anterior and neurointermediate lobes, total RNA isolated, and POMC mRNA quantitated by the filter hybridization method described in Fig. 8. The results of these experiments are presented in Fig. 9. Adrenalectomy caused a 7-fold increase and dexamethasone treatment a 6-fold decrease in the POMC mRNA levels of the anterior lobe relative to control animals. In contrast, RNA isolated from the neurointermediate lobe shows no change in POMC mRNA levels in the adrenalectomized rat and only a 3-fold decrease with dexamethasone treatment relative to control animals. Similar results were obtained in two other studies. In one the steroid treated animal was not adrenalectomized and in the other dexamethasone was given after 1 week of adrenalectomy. In addition, the naturally occurring glucocorticoid in the rat, corticosterone, gave similar results, but the magnitude of the effect was lower. Thus, it appears that the POMC mRNA levels parallel exactly the rates of POMC synthesis seen in the organ cultures, implying that, as with the AtT20 cells, the decreased rate of POMC synthesis is due to a decreased level of POMC mRNA.

Glucocorticoids decrease POMC mRNA levels to a much greater extent (10- to 30-fold) in the anterior pituitary than in cultured tumor cells (2- to

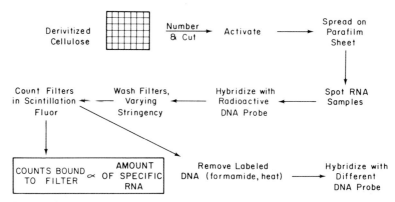

FIG. 8.   Filter hybridization assay. This assay is used to determine the relative abundance of POMC mRNA sequences in various pituitary total RNA preparations. Aminophenyl-thioether-cellulose sheets (prepared by the method of B. Seed, personal communication) were gridded and numbered with India ink, cut into 1 cm squares, diazotized, then soaked in 20 mM NaPO buffer pH 6.8, as described by Alwine *et al.* (1977), spread out on a sheet of parafilm, and blotted to remove superficial moisture. RNA samples were dissolved in the phosphate buffer; aliquots of three concentrations of each RNA were spotted in triplicate into individual filters. Filters were left overnight at 4°C to allow the RNA to couple, then dried at room temperature. The batch of filters was prehybridized with a ^{32}P-POMC cDNA probe (Roberts *et al.*, 1979a), labeled by the method of O'Farrell (1981). Hybridization and subsequent washing of filters used the conditions of Alwine *et al.* (1977) with the following modification: Prehybridization, in 10 ml of solution, and hybridization, in 5 ml, was done in a capped 20 ml vial attached to an end-over-end rotator in a 42°C oven. This ensured thorough mixing of unhybridized DNA during the incubation. The washed filters were air dried, and counted individually in a PPO/POPOP/toluene scintillation cocktail. Each assay included filters containing yeast RNA; POMC DNA counts bound to these filters were not significantly above the background on blank filters and showed no RNA dose–response. After counting, the hybridized DNA can be removed by soaking the filters in 99% formamide at 65°C. The RNA can then be reassayed with a second DNA probe, e.g., to determine the abundance of another pituitary peptide hormone mRNA.

3-fold). This difference may be partially attributable to the effects of glucocorticoids on other factors, e.g., hypothalmic CRF, which modulate POMC production in the pituitary of the intact animal but which are not present in cultured tumor cell lines. Additionally, adrenalectomy influences both corticotroph cell number and volume, thereby resulting in a corresponding 2-fold increase in cell population and hypertrophy within several days following surgery (Moriarity and Moriarity, 1975). Because our results (Fig. 9) are expressed relative to micrograms of anterior pituitary total RNA, this hyperplasia of corticotrophs would correspond to an observed 2-fold increase in the amount of POMC mRNA prior to considering other changes in the quantity of POMC mRNA per cell. Thus, our methods of analysis may, in part, account for the larger magnitude of the

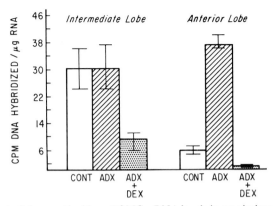

FIG. 9.   Effect of glucocorticoids on POMC mRNA levels in rat pituitary. Total RNA was extracted from rats treated as in Fig. 7 (with the exception that the dex treatment was given on top of adrenalectomy) and analyzed by the filter hybridization method described in Fig. 8. Values given are averages and the error bars represent the range of data points.

glucocorticoid effect on POMC mRNA levels in the anterior pituitary of the intact animal.

V. Possible Mechanisms for Differential Gene Regulation

The experiments described in Section IV demonstrate that glucocorticoids negatively regulate the production of anterior lobe POMC by causing a selective decrease in the level of the POMC mRNA. In contrast to the marked effect of adrenalectomy and hormone replacement on anterior lobe POMC mRNA levels, removal of the adrenals did not increase the intermediate lobe POMC mRNA concentration, and hormone treatment had only minimal inhibitory effects.

The observation that POMC gene expression is far more sensitive to glucocorticoid regulation in one tissue than another is explainable in several ways. We will consider two of the most likely possibilities:

1. The POMC gene products may be derived from multiple nonallelic genes, which have different sensitivities to glucocorticoid action. In order to test this possibility, it is necessary to analyze POMC mRNAs from the various tissues in addition to analyzing POMC gene structure. Several laboratories have studied POMC mRNA and gene structure in a variety of species. For example, Nakanishi et al. (1981) and Chang et al. (1980) have examined the structures of bovine POMC mRNA and human and bovine POMC genes. Drouin and Goodman (1980) reported the existence of two POMC genes based on Southern blot analysis of rat genomic DNA and determined the partial nucleotide sequence of one gene. Subsequent efforts to isolate the other gene have not been successful, and it is thought

that its initial identification was attributable to contamination of the genomic DNA with plasmid DNA (Chen and Roberts, unpublished results). In mouse genomic DNA, however, clear evidence for at least 2 nonallelic POMC genes is furnished by Southern blot analysis. Two bands which hybridize with the mouse β-endorphin probe are generated with every restriction enzyme tested (Shine, Euler, and Herbert, personal communications; Chen and Roberts, unpublished observations). Thus, the mouse is the only mammalian species studied so far which clearly possesses 2 nonallelic POMC genes.

The inability to resolve a particular gene into multiple bands by Southern blot analysis does not necessarily imply that there is only one copy of that gene. The radioactive probes used for identification of these genes are cDNAs which often recognize only that area of the genome coding for the structural portion of the gene and not the regulatory regions which are probably located in regions flanking the coding sequences. Multiple copies of specific genes typically share a large amount of homology in structural sequences, whereas flanking sequences may show great variation, as for example observed in the growth hormone gene family discussed in the preceding section. Briefly, although many restriction enzymes generate a single one band for a specific gene with Southern blot analysis in this system, some restriction enzymes result in multiple bands, thereby implying that the genes coding for growth hormone in human are very similar, but do exhibit some differences in sequence.

Because the POMC gene system has not been analyzed to the same extent as the GH system, it therefore remains distinctly possible that multiple, different copies of the POMC gene may yet be identified in this system. Toward this end, our laboratory has examined POMC cDNAs derived from different pituitary tissues in addition to characterizing POMC genes isolated from genomic DNA libraries. In order to determine if the anterior and intermediate lobe of the pituitary express the same POMC mRNA, cDNAs were synthesized from poly(A)+ RNA isolated from each of these tissues and cloned into bacteria. POMC-containing clones have been identified by the method of Grunstein and Hogness (1975) using a DNA probe to the endorphin/β-MSH region of the mouse POMC cDNA. Restriction endonuclease analyses of several of the POMC clones derived from the intermediate lobe mRNA are shown in Fig. 11. Three different cDNAs representing all but the 5' end of the POMC mRNA provide identical restriction endonuclease patterns which also correspond to that predicted from the rat POMC gene clone (Drouin and Goodman, 1980). Although analogous studies of cDNAs derived from the anterior lobe are in progress, we are currently unable to identify different POMC mRNAs in the anterior and intermediate lobes of the rat pituitary.

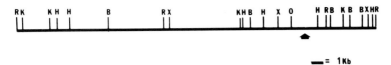

= 1Kb

FIG. 10. Restriction endonuclease analysis of an isolated rat POMC genomic DNA. From the Sprague–Dawley rat RI library generously provided by Dr. James Bonner of Cal Tech, California. R = *Eco*RI, K = *Kpn*I, H = *Hind*III, B = *Bam*HI, X = *Xba*I, O = *Xho*I. The arrow points to the region of the gene that hybridizes with the mouse endorphin cDNA.

POMC genes have also been isolated from several phage lamda genomic DNA libraries. Two different rat genomic DNA libraries, one made from an *Eco*RI digest of DNA and the other from an *Hae* III/*Alu* I partial digest have been screened (Benton and Davis, 1977) using the β-MSH/endorphin mouse cDNA probe. Positive clones were then subjected to restriction endonuclease analysis, thereby generating the restriction map of the rat POMC gene shown in Fig. 10. Comparisons of this map with those for the human (Chang *et al.*, 1980) and bovine (Nakanishi *et al.*, 1981) genes indicate that our clone probably contains the entire rat gene. In addition, further comparison of our map with that published by Drouin and Goodman (1980) for rat reveals extensive homology in the 3′ end of both genes. Additionally, POMC genes have been isolated and further characterization will resolve whether any differences exist between these POMC genes. Thus, no evidence currently exists which clearly demonstrates the

A. RAT POMC GENE

100 bp

B. RAT POMC cDNA

FIG. 11. Restriction enzyme maps of rat (A) POMC gene and (B) POMC cDNA. The restriction enzyme map of rat POMC gene is derived from the genomic sequence published by Drouin and Goodman (1980). The POMC cDNA is generated from rat (Sprague–Dawley) intermediate pituitary RNA and cloned into *Pst*I site of plasmid pBR322 by G-C tailing. The cloned POMC cDNA containing approximately 557 base pairs encodes almost the entire 3′ untranslated region, β-LPH, ACTH, and part of N-terminal glycopeptide (C.-L. Chen and J. L. Roberts, unpublished results). The symbols used to indicate the sites of restriction endonuclease cleavage are: E, *Hae*III; P, *Hpa*II.

presence (or absence) of multiple POMC genes that might encode differentially regulated genes. Hence, we await further analysis of the POMC system to determine if there are indeed multiple POMC genes.

2. The glucocorticoid receptor system may be functionally different in the two lobes of the pituitary. This idea is consistent with observations from several studies on the intracellular distribution of radiolabeled glucocorticoids in adrenalectomized rats. Autoradiographic analyses of pituitary sections have demonstrated that anterior lobe cells concentrate the label in their nuclei while intermediate lobe cells do not (Warembourg, 1975; Rees *et al.*, 1977). Moreover, the anterior pituitary cells with the highest concentration of label were identified as corticotrophs (Rees *et al.*, 1977).

Steroid hormones are currently thought to regulate gene expression primarily via their interaction with a cytoplasmic receptor which, upon binding the hormone, translocates to the nucleus. Correspondingly, the absence of a translocatable glucocorticoid receptor in the intermediate lobe cells should result in the absence of glucocorticoid-dependent gene regulation. The classic example of a correlation between a translocatible glucocorticoid receptor and the biological function of the hormone is provided by the S49 lymphoma cells. While lymphocytes are normally killed by high doses of glucocorticoids, hormone-resistant cells have been isolated (Sibley and Tomkins, 1974a,b; Gehring and Tomkins, 1974). Subsequent characterization has revealed that some of these cells, while still possessing cytoplasmic glucocorticoid binding proteins, no longer contain translocatible receptors. Conceivably, the intermediate lobe of the pituitary may, in its normal state, contain a hormone binding protein which is functionally analogous to that described for the S49 mutant.

Although the above observations may explain the different responses of POMC production to adrenalectomy, they cannot account for the small, but reproducible inhibition of intermediate lobe POMC production that occurs in response to exogenous steroids. Further studies are therefore necessary to resolve whether the hormones directly affect pituitary tissues, or exert indirect effects, perhaps via modulation of hypothalamic factors. Additionally, it must be determined whether other adrenal factors influence the intermediate lobe as a balance to the inhibitory effects of glucocorticoids.

VI. *In Situ* Hybridization: A New Technique for Studying Gene Expression in Heterogeneous Tissue

When studying hormonal effects on gene regulation in a heterogeneous tissue such as the pituitary, it is possible to misinterpret the results if the tissue is being considered homogeneous. For example, the early studies of Nakanishi and colleagues (1977b) on the glucocorticoid effects on whole rat pituitary POMC mRNA levels reported only a 3-fold inhibition in POMC mRNA levels upon administration of large doses of dexamethasone. This observation was derived from a mixture of two pools of POMC mRNA, one glucocorticoid sensitive and the other glucocorticoid insensitive, as previously discussed in Sections III and IV. Even separation of the neurointermediate lobe from the anterior lobe may not be sufficient to permit an unambiguous analysis of hormonal regulation of POMC gene expression, particularly if heterogeneity exists among the population of POMC-producing cells in the individual lobes. Indeed, heterogeneity has been demonstrated in cells of the dog intermediate lobe at the immunohistochemical level (Halmi *et al.*, 1981). *In situ* hybridization, a technique that allows for the localization and quantitation of specific mRNA or DNA species at the cellular level (Brahic and Haase, 1978), should be directly applicable to studying gene regulation in heterogeneous tissue.

In situ hybridization, also referred to as hybridization-histochemistry (Hudson *et al.*, 1981), is similar in some regards to immunohistochemistry. Instead of identifying specific proteins with antisera, radioactive DNA probes are used to identify specific mRNA sequences within cells of histological sections of tissues. Whereas immunohistochemistry distinguishes protein conformation and charge difference as criteria for recognition, molecular hybridization utilizes complementary base-pairing between a cDNA and a cellular mRNA. Thus, with careful control of the temperature, pH, and ionic conditions, the cDNA/mRNA hybridizations provide greater recognition specificity than the antibody–antigen interactions. This technique allows one to examine a very small number of cells in a large cell population. Since the amount of radioactive cDNA bound to mRNAs in tissue sections should correspond to the mRNA levels in the cells, this technique can be used to study cellular mRNA levels in a semiquantitative fashion.

During the development and refinement of this technique for localization of POMC mRNA, the previously determined distribution of growth hormone in specific cell types of the pituitary served as an internal standard. Hybridization of the GH probe would be expected, on the basis of immunohistochemical evidence, to occur in greater than 50% of the anterior pituitary cells, whereas *no* hybridization should be expected in tissue sections from the posterior and intermediate lobes. In contrast, the β-endorphin probe should hybridize to only 3–10% of the anterior lobe cells, to none of the posterior lobe cells, and essentially all of the intermediate lobe cells. Using these two hormonal systems to verify the specific-

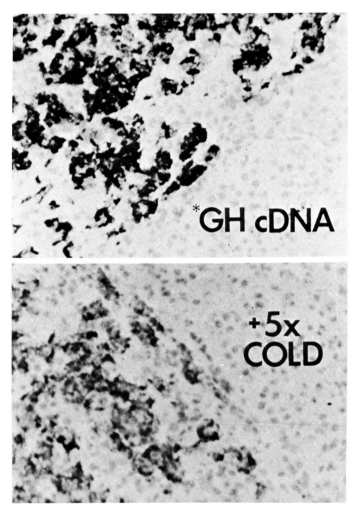

FIG. 12. *In situ* hybridization of normal rat pituitary: GH competition study. Top figure: A frozen section is hybridized to 1.2 × 10 cpm/20 ng of tritium-labeled nick-translated rat growth hormone probe. Bottom figure: A frozen consecutive section is prehybridized with 100 ng of unlabeled DNase-nicked rat GH cDNA, and then hybridized to 1.2 × 10 cpm/20 ng of tritium-labeled nick-translated rat GH probe. The exposure time and development procedure of the two sections are identical. This shows that a 5-fold excess of cold GH cDNA is not enough to compete totally with the hybridizable ^{3}H-GH cDNA, but it significantly decreases the signal. ×287.

ity of the technique, we have derived an experimental protocol for *in situ* hybridization that results in the expected mRNA distribution. This protocol is described in detail in Figs. 12 and 13. Use of tritium labeled GH cDNA gave the hybridization pattern shown in the top of Fig. 12. As expected, silver grains were localized in the cytoplasm of approximately 50% of the anterior lobe cells. In contrast, few grains were seen in the intermediate and posterior lobe regions of this section (Fig. 12, top panel). In order to verify that the distribution of silver grains indicates the presence of nucleic acid sequences complementary to GH cDNA, the hybridization was conducted in the presence of a 5-fold molar excess of unlabeled, denatured, double-stranded GH DNA. As shown in the lower panel of Fig. 12, a large portion of the hybridization of radiolabeled GH

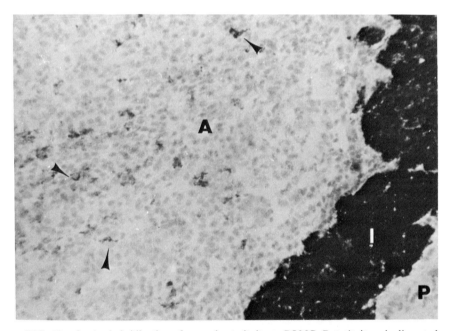

FIG. 13. *In situ* hybridization of normal rat pituitary: POMC. Rat pituitary is dissected and frozen in cold isopentone immediately after decapitation. Sections are cut at −25°C, then immersed in dry-ice cooled 95% ETOH for 1 hour. Sections are then hydrated through graded alcohols at room temperature, equilibrated in hybridization buffer consisting of 3× SSC, 50% formamide, and 1× Denhardt solution, and 3 × 10^5 cpm of the tritium-labeled single-strand mouse endorphin probe is added. Hybridization is done at 28°C for 40 hours. The sections are then washed in 2× SSC at 28°C for 4 hours, dehydrated through graded alcohols, and nuclear emulsion coated. Autoradiographic exposure is done at 6°C for 12 weeks. P, Pars nervosa; I, pars intermedia; A, pars distalis; arrows are pointing at some corticotrophs. ×198.

DNA has been successfully completed by the nonradioactive GH cDNA, thus suggesting that the presence of silver grains in cells in the upper panel was indeed attributable to specific GH mRNA : GH cDNA hybridization.

Analogous *in situ* experiments employing the mouse β-endorphin cDNA probe also confirmed immunohistochemical reports on the distribution of POMC in the anterior and intermediate lobes of the pituitary (Figs. 13–15). With a single-stranded tritium-labeled endorphin cDNA, POMC mRNA was detected in essentially all intermediate lobe cells. Only 3–6% of the cells in the anterior lobe and no cells in the posterior lobe hybridized with the endorphin cDNA probe (Fig. 13). A magnification of POMC mRNA-containing cells in the anterior lobe is shown in Fig. 14. Silver grains are located not only in the cytosol around the corticotroph nucleus, but also in the cellular processes that give the corticotroph its classical stellate shape. This observation would indicate that the RER located in these processes is involved in POMC biosynthesis. The grain distribution in the intermediate lobe cells (Fig. 15) provides a striking example of the resolution obtained by using a tritiated cDNA for a probe. In this tissue section, the arrows designate cells which do not contain POMC mRNA in the midst of POMC-producing cells. By comparison of

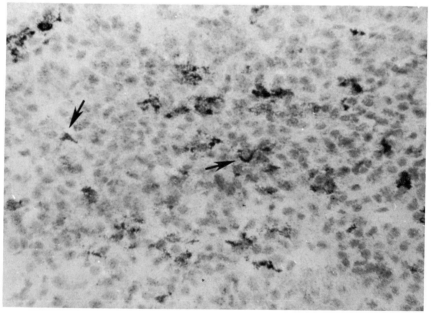

FIG. 14.   Close up of pars distalis corticotrophs. A frozen section hybridized with B.0 × 10 cpm of tritium-labeled single-stranded mouse endorphin probe (×313). This clearly shows that the silver grains are in the cytoplasm of the cells. Note the stellate-shape of the cortico-trophs and the presence of silver grains in the processes of the cells.

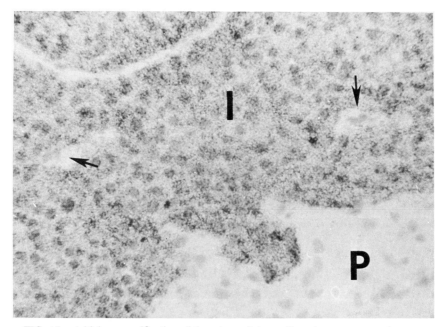

FIG. 15. A higher magnification of the rat pars intermedia and pars nervosa. Arrows are pointing at cells which have very few silver grains, that is, no apparent hybridizable POMC mRNAs. I, Pars intermedia; P, pars nervosa. ×250.

POMC immunohistochemistry and *in situ* hybridization in serial sections of pituitary tissue we are currently correlating the presence of POMC mRNA with the presence of POMC proteins. This technique should permit us to resolve the recurring issue of whether a protein localized by immunohistochemistry is synthesized locally or whether its presence is due to uptake or axonal transport.

VII. Conclusion

Proopiomelanocortin possesses all the features of a model system for examining the hormonal regulation of peptide hormone gene expression. The primary advantages which establish POMC as such an ideal prototype for these studies include the wealth of information known about the biosynthesis of the precursor and its component hormones, the factors regulating the secretion and tissue levels of these peptides, and the anatomy of the POMC system in a variety of species. More importantly, the application of recombinant DNA techniques now permits us to analyze the structure of the POMC gene itself and to define those factors which modulate the expression of this gene in its various expressing tissues.

The study of POMC gene regulation becomes both complicated and intriguing by the fact that POMC synthesis is subject to differential hormonal regulation in the distinct cell types where it is processed. Clearly, the production of POMC peptides in the anterior pituitary is under the negative control of glucocorticoids. These steroids decrease the intracellular levels of POMC peptides by directly reducing the level of POMC mRNA (and thus POMC translation) and not by altering posttranslational processing events. The absence of a functional glucocorticoid receptor system in the intermediate lobe of the pituitary may explain the corresponding lack of glucocorticoid effects in that tissue. Alternatively, the different responses of the intermediate and anterior lobe corticotrophs may be attributable to the presence of multiple POMC genes, each of which is modulated individually by other hormones. Because these hypotheses are as yet untested, current studies on POMC gene structure and cDNAs will provide a necessary and important foundation for understanding hormonal regulation of the POMC gene(s).

The techniques that have been described in this article for examining the hormonal regulation of gene expression may be applied directly to other systems in which a corresponding cDNA probe is available for measuring levels of a specific mRNA. The usefulness of this methodology in a system as complex as POMC clearly demonstrates the general applicability of this technology. The new technique of *in situ* hybridization will prove to be infinitely valuable for analyzing gene expression in a heterogeneous tissue for it enables one to identify specific mRNAs within a single cell and to semiquantitatively assess the amount of a particular message. In fact, *in situ* hybridization currently provides the most direct, specific, and definitive approach for examining individual gene expression in the extremely complex and highly heterogeneous tissues of the brain.

ACKNOWLEDGMENTS

This work was supported by NIH grants AM27484 to J.L.R. and AM06044 to B.S.S. We would like to gratefully acknowledge Pamela Ross for typing the manuscript.

REFERENCES

Alwine, J., Kemp, D., and Stark, G. (1977). *Proc. Natl. Acad. Sci. U.S.A.* **75,** 5350.
Benton, W. D., and Davis, R. W. (1977). *Science* **196,** 180.
Bertagna, X. Y., Nicholson, W. E., Sorenson, G. D., Pettengill, O. S., Mount, C. D., and Orth, D. N. (1978). *Proc. Natl. Acad. Sci. U.S.A.* **75,** 5160.
Brahic, M., and Haase, A. T. (1978). *Proc. Natl. Acad. Sci. U.S.A.* **75,** 6125.
Chang, A. C. Y., Cochet, M., and Cohen, S. N. (1980). *Proc. Natl. Acad. Sci. U.S.A.* **77,** 4890.
Chirgwin, J. M., Przybyla, A. E., MacDonald, R. J., and Rutter, W. J. (1979). *Biochemistry* **18,** 5294.

Drouin, J., and Goodman, H. M. (1980). *Nature* (*London*) **288**, 610.

Eipper, B., and Mains, R. (1980). *Endocrinol. Rev.* **1**, 1.

Gehring, U., and Tomkins, G. M. (1974). *Cell* **3**, 301.

Gillies, G., and Lowry, P. (1978). *Endocrinology* **103**, 521.

Grunstein, M., and Hogness, D. S. (1975). *Proc. Natl. Acad. Sci. U.S.A.* **72**, 3961.

Halmi, N. S., Peterson, M. E., Colurso, G. J., Liotta, A., and Krieger, D. T. (1981). *Science* **211**, 72.

Herbert, E., Roberts, J., Phillips, M., Allen, R., Hinman, M., Budarf, M., Policastro, P., and Rosa, P. (1980). *Front. Neuroendocrinol.* **6**, L.

Herbert, E., Birnberg, N., Lissitsky, J. C., Civelli, O., and Uhler, M. (1981). *Neurosci. Newslett.* **12**, 16.

Hudson, P., Penschow, J., Shine, J., Ryan, G., Niall, H., and Coghlan, J. (1981). *Endocrinology* **108**, 353.

Krieger, D. T., and Liotta, A. S. (1979). *Science* **205**, 366.

Larson, L. (1977). *Lancet* **2**, 1321.

Liotta, A. S., and Krieger, D. T. (1980). *Endocrinology* **106**, 1504.

Liotta, A. S., Osathanondh, R., Ryan, K. J., and Krieger, D. T. (1977). *Endocrinology* **101**, 1552.

Liotta, A. S., Gildersleeve, D., Brownstein, M. J., and Krieger, D. T. (1979). *Proc. Natl. Acad. Sci. U.S.A.* **76**, 1448.

Mains, R. E., Eipper, B. A., and Ling, N. (1977). *Proc. Natl. Acad. Sci. U.S.A.* **74**, 3014.

Miller, W. L., Johnson, L. K., Baxter, J. D., and Roberts, J. L. (1980). *Proc. Natl. Acad. Sci. U.S.A.* **77**, 5211.

Moriarity, C., and Moriarity, C. (1975). *Endocrinology* **96**, 1419.

Nakamura, M., Nakanishi, S., Sucoka, S., Imura, H., and Numa, S. (1978). *Eur. J. Biochem.* **86**, 61.

Nakanishi, S., Inoue, A., Taii, S., and Numa, S. (1977a). *FEBS Lett.* **84** (1), 105.

Nakanishi, S., Kita, T., Taii, S., Imura, H., and Numa, S. (1977b). *Proc. Natl. Acad. Sci. U.S.A.* **74**, 3283.

Nakanishi, S., Inoue, A., Kita, T., Numa, S., Chang, A. C. Y., Cohen, S. N., Nunberg, J., and Schimke, T. (1978). *Proc. Natl. Acad. Sci. U.S.A.* **75**, 6021.

Nakanishi, S., Inoue, A., Kita, T., Nakamura, M., Chang, A. C. Y., Cohen, S. N., and Numa, S. (1979). *Nature* (*London*) **278**, 423.

Nakanishi, S., Teranishi, Y., Watanake, Y., Notake, M., Noda, M., Kakidani, M., Jingami, M., and Numa, S. (1981). *Eur. J. Biochem.* **115**, 429.

O'Farrell, P. H. (1975). *Biochemistry* **250**, 4007.

O'Farrell, P. H. (1981). *Focus* **3**, 1.

O'Farrell, P. Z., Goodman, H., and O'Farrell, P. H. (1977). *Cell* **12**, 1133.

Palade, G. (1975). *Science* **189**, 347.

Rees, H., Stumpf, W., Sar, M., and Petrusz, P. (1977). *Cell Tissue Res.* **182**, 3347.

Roberts, J. L. (1982). *In* "Behavioral Neuroendocrinology" (C. Nemeroff and A. Dunn, eds.). Raven, New York, in press.

Roberts, J. L., and Herbert, E. (1977). *Proc. Natl. Acad. Sci. U.S.A.* **74**, 4826.

Roberts, J. L., Phillips, M., Rosa, P. A., and Herbert, E. (1978). *Biochemistry* **17**, 3609.

Roberts, J. L., Budarf, M., Baxter, J., and Herbert, E. (1979a). *Biochemistry* **18**, 4907.

Roberts, J. L., Seeburg, P., Shine, J., Herbert, E., Baxter, J. D., and Goodman, H. M. (1979b). *Proc. Natl. Acad. Sci. U.S.A.* **76**, 2153.

Rosa, P., Policastro, P., and Herbert, E. (1980). *J. Exp. Biol.* **89**, 215.

Schachter, B. S., Johnson, L. K., Baxter, J. D., and Roberts, J. L. (1982). *Endocrinology*, in press.

Seeburg, P. H., Shine, J., Martial, J. A., Baxter, J. D., and Goodman, H. N. (1977). *Nature (London)* **270**, 486.

Sibley, C. H., and Tomkins, G. M. (1974a). *Cell* **2**, 213.

Sibley, C. H., and Tomkins, G. M. (1974b). *Cell* **2**, 221.

Steiner, D. F., Kemmler, W., Tager, H. S., and Peterson, J. D. (1974). *Fed. Proc. Fed. Am. Soc. Exp. Biol.* **33**, 2105.

Vale, W., Rivier, C., Yang, L., Minick, S., and Guillemin, R. (1978). *Endocrinology* **102**, 1910.

Vale, W., Spiess, J., Rivier, C., and Rivier, J. (1981). *Science* **213**, 1394.

Warembourg, M. (1975). *Cell Tissue Res.* **161**, 183.

DISCUSSION

R. Levine: I should like to ask two questions, Dr. Roberts, in relation to your beautifully presented paper. Do the glucocorticoids inhibit the secretion of all of the fragments simultaneously and to the same extent, as they do the synthesis?

J. Roberts: That has been the general observation of a variety of laboratories. Basically you are inhibiting the release of the secretory granule which does contain within it all of the peptide fragments. In some cases people have seen dissociation of coordinate release, whether this is due to an increased turnover within the granule of specific peptides or not, it is not clear.

R. Levine: The second question: I noticed that in the intermediate lobe the total values for mRNA content are much higher than in the anterior pituitary. Is that due to the fact that there are no corticoid receptors, and therefore this has allowed the original control values to be higher?

J. Roberts: That makes perfect sense because the levels you see in the intermediate lobe are approximately 5 times the level that one would see in the anterior lobe and if you were to look at the adrenalectomized levels that would be perfectly parallel to what you are saying, that it could be why there is more POMC message per cell in the intermediate lobe.

H. P. J. Bennett: Thank you very much for a most lucid presentation. I would like to present some results which Dr. Chris Browne and I have obtained in the laboratory of Dr. Sam Solomon. These data confirm the complex nature of the posttranslational events which takes place in the processing of the ACTH/β-LPH precursor in the intermediary lobe of the rat pituitary. As you have already explained, it has been speculated for a number of years that ACTH acts as a biosynthetic precursor for α-MSH and CLIP (i.e., ACTH$_{8-39}$) in the intermediary lobe. We have recently isolated and characterized 8 forms of rat CLIP from this tissue using reversed-phase HPLC techniques. Through structural analysis we have determined that these multiple forms of CLIP result from the presence or absence of 3 posttranslational modifications, namely, glycosylation of asparagine$_{29}$ phosphorylation of serine$_{31}$ and removal of the C-terminal phenylalanine$_{39}$. All 8 forms can easily be resolved by reversed-phase HPLC and to illustrate this point we have recombined approximately 0.5 μg of each of the purified peptides and rechromatographed them under standard conditions (Fig. A). The upper panel shows UV absorption at 210 nm and the lower panel shows immunoreactive CLIP. To summarize their identity, peaks 1 to 5 and 6 are glycosylated peptides while peaks 3, 4, 7, and 8 are nonglycosylated peptides, peaks 1, 3, 5, and 7 are phosphorylated peptides while peaks 2, 4, 6, and 8 are nonphosphorylated peptides, and peaks 1, 2, 3, and 4 are ACTH$_{18-38}$ peptides while peaks 5, 6, 7, and 8 are ACTH$_{18-39}$ peptides.

In Fig. B we have used a modification of a diagram of Drs. Mains and Eipper to summarize our findings and to show how they fit into the generally accepted scheme of the processing of the ACTH/β-LPH precursor. We have evidence from biosynthetic studies to indicate that all three modifications are early posttranslational events. This suggests that eight forms of both

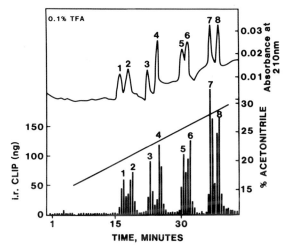

FIG. A.   Reversed phase HPLC of eight forms of rat CLIP.

ACTH and the ACTH biosynthetic intermediate are formed as transient intermediates in CLIP biosynthesis. This would also suggest that four forms of the precursor itself are formed. Interestingly within the structure of the so-called 16K fragment a glycosylation site similar to that present in CLIP is found. We have observed no evidence for phosphorylation of the appropriate serine residue. It is now incumbent upon us to discover biological roles for all these various peptides.

J. Roberts: I think this points up one of the interesting parameters of these polyprotein systems. Although you do have coordinate initial synthesis of these peptides, in the end,

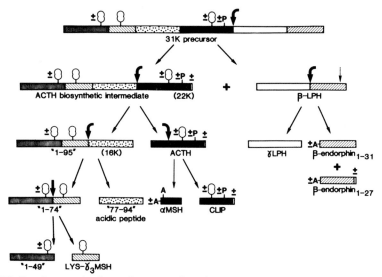

FIG. B.   Proposed scheme for processing of 31K precursor in the rat intermediary pituitary.

after posttranslational modifications, there can be changes in biological activity, either enhancing the biological activity or completely inhibiting the biological activity such as with the acetylation of endorphin. So it may be a primary function of these posttranslational modifications to alter the initial bioactivity, say if you want to kill one activity and leave the other alone.

E. Zimmerman: The *in situ* hybridization results are quite beautiful and the resolution very encouraging in the pituitary. My question is whether at this point you have further data, or could comment on, two tissues that you might be able to resolve in the brain. The first has to do with a group of cells that was described by Watson, as well as others, which seem to react with immunoreactive α-MSH but with antiserum to other parts of the ACTH/β-LPH system which are dorsal and lateral to the arcuate group. The second issue would be the localization of the message for growth hormone in brain in view of reports of growth hormone in brain tissue.

J. Roberts: Well, first off, Stan Watson has looked at these figures and is not clear that we are actually in the α-MSH system you mentioned without other anatomical markers to orient ourself. I think we should take these figures from the point of view that we can identify mRNA in specific neural cells. The experiments are actually now being done using serial sections, on being stained for α-MSH and the other hybridized with the cDNA. The presence of growth hormone mRNA in the brain is being studied using this system by Beth Schachter in our lab.

B. S. McEwen: I believe that you showed that there was an effect of dexamethasone on the intermediate lobe even though there was not an effect of adrenalectomy. I was wondering what is your explanation for the dexamethasone action.

J. Roberts: You didn't because I neglected to mention it. The only possibility I can think of, in lieu of the results that we have that the only thing changing message level in the intermediate lobe is dopamenergic compounds, is that the high level of glucocorticoids are somehow increasing the level of dopamine getting to the intermediate lobe, thus decreasing the mRNA level. Thus the type of inhibition seen in the intermediate lobe would be an indirect effect of the glucocorticoids.

E. J. Peck: First, in your latter studies, is the sequence for enkephalin within your cDNA probe, and if so, second, are your hybridization conditions sufficiently stringent to avoid hybridization to the enkephalin precursor sequence? The brain is reported to have an enkephalin precursor, not POMC.

J. Roberts: Yes, the amino acid sequence of met-enkephalin is within the endorphin sequence, however, in the regions outside of that there is no homology between the amino acid enkephlin precursor and endorphin. Although cDNA clones have been obtained from the pro-enkephalin molecule, I have not seen the data to know if there is a strong nucleic acid sequence homology. If the hybridization was only coming from the 15 nucleotides derived out of the enkephalin 5 amino acid sequence, I would say we would not be seeing a cross-reaction because of the type of stringent washes that we are doing.

N. Varsano-Aharon: Dr. Roberts, you have described beautifully the difference in the precursor processing between the anterior and intermediate lobes of the pituitary. You have also shown that mouse pituitary AtT20 tumors are identical in processing to the normal human anterior lobe. We also know that in human pituitary tumors (as in Cushing's disease) and in the intensely stimulated human pituitary (such as in Addison's disease) the relative proportions of precursor to product remain those of the unstimulated anterior lobe. My first question is: Do you know what happens or do you have data on the processing of the ACTH precursor "ectopically" produced by nonpituitary human cancer cells? There, we know, the bulk of what is extractable from the tumor is precursor. My second question: If you have personal data do you know what the effect of glucocorticoids might be and whether it is such as to explain the isolated cases of supressible "ectopic" ACTH. Is it an effect on production, processing, or release?

J. Roberts: To answer the second question first, I think from all the studies I have seen, one can suppress ectopic production of ACTH only 2- to 3-fold with glucocorticoids. This is not the 5- to 10-fold that we are seeing with the anterior pituitary of the rat. Whether this difference is due to the expression of different POMC gene which is not as suppressible or say a gene whose basal level of expression starts out much lower is just not clear. The fact that primarily precursors are seen in the tumor tissues may be due to the absence of processing enzymes. There is evidence being obtained now from other laboratories that the processing enzymes for cleaving the diabasic residues are not ordinary housekeeping proteases. They are expressed only in specific cells such as the ones that produce the complex peptide hormones. Therefore, if somehow the POMC gene is turned on in this tumor and there is not a concomitant turn on of the processing enzyme gene(s), there will not be effective processing of the precursors. That would be my interpretation of the results. However, I have no evidence to show that there aren't processing enzymes.

J. Pierce: Could you make a brief comment on the status of the characterization of some of the processing enzymes from the anterior vis-à-vis the intermediate lobe?

J. Roberts: They were initially described in the insulin system as being intrinsic membrane proteins, but then very little was heard about it for years, probably because intrinsic membrane enzymes are not an easy thing to work with. Several laboratories have now been able to isolate the POMC secretory granule with the intention of using them to get an enriched fraction for the proteolytic enzymes. People have also been able to come up with synthetic substrates or purified natural substrates for these enzymes which will allow for a burst of activity in this direction.

H-C. Blossey: As the intermediate lobe is beyond the normal regulatory mechanisms, do you think that it may be that the intermediate lobe is responsible for maintaining a basic level of ACTH in the gland?

J. Roberts: The intermediate lobe is essentially not producing any ACTH; the ACTH that is seen there, as shown in elegant studies done by Mains and Eipper and others, is a precursor to α-MSH and CLIP. Actually, the function of all the peptides in the intermediate lobe is not entirely clear at this point. The endorphins that are produced are all acetylated so they have no opiate activity. The possibility exists that the short portal vessels crossing through the intermediate lobe into the anterior lobe may be transporting these intermediate lobe peptides to the anterior lobe where they have a modulatory influence on peptide hormone secretion in a manner much analogous to that seen with the hypothalamic peptides from the major portal vessel system.

B. Hudson: A spectacular talk, but if I may comment there is one omission. I am referring to the paper that was published by my colleagues on hybridization histochemistry earlier this year (P. Hudson, J. Penschow, J. Shine *et al. Endocrinology* **108**, 353, 1981). We did not use ^{3}H label, we use ^{32}P by which we could get an autoradiograph within 3 days. My colleagues used endorphin, a growth hormone, and relaxin probes. The latter was used to show the changing in the concentrations of relaxin message through pregnancy in rats.

J. Roberts: Definitely, I totally agree that the studies you mentioned, which were described in *Endocrinology,* show similar results to ours. However, our techniques allow for identification of single cells whereas the Australian methods can only resolve at the tissue level. The use of ^{32}P instead of tritium may allow for shorter exposure time, but you cannot resolve at the single cell level, which is the point of our use of this technique and why I did not mention their work.

K. Sterling: That was a magnificent presentation. I wanted to ask you to fill in your last comment now on the last two figures where you had gotten the POMC down to the single cell level, following it in serial sections. The particular picture you used to illustrate that, I think, was a cell near the third ventricle or at the third ventricle ependyma and what I wanted to ask you is a little more about the distribution and the extent of some of the cells in the rat hypothalamus. What can you tell us about them?

J. Roberts: First I must mention that these are preliminary studies which you have described. You can find two groups of cells, one localized on each side at the top of the third ventricle, and in addition throughout other regions of the hypothalamus one can find scattered individual cytoplasmic localization of cells. I should mention that the probe that was used for doing these studies was a large 9 kilobase genomic DNA probe which not only contains POMC coding sequence but also contains 4–5 kilobases of an intervening sequence and 3 kilobases of a 3′ flanking sequence. Thus, it is not only POMC coding sequence, but also flanking and intervening sequence; however, there is no repetitive sequence DNA. In talking with the gene structure people, everyone agrees that you would not expect to find a different gene located so near (within 3 kb) an already identified gene, so I'm convinced that what we're seeing is in some manner derived from POMC DNA sequences. Whether the signal is coming from sequences directly from POMC itself, from a different type of precursor, such as what Watson is seeing with the α-2 system, where you only see α-MSH and essentially none of the other peptides, or whether it's from a totally different precursor about which we know nothing, we just don't know yet. It's possible that you could be seeing the enkephalin type of cells, but seeing it in this particular region does not agree with say any localized distribution that's already known for the enkephalin-containing neurons. So actually I can't really answer your question. These are experiments that we're doing right now and I think it really requires the ability to do the serial sections where you can do the immunohistochemistry in one set and the hybridization histochemistry in the other set.

J. H. Oppenheimer: Do you have any preliminary data on the stability of the messenger population? Also, do you think that the inhibition process itself requires protein synthesis?

J. Roberts: Well, there was a set of experiments that I did when I was in John Baxter's laboratory looking at the effect of cyclohexamide on the glucocorticoid inhibition of POMC message and in the presence of cyclohexamide we did still see a decrease in translatable POMC messenger. However, since it takes about 8 hours to see the decrease in the first place, and if you have the protein synthesis inhibited to the level of 98% which was the way we did it, they're clearly dying and the whole pattern of protein synthesis changes, so I was a bit reluctant to go further with this study. So it is not clear that it does require new protein synthesis. One possible mechanism of increased turnover in the cytoplasm which would be a decreased translation efficiency of POMC mRNA and thus leading more of the message exposed for a nuclease action. We have no labeling experiments analyzing the steady-state labeling kinetics or steady-state levels of the message. These are studies being done in our laboratory right now by Jim Eberwine.

D. Shields: In relation to Hugh Bennett's question about multiple forms of CLIP, and its different posttranslation modifications, we found that there are 8 or 9 different precursors to somatostatin (prepro somatostatins) among the cell-free translation products of pancreatic islet messenger RNA. I wonder if you found multiple forms of ACTH precursors in your experiments of the translation of POMC mRNA when analyzed by two-dimensional gels. You mentioned that you translated the messenger RNA from both anterior and intermediate lobes, do you have any evidence that there may be multiple genes or multiple primary translational products from these different cells?

J. Roberts: We always did see two bands, but sometimes you saw them and sometime you did not in cell-free translation. So, I attributed more to a preparation artifact. I think Chretien's group is now getting clear evidence in the pig pituitary for two POMC messenger RNA transcripts. If I understand correctly, they are actually seeing two sizes of mRNA differing by only small number of bases. So it could be that there is more than one mRNA coding for very similar peptides. I might mention that although we haven't done as clearly an extensive study as has been done in the growth hormone systems, we are starting to obtain significant evidence that there is more than one POMC-related gene for the POMC protein in the rat cells. In the human we still have been unable to identify any more than one, but this could be very similar to the human GH system. One has to do a substantial amount of structural work until one is really able to identify separate genes when maybe only 20 bases are different out of 2 or 3 kilobases in the whole thing.

H. Friensen: I wonder if I could pursue the question raised by Ernie Peck a little further and see if I can establish what the minimal length of nucleotides required for hybridization is. It seems to me that synthetic oligonucleotides have been used which are shorter in length than 50 for successful hybridization. What is your impression of the minimal length required by hybridization?

J. Roberts: Yes, successful hybridization can be seen in primed DNA synthesis studies where the primer is as small as 9 nucleotides. However, you're working then in a 3–4 order of magnitude molar excess of the primer over the template. A stable hybrid, stable at room temperature, which is how we do our experiments with washing in a low salt buffer, I would think would have to be something like a perfect match of at least 20 nucleotides. It also depends upon whether the nucleotides are all A-T pairs, where you only have two hydrogen bonds or if they were all G-C pairs where you have three. There is also the problem of where in the hybrid the mismatch occurs. This is the kind of experiment that Connie Gee would like to be able to do once we can just get the basic experiments done, of being able to go through and show hybridization with probes that are 10–20–50–100 nucleotides in length and see if one does see a difference in signal. If hybridization does work with small probes, I could envision methods of working with small synthetic probes of 15 nucleotides where you merely kinase the 5′ end with ^{32}P or ^{35}S and then you have all the probe you want. This would be a much simpler method than the long laborious nick translations or the single-stranded priming off M13.

P. K. Siiteri: Your experiments showing steroid inhibition of mRNA synthesis might be described as a chronic effect since you were giving steroid over a period of 7 days. I wonder if you have looked at short-term pulses of glucocorticoid, say over a period of 2 hours. Do you think that the synthetic mechanism is not modulated by rapidly changing hormone levels? Do you have any information about short-term changes?

J. Roberts: No, we've done no experiments giving glucocorticoids in a pulsatile fashion. With regard to short-term treatment, Ed Herbert's laboratory has done a marvelous job by being able to show that it takes about 4 hours after giving the steroid to the adrenalectomized animals to start to see the decrease in anterior pituitary POMC mRNA. They've followed a time course of inhibition and the intact animal looks very similar to what we reported in the AtT20 tumor cells. In similar studies reported by Nakonishi *et al.* using the whole undissected rat pituitary they showed a time course of decrease in POMC mRNA on the order of say 14–24 hours for half deinduction. No one has really done a real fine tune analysis to see what has happened at short time periods. The problem is that with most of the polypeptide messenger RNA systems, the specific mRNA pool size is so large relative to the synthetic input of mRNA from the nucleus that small changes, even if you're shutting off mRNA synthesis or are stimulating synthesis 10-fold, you just aren't changing the pool size quick enough to be able to detect the change with the techniques that are available.

G. Aguilera: Have you seen any effect of CRF in the processing of the precursor molecule? And do you have any *in vitro* experiments in which you have shown effect of glucocorticoids directly?

J. Roberts: We have not looked at any effects of CRF in this system because purified CRF is not available. If I were to postulate on CRF effects on POMC mRNA levels, I would think that repeated CRF stimulation of the anterior pituitary corticotroph would cause an eventual rise in POMC mRNA through some type of coupling of increased secretion and POMC synthesis to POMC mRNA stability. As for direct effects of glucocorticoids on POMC mRNA levels, the only clear data comes from the AtT20 tumor cell experiments where we see a 3-fold decrease. Since we're seeing 50- to 80-fold changes in POMC mRNA levels in response to glucocorticoids in the intact animals, there could indeed be other indirect effects of glucocorticoids, possibly mediated through CRF, or POMC mRNA levels. Unfortunately, I don't see an easy way to get at any CRF effects of POMC mRNA in the whole animal.

C. T. Sawin: In the intermediate lobe you noted that there are no apparent glucocorticoid receptors but that glucocorticoids caused an approximately 70% reduction in POMC mRNA. You hypothesized that perhaps glucocorticoids caused increased dopamine to reach that area. Is it possible that a combined experiment using a dopamine blocker and corticoids would then result in a level of mRNA that would be the same as if the dopamine blocker alone were used?

J. Roberts: No, we haven't done that and I think we'll try that when we get back.

C. T. Sawin: The second thing is with regard to your *in situ* hybridization findings in the brain. Have you had a chance to study glucocorticoid effects on it, if it's quantifiable, to see if there is any effect on the brain POMC mRNA?

J. Roberts: Yes, the experiments on glucocorticoid effects on brain POMC mRNA are being done but the results are not out—the slides are still exposing. We have tried these experiments before, but the *in situ* hybridization has not worked. There are still some variables in this system that we still don't have totally under control, but we've made substantial progress at single cell analysis of specific mRNAs. Thus, we don't as yet have any data on hormonal regulation of POMC genes in the brain, but that is a primary reason for our going about doing this type of study in the first place. In a heterogeneous tissue, such as the brain, the *in situ* hybridization experiments are going to be the only way to study differential hormonal regulation of specific gene products in different cells.

Molecular Studies of Genetic Disorders Affecting the Expression of the Human β-Globin Gene: A Model System for the Analysis of Inborn Errors of Metabolism

BERNARD G. FORGET

Department of Medicine, Hematology Section, Yale University School of Medicine, New Haven, Connecticut

I. Introduction

The thalassemias are a heterogeneous group of inherited disorders of hemoglobin synthesis characterized by absent or diminished synthesis of one of the polypeptide chains of human adult hemoglobin (Hb A: $\alpha_2\beta_2$) (for reviews see: Bunn *et al.*, 1977; Weatherall and Clegg, 1981; and Nienhuis and Propper, 1981). A number of advances in molecular biology have allowed a detailed study of the molecular basis of these disorders and have recently led to a considerable body of new information concerning the precise molecular mechanisms that are associated with the various abnormalities of globin gene expression that characterize the thalassemias (for reviews see Forget, 1979; Maniatis *et al.*, 1980; Bank *et al.*, 1980; Orkin and Nathan, 1981; Weatherall and Clegg, 1979; Benz and Forget, 1982). In this article, we will focus on the molecular defects causing the β-thalassemias in which β-globin chain synthesis is abnormal; analogous molecular defects, though in different relative frequencies, are associated with the α-thalassemias. From the point of view of molecular pathology, the thalassemias can potentially serve as a general model system for the study and understanding of other inborn errors of metabolism such as those that affect the expression of the genes for various polypeptide hormones.

II. Normal Human Globin Genes and Their Expression

Before describing in detail the molecular defects that are associated with the β-thalassemias, it would be useful to review the normal structure, organization, and mechanism of expression of the human globin genes.

There are three normal nonembryonic human hemoglobins. Hb A is the major hemoglobin component of adult red blood cells and is composed of two α chains and two β chains. Hb A_2 is a minor hemoglobin constituent

Copyright © 1982 by Academic Press, Inc.
All rights of reproduction in any form reserved.
ISBN 0-12-571138-7

of normal adult red cells, usually accounting for up to 3% of the total hemoglobin. It is composed of two α chains and two δ chains which are similar in structure to the normal β chain of Hb A; the sequence of the δ chain differs from that of the β chain by only 10 out of 146 amino acids. Hb F is the major hemoglobin component of red blood cells in the developing fetus and newborn infant; it is made up of two α chains and two γ chains. The γ chain shares some structural similarities with the β chain but these similarities are less striking than in the case of the δ chain: γ and β chain sequences differ in 39 out of 146 amino acids. During the neonatal period γ chain synthesis rapidly decreases and is replaced by β chain synthesis in the phenomenon termed the fetal to adult hemoglobin "switch." The precise mechanisms which control this switch are not known. In addition to the globin chains described above, two different embryonic globin chains, ζ (α-like) and ϵ (β-like), are synthesized early in gestation.

Analysis of fetal hemoglobin shows that it contains two structurally different γ chains that differ in sequence by a single amino acid at position 136: it is glycine ($^G\gamma$ chain) in some chains and alanine ($^A\gamma$ chain) in others. Since these structurally different globin chains must have derived from separate genes, it was known for some time that the γ-globin gene in man must be duplicated. A number of genetic studies also strongly suggested that the human α-globin gene must be duplicated, a conclusion that has been subsequently confirmed by gene mapping and cloning studies (see below).

The chromosomal localization and organization of the human globin genes have recently been defined by the use of somatic cell hybrid, molecular hybridization, and recombinant DNA technologies. The α-globin genes are situated on chromosome 16 (Deisseroth *et al.*, 1977) whereas the non-α-globin genes are located on chromosome 11 (Deisseroth *et al.*, 1978). Molecular cloning of the α- and non-α-globin genes (Fritsch *et al.*, 1980; Lauer *et al.*, 1980) has led to the determination of a map of the fine structure of the human globin gene clusters that is illustrated in Fig. 1 (for reviews see Proudfoot *et al.*, 1980; Forget, 1981). In addition to the expected globin genes, a number of abnormal or nonfunctional globin-like genes are present in the cluster and have been termed "pseudogenes": $\psi\alpha 1$ (Proudfoot and Maniatis, 1980), $\psi\beta 1$, and $\psi\beta 2$ (Fritsch *et al.*, 1980). Such pseudogenes have also been found in globin (as well as nonglobin) gene clusters in other animal species and their evolutionary significance remains unknown.

Until recently it had been assumed that the genetic information in the DNA of a gene for a protein such as a globin chain was colinear in DNA with the amino acid sequence of the protein and the nucleotide sequence of its messenger RNA (mRNA). Recent gene mapping studies, however,

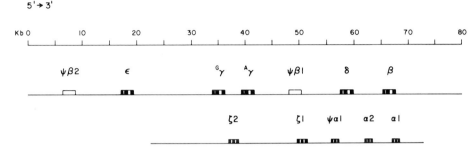

FIG. 1. Chromosomal organization of the human globin genes. The genes are represented by the blocks and the intergene DNA by the straight lines. Intervening sequences are indicated by the open blocks that interrupt the filled blocks representing the coding regions of the genes. The presence and extent of intervening sequences in the pseudogenes, ψβ1 and ψβ2 have not yet been determined and these genes are represented as totally open blocks. 5′ → 3′ indicates the direction of transcription of the genes and the scale indicates the distance between genes in kilobases (1 kb = 1000 nucleotides). [Reproduced with modification from Forget (1981) with permission.]

as well as direct nucleotide sequence analysis of cloned genes for globins (and other proteins) have revealed the remarkable fact that the coding portions of eukaryotic genes are almost invariably interrupted by intervening sequences of DNA (or introns) of variable length that are not represented in the mature mRNA corresponding to the gene. These intervening sequences, however, are initially transcribed from the gene into

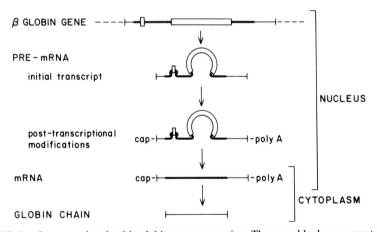

FIG. 2. Processes involved in globin gene expression. The open blocks represent intervening sequences present in the gene and pre-mRNA but absent from mature mRNA; the bold line represents coding sequences and the finer line noncoding sequences of the gene and mRNA. [Reproduced from Forget (1980) with permission.]

precursor mRNA molecules and are then removed by an enzymatic process called splicing in the cell nucleus before transport of the mRNA to the cell cytoplasm. Two introns (one small and one large) have been identified in the coding regions of the non-α-globin genes in man; two small introns have also been identified in the human α-globin genes. These introns are represented by the open (white) blocks interrupting the normal globin genes in Fig. 1, and the posttranscriptional processing (or "splicing") of globin precursor mRNA molecules is illustrated schematically in Fig. 2.

III. Molecular Basis of the β-Thalassemia Syndromes

The β-thalassemias are genetically and biochemically heterogeneous. The major subtypes of β-thalassemia and their associated biochemical manifestations and molecular defects (in the homozygous state) are listed in Table I. We will consider below each subtype separately.

A. β^+-THALASSEMIA

The most common type of β-thalassemia is that in which there is some synthesis of β globin chains but in significantly reduced amounts: usually 10 to 20% of normal. The β chains which are synthesized, when analyzed by peptide mapping, appear to be structurally normal β chains, although such studies have in fact been carried out in only a limited number of cases. All of the various patients with β^+-thalassemia who have been studied reveal a common biochemical defect. When RNA isolated from reticulocytes of these patients is analyzed by molecular hybridization assays using α and β cDNA to quantitate the α to β mRNA content of the RNA, a quantitative deficiency of β-globin mRNA relative to α-globin mRNA can be demonstrated. The deficiency of β mRNA in individual cases is closely proportional to the deficiency of β-globin chain synthesis in the same patient.

A considerable body of recent experimental evidence indicates clearly that the cause of the decreased accumulation of cytoplasmic β-globin mRNA in β^+-thalassemia is not due to decreased transcription of the affected β-globin gene but to posttranscriptional processes.

By molecular hybridization assays using labeled α- and β-globin cDNAs, Nienhuis et al. (1977) were the first to study the relative amounts of α- and β-globin mRNA in nuclear and cytoplasmic RNA of bone marrow erythroid cells in three patients with β^+-thalassemia. In all three cases, the bone marrow nuclear RNA contained higher amounts of β mRNA (compared to α mRNA) than did the marrow cytoplasmic RNA or

TABLE I

Major Categories of β-Thalassemia Syndromes and Their Associated Biochemical and Molecular Defects

| | Hb A (β chain) | Hb A$_2$ (δ chain) | Hb F (γ chain) synthesis | | α : non-α-globin chain imbalance | β-Globin mRNA | β-Globin gene DNA |
			Amount	Cellular distriction			
β^+-Thalassemia	→	+	+	Heterogeneous	++++	→	+
β^0-Thalassemia	0	+	+	Heterogeneous	++++	(a) 0 → (b) →	+
$\delta\beta$-Thalassemia	0	0	++/+++	Heterogeneous	++/+++	0	0
Hereditary persistence of fetal hemoglobin	0	0	++++	Uniform	+	0	0

reticulocyte RNA of the same patients. In one case nuclear RNA actually contained nearly equal amounts of α and β mRNA sequences. The results of this study clearly suggested that, in the cases studied, the β⁺-thalassemic defect is characterized by a defect in mRNA processing and/or nuclear transport rather than being due to a primary transcription defect. Subsequent studies by Kantor *et al.* (1980), Maquat *et al.* (1980), and Benz *et al.* (1981) using newer technologies for the analysis of bone marrow nuclear RNA pulse-labeled with [³H]uridine and/or using hybridization assays with probes specific for the large intervening sequence of the β-globin gene (that is present only in precursor and not mature β mRNA molecules) have clearly demonstrated that in all cases of β⁺-thalassemia tested, the synthesis of precursor and nascent β-globin mRNA is equal to that of α mRNA. Furthermore, some cases demonstrated abnormal accumulation and/or abnormal processing of sequences in precursor β mRNA that correspond to the large intervening sequence (IVS-2) of the β-globin gene. Other cases however showed no abnormality of IVS-2 processing but nevertheless demonstrated decreased accumulation over time of the nascent β-globin mRNA that was initially synthesized in normal amounts (Benz *et al.*, 1981).

Cloning and nucleotide sequence analysis of β⁺-thalassemic globin genes has pinpointed the molecular basis for at least one form of β⁺-thalassemia that does not involve an abnormality in IVS-2.

Abnormal β-globin genes from two unrelated Cypriot individuals with β⁺-thalassemia have been cloned and their nucleotide sequence determined (Spritz *et al.*, 1981; Westaway and Williamson, 1981). Both genes revealed the same abnormality: a single nucleotide difference when compared to the nucleotide sequence obtained for a normal β-globin gene by Lawn *et al.* (1980). This one base substitution was found in the small intervening sequence (IVS-1), 22 nucleotides from the 3'-junction between this IVS and the adjacent coding sequence (Fig. 3). It should be noted that the nucleotide sequence analysis of these β⁺-thalassemic genes revealed no abnormalities at the junction points between intervening sequences and coding sequences; no abnormalities in the 5'- and 3'-untranslated sequences corresponding to the β mRNA; and no abnormalities in the 5'-flanking sequences thought to be important or responsible for the initiation of transcription of the gene.

Examination of the region of the base substitution in the small IVS of the β⁺-thalassemic gene reveals a finding that might mediate a posttranscriptional defect in mRNA metabolism and possibly explain the molecular basis of this type of β⁺-thalassemia. Specifically, the base change creates in the β⁺-thalassemic globin gene a heptanucleotide sequence which is identical, in all but one nucleotide, with the heptanucleotide

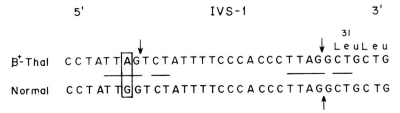

FIG. 3. Nucleotide sequence of the human β-globin gene near the 3'-junction between the small intervening sequence (IVS-1) and the adjacent protein encoding sequence. The homologous authentic and putative internal 3'-splice regions are indicated by the solid lines and the potential sites of intron excision are indicated by the arrows. The single nucleotide change in the β⁺-thalassemic DNA sequence is indicated by the box. Normal β-globin mRNA codon position 31 is numbered. [Reproduced with modification from Spritz *et al.* (1981) with permission.]

sequence situated at the 3'-junction between IVS-1 and the adjacent coding region; the one nucleotide that differs has been found to be variable in other non-α-globin genes in man. More importantly the base change of A to G creates an AG dinucleotide in this sequence and it is now recognized that the dinucleotide AG constitutes the necessary 3'-splicing signal for the excision of intervening sequences. In Fig. 3, the heptanucleotide region of sequence homology is shown by the horizontal line and the potential splicing sites following AG nucleotides are shown by arrows.

It has been suggested (Spritz *et al.*, 1981) that the base substitution in the β⁺-thalassemic globin gene may create an alternative splicing site for processing of the β mRNA precursor molecules, and a model of the hypothesis is illustrated in Fig. 4. A given β mRNA precursor molecule could be spliced in two ways, either normally, as shown in the lower portion of Fig. 4, or abnormally, as shown in the upper portion of the figure. The abnormal splicing pathway would not be expected to cause a defect in the metabolism or processing of IVS-2 sequences in this patient and, in fact, [³H]uridine labeling of the bone marrow cells of the individual studied by Spritz *et al.* does not show accumulation of IVS-2 sequences (Benz *et al.*, 1981). The abnormal alternative splicing pathway however would lead to the synthesis of a mRNA molecule containing an additional 19 nucleotides derived from the 3'-end of IVS-1. The nucleotide sequence of this abnormal region of the mRNA, in the expected reading frame, would be as follows:

```
      30                          35
      Ser  Leu  Phe  Ser  His  Pro  Term
  —  AGT  CTA  TTT  TCC  CAC  CCT  TAG  —
```

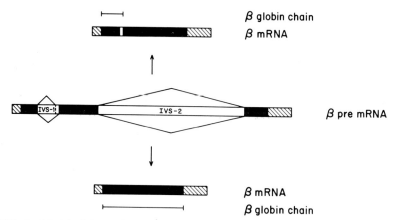

FIG. 4. Model of alternative splicing of precursor β mRNA molecules as a result of the base substitution within IVS-1 of the β^+-thalassemic gene. See text for detailed explanation. [Reproduced from Forget *et al.* (1982), with permission.]

This abnormal β mRNA would therefore contain a nonsense codon following amino acid position 35 that should cause premature termination of translation of the mRNA at that point. It is also interesting to note that the downstream sequence of the mRNA, put out of phase by insertion of the additional 19 nucleotides, contains a number of additional in-phase termination or nonsense codons. It has been previously shown by Chang and Kan (1979) that one form of β^0-thalassemia is caused by a nonsense mutation in the coding region of β mRNA. This mutation would not necessarily be expected, in itself, to lead to a decreased accumulation of β-globin mRNA in the cell. However, it is well established that β mRNA levels in such β^0-thalassemic patients are quite low: 5 to 15% of normal. β-Globin mRNAs that contain nonsense mutations must therefore be unstable and decay more rapidly than normal β-globin mRNA. Hence, our theory postulates that the deficient β-globin mRNA that is observed in β^+-thalassemia probably represents the normal β mRNA that accumulates through the normal splicing pathway (lower portion of Fig. 4). The mRNA that results from the abnormal processing pathway (upper portion of Fig. 4) contains a nonsense mutation and therefore is presumably unstable and rapidly degraded in the cell.

The theory has one additional corollary: all things being equal, approximately 50% of the precursor β-globin mRNA molecules in β^+-thalassemia should be processed normally and 50% should be processed abnormally. However in β^+-thalassemia, the β-globin mRNA level in reticulocytes is not 50% of normal but only 10 to 20% of normal. If the theory as illustrated in Fig. 4 is correct, then the presence of only 10 to

20% of normal β mRNA implies that there is preferential splicing of the β^+-thalassemic precursor β mRNAs at the alternative or abnormal splicing site rather than at the normal splicing site. As a result, one would observe a more marked deficiency of normally spliced β mRNA sequences than would normally be expected if splicing occurred only randomly at one site versus the other. Confirmation of the theory requires the demonstration, in β^+-thalassemic erythroid cell RNA, of RNA sequences that contain the abnormal additional nucleotides. Results of experiments in our laboratory and by others indicate that the predicted abnormal mRNA can in fact be detected (Fukumaki *et al.*, 1982; Busslinger *et al.*, 1981).

In summary then, β^+-thalassemia is characterized by a quantitative deficiency of cytoplasmic β-globin mRNA in erythroid cells of affected individuals. The basis of this deficiency, in all cases thus far tested, appears to be a posttranscriptional defect in precursor β mRNA processing, and/or stability and transport of nascent β mRNA. In some patients the defect is caused by a base substitution in the small IVS of the β-globin gene that results in alternative splicing of the majority of precursor β mRNA molecules to yield an abnormal and presumably unstable β mRNA; the minority of precursor β mRNA molecules that are processed correctly yield the reduced amount of functionally normal β mRNA that accumulates in reticulocytes. It is likely that other specific mutations will be identified in the future as causes of β^+-thalassemia, possibly base changes in the large intervening sequence (IVS-2) of the gene resulting in abnormal processing of precursor β mRNA molecules.

B. β^0-THALASSEMIA

In β^0-thalassemia, which accounts for approximately 10% of the cases of homozygous β-thalassemia, there is total absence of β chain synthesis but intact synthesis of δ chains. This condition is found in many different racial groups and various clinical and/or genetic subtypes have been described which were thought likely to have different molecular bases. Variable results have been obtained in the analysis of reticulocyte globin mRNA of such patients (Benz *et al.*, 1978; Old *et al.*, 1978). In some patients (approximately half) molecular hybridization assays reveal a marked deficiency or virtual absence of β mRNA: less than 1% as much β-like mRNA as α mRNA is detected. The small amount of β-like mRNA seen in these cases may in fact represent trace amounts of the mRNA for δ chains. In the other half of cases however hybridization assays reveal a substantial amount of β or β-like mRNA: anywhere from 5 to 30% as much β mRNA as α mRNA. The amount of hybridization to β cDNA in these cases is probably too great to be explained by cross-hybridization of δ chain mRNA with the β cDNA probe. The β mRNA demonstrable by hybridization assays is nonfunctional: in heterologous cell-free protein-synthesizing systems it fails to direct the synthesis of any normal human β-globin chains. The β-globin mRNA in many of these cases is nonfunctional because of a base substitution in the coding region of the gene (and hence the mRNA) that changes an amino acid codon to a termination codon, a so-called nonsense mutation. This mutation was first demonstrated in the β mRNA of a Chinese patient with approximately 15% as much β mRNA as α mRNA. Nucleotide sequence analysis of the abnormal β mRNA by Chang and Kan (1979) demonstrated a single base substitution in the sequence of codon 17 from AAG (Lys) to UAG (Term) (Fig. 5). In patients of Mediterranean ancestry, a second type of nonsense mutation has subsequently been demonstrated (Trecartin *et al.*, 1981) and appears to be quite widespread: a base substitution in codon 39 from CAG (Gln) to UAG (Term) (Fig. 5). Both of these nonsense mutations are associated with low levels of β mRNA (only approximately 5% as much β mRNA as α mRNA in the Mediterranean mutation). This low level of mRNA may be due to accelerated turnover (instability) of the abnormally translated β mRNA.

In a Greek patient with β⁰-thalassemia, a different type of mutation has been described by Proudfoot *et al.* (1981): a base substitution at the junction between the coding sequence and the 5'-extremity of the second or large intervening sequence (IVS-2) of the β-globin gene, that was detected by cloning and nucleotide sequence analysis of the gene. This mutation involves the dinucleotide GT, which is conserved at the 5'-extremity of all introns and is thought to constitute a splicing signal for the mRNA processing enzyme(s) of the cell. The GT to AT change (Fig. 6) presumably prevents normal processing or splicing of the pre-β mRNA transcripts and results in the absence of functional β mRNA in the cell. The precise

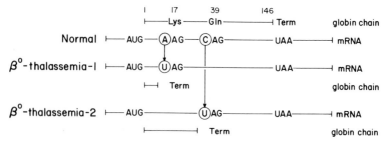

FIG. 5.   Nonsense mutations in cases of β⁰-thalassemia. Single nucleotide base substitutions at amino acid codons 17 and 39 lead to premature termination of β-globin chain synthesis and therefore total absence of intact β chains and Hb A.

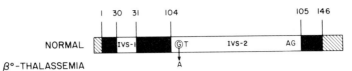

FIG. 6. Mutation in the large intervening sequence of the β-globin gene causing β⁰-thalassemia. A single base substitution at the splice junction between coding sequence and IVS-2 changes the consensus splice signal dinucleotide from GT to AT thereby presumably preventing the excision of IVS sequences at this point from precursor β mRNA molecules.

structure of the β mRNA that is synthesized in these cases has not yet been determined. This mutation alters a recognition site, normally present at the 5'-IVS-2 splice junction of the β-globin gene, for the restriction endonuclease HphI. Presumably the same mutation was therefore detected using HphI restriction endonuclease analysis of total cellular DNA by Baird et $al.$ (1981) in three other patients with β⁰-thalassemia, two Iranian and one Italian.

Even in those cases of β⁰-thalassemia where there is apparently absent β-globin mRNA, gene mapping studies do not usually reveal any evidence for β-globin gene deletion or rearrangement, with one exception. Three cases of homozygous β⁰-thalassemia have been identified, all from the same region of India, in which the 3'-extremity of one of the two β-globin genes is deleted, including the 3'-one-third of IVS-2 (Orkin et $al.$, 1979a, 1980; Flavell et $al.$, 1979). The relationship between the deletion and the precise molecular basis of this type of β⁰-thalassemia remains to be determined. Certainly any transcripts from such a gene would not be processed normally due to the absence of the normal splicing signal at the 3'-extremity of IVS-2.

In summary, three different types of molecular defects have been identified in β⁰-thalassemia.

1. Nonsense mutations at two different points of the coding region of the gene resulting in presumably unstable nonfunctional (nonsense) globin mRNAs.

2. A base substitution of the 5'-splice junction of one of the intervening sequences (IVS-2) of the β-globin gene, presumably preventing the normal processing of precursor β mRNA molecules to normal mature β-globin mRNA.

3. A partial β-globin gene deletion involving the 3'-extremity of the gene including the distal one third of the large intervening sequence (IVS-2).

Other defects may cause β⁰-thalassemia, including possibly defects that prevent transcription of the gene, but they remain to be demonstrated.

C. δβ-THALASSEMIA

δβ-Thalassemia is a relatively rare type of thalassemia that is characterized by total absence of both β chain synthesis of Hb A and δ chain synthesis of Hb A_2. Homozygous patients have 100% fetal hemoglobin (Hb F). These patients manifest a thalassemic phenotype because γ chain synthesis (of Hb F) is not equal to α chain synthesis: there is only approximately one-third as much γ chain synthesis as α chain synthesis. These patients are anemic, and in heterozygotes there is an increased amount of Hb F that is heterogeneously distributed amongst the red cells.

Molecular hybridization of reticulocyte RNA from homozygous patients reveals a total absence of β or β-like mRNA. When cellular DNA from such patients is analyzed by molecular hybridization assays, a marked reduction in hybridization of the DNA to β cDNA is observed, indicating the presence of a substantial deletion of the β- (and presumably δ)-globin genes.

Gene mapping studies in the common Mediterranean type of δβ-thalassemia have revealed that the entire β globin gene and the 3′-terminal half of the δ gene are deleted, starting somewhere in the large intervening sequence (IVS-2) of the δ gene as illustrated in Fig. 7 (Fritsch et al., 1979). The 5′-terminal (or C-coding) portion of the δ gene up to codon 104 and a portion of the intervening sequence are thus intact in this common type of δβ-thalassemia that is associated with the synthesis of both $^Gγ$ and $^Aγ$ types of Hb F. A rare variant of δβ-thalassemia in which only the $^Gγ$ type of Hb F is synthesized has been described in a Turkish family (Orkin et al., 1979b). Gene mapping studies have shown that this disorder is associated with total deletion of $^Aγ$, δ, and β-globin gene sequences as well as their associated intergene DNA sequences as illustrated in Fig. 7 (Fritsch et al., 1979; Orkin et al., 1979b).

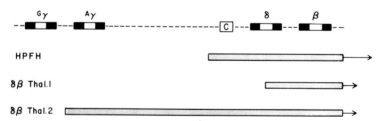

FIG. 7.   Extent of non-α-globin gene deletions in various β-thalassemia syndromes. Stippled boxes represent the areas of chromosomal DNA that are deleted as detected in gene mapping (gel blotting) experiments. Arrows to the right of the stippled boxes indicate that the 3′-end points of these deletions have not been precisely mapped with respect to normal chromosomal DNA. C represents a hypothetical control gene involved in the regulation of γ gene expression (see text for details). [Reproduced with modifications from Forget (1979) with permission.]

Other subtypes of δβ-thalassemia have also been described that are associated with different molecular defects:

1. A nondeletion form of the disorder in Sardinian patients (Ottolenghi *et al.*, 1981).
2. In a Spanish family, a total deletion of the δ- and β-globin genes extending at least 1.2 kb into the inter-γ-δ gene DNA (Ottolenghi *et al.*, 1981).
3. In a family from India, a major rearrangement of the β gene cluster, with deletion of portions of the β-, δ-, and ^{A}γ-globin genes and an inversion of the preserved intergene DNA between the ^{A}γ- and δ-globin gene (Jones *et al.*, 1981); this form of δβ-thalassemia is associated with the synthesis of only the ^{G}γ type of Hb F.

Finally, a rare disorder somewhat related to δβ-thalassemia is the so-called γδβ-thalassemia described in two northern European families, in which heterozygotes have a β-thalassemia phenotype but without elevations of Hb A_2 or Hb F. Gene mapping studies in both families have revealed the presence of extensive gene deletions involving the δ, both γ and probably the ε gene as well. The 3'-endpoint of the deletion however is different in the two families: in one case, the deletion ends in the inter-δ-β DNA leaving the β-globin gene and 2.5 kb of its 5'-flanking DNA intact (van der Ploeg *et al.*, 1980) but in the other family, the deletion involves the 5'-end of the β gene up to the codon for amino acid 64 (Orkin *et al.*, 1981). The basis for the abnormal expression of the apparently intact β gene in the first family has not yet been determined.

D. HEREDITARY PERSISTENCE OF FETAL HEMOGLOBIN (HPFH)

HPFH is a condition that is genetically and hematologically quite heterogeneous. In the usual form of HPFH which occurs in blacks, there is a total absence of β as well as δ chain synthesis directed by the chromosome bearing the HPFH gene. γ chain synthesis is present in the adult at a high level and in contrast to the findings in β-thalassemia or δβ-thalassemia the synthesis of Hb F is uniformly distributed among all red cells rather than being heterogeneously distributed. Red blood cells of homozygotes contain 100% Hb F, and both types of γ chains (^{G}γ and ^{A}γ) are present in roughly equal amounts. In heterozygotes there is no imbalance of globin chain synthesis: the β + γ/α synthetic ratio is equal to 1.0. In homozygotes, there is 100% fetal hemoglobin with no synthesis of Hb A or Hb A_2. However homozygotes do manifest a slight imbalance in globin chain synthesis with γ/α synthetic ratios of approximately 0.5 to 0.6. In homozygous HPFH therefore there is a degree of imbalance of globin chain synthesis similar to that found in heterozygous β-thalassemia. Molecular hybridization assays for β mRNA and β-globin structural genes in homozygous HPFH have shown that β mRNA is totally absent in reticulocyte RNA of these patients and that the β- (and δ)-globin structural genes are essentially deleted.

Gene mapping studies have revealed the presence of two different types of gene deletions in the common black type of HPFH. In both types, the δ- and β-globin genes are totally deleted but the 5'- and 3'-endpoints of the deletions differ. In one case, the 5'-endpoint of the deletion extends approximately 4 kb into the inter-γ-δ gene DNA as illustrated in Fig. 7 (Fritsch *et al.*, 1979; Tuan *et al.*, 1979); in the other case, the deletion involves an additional 4 to 5 kb of this intergene DNA (Tuan *et al.*, 1980). The 3'-endpoints of the two deletions also differ; they are located at least 16 kb beyond the β-globin gene but have not yet been precisely mapped in relation to normal DNA. Despite these differences in the extent of the deletions, the phenotype in affected individuals is quite similar. The implications of these gene deletions with respect to the control of γ-globin gene expression are discussed in the next section.

Although the usual variety of HPFH in blacks is associated with a deletion of the β- and δ-globin structural genes, there are several different rarer subtypes of HPFH in blacks as well as in other racial groups that are not associated with β gene deletions because these syndromes are associated with intact synthesis of β-globin chains from the chromosome that bears the HPFH determinant. In particular, gene mapping studies of the Greek type of HPFH, in which $^A\gamma$ chains are predominantly synthesized, have not revealed the presence of any gene deletions detectable by restriction endonuclease analysis (Tuan *et al.*, 1980; Bernards and Flavell, 1980).

IV. Effect of Gene Deletions on the Expression of γ-Globin Genes

The different extent of the δ- and β-globin gene deletions in $\delta\beta$-thalassemia and HPFH allows one to construct hypothetical models to explain the different effects of the mutations on the level and pattern of Hb F synthesis that occurs in these syndromes and to attempt to understand possible factors that regulate the fetal-to-adult hemoglobin switch in normal persons. As previously stated, in HPFH Hb F synthesis occurs at a high level in all erythroid cells whereas in $\delta\beta$-thalassemia Hb F synthesis occurs at a lower level and in a heterogeneous fashion.

Huisman *et al.* (1974) first proposed the existence of hypothetical control genes situated between the globin genes that might regulate the extent and level of Hb F synthesis in normal persons and in different hemoglobinopathies. One such hypothetical control gene is represented by C in

Fig. 7. This neonatal "switch" gene would have two possible functions in the perinatal period: (1) activation of the β- (and δ)-globin genes, and (2) suppression of the activity of the γ-globin genes. Deletion of this gene could theoretically lead to the HPFH phenotype because absence of this control gene would allow γ-globin gene activity to continue uninhibited. One particular genetic syndrome in fact strongly supports the presence of such a control gene between the $^A\gamma$ and δ-globin genes: Hb Kenya is a hemoglobin variant in which the non-α-globin chain consists of a fused (or hybrid) γβ-globin chain. It presumably arose by nonhomologous crossover between the $^A\gamma$- and β-globin genes and thus all of the normal inter-γ-δ gene DNA is presumably deleted in this condition, although this conclusion has not been confirmed by gene mapping studies. The fascinating feature about Hb Kenya is that the condition is associated with a HPFH phenotype thus giving credence to a possible function of the inter-γ-δ gene DNA in the control of γ-globin gene expression.

The recent gene mapping studies summarized in Fig. 7 provide additional support for the model proposed above, at least in the case of the usual form of HPFH and the common variety of δβ-thalassemia (δβ-thalassemia-1). In both types of black HPFH, the deletion of δ- and β-globin genes is complete, extends into the inter-γ-δ gene DNA, and could thus encompass a hypothetical inter-γ-δ control gene, whereas in δβ-thalassemia-1 the deletion stops within the δ gene and leaves the hypothetical control gene intact and capable of suppressing γ gene activity. In δβ-thalassemia, presumably only a certain subpopulation of erythrocytes with a predetermined (?genetic) commitment to Hb F synthesis ("F cells") synthesize Hb F and selectively survive over the other erythroid cells that lack Hb F and are destroyed because of the effects of unbalanced globin chain synthesis and precipitation of excess α-globin chains.

It should be noted that the inter-γ-δ gene DNA that is deleted in both types of black HPFH contains a pair of repetitive DNA sequences, called Alu I sequences, that are transcribed (at least *in vitro*) by RNA polymerase III to yield low-molecular-weight RNA species of as yet unknown function (Duncan *et al.*, 1979). It is difficult to avoid speculating that these repetitive DNA elements may, in some as yet undefined manner, be involved in the control of normal γ-globin gene expression and, when deleted, contribute to the HPFH phenotype. Certainly, this pair of Alu I repetitive DNA sequences is not deleted in δβ-thalassemia-1. In the case of Spanish δβ-thalassemia mentioned above (Ottolenghi *et al.*, 1981) the DNA deletion does involve a portion of the inter-γ-δ DNA flanking the 5'-end of the δ gene, but it is possible that the Alu I repetitive DNA elements may not be deleted.

The case of $\delta\beta$-thalassemia-2 (Fig. 7) is more difficult to fit into the simple model presented above. In this syndrome, a $\delta\beta$-thalassemia phenotype, rather than a HPFH phenotype, is associated with deletion of all of the inter-γ-δ gene DNA. Deletion of the latter region of DNA alone is therefore not the only factor responsible for the HPFH phenotype. It is possible that the HPFH phenotype requires two intact γ-globin genes (a hypothesis refuted by the findings in the Hb Kenya syndrome) or an intact inter-$^G\gamma$-$^A\gamma$ gene DNA region (the latter is substantially deleted in $\delta\beta$-thalassemia-2). Alternatively, differential deletion of DNA sequences situated to the 3'-side of the β gene may explain the different phenotypes. The 3'-endpoints of the deletions in HPFH and $\delta\beta$-thalassemia have not been precisely mapped with respect to normal DNA sequences, but they are known to be different from one another.

V. Summary and Conclusions

Different molecular mechanisms are responsible at the gene level for hemoglobinopathies that are characterized by absent or reduced synthesis of the β-globin chain of Hb A. In some cases, total or partial deletions of globin genes have been demonstrated and their extent has been precisely mapped by the use of newer gene mapping techniques. However, in many β-thalassemia syndromes, the affected globin gene is structurally intact and the precise cause of its abnormal expression is unknown. Some types of β^0-thalassemia are associated with functionally abnormal β-globin mRNAs, due to the presence of nonsense mutations that cause premature termination of β-globin chain synthesis. In other cases of β^0-thalassemia, a mutation at the junction between the coding sequence and the large intervening sequence of the β-globin gene presumably prevents normal processing of precursor β-globin mRNA molecules. Finally, in β^+-thalassemia, transcription of the β-globin gene appears to be normal but posttranscriptional defects of precursor β mRNA molecules prevent the accumulation of normal amounts of cytoplasmic β mRNA molecules. In one type of β^+-thalassemia, a base substitution has been identified within the small intervening sequence of the gene that creates an alternative splicing site within the precursor β mRNA molecules; preferential splicing at this site generates an abnormal β mRNA that is presumably unstable.

ACKNOWLEDGMENTS

The author's research described in this article was supported in part by grants from the National Institutes of Health. The author thanks Ms. N. Grinnell for help in the preparation of this manuscript.

REFERENCES

Baird, M., Driscoll, C., Schreiner, H., Sciarratta, G. V., Sansone, G., Niazi, G., Ramirez, F., and Bank, A. (1981). *Proc. Natl. Acad. Sci. U.S.A.* **78,** 4218.

Bank, A., Mears, J. G., and Ramirez, F. (1980). *Science* **207,** 486.

Benz, E. J., Jr., and Forget, B. G. (1982). *Annu. Rev. Med.* **33** (in press).

Benz, E. J., Jr., Forget, B. G., Hillman, D. G., Cohen-Solal, M., Pritchard, J., Cavallesco, C., Prensky, W., and Housman, D. (1978). *Cell* **14,** 299.

Benz, E. J., Jr., Scarpa, A. L., Tonkonow, B. L., Pearson, H. A., and Ritchey, A. K. (1981). *J. Clin. Invest.* **68,** 1529.

Bernards, R., and Flavell, R. A. (1980). *Nucleic Acids Res.* **8,** 1521.

Bunn, H. F., Forget, B. G., and Ranney, H. M., eds. (1977). "Human Hemoglobins," pp. 140–192. Saunders, Philadelphia, Pennsylvania.

Busslinger, M., Moschonas, N., and Flavell, R. A. (1981). *Cell* **27,** 289.

Chang, J. C., and Kan, Y. W. (1979). *Proc. Natl. Acad. Sci. U.S.A.* **76,** 2886.

Deisseroth, A., Nienhuis, A., Turner, P., Velez, R., Anderson, W. F., Ruddle, F., Lawrence, J., Creagan, R., and Kucherlapati, R. (1977). *Cell* **12,** 205.

Deisseroth, A., Nienhuis, A., Lawrence, J., Giles, R., Turner, P., and Fuddle, F. H. (1978). *Proc. Natl. Acad. Sci. U.S.A.* **75,** 1456.

Duncan, C., Biro, P. A., Choudary, P. V., Elder, J. T., Wang, R. R. C., Forget, B. G., deRiel, J. K., and Weissman, S. M. (1979). *Proc. Natl. Acad. Sci. U.S.A.* **76,** 5095.

Flavell, R. A., Bernards, R., Kooter, J. M., deBoer, E., Little, P. F. R., Annison, G., and Williamson, R. (1979). *Nucleic Acids Res.* **6,** 2749.

Forget, B. G. (1979). *Ann. Int. Med.* **91,** 605.

Forget, B. G. (1980). *In* "Current Topics in Hematology" (S. Piomelli and S. Yachnin, eds.), Vol. 3, pp. 1–74. Liss, New York.

Forget, B. G. (1981). *Tex. Rep. Biol. Med.* **40,** 77.

Forget, B. G., Benz, E. J., Jr., Spritz, R. A., and Weissman, S. M. (1982). *In* "Advances in Red Blood Cell Biology" (D. J. Weatherall, G. Fiorelli, and S. Gorini, eds.). Raven, New York (in press).

Fritsch, E. F., Lawn, R. M., and Maniatis, T. (1979). *Nature (London)* **279,** 598.

Fritsch, E. F., Lawn, R. M., and Maniatis, T. (1980). *Cell* **19,** 959.

Fukumaki, Y., Ghosh, P. K., Benz, E. J., Jr., Reddy, V. B., Lebowitz, P., Forget, B. G., and Weissman, S. M. (1982). *Cell* **28,** 585.

Huisman, T. H. J., Schroeder, W. A., Efremov, G. D., Duma, H., Mladenovski, B., Hyman, C. B., Rachmilewitz, E. A., Bouver, N., Miller, A., Brodie, A., Shelton, J. R., Shelton, J. B., and Apell, G. (1974). *Ann. N.Y. Acad. Sci.* **232,** 107.

Jones, R. W., Old, J. M., Trent, R. J., Clegg, J. B., and Weatherall, D. J. (1981). *Nature (London)* **291,** 39.

Kantor, J. A., Turner, P. H., and Nienhuis, A. W. (1980). *Cell* **21,** 149.

Lauer, J., Shen, C. K. J., and Maniatis, T. (1980). *Cell* **20,** 119.

Lawn, R. M., Efstratiadis, A., O'Connell, C., and Maniatis, T. (1980). *Cell* **21,** 647.

Liebhaber, S. A., Trecartin, R. F., Kan, Y. W., Agius, A., Furbetta, M., and Cao, A. (1981). *Clin. Res.* **29,** 568A.

Maniatis, T., Fritsch, E. F., Lauer, J., and Lawn, R. M. (1980). *Annu. Rev. Genet.* **14,** 145.

Maquat, L. E., Kinniburgh, A. J., Beach, L. R., Honig, G. R., Lazerson, J., Ershler, W. B., and Ross, J. (1980). *Proc. Natl. Acad. Sci. U.S.A.* **77,** 4287.

Nienhuis, A. W., and Propper, R. D. (1981). *In* "Hematology of Infancy and Childhood" (D. G. Nathan and F. A. Oski, eds.), 2nd Ed., pp. 726–799. Saunders, Philadelphia, Pennsylvania.

Nienhuis, A. W., Turner, P., and Benz, E. J., Jr. (1977). *Proc. Natl. Acad. Sci. U.S.A.* **74,** 3960.

Old, J. M., Proudfoot, N. J., Wood, W. G., Longley, J. I., Clegg, J. B., and Weatherall, D. J. (1978). *Cell* **14,** 289.

Orkin, S. H., and Nathan, D. G. (1981). *In* "Advances in Human Genetics" (K. Hirschhorn and H. Harris, eds.), Vol. 2, pp. 233–270. Plenum, New York.

Orkin, S. H., Old, J. M., Weatherall, D. J., and Nathan, D. G. (1979a). *Proc. Natl. Acad. Sci. U.S.A.* **76,** 2400.

Orkin, S. H., Alter, B. P., and Altay, C. (1979b). *J. Clin. Invest.* **64,** 866.

Orkin, S. H., Kolodner, R., Michelson, A., and Husson, R. (1980). *Proc. Natl. Acad. Sci. U.S.A.* **77,** 3558.

Orkin, S. H., Goff, S. C., and Nathan, D. G. (1981). *J. Clin. Invest.* **67,** 878.

Ottolenghi, S., Giglioni, B., Taramelli, R., Comi, P., Mazza, U., Saglio, G., Camaschella, C., Izzo, P., Cao, A., Galanello, R., Gimferrer, E., Baiget, M., and Gianni, A. (1981). *In* "Organization and Expression of Globin Genes" (G. Stamatoyannopoulos and A. W. Nienhuis, eds.), pp. 287–298. Liss, New York.

Proudfoot, N. J., and Maniatis, T. (1980). *Cell* **21,** 537.

Proudfoot, N. J., Shander, M. H. M., Manley, J. L., Gefter, M. L., and Maniatis, T. (1980). *Science* **209,** 1329.

Proudfoot, N., Shander, M., vande Woude, S., and Maniatis, T. (1981). *J. Supramol. Struct. Cell. Biochem. (Suppl.)* **5,** 381.

Spritz, R. A., Jagadeeswaran, P., Choudary, P. V., Biro, P. A., Elder, J. T., deRiel, J. K., Manley, J. L., Gefter, M. L., Forget, B. G., and Weissman, S. M. (1981). *Proc. Natl. Acad. Sci. U.S.A.* **78,** 2455.

Trecartin, R. F., Liebhaber, S. A., Chang, J. C., Lee, K. Y., Kan, Y. W., Furbetta, M., Angius, A., and Cao, A. (1981). *J. Clin. Invest.* **68,** 1012.

Tuan, D., Biro, P. A., deRiel, J. K., Lazarus, H., and Forget, B. G. (1979). *Nucleic Acids Res.* **6,** 2519.

Tuan, D., Murnane, M. J., deRiel, J. K., and Forget, B. G. (1980). *Nature (London)* **285,** 335.

Van der Ploeg, L. H. T., Konings, A., Oort, M., Roos, D., Bernini, L., and Flavell, R. A. (1980). *Nature (London)* **283,** 637.

Weatherall, D. J., and Clegg, J. B. (1979). *Cell* **16,** 467.

Weatherall, D. J., and Clegg, J. B. (1981). "The Thalassemia Syndromes," 3rd Ed. Blackwell, Oxford.

Westaway, D., and Williamson, R. (1981). *Nucleic Acids Res.* **9,** 1777.

DISCUSSION

G. D. Aurbach: You have identified an abnormal splicing site from mutation of a nucleotide sequence which represents one type of abnormality in splicing. Would it also be possible to have an abnormal spligase enzyme as another abnormality? The second part of that question would be, are there more than one type of spligase enzymes recognizing other signals for splicing?

B. G. Forget: I think I would answer that question by saying that all of the evidence that has so far accumulated points to the fact that the splicing mechanism is universal and is the same for all of the structural genes in different differentiated cell types. There is no evidence for a specific splicing enzyme for a specific precursor RNA transcript of a specific gene. For instance, you can take a rabbit globin gene, put it into monkey kidney cells (using an SV40 virus vector) and the splicing enzymes of the monkey kidney cells will process the rabbit globin gene transcript perfectly well. So I think that if functionally abnormal "spligases" were to occur, the result would be a fatal disorder because the defect would affect the expression of all genes. There is really no evidence to point to a specific splicing enzyme defect affecting the transcript of one particular globin gene. When introns were first discovered, people thought that maybe there would be a special splicing enzyme for each different globin gene and that abnormalities of globin gene expression might be associated in some cases, with defective splicing enzymes. However, that was premature speculation that has not been proven to be correct because of the subsequent demonstration of the universality of the enzyme. The splicing enzymes themselves have not been characterized that well. I think the best characterized splicing enzymes are those for the processing of transfer RNA precursors in yeast and those are a different set of splicing enzymes than those that process the transcripts of eukaryotic structural genes. Very little is known about the enzymology of the splicing of such transcripts. I might also point out that classical genetic studies indicate that the β-thalassemias map to the structural loci for the β-globin genes; there is no genetic evidence in any of the thalassemias, that the genetic locus is very remote from that of the structural globin gene locus. If thalassemia were due to a splicing enzyme defect, one would not expect the gene to map close to the β-globin gene structural locus.

L. P. Bullock: You mentioned that, in these thalassemias where the production of fetal hemoglobin increases, the production is spotty. Do you know the etiology of this? Is it related to the stem cell or its microenvironment?

B. G. Forget: It is a stem cell phenomenon. There are two basic types of erythroid precursor cells in man, and two distinct red blood cell populations: (1) a minority population of red cells, the so-called F-cells, that account for 3–5% of the erythroid cells in adults and contain variable amounts of HbF in addition to adult HbA and (2) the majority of red cells that contain only HbA. The 1% HbF that is present in normal adults is not present as 1% of the total hemoglobin in all red cells. Approximately 3–5% of our red cells contain large amounts of HbF, while most of our red cells contain none. It is a cell biology phenomenon that is programmed at the level of the committed erythroid stem cell. The F-cells are in fact amplified by selective survival in the β-thalassemias and, as a result, one observes an apparent increase in HbF. What really occurs is the selection of a red cell population that is present in normal adults: in β-thalassemia, the cells that contain no HbF are preferentially destroyed whereas those that do contain some HbF preferentially accumulate because they have a longer life span.

D. Moore: The HPFH and δβ-thalassemia deletions are certainly a fascinating developmental paradigm. Are there other HPFH genotypes that could be looked at to test further the idea that the Alu family repeats are involved in the fetal to adult switch?

B. G. Forget: There is one other type of HPFH in which there is a gene deletion that extends even further into the intergene DNA and therefore also removes the Alu repeats that are 5' to the δ gene. On the other hand, there do exist nondeletion types of HPFH that are associated with the usual phenotype but in which no gene deletion can be detected. However, it is not known, in those cases, whether or not the Alu sequences have some subtle defects such as the deletion or substitution of only one (or a few) nucleotides. One form of δβ-thalassemia is associated with the deletion of the entire inter γδ gene DNA without a resulting HPFH phenotype; this finding therefore puts the HPFH theory somewhat in question.

M. I. New: These patients don't live to a reproductive age and hence are genetically dead. I would like to ask the following question: since this is a disease which occurs with relative frequency, is there a heterozygote advantage?

B. G. Forget: Yes, just as there is a survival advantage for heterozygotes with sickle cell trait in malaria-infested areas, similarly heterozygotes for β-thalassemia and heterozygotes for another red blood cell disorder G6PD (glucose-6-phosphate dehydrogenase) deficiency also have a selective advantage. There are now some *in vitro* culture studies that show that the malaria parasite does not grow normally in these abnormal red cells. The gene frequency for thalassemia was amplified in areas where malaria was epidemic or endemic, presumably because those individuals who did not have the trait were more likely to die of malaria whereas those who had the trait selectively survived and reproduced, thereby increasing the gene frequency.

K. Sterling: I have another question with regard to the interesting disorder HPFH; if the fetal hemoglobin or globin exactly balances the absent β chain and they don't have anemia, don't have target cells, don't have the "hair-on-end," etc. and are asymptomatic and normal, how do you discover them?

B. G. Forget: These individuals are usually detected by chance: in screening programs or if someone obtains a hemoglobin electrophoresis for one reason or another. They are totally asymptomatic, and do not seek medical attention for the disorder. That is why very few cases of HPFH have been identified. I think that there have been only 10 or so homozygotes described in the world. I'm sure there are many more out there, but finding them is pure luck.

K. Sterling: So the incidence may be much higher than realized in the Mediterranean basin?

B. G. Forget: In fact I might point out that the typical form of HPFH occurs primarily in blacks and is rare in Mediterranean caucasians.

K. Sterling: And most of the Mediterranean anemias are classic thalassemias, in caucasian Mediterraneans, Greeks, Italians, and so on, although it does occur in blacks, but at a lower frequency. Now the next question about this is, you showed, I think, a gene with a C in a box, the controller that turns off fetal hemoglobin.

B. G. Forget: That is a very hypothetical gene.

K. Sterling: Well my question is, if fetal hemoglobin is just as good as the ordinary adult type, why in evolution has this come about?

B. G. Forget: I can try to answer that, but, once again, the arguments consist of unproven hypotheses. HbF is just as good as HbA for the thalassemic person. It is even better, because it substitutes for something that is missing. However, HbA is probably better than HbF for a normal person because it delivers oxygen more readily to the tissues due to differences in oxygen affinity between fetal and adult red cells. HbF is good for the fetus, because fetal red cells have a high oxygen affinity: the oxygen dissociation curve is shifted to the left which means that it takes more hypoxia, a lower PO_2, in order to have 50% of the oxygen removed from that hemoglobin. Therefore, in the low oxygen tension environment of the placenta, the fetus having HbF in its red cells can preferentially extract oxygen from the maternal red cells. So, for the fetus, there is a definite advantage to have HbF because it facilitates transport, or passage, of oxygen from the maternal circulation to the fetal circulation. Now in the adult having 100% HbF, there develops a mild degree of tissue hypoxia: homozygotes for HPFH do not have a normal hematocrit; in fact, they have a mild polycythemia, i.e., a higher hematocrit than normal. As a result, the tissue hypoxia from the high oxygen affinity causes the stimulation of erythropoietin and consequently the production of increased numbers of red cells. For an adult, having 100% HbF appears to constitute a mild hypoxic stress.

K. Sterling: I wonder how HPFH subjects would do at the top of the Andes or in the Himalayas. Has that been looked at?

B. G. Forget: No, that has not been looked at to my knowledge in HPFH. However, another interesting experiment of biology has occurred. If HbF were essential to the fetus, one would expect that a woman who is homozygous for HPFH might have trouble carrying a normal infant to term. In fact, such women have conceived and have delivered normal healthy infants. Therefore, the differential oxygen affinity might provide an advantage but it does not appear to be absolutely essential for normal gestation.

B. M. Dobyns: About 45 years ago I took a short excursion into hematology. I had occasion to trace down members of a family in which there was thalassemia (*J. Am. Med. Assoc.* **114**, 1530, 1940). There were about 15 cases. I had no further interest in the subject shortly after I finished the study. As I recall in tracing the members of that family, they had a rather high death rate in infancies. The way I stumbled onto the problem in one member of the family was anemia and decreased fragility of the red cells. I recall on seeing your figure here the desiccated appearance of the content within the red cell. There was also poikilocytosis and target cells. This is as much as I know or can recall, but I am curious to know how your finding or any other findings in the last 35 years in thalassemia relate to those findings of red cells as we tried to identify the members of that family?

B. G. Forget: Osmotic fragility has long been used as a screening test for the detection of heterozygous β-thalassemia. The observed abnormality is a decrease in osmotic fragility, in contrast to the increased fragility that is seen in hereditary spherocytosis. The red cells of heterozygotes for β-thalassemia (or α-thalassemia for that matter) can support a greater than normal hypotonic stress. In other words, it takes more of a hypotonic stress to lyse these cells than it does to lyse normal red cells. This phenomenon is not specific for thalassemia: it is also seen in iron deficiency anemia and is related to the decreased intracellular hemoglobin content or hypochromia of these cells. Because of the decreased amount of intracellular contents, there is more room in the cell to accept water and swell in the face of a hypotonic stress.

J. E. Rall: My recollection is that a few years back I read about a case in which there had been read through, namely, there had been a frame shift or a deletion so that the stop signal was changed to a codon.

B. G. Forget: Yes, that is Hemaglobin Constant Spring, one of the forms of α-thalassemia. It is due to a chain termination mutation: a single base substitution in the termination codon of the α messenger RNA, that allows readthrough of the normally un- translated 3'-portion of the messenger RNA and the synthesis of an α-globin chain with 31 additional C-terminal amino acid residues. It is associated with an α-thalassemia phenotype, for reasons that are unclear. Presumably, the abnormal messenger RNA is unstable and that is why very little of the gene product is made. It is yet another example of a posttranscrip- tional defect leading to instability and decreased accumulation of a specific globin messenger RNA.

J. E. Rall: It seems strange that a single mutation in the message is going to change its stability.

B. G. Forget: Presumably it is not the base change itself but the effect on the secondary structure or conformation of the α messenger RNA that results from the translation of usually untranslated sequences. This change in conformation might make the messenger RNA more susceptible to breakdown by nucleases in the cell. The precise mechanism of the messenger RNA deficiency remains unknown.

G. W. Moll, Jr.: Are there any significant changes in porphyrin synthesis in thalassemia patients?

B. G. Forget: There are a number of abnormalities in porphyrin metabolism in β-thalassemia but they are thought to be secondary to the basic abnormality of globin chain synthesis. The precipitation of α chains leads to considerable metabolic disturbances within the red cells and as a consequence of those metabolic disturbances, porphyrin and heme synthesis are affected. For instance, dipyrroles accumulate in these patients due to abnormal heme catabolism.

G. W. Moll, Jr.: Would the porphyrin by-products feedback upon globin synthesis?

B. G. Forget: I do not believe that there is any direct evidence, for a significant effect of porphyrin by-products on globin synthesis in thalassemia.

Müllerian-Inhibiting Substance: An Update

PATRICIA K. DONAHOE, GERALD P. BUDZIK, ROBERT TRELSTAD,
MEREDITH MUDGETT-HUNTER, ARLAN FULLER, JR., JOHN M. HUTSON,
HIROMICHI IKAWA, AKIRA HAYASHI, AND DAVID MACLAUGHLIN

*Division of Pediatric Surgery, Massachusetts General Hospital,
Boston, Massachusetts*

I. Introduction

A. MÜLLERIAN-INHIBITING SUBSTANCE—A FETAL REGRESSOR

Nature abounds with natural inhibitors. Apparent regression can result from of failure of stimulation, such as occurs in patients with testosterone deficiency and in whom there is failure of development of the male genitalia. Regression can occur passively when a stimulus is withdrawn, e.g., atrophy of the breasts when estrogen production is ablated. Regression can also occur actively under the direct influence of a regressor, without which an organ will persist autonomously. Müllerian-inhibiting substance is such a natural active regressor.

Müllerian-inhibiting substance was first proposed by Jost (1946a,b, 1947, 1953) after a series of elegant *in vivo* rabbit embryo experiments in which he established the autonomy of the development of the uterus, fallopian tubes, and vagina from the embryonic Müllerian duct unless a testicular substance was present to prevent development. He gonadectomized fetuses when both Wolffian and Müllerian ducts were present, i.e., before regression of either duct had occurred. If the gonad was replaced with ovary or with no gonad, then the Müllerian ducts persisted and the Wolffian ducts regressed. If the gonad was replaced with testis, then the Wolffian ducts developed into seminal vesicles, vas deferens, and epididymis, and the Müllerian duct regressed. If the gonad was replaced with testosterone alone then the Wolffian duct was stimulated but the Müllerian ducts did not regress. This lack of regression after implantation of testosterone alone lead Jost to suggest the existence of a nonsteroidal testicular substance which he called "Müllerian-inhibiting substance."

279

Natural inhibitors such as Müllerian-inhibiting substance may be produced in small quantity representing less than 1% of the gene product of a cell, or may be produced only during a small window of embryonic development, thereby making their analysis difficult. The advent of hybridoma technology and molecular biology now may make these rare products susceptible to more precise analysis. A knowledge of the properties of natural fetal regressors or inhibitors may be harnessed for the manipulation of tumors. Müllerian-inhibiting substance may serve as a prototype for similar molecules or products which may give us clues regarding intercellular and intracellular transport, as well as mechanisms of action that lead a cell or organ system to self destruct or to transform.

B. ASSAY FOR DETECTION OF MÜLLERIAN-INHIBITING SUBSTANCE

Picon (1969) devised an *in vitro* organ culture assay to detect Müllerian inhibiting substance using the 14 day rat agonadal urogenital ridge. If cultured for 3 days with embryonic mammalian testis from midgestation to term and for intermittant days during the subsequent 3 weeks after birth, regression of the Müllerian duct could be detected histologically. Using the same organ culture assay technique, Josso demonstrated that Müllerian-inhibiting substance was present in human (Josso, 1972) and bovine (Josso, 1973) testis during mid and late gestation, and that the biologic activity was limited to the seminiferous tubules and most probably to the Sertoli cells (Blanchard and Josso, 1974). Nontesticular tissue did not cause regression of the ducts (Josso, 1972).

The organ culture assay of Picon was adapted in our laboratory for semiquantitative measurement of Müllerian-inhibiting substance (Donahoe *et al.,* 1977a). We originally used both male or female agonadal urogenital ridges, but now use only female 14 day urogenital ridges with retained ovary, since mammalian ovary has no detectable biological activity. Dissection is faster and trauma is minimized. The female urogenital ridge is placed on an agar-coated stainless-steel grid of a Falcon organ culture dish (Fig. 1). Small 1-mm^3 tissue fragments to be assayed for the presence of Müllerian-inhibiting substance are placed adjacent to the duct, or aqueous samples are mixed with the media beneath the agar-coated stainless-steel grid. Media with fetal calf serum is added to the level of the agar and incubation proceeds at 37°C in a humidified 5% CO_2 atmosphere for 3 days, after which the urogenital ridge is fixed, embedded, and serially sectioned from the cephalic end of the duct. Stained sections are inspected for regression which is graded from 0 to 5+ by two independent, experienced observers.

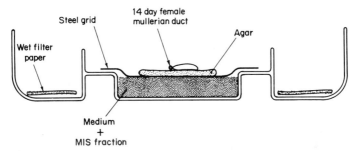

FIG. 1. Fourteen and one-half day rat urogenital ridge either cocultured with whole testis or cultured with soluble test fractions added to media of organ culture dish.

C. POSTNATAL MÜLLERIAN-INHIBITING SUBSTANCE

Using this assay, this laboratory confirmed the findings of Picon (1969) and Constantinople and Walsh (1973) in the postnatal rat, and demonstrated a gradually diminished production of Müllerian-inhibiting substance (MIS) until 20 days after birth (Donahoe et al. 1976), after which MIS could no longer be detected by organ culture methodology. We demonstrated that Müllerian duct regression could be elicited by fetal testis placed at a distance from the duct without requiring direct cell to cell contact. Müllerian-inhibiting substance, in addition, could be detected in the human testis (Donahoe et al., 1977b) for approximately 2 years after birth.

In order to proceed with purification, it was necessary to find a large "nonfetal" source of this fetal regressor. After standardizing methods of handling, transporting, and freezing (Donahoe et al., 1977c) fetal and postnatal testis with retained MIS activity, we discovered that the bovine testis continued to produce MIS after birth for 8–10 weeks (Donahoe et al., 1977d). The bovine neonatal testis now provides an excellent extrafetal source for the isolation and characterization of Müllerian-inhibiting substance.

II. Purification of Müllerian-Inhibiting Substance

With an in vitro assay and an extrafetal source of MIS, we began purification and characterization of the biologically active moiety.

A. EXTRACTION METHODS

Preliminary extractions with saline, urea, or media or media incubations failed to yield active biological fractions. However, extraction in 1 M guanidine with the addition of 5 mM benzamidine, a protease inhibitor, yielded consistently active extracts (Swann et al., 1979). The biologically active supernatant from the guanidine extract was then subjected to cesium chloride density gradient sedimentation which separated the nucleic acids from the protein fractions. We pursued extraction with this highly dissociative solvent in order to ascertain whether the active moiety was a small active fragment as part of a large carrier protein or itself a large molecular weight moiety. The most buoyant protein fraction had good biological activity. Since low-molecular-weight constituents tend to assume a diffuse distribution in these gradients, the presence of MIS activity in a single fraction suggested that the activity was associated with a macromolecular constituent. This presumption confirmed the finding that activity was retained by dialysis as demonstrated by Josso (Josso et al., 1975), and after ultrafiltration (Picard and Josso, 1976; Josso et al., 1977). The active buoyant fraction was further fractionated by gel filtration chromatography on BioGel A 0.5M yielding an active protein fraction which eluted between K_{av} values of 0.19 and 0.38. The active fraction after gel chromatography was then placed on a DEAE anion exchange column. Running the DEAE column at pH 8 allowed nearly quantitative elimination of albumin, as well as many other serum proteins, from the biologically active unbound fraction. Biological activity was better preserved by loading the column at 0.05 M NaCl rather than at lower ionic strength (Donahoe et al., 1981a). These sequential steps resulted in a 200-fold purification of a macromolecular glycoprotein fraction with biological activity for MIS in the unbound fraction of the DEAE column.

B. MEDIA INCUBATION

Labeling experiments with [^{35}S]methionine yielded interesting results which changed our purification approach. Both the labeled media after incubation for 45 minutes and the extracted whole tissue were purified. Labeled bands were localized by gel electrophoresis and autoradiography. Matched experiments with unlabeled material were handled in a similar fashion and biological activity monitored. After a 45-minute incubation, all biological activity was in the media, none remaining in the tissue. As a result, we elected to purify MIS directly from the incubation media. Since we had documented the macromolecular nature of MIS by dissociative solvent extraction with guanidine and density gradient sedimentation, we felt secure pursuing the purification of MIS from the incubation media.

C. SEQUENTIAL ION EXCHANGE CHROMATOGRAPHY

As summarized in Fig. 2, minced tissue was suspended in serum-free Ham's F10 nutrient, media and incubated at 37°C for 45 minutes with gentle agitation. The order of purification was changed since the ion exchange chromatography could now be done without loss of biological activity. The media was concentrated, rapidly reequilibrated with 0.05 M NaCl, 10 mM sodium phosphate (pH 8) by Sephadex G-25 chromatography and then applied to a DEAE column. High biological activity was found in the unbound fraction. The pH of this fraction was gently adjusted to 6 with dilute HCl and the material passed through a CM BioGel A column. The unbound fraction again showed high biological activity.

D. SEQUENTIAL LECTIN AFFINITY CHROMATOGRAPHY

Earlier attempts at carbohydrate affinity chromatography using guanidine extracts were unsuccessful. Biologically active material could neither be washed through nor eluted. However, in view of the change in the initial handling of the tissue from a disruptive extraction to a more gentle incubation and secretion, we reasoned that the active moiety might now be more highly glycosylated; therefore, a concanavalin A (Con A) or a wheat germ lectin affinity column might be successful. Aliquots of biologically active material from the CM BioGel unbound fraction were directly applied to a Con A or wheat germ lectin affinity column, both equilibrated and initially washed with PBS. In the first case, biological activity was initially bound and eluted only by 0.2 M 1-O-methyl-α-D-glucopyranoside in PBS. Similarly, on the wheat germ lectin column, the active fraction was released with 100 mg/ml N-acetyl glucosamine in PBS. The biologically active fraction eluted from the Con A column was then run on a BioGel A 0.5M column, and a single bioactive peak eluted with a 2000-fold purification from the protein content of the starting material. The affinity columns were then run sequentially. CM fraction I was concentrated 3-fold and loaded on a wheat germ lectin Sepharose 6 MB column washing with PBS. The biologically active bound fraction which eluted with N-acetyl glucosamine was then applied to a Con A Sepharose 4B column and eluted with PBS. The bound fraction, which was biologically active, was eluted with 1-O-methyl-α-D-glucopyranoside and concentrated back to the same loading volume (Budzik et al., 1980). Figure 3 demonstrates the regression achieved with the biologically active fractions.

The five biologically active purifications fractions were analyzed by

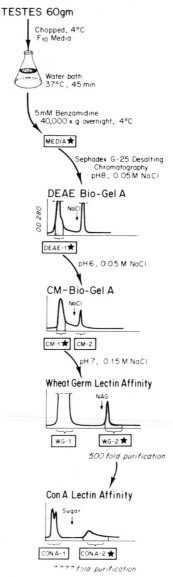

FIG. 2. Purification procedure used to obtain fractions with biological activity for MIS includes sequential DEAE BioGel A and CM BioGel A ion exchange chromatography and sequential carbohydrate affinity chromatography on wheat germ lectin (WG)-Sepharose 6MB and concanavalin A (Con A)-Sepharose 4B. Biologically active fractions and degree of purification at each step are indicated by the asterisks.

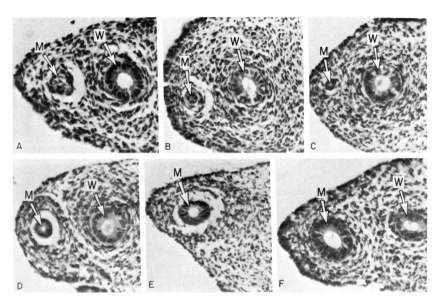

FIG. 3. Photomicrographs (×400) of 8-μm sections of 14 day female fetal rat urogenital ridges after incubation with purification fractions. M, Müllerian duct; W, Wolffian duct. (A) Incubation media, (B) DEAE-I, (C) CM-1. These fractions were diluted 1 : 1 with media for organ culture assay. Excellent (3–4+) regression results from each; the Müllerian duct is either very small or simply replaced by a whorl of cells, while the Wolffian duct is well developed. (D) WGL-II, (E) Con A-II. The lectin affinity fractions were diluted with media to the same concentration (one testis/ml) as the preceding fractions. WGL-II (2–3+) and Con A-II (2+) show high, but reduced, activity relative to preceding steps. The Müllerian duct is small and surrounded by a large area of vacuolization; the tip of the urogenital ridge is poorly differentiated distal to the Wolffian duct. (F) Con A-I. An inactive fraction does not affect development of the Müllerian duct; it is well developed with a wide lumen lined with columnar epithelial cells.

SDS gel electrophoresis gels using an 11% polyacrylamide slab gel topped with a 3% stacking gel according to Laemmli (1970). Fraction Con A-II purified 7000-fold showed a highly reduced number of bands localized to three regions. Single bands were seen at approximately 130,000 and 30,000 and a group of bands between 70,000 and 50,000 daltons. When Con A-II is electrophoresed under identical conditions but without prior reduction by 2-mercaptoethanol, a similar band pattern emerges although the mobilities of some components are slightly higher.

Amino acid analysis of fraction Con A-II was performed by the method of Moore *et al.* (1958) and verified the protein character of the sample. The protein components appear not to have an unusual amino acid composition (Budzik *et al.*, 1980).

As expected from their lectin affinities, all components of fractions

WGL-II and Con A-II stain with periodic acid–Schiff reagent on comparable gels indicating their glycoprotein nature. Carbohydrate analysis of fraction Con A-II was performed by gas–liquid chromatography after hydrolysis of the sample with methanolic-HCl and formation of the trimethylsilyl derivatives (Rheinhold, 1972). Galactosamine and glucosamine were determined using the amino acid analyzer following hydrolysis of samples with 6 N HCl for 3 hours at 100°C (Swann *et al.,* 1977). This analysis indicated a total sugar content of 8.3% (w/w). As expected from the sequential affinity of this MIS-containing fraction from wheat germ lectin and concanavalin A, both 2.8% glucosamine and 0.7% mannose were detected. In addition, 1.3% galactose, 0.9% galactosamine, and 2.6% N-acetyl neuraminic acid were obtained in the same analysis (Budzik *et al.,* 1980).

E. DYE AFFINITY CHROMATOGRAPHY

To achieve greater purification of MIS, we have resorted to dye-ligand affinity chromatography. Early in the development of the present purification protocol, we had attempted chromatography of the incubation medium on Cibacron Blue F3GA-agarose to remove the large amounts of albumin present in this fraction (Travis and Pannell, 1973; Travis *et al.,* 1976). Unexpectedly, the MIS also bound to the dye matrix but could not be reproducibly eluted with retention of good biological activity. A related gel, Matrex Gel Green A (Amicon Corp.) (Fulton and Marois, 1980), has been found to give consistently better results with regard to elution of biologically active MIS. However, the addition of 5 mM 2-mercaptoethanol to eluting buffers is absolutely essential for recovery of active MIS; EDTA was also somewhat effective as a protecting agent, but the mercaptide was superior.

The results of a typical separation on Matrex Gel Green A are summarized in Fig. 4. Prior to chromatography, fraction WGL-2 was dialyzed

(~7.8 mg WGL-2 Loaded)

ELUTION	PROTEIN (mg)	ACTIVITY
0.15 M NaCl pH 8.0	7.3	ō
1.0 M NaCl pH 8.0	0.87 ~15,000 fold purification	2-3+
5.0 M Gu-HCl	0.01	N.D.

FIG. 4. Elution of wheat germ lectin fraction 2 from Matrex Gel Green A dye ligand affinity column. The purification factor of the biologically active fraction is indicated.

FRACTION	TOTAL PROTEIN (mg)	PURIFICATION FACTOR	BIOLOGICAL ACTIVITY
Testis tissue(40)	14,000.0	—	5 +
Incubation media	1245.7	11.2	3–4 +
DEAE – 1	549.1	25.5	3–4 +
CM–1	329.4	42.5	3–4 +
WGL –2	7.8	1794.9	2–3 +
Green – 2	0.93	15,053.8	2–3 +

FIG. 5.   Sequential purification steps of MIS with dye affinity chromatography following wheat germ lectin showing the purification factor and the biological activity at each step.

against 0.15 M NaCl, 10 mM sodium phosphate (pH 8), 5 mM 2-mercaptoethanol at 4°C. A column (2 ml) of Matrex Gel Green A was prepared in the same buffer and the sample loaded. The column was washed with approximately 10 volumes of loading buffer and subsequently eluted with 10 volumes of 1.0 M NaCl, 10 mM sodium phosphate (pH 8), 5 mM 2-mercaptoethanol. Removal of residual protein and regeneration of the column was achieved with 5 M guanidine–HCl. The biologically active MIS eluted in the 1.0 M NaCl wash was purified approximately 15,000-fold relative to newborn calf testis (Fig. 5). Further refinements of this procedure are under investigation to achieve even greater enhancement of purity.

III. Monoclonal Antibody to Müllerian-Inhibiting Substance

Immunologic techniques should provide a logical way to circumvent some of the problems encountered in the purification of MIS from calf testes where large quantities of material are consumed in the bioassay required for activity confirmation. Traditional methods of raising antisera to MIS cannot be used since MIS preparations are not sufficiently pure to raise monospecific antisera. The technique of somatic cell fusion as described by Kohler and Milstein (1976) offered the possibility of obtaining a monospecific antibody to MIS regardless of the purity of the immunizing antigen.

BALB/c mice were immunized intraperitoneally with 30-fold purified MIS in complete Freund's adjuvent with booster doses at 1 and 2 months, and 3 days prior to fusion (Fig. 6). Spleen cells from the immunized mice were fused with an HAT-sensitive myeloma cell line, P3-NS1/1 Ag4-1 (NS-1) (Kohler *et al.*, 1976) as described by Marshak-Rothstein *et al.* (1979), using polyethylene glycol as the fusion mediator and HAT media

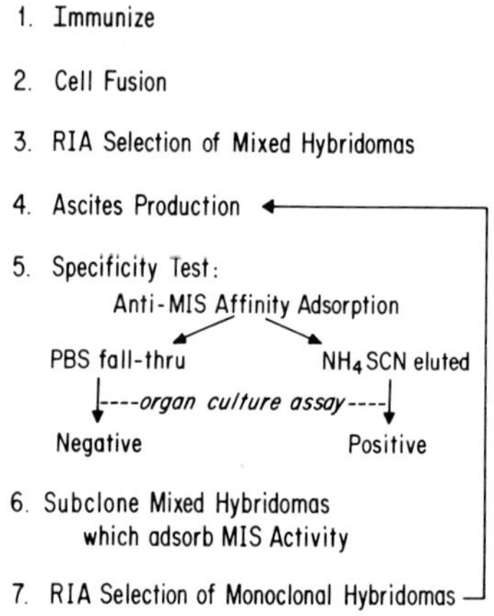

1. Immunize

2. Cell Fusion

3. RIA Selection of Mixed Hybridomas

4. Ascites Production ◄——————————————┐

5. Specificity Test:
        Anti-MIS Affinity Adsorption

     PBS fall-thru   NH₄SCN eluted

     │----organ culture assay----│
     Negative   Positive

6. Subclone Mixed Hybridomas
     which adsorb MIS Activity

7. RIA Selection of Monoclonal Hybridomas ──┘

FIG. 6.   Steps in the selection of anti-MIS monoclonal antibodies.

(hypoxanthine $1 \times 10^{-4} M$, aminopterin, $4 \times 10^{-7} M$, and thymidine $1.6 \times 10^{-5} M$) (Littlefield, 1964) as the selector of hybridoma cell cultures. Cells distributed into 96 well plates were screened for antibody production by a solid phase radioimmunoassay performed on flexible polyvinyl chloride (PVC) microtiter plates (Cook Laboratories) (Klinman $et\ al.$, 1976). A crude MIS preparation was used to coat the plates and anti-MIS antibody detected using a double antibody technique with ^{125}I goat anti-mouse IgG antibody. Increasingly pure fractions of MIS (7000- or 15,000-fold purification) were used to screen for anti-MIS antibody during subsequent subcloning (Mudgett-Hunter $et\ al.$, 1982).

A. MIXED HYBRIDOMAS

Mixed hybridomas were augmented by growth in the peritoneal cavity of pristane primed BALB/c mice. After 10 to 14 days the resulting ascites fluid was collected from each mouse and tested for the presence of anti-MIS antibody by both radioimmunoassay and by its ability to remove biologically active MIS from an MIS preparation. The IgG fraction from the peritoneal fluid was isolated from approximately 10 ml of ascites fluid by DEAE chromatography and then coupled to the solid support N-hydroxysuccinimide-activated Sepharose (HAS) (Gottlieb $et\ al.$, 1975). MIS fractions with high biological activity were then passed over columns of the HAS anti-MIS IgG and eluted with PBS. The bound MIS was eluted from the column with $3\ M$ ammonium thiocyanate (NH₄SCN) (Mudgett-Hunter $et\ al.$, 1978), concentrated, and dialyzed against PBS. The crude MIS preparation, before and after passage through the HAS anti-MIS IgG

column, and the ammonium thiocyanate-eluted MIS were tested for biological activity in the organ culture assay. Monoclonal antibody specific
for digoxin (Mudgett-Hunter et al., 1980) served as control antibody.

B. MONOCLONAL HYBRIDOMAS

The cells in the peritoneal fluid which produced an IgG capable of
binding MIS were then cloned by limiting dilution using BALB/c spleen
cells as feeder layers. Colonies grown in wells seeded at 1 cell/well were
considered monoclonal and were tested for anti-MIS antibody both by the
polyvinyl chloride radioimmunoassay and again after augmentation in ascites fluid, by binding and eluting MIS on the anti-MIS HAS column.

After Fusion 5, 28 of the hybridomas with the highest counts were
chosen for further analysis, but after 4 weeks of growth in HT media, only
5 of the original mixed hybridomas still remained positive by the radioimmunoassay. Two of the five mixed hybridomas (ID1 and IIH6) were tested
for their ability to adsorb MIS (Fig. 7). The fall-through PBS-eluted fraction showed markedly diminished MIS activity when tested in the organ
culture assay as compared to the MIS fraction passed over a digoxin
antibody column (data not shown). These two mixed hybridomas were
subcloned by limiting cell dilution, but only the ID1 mixed hybridoma
yielded clones which tested positive in the radioimmunoassay. Ascites
fluid was obtained for ID1 subclones (IB2, IIB6, IIG7, and IIIB4), but
only IB2 was capable of adsorbing biological activity (Fig. 8). Biological
activity was successfully eluted from the IB2 affinity column with the
ammonium thiocyanate wash.

In another fusion, #7, a 7000-fold purified MIS preparation used to
immunize BALB/c mice prior to fusion proved to be less antigenic, since
culture media from only one well (IVA6) contained antibody reactive to

FUSION	MIXED HYBRIDOMA	CULTURE MEDIA DAYS POST-FUSION =counts/min=		ASCITES (1 : 10 dil.) =counts/min=	ADSORBED BIOLOGICAL ACTIVITY
		19	49		
#5	ID1	2412	1346	n.d.	+
	IG10	2524	499	2643	−
	IID5	1747	505	6858	−
	IIH6	2461	730	6050	+
	IVF4	2146	651	2734	−
#7	IVA6	4435	3691	n.d.	n.d.

FIG. 7. RIA counts of media and ascites from mixed hybridomas from two separate
fusions.

FUSION	MIXED HYBRIDOMA	SUBCLONE	CULTURE MEDIA	ASCITES	ADSORBED BIOLOGICAL ACTIVITY
			=counts / min=		
#5	ID1	IB2	4515	6167	+
		IIB6	5146	5663	−
		IIG7	2975	6459	−
		IIIB4	3271	4531	−
#7	IVA6	IIIB3	4783	5947	+

FIG. 8. RIA counts from subclones of mixed hybridomas which had adsorbed biological activity. Of the subclones from fusion 5 with high counts in the RIA, only one (IB2) adsorbed biological activity. From fusion 7, the single subclone with high counts (IIIB3) from the only mixed hybridoma with high counts, also adsorbed biological activity.

MIS by polyvinyl chloride plate RIA (Fig. 7). Consequently the cells from this well were first subcloned by limiting dilution and several selected clones were augmented in peritoneal fluid. One of these clones, IIIB3, was expanded in ascites fluid and its IgG found to successfully remove MIS after coupling the antibody to HAS (Fig. 8).

C. SPECIFICITY OF MONOCLONAL HYBRIDOMA

In an attempt to assess the crossreactivity of monoclonal antibody IIIB3 with other proteins, several proteins were tested for their ability to inhibit the binding of IIIB3 to MIS-coated wells by radioimmunoassay in polyvinyl chloride plates. Myoglobin, hemocyanin, insulin, and biologically negative fractions of MIS did not significantly inhibit the binding of IIIB3 to the MIS preparation coating the wells. In contrast to these protein solutions, a 15,000-fold purified fraction of MIS gave significant inhibition of binding to MIS (Fig. 9).

In summary, impure fractions of MIS were used to immunize BALB/c mice. Spleen cells from mice were fused with the murine myeloma NS1 and two monoclonal hybridomas secreting antibody specific for MIS were isolated. Specificity of these antibodies was demonstrated by their ability (1) to absorb biologically active MIS prior to an organ culture assay, and (2) to compete favorably with other potentially crossreacting preparations in a solid phase radioimmunoassay.

In the course of our studies, the power of the somatic cell fusion technique was realized 2-fold. First, in spite of the impurities present in the MIS preparation used for immunization, a monoclonal antibody specific for MIS was obtained. Recent literature lists several examples of hybridoma-secreting monoclonal antibodies to a single differentiation antigen where the immunizing agent was whole cells (Marshak-Rothstein *et al.*, 1979; Hammerling *et al.*, 1979; Herlyn *et al.*, 1979; and Springer *et al.*, 1978). Production of monoclonal antibody specific for one protein present in an impure fraction has only recently been reported for human leukemia interferon (Secher and Burke, 1980; Staehelin *et al.*, 1981). The present study emphasizes the efficacy of obtaining a monoclonal antibody specific for a single component present in low concentration in the immunizing preparation. Second, this study demonstrates that even uncloned hybridoma mixtures may be used to raise ascites with preservation of specific antibody production. Although not recommended as standard practice, raising ascites from a mixed hybridoma cell population was necessary here in order to obtain antibody in sufficient quantity (milligram) to assess antibody specificity for MIS prior to subcloning. If this step were omitted, ascites from many subclones would have had to be screened in the bioassay in order to determine which had the requisite specificity for MIS.

A library of monoclonal antibodies to MIS will be used to purify MIS, to identify translation products of mRNA, to establish a standardized RIA for MIS, and to determine tissue localization and distribution. Monoclonal antibodies both to MIS and MIS receptors will be manipulated for chemotherapeutic applications.

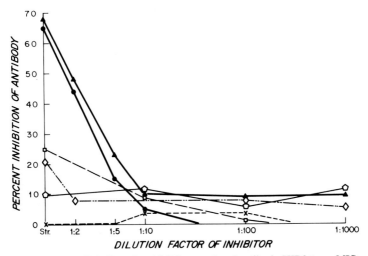

FIG. 9.   Inhibition of binding of anti-MIS monoclonal antibody IIIB3 to an MIS preparation (Con A-2 7000-fold purified) in the polyvinyl chloride plate. Protein solutions: ●, green-2 against IIIB3 culture media, and ▲, green 2-against IIIB3 ascites fluid show good inhibition; ◇, green-1, ×, insulin, □, hemocyanin-digoxin, and ⟠ myoglobin show little inhibition against IIIB3 culture media.

IV. Efficacy of MIS as a Chemotherapeutic Agent against Human Ovarian Cancer *in Vitro*

Natural inhibitors such as MIS may prove to be effective chemotherapeutic agents since they should be endowed with specificity and in addition may possess molecular configurations which permit protected intercellular and intracellular transport. These substances may themselves be directly applicable as chemotherapeutic agents, or may act as homing carriers for other less specific chemotherapeutic or other radiomimetic agents. In addition they may provide examples for analog modulations. We have studied MIS in depth, encouraged by the hypothesis that a fetal regressor may act as a tumor regressor against tumors originating from the same cells or organs that regress under the influence of the fetal regressor during embryonic development (Donahoe *et al.*, 1979).

The Müllerian duct, the embryonic anlagen of the uterus, fallopian tube, and upper vagina in the mammalian species, regresses under the influence of MIS. We therefore investigated semipurified fractions of MIS for their ability to bring about regression of tumors of Müllerian duct origin. We turned to human ovarian carcinoma, both because of its availability and because of its secondary Müllerian structure. Endometrial, cervical, or fallopian tube tumors, as more obvious Müllerian duct tumors, were not available to us in tissue culture at the outset of these studies.

A. WHY OVARIAN CANCER?

The serous carcinoma accounts for most of the human ovarian cancers encountered in the western world. Several pathological observations indicate that this tumor originates from the surface epithelium of the ovary and differentiates toward a Müllerian type of epithelium. The best differentiated areas of a serous carcinoma of the ovary are composed of typical ciliated epithelium, which mimics the lining of the fallopian tube. Exophitic serous carcinomas appear to arise from the surface epithelium (Scully, 1979). Cystic serous carcinomas apparently originating from surface epithelial inclusions cysts within the ovarian stroma (Donahoe *et al.*, 1981b) (Fig. 10) are thought to arise after ovulation when proliferation of the stromal and epithelial elements at the site of perforation leads to incorporation of the surface epithelium into the ovarian cortex during repair at the site of rupture of the follicle. Although the surface epithelium of the ovary is not a direct derivative of Müllerian duct epithelium, it is thought to have Müllerian potential on undergoing neoplasia, since it forms from the coelomic epithelium, which covers the urogenital ridge and gives rise to the Müllerian duct in close proximity to the developing ovary (Fig. 11).

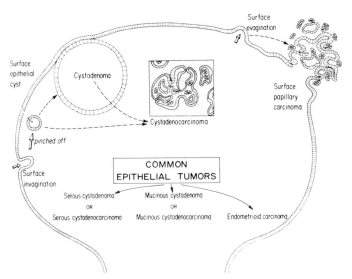

FIG. 10. Proposed genesis of common epithelial ovarian carcinomas from invagination or evagination of the surface coelomic epithelium.

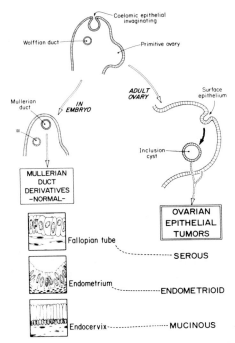

FIG. 11. Proposed scheme demonstrating parallelism between the development of the Müllerian duct from coelomic epithelium and the formation of ovarian epithelial tumors from the coelomic epithelium.

A human ovarian cancer cell line (HOC-21), obtained from Dr. T. Yamada, Keio University, Japan, doubles every 28 hours in tissue culture. Its previous diploid number of 46 XX noted in a karyotype done in 1974 (Yamada, 1974), changed to a modal number of approximately 70 in 1981 after continuous serial subculture. The histologic appearance of the tumor, however, has remained similar to that of the original tumor removed in 1971, if 10^4 or more cells are heterotransplanted into the hamster cheek pouch or 10^5 or more cells are transplanted into homozygous nude mice (Donahoe et al., 1981b). Since 1978, this cell line has been subcultured twice weekly in our laboratory from stationary monolayers at 37°C in Eagle's minimal essential media (MEM) containing 15% fetal calf serum, 1% penicillin (10,000 units/ml), and streptomycin (10,000 μg/ml). We were encouraged by initial observations made when we harvested media from beneath fetal testis that had been incubating in organ culture and applied this media to a tissue culture flask containing a monolayer of HeLa cells. The cells treated with media from beneath the fetal testis lifted from the dish in sheets or were destroyed. We then attempted to quantitate these observations using the HOC-21 cell line. As control lines we used a human fibroblast strain derived from the foreskin of a 1-year-old undergoing circumcision and a glioblastoma (non-Müllerian duct tumor) line (Donahoe et al., 1979).

B. MONOLAYER MICROCYTOXICITY

Monolayers of these cells lines after they approach confluency (3 day after a 1:2 subculture) (Macieira-Coelho, 1973), were washed, dispersed, and counted. Appropriate dilutions for each cell line were made with either MEM or F10 with 20% fetal calf serum, and 300–400 cells were delivered to each well of a Falcon 3034 microtest plate in a 0.01 ml volume (Wood and Morton, 1970). Plates were incubated and the following morning media was blotted from the wells and replaced with new media. Testis and control fractions were then added (total volume, 0.02 ml/well) in a template pattern to equalize drying effects. After a 24-hour incubation period, the plates were washed and stained, and the adherent cells counted on a projection screen. Six replicate wells were used for each test fraction. The microtest plates contained phosphate-buffered saline (PBS) as a negative control, fractions from newborn calf heart (no Müllerian duct regression) as a tissue negative control, and fractions from newborn calf testes that were either inactive (biochemical negative controls) or active (test substance) in the organ culture assay. The counts of the 18 PBS control replicate wells were averaged and compared with the average of the six replicates of each fraction tested, and a cytotoxicity index [CI =

(control well counts − test well counts)/control well counts] was calculated separately for each plate. A CI greater than 0.25 differed significantly from the controls ($p < 0.01$, Student's t test). Müllerian duct regression activity was simultaneously determined for each test fraction, and the activity in an organ culture assay was correlated with the cytotoxicity assay on the human ovarian cancer cells.

Newborn calf testes were extracted in guanidine hydrochloride and sequentially purified using cesium chloride density gradient sedimentation and gel chromatography and used for subsequent microcytotoxicity assay.

A significant cytotoxic index against the human ovarian carcinoma was obtained when the biologically active Fraction 11, obtained by density gradient sedimentation of the guanidine extract, was applied to the cells in the microtest wells (Fig. 12). A significant cytotoxic effect was not obtained when similar fractions from newborn calf heart were tested against the human ovarian carcinoma cells (HOC-21) (Donahoe *et al.*, 1979). Similarly, none of these fractions from nontesticular tissue demonstrated Müllerian duct regression in the organ culture assay. When biologically active fractions from calf testis were tested in the microtest system against a

Row	TOXICITY TEST SOLUTION	SKIN FIBROBLASTS (Human, 1 yr.)		OVARIAN CARCINOMA (Human – 1971)	
		Avg. cells per well	C.I.	Avg. cells per well	C.I.
2	PBS (Control)	64.0		96.7	
3	BB 144 F₁₁ 1:1	60.0	-0.01	54.0	0.37
4	CMRL	68.3	-0.15	91.2	-0.06
5	PBS (Control)	61.2		83.7	
6	PBS (Control)	53.5		86.8	
7	BB 144 F₁₁ 1:3	54.3	0.09	65.3	0.24
8	CMRL	70.7	-0.19	91.8	-0.07
9	PBS (Control)	58.3		84.8	

FIG. 12.   Newborn calf testes were extracted with guanidine, subjected to density gradient sedimentation in $CsCl_2$ and ultrafiltration, then dialyzed and concentrated. Fractions were then assayed for Müllerian duct regression. Those with positive biological activity were mixed with media and added to the wells of a microtest plate over either skin fibroblasts or human ovarian cancer cells that were at appropriate density and synchronized in the S phase of the cell cycle. BB 144 F11 is a density gradient sedimentation fraction with 2–3+ MIS biological activity.

Row	TOXICITY TEST SOLUTION	GLIOBLASTOMA (Human-1973)		ORGAN CULTURE RESULTS
		Avg. cells per well	C. I.	
2	PBS (Control)	108.8		
3	BB 149 Biogel B	119.0	−0.08	0
4	BB 157 F_{11}	104.0 ppt	0.05	3-4 +
5	BB 157 Biogel B	116.0	−0.05	0
6	PBS (Control)	105.5		
7	BB 158 F_{11}(redia.)	107.2 ppt	0.03	1-2 +
8	BB 159 Biogel	122.2 ppt	−0.11	2-4+ ppt
9	PBS (Control)	115.7		

FIG. 13.　Fractions from newborn calf testes or heart fragments were added to microtiter plates containing glioblastoma cells. No cytotoxicity was seen against the non-Müllerian glioblastoma cells. BB 149 represents fractions derived from newborn calf heart. BB 157, 158, and 159 are fractions from newborn calf testes.

human fibroblast line (Fig. 12) or a glioblastoma line (Fig. 13), no significant cytotoxic effect was observed. A cytotoxic effect was not observed when biologically active fractions were applied against the human ovarian cancer line which had been subcultured more than 3 days earlier. This effect also was not present when the plates were sparsely (less than 50 cells/well) or densely (greater than 100 cells/well) seeded. The cytotoxic effect was not observed unless S phase synchrony of the cell cycle was controlled (Macieiro-Coelho, 1973).

Whether this cytotoxic response following the interaction of these fractions with the tumor is due to loss of cell adherence or cell death has not been addressed by this study.

C. COLONY INHIBITION

Since the monolayer microcytotoxicity method could not differentiate clearly between cell detachment and cell death, we turned to the clonogenic soft agar assay where the end point was growth inhibition of clonogenic cells. More highly purified biologically active MIS, prepared by incubation rather than by guanidine extraction techniques, was used to study colony inhibition of the human ovarian carcinoma cell line, HOC-21. Newborn calf testes were incubated in F10 media with the antiprotease benzamidine at 37°C for 45 minutes, following which the supernatant was reequilibrated on a Sephadex G-25 column and fractionated by sequential anion and cation exchange chromatography as previously described (Budzik *et al.*, 1980). The biologically active fraction which did not bind to the CM BioGel A column (CM-1), and which represented a 50-fold purification, was then aliquoted in 0.5 ml volumes and stored in Nunc tubes at −80°C. Biologically inactive CM-1 fractions prepared from newborn bovine heart tissue (rather than testis) and PBS were used as negative controls. In addition, bioactive CM-1 was inactivated by heating to 100°C for 10 minutes and, following centrifugation, the supernatant, which was biologically inactive in the assay, used as yet another negative control. All fractions were tested in the organ culture assay for biological activity and this activity correlated with colony inhibition activity. The colony inhibition activity of Adriamycin, cis-platinum, and hexamethylmelamine in therapeutic doses (Fuller *et al.*, 1982) was compared to that produced by the biologically active MIS fractions.

HOC-21 cells were again harvested 3 days after subculture just as the cells reached confluency in an attempt to synchronize the cells in the S phase of the cell cycle. Cells in a 75-cm² flask were washed, trypsinized, and were resuspended in the "plating" or upper layer according to the method of Hamburger and Salmon over a lower layer containing both conditioned medium and promoting factors (Fig. 14) (Hamburger and Salmon, 1977; Salmon *et al.*, 1978; Hamburger *et al.*, 1978, Salmon and Buick, 1979). Viability, as determined by trypan blue exclusion, was greater than 95% after passage through a 25-gauge needle immediately prior to counting and plating. Our first series of experiments were done with a cell number of 250,000 per plate in order to compare results achieved by previous investigators using standard chemotherapeutic agents in colony inhibition against other human ovarian cancer. Cells at this number gave both acceptable plating efficiency and colony growth at 14–21 days.

HOC-21 cells were mixed with substances to be tested and the growth factors asparagine, DEAE Dextran, and mercaptoethanol were added to the upper layer prior to plating in agar. The upper cell layer was pipetted into coded 35-mm gridded petri dishes (Lux #5217) and allowed to harden at room temperature for 0.5 hour. Plates were incubated at 37°C, in 5% CO_2 for 14 to 21 days, and colonies counted in a standardized cruciate pattern by two independent observers. Colony inhibition by the biologically active MIS fraction (CM-1) at various dilutions was compared with either the negative and positive control plates and results of these experiments were compared by Student's t test; a value of $p < 0.05$ was considered significant.

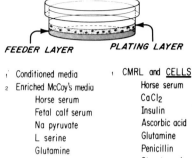

FEEDER LAYER   PLATING LAYER

1	Conditioned media	1	CMRL and CELLS
2	Enriched McCoy's media		Horse serum
	Horse serum		CaCl₂
	Fetal calf serum		Insulin
	Na pyruvate		Ascorbic acid
	L serine		Glutamine
	Glutamine		Penicillin
	Penicillin		Streptomycin
	Streptomycin	2	MIS or CONTROL
3	Tryptic soy broth	3	Asparagine
4	Asparagine	4	DEAE dextran
5	DEAE dextran	5	Mercaptoethanol
6	Agar	6	Agar

FIG. 14.   The colony inhibition assay employed a two-layer agar plate with a feeder layer containing conditioned media and a plating layer containing cells and MIS or control. The 1 ml feeder layer contained 0.5 ml modified McCoy's 5a medium, 0.25 ml 2% Gibco agar, and 0.25 ml of conditioned media prepared from adherent spleen cells of BALB/c mice intraperitoneally primed with 0.5 ml Pristane 4 to 6 weeks previously. Modified McCoy's 5a medium (Gibco) as a stock solution was enriched to a final concentration of 4.2% horse serum, 8.5% heat-inactivated fetal calf serum, 1.7 mM sodium pyruvate, 0.03 mM L-serine, 1.7 mM glutamine, 85 units/ml penicillin, and 85 μg/ml streptomycin. At the time of preparation of the under or feeder layer, 3 ml of 3% tryptic soy broth was added to 12 ml enriched McCoy's medium, alone with 180 μl of 50 mM asparagine and 90 μl of DEAE dextran (50 mg/ml). After incubation of the cells with MIS or control, 45 μl of 50 mM asparagine, 22.5 μl of DEAE dextran (50 mg/ml), and 11 μl of 14.3 mM mercaptoethanol were added to each tube of 7.5 × 10⁵ cells suspended in enriched CMRL which constituted the upper layer. This was plated with 0.53 ml agar into 3 gridded petri dishes. CMRL 1066 (Gibco) was enriched with 12% horse serum, 3.2 mM calcium chloride, 1.6 units/ml insulin, 0.23 mM vitamin C, 80 units/ml penicillin, 80 μg/ml streptomycin, and 3.2 mM glutamine (Hamburger and Salmon, 1977).

Fractions with high MIS biological activity as demonstrated in organ culture inhibited colony growth in the soft agar colony inhibition assay in a dose-dependent manner. A significant difference was seen when CM-1 from 10^{-1} to 10^{-4} ml were compared to control PBS plates. Doses of 10^{-5} and 10^{-6} did not show significant differences (Fuller *et al.*, 1982) (Fig. 15). Mean colony growth of control plates was established as 100% and inhibition was calculated as a percentage of control colony counts. A dose–response relationship was evident when the data were plotted on a semilog scale. Fifty percent inhibition occurred with 3×10^{-3} ml MIS preparation, which corresponded to 2 μg total protein or 1/300 of the purified product of a single testis. Heat inactivated CM-1 did not inhibit colony growth significantly when compared to PBS controls. Adriamycin exhibited significant colony inhibition when compared to PBS controls and served as a positive control. Heat-inactivated CM-I failed to exhibit a significant colony inhibition at similar doses. Newborn calf heart tissue was prepared in a manner identical to newborn calf testis. Human ovarian cancer cells incubated with the CM-1 fraction from heart produced the same number of colonies (202 ± 43), as did those cells incubated with PBS (202 ± 42).

The ability of MIS to inhibit HOC-21 in soft agar in a dose-dependent manner and to lose that ability with heat inactivation supports our earlier observation of cytotoxicity in a microcytotoxicity assay. Fractions inactive in organ culture assay were unable to inhibit HOC-21 colony growth, again demonstrating the specificity of MIS. The inhibition caused by MIS compares favorably with that caused by adriamycin, even though the adriamycin was tested in a continual exposure system since it is not inactivated at 37°C as is the glycoprotein MIS. The efficacy of MIS as a chemotherapeutic agent has been strengthened by these colony inhibition studies which will be continued (1) with the same cell line at different cell numbers, (2) with more purified preparations of MIS, (3) against other Müllerian-derived tumor cell lines, and (4) against fresh human ovarian cancer cells obtained directly from patients in the operating room.

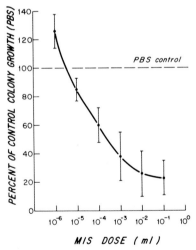

MIS DOSE (ml)

FIG. 15. Colony inhibition by the biologically active CM-I fraction was expressed as a percentage of PBS control colony growth and the results from multiple doses in each of 5 experiments (3 plates each) were combined to form the dose–response curve. The vertical lines indicate the standard deviation at each dose. Colony growth at doses of 10^{-1} to 10^{-4} were significantly different from controls. One milliliter of CM-1 corresponds to the product of one testis: 3×10^{-3} ml, equivalent to 2 μg semipurified protein, produces 50% inhibition of colony growth with PBS controls.

D. *In Vivo* INHIBITION OF HUMAN OVARIAN CANCER BY MIS IN NUDE MICE

As larger quantities of biologically active more purified MIS became available, we proceeded to *in vivo* studies as the next logical step to investigate the chemotherapeutic potential of MIS. Since there are no readily available syngeneic transplantable ovarian common epithelial tumors of Müllerian duct derivation in small animals, we turned to the nude mouse (Donahoe *et al.*, 1981b). Athymic, hairless, homozygous nude mice nu/nu (Rygaard and Povlsen, 1969) are deficient in thymus-derived lymphocytes, and therefore lack the ability to mount a cell-mediated immune response.

HOC-21 cells were harvested after multiple 3-day cultures (Donahoe *et al.*, 1979) and disaggregated to create a single cell suspension by passage through a 25-gauge needle. The cells were counted in a hemocytometer chamber, and viability ($> 95\%$) was assessed. The appropriate cell number (1 to 5×10^6) was resuspended in enriched CMRL-1066 (Connaught Medical Research Laboratory) containing either (1) an MIS preparation, (2) heat-inactivated MIS, (3) a heart preparation, (4) PBS, (5) doxorubicin (adriamycin, Adria Laboratories, Inc., Columbus, Ohio 43215) 0.1 μg/ml, or *cis*-diaminedichloroplatinum (Platinol, Bristol Laboratories, Syracuse, N.Y. 13201) 0.04 μg/ml, after which they were incubated by gentle manual agitation with each of these substances for 1 hour at 37°C prior to injection. The injection of 0.5 ml was done with a 25-gauge needle in the subcutaneous tissue of the mid-dorsal right flank (Auerbach *et al.*, 1978). Selected animals were reinjected at 24 and 48 hours at the site of the original inoculation.

The animals were inspected daily and the length and width of each tumor was measured. The earliest day of tumor appearance was noted. The animals were sacrificed at selected intervals throughout and at the conclusion of the study, and the presence or absence of tumor confirmed histologically. The proportion of animals free of tumor in each group was plotted against time from inoculation using Kaplan–Meier life table calculations, and the significance of the delay in tumor appearance was determined by the log rank test of Mantell on a programmable calculator (Peto *et al.*, 1977; Tepperman, 1980). Tumor-free MIS-treated animals were compared with tumor-free control animals by the Fisher exact test; $p <$ 0.05 was considered statistically significant.

Tumors grew readily in control animals, invading locally but not metastasizing. Nodules of 3 to 4 mm in diameter could be palpated at 48 hours which is consistent with the kinetics of the HOC-21 tumor observed in tissue culture (Yamada, 1974).

In a preliminary experiment 5×10^6 HOC-21 cells were injected into BALB/c nude mice after pretreatment of the cells with 0.02 to 0.5 ml of MIS preparation per animal. A statistically significant delay in appearance of tumor was observed when pretreatment with MIS ($n = 8$) was compared with pretreatment with heat-inactivated MIS or PBS ($n = 9$). A cell inoculum of 2×10^6 or 1.5×10^6 produced tumors in all the control mice whereas an inoculum of 1×10^6 produced tumors in only 60%.

One or 2×10^6 cells were present in the inoculum used in the experiments ($n = 29$), which explored the effects of varying doses of MIS on tumor growth. An MIS dose–response relation was observed both when the time of appearance of the tumor and the tumor-free survival of the animals were evaluated (Figs. 16 and 17). Pretreatment with adriamycin also delayed the appearance of the ovarian tumor. A biologically inactive preparation from bovine heart (not shown), purified in the same manner as the CM-1 preparation of MIS from bovine testes, did not prolong the tumor-free survival. The tumor nodules were sampled histologically for confirmation at the end of the experiment in all the animals, and at 2, 3, and 5 days after injection in selected control animals. The histologic appearance was similar to that seen in the original tumor (Yamada, 1974).

An inoculum of 5×10^6 human colon carcinoma cells (SW-48) was required to produce a palpable tumor in all the control animals within 5 days: 1×10^6 cells produced a tumor in only 40%, and 2×10^6 cells in only 60% of the animals injected. Pretreatment of the SW-48 cells with MIS

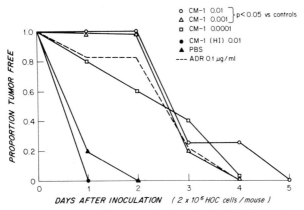

FIG. 16. HOC-21 cells (2×10^6) were preincubated with MIS. Increasing concentrations of CM-I (MIS) prolonged the tumor-free interval ($p < 0.05$) in Swiss nude mice. A similar prolongation is seen after pretreatment of the cells with adriamycin. Heat-inactivated MIS did not prolong the tumor-free interval in comparison to PBS. Each group tested consisted of 5 mice except at the highest dose where $n = 4$.

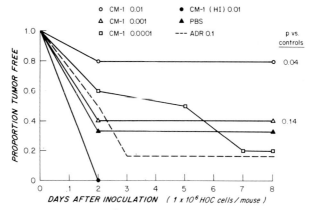

FIG. 17. Pretreatment of 1×10^6 HOC-21 cells with increasing concentrations of CM-I (MIS) prolonged the tumor-free interval in a dose-dependent manner in Swiss nude mice. The highest concentration of CM-I at this cell number resulted in 80% tumor-free interval ($p < 0.04$). $n = 5$ in each group except for the PBS-treated group where $n = 6$.

resulted in no delay in the appearance of the tumor in comparison to that observed with the use of PBS or heat-inactivated MIS (Fig. 18).

The inhibition of HOC-21 by MIS in contrast to the failure of inhibition of colon carcinoma by MIS indicated again that the human ovarian serous carcinoma may be sensitive to MIS as a chemotherapeutic agent, as suggested by previous *in vitro* observations in the microcytotoxicity assay (Donahoe *et al.*, 1979) and the colony inhibition assay (Fuller *et al.*, 1982).

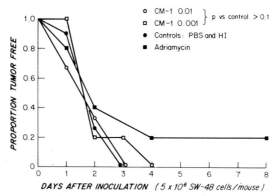

FIG. 18. Pretreatment of colon carcinoma cells (5×10^6) with MIS did not delay tumor appearance when compared with PBS or heat inactivated MIS. $n = 6$ in each group.

E. INHIBITION BY MÜLLERIAN-INHIBITING SUBSTANCE OF FRESH HUMAN OVARIAN CANCER CELLS OBTAINED FROM PATIENTS UNDERGOING DIAGNOSTIC PARACENTESIS

Preliminary data derived from fresh human ovarian cancer cells obtained from patients with ovarian cancer who were undergoing diagnostic and therapeutic paracentesis demonstrated inhibition of colony growth after pretreatment of the cells with biologically active MIS fractions (Fuller et al., 1982). The tumor cells were collected by suction-filtration into sterile containers and the red cells lysed with ammonium chloride. Washed cells (250,000) in single cell suspension were then plated in soft agar over the conditioned media underlayer as previously described for the established cell line (HOC-21) (Fuller et al., 1982). Significant colony inhibition was observed against the tumor cells of 4 out of 5 patients when the cells were incubated with the biologically active MIS fraction CM-I at doses of 10^{-2} and 10^{-3} ml.

F. SUMMARY OF CHEMOTHERAPEUTIC STUDIES

Additional studies are underway to determine the colony inhibitory effect of more purified fractions of MIS against other cell lines of ovarian carcinoma and against endometrial and cervical carcinoma cell lines at varying cell numbers, as well as against fresh Müllerian duct tumors and ovarian tumors both in ascites and solid form. Other fresh tumors and established cell lines will be tested in this system to determine if MIS is specific to Müllerian derivative tumors. If a tumor such as HOC-21 remains susceptible to MIS then this line will be used to investigate MIS receptors and the mechanism of action of MIS.

Rosenwaks and his colleagues (Rosenwaks et al., 1981) described inhibition of an established endometrial cancer (HEC-1) in culture since 1968, by a newborn rat testicular homogenate as well as media from beneath an organ culture of a 7-day-old rat testis. Monkey kidney cells were not inhibited. Neither heart, liver, kidney, nor adult testis media inhibited the endometrial monolayer. This study demonstrates cytotoxicity of a testicular homogenate and of incubation media from testis for a cell line that is unquestionably of Müllerian duct origin. The cytotoxic effect on this cell line was also observed to occur in the growth phase, but not in the stationary phase of the cell cycle.

This accumulated evidence has encouraged us to continue studies of MIS as a chemotherapeutic agent against tumors of Müllerian duct origin. The potential specificity afforded by natural inhibitors may make them valuable adjuncts in the multimodality therapy of cancer patients.

V. Matrix Ultrastructure and Biochemistry during Müllerian Duct Regression

A. ULTRASTRUCTURE OF MÜLLERIAN DUCT DURING REGRESSION

The association of Müllerian duct regression with increased activity of hydrolytic enzymes (Scheib, 1963) encouraged our early transmission electron microscopy studies both *in vivo* (Price *et al.*, 1977) and *in vitro* (Price *et al.*, 1979), which suggested that programmed cell death played an important role in the regression of the Müllerian duct. This assumption was supported by the appearance within ductal cells of lysosomes and infiltration of the epithelium by macrophage-like cells. Recent studies (Hayashi *et al.*, 1982) in this laboratory indicated that significant synthesis and degradation of hyaluronate and sulfated glucosaminoglycans occurred at the interface of the ductal epithelium and mesenchyme. Further observations indicated that turnover of the Müllerian duct basement membrane is the significant event in ductal development and further suggested that in addition to cell death some epithelial cells may reenter the mesenchymal cell population after shedding their basement membranes (Trelstad *et al.*, 1982).

Urogenital ridges of rat embryos at days 14, 15, 16, and 17 were fixed in formaldehyde–glutaraldehyde (Karnovsky, 1965) after buffering. The tissues were postfixed in osmium tetroxide, buffered with S-colloidin, and then immersed in uranyl acetate followed by dehydration and embedding in Alderite and Epon (Trelstad *et al.*, 1982). Sections were then cut on a ultramicrotome and, after staining, were examined using the Phillips 300 transmission electron microscope. In some specimens, ruthenium red was added to the fixative to enhance polyanionic materials and to demonstrate glucosaminoglycans. Large composite montages were reconstructed from micrographs taken at the perimeter of the Müllerian and Wolffian ducts at 10,000×.

At day 14 the basement membrane was intact and the cells were oriented perpendicular to the membrane. Early in day 15, the nuclei were still euchromatic and the epithelial cells were oriented perpendicular to the basal cell surface. Large phagosomal vacuoles containing debris were present in both epithelial and mesenchymal cells and in extracellular spaces. During the latter half of day 15, patchy discontinuities appeared in the basement membrane of the Müllerian duct at multiple sites around the perimeter of the duct and, in some regions, the mesenchymal cell processes were closely applied to the remnants of the basement membrane, at some points, making direct contact with the epithelial cells (Fig. 19).

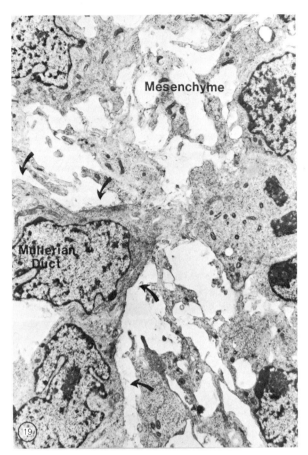

FIG. 19. Arrows demonstrate breakdown of basement membrane, and migration of epithelial cell out of the epithelial basement membrane compartment into the mesenchyme. The nucleus is euchromatic and not pycnotic; therefore transformation to mesenchyme is more likely than cell death.

Many of the epithelial cells within the Müllerian duct become reoriented with their axes parallel to the original basal surface and some appear to migrate or extrude from the epithelium to the mesenchyme cell compartment (Fig. 19). This process continued into day 16. Here again, vacuoles, principally of the autophagic nature, were present in both mesenchymal and epithelial cells and large electron dense aggregates of cellular debris were present in the extracellular space. The epithelial basal surface was devoid of basement membrane and epithelial–mesenchymal contact was obvious. By day 17 the site of the Müllerian duct consisted of a few cells of epithelial derivation as well as mesenchymal cells and macrophages. Aggregates of cellular debris, mostly in the extracellular space, were present within the mesenchymal compartment.

The possibility that some of the Müllerian epithelial cells persisted and entered the mesenchymal compartment was unexpected. Transformations from mesenchyme to epithelium and epithelium to mesenchyme are known to occur during earlier stages of embryonic development. The coelomic epithelium, the source of the Müllerian duct epithelium, is derived from the primary mesenchyme which invades at gastrulation. The Müllerian duct is therefore a mesodermally derived epithelium. Retransformation to the mesenchymal compartment therefore is not unexpected.

B. MATRIX BIOCHEMISTRY

Out attention having been focused on the basement membrane and the processes of epithelial–mesenchymal interactions, we undertook a number of biochemical and histochemical investigations of the tissue aimed at defining changes in the matrix macromolecules. Initial studies using tritiated proline to define collagen biosynthesis in the gonadal ridge indicated that this family of macromolecules was being synthesized in relatively small amounts. On the other hand, studies using tritiated glucosamine indicated a major biosynthetic activity, and accordingly we directed our attention to the biosynthesis and degradation of glycoproteins, proteoglycans, and hyaluronic acid (Hayashi *et al.*, 1982).

Urogenital ridges from timed pregnant rat embryos were placed in organ culture for either autoradiographic or biochemical studies. The ridges were labeled with either 25 μCi/ml of tritiated proline, 40 μCi/ml $H_2{}^{35}SO_4$, or 40 μCi/ml of tritiated glucosamine. Urogenital ridges were labeled for pulse or pulse-chase experiments (Banerjee *et al.*, 1977) and fixed for autoradiography using glutaraldehyde. One-micron sections were covered with Kodak NTB-2 nuclear track emulsion and developed in Kodak D19. Glucosamine and H_2SO_4-treated autoradiography slides were viewed unstained and selected specimens were stained with alcian blue at pH 1 and pH 4 (Alexander and Donoff, 1980). Hyaluronidase activity was determined using a histochemical technique in which a hyaluronate substrate was prepared in a gel and the entire retroperitoneum of the embryo with its inherent hyaluronidase activity placed over the gel (Alexander and Donoff, 1979). Digestion of the hyaluronate film by tissue bound hyaluronidase was then observed, after the slides were appropriately fixed and stained with Toluidine blue, by absence of stain in the tissue areas of note.

The major biosynthetic products produced from tritiated glucosamine were obtained by chemical analysis after enzymatic digestion. Urogenital ridges were dissected from 14, 15, or 16.5 day male or female embryos and the gonads removed. Twenty agonadal ridges of the same sex were then labeled with 50 μCi/ml tritiated glucosamine for 6 hours. Specimens were homogenized, proteins precipitated with trichloroacetic acid, and the supernatant subjected to sequential enzymatic digestion (Fig. 20) using fungal hyaluronidase, testicular hyaluronidase, and testicular hyaluronidase plus nitrous acid (Toole and Gross, 1971). Undigested radiolabeled GAGs were then precipitated with cetylpyridinium chloride and counted. The relative amounts of each GAG was calculated according to their differential susceptibility to enzymatic degradation shown in Fig. 20.

Glycoproteins were calculated by modifying the analysis above. Specimens, after labeling, were extracted with 4 M guanidine hydrochloride. The supernatant was then applied to a DEAE 52 (Whatman) column to separate glycoprotein and hyaluronate from the glucosaminoglycans using differential salt elution. The low salt fraction was then digested with pronase and precipitated with cetylpyridinium chloride. The supernatant contained the glycoproteins and the precipitate hyaluronate.

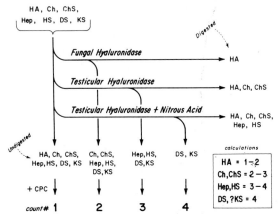

FIG. 20. Sequential enzymatic digestions of the CPC precipitate as described in the text. Aliquots of the CPC precipitate containing HA (hyaluronate), Ch (chondroitin), ChS (chondroitin sulfate), Hep (heparan), HS (heparan sulfate) were treated with the several hyaluronidases and nitrous acid as indicated. Following such treatments the portions either digested or undigested which remained are indicated. The four separate fractions constituting predominantly hyaluronate, chondroitin sulfate, heparan sulfate, and dermatan sulfate (DS) were calculated as indicated. The exact behavior of keratan (KS) sulfate in this process has not been rigorously established (Toole, 1976).

To allow us to focus on changes more specific to the Müllerian duct, the development of the Wolffian duct was stabilized by the addition of $10^{-6} M$ testosterone to the culture media. The 14 day agonadal fetal urogenital ridges were then incubated for 18 or 42 hours either with or without MIS as a CM-1 preparation. The collected ridges were then labeled for 6 hours with tritiated glucosamine and digested and analyzed biochemically as described above. The Müllerian duct in the ridge tissue that was not treated with MIS developed, whereas the Müllerian duct in the ridge tissue which was exposed to MIS regressed.

Although the labeling of the gonad ridge with proline and sulfate was nonspecific, the incorporation of tritiated glucosamine showed a remarkable restriction to the Wolffian and Müllerian ducts. Autoradiographic grains were dense in the basement membrane and periductal region and also covered the epithelial cell surfaces, particularly the luminal surfaces. The tritiated glucosamine pulse-chase and pulse studies revealed that although the Müllerian duct was regressing, there was a rapid turnover of matrix macromolecules with uptake of tritiated glucosamine evident even in the latter stages of regression of the Müllerian duct (Fig. 21). Remarkable persistence of label was found in the mesenchyme cells surrounding the regressing Müllerian duct as late as 42 hours in male chase experiments, both in the immediate vicinity of the remnant of the Müllerian duct, and also at some distance from the site (Fig. 21). Histochemical studies with alcian blue at pH 1 coupled with prior treatment of the tissues with chondroitinase ABC indicated the presence of some sulfated glucosaminoglycans among the matrix macromolecules. The persistence of weak staining in the basement membrane indicated also the presence of some other anionic materials such as heparan sulfate. Alcian blue at pH 4 with or without prior digestion with fungal hyaluronidase indicated that hyaluronate is an active constituent of the periductal region (Hayashi *et al.*, 1982).

Biochemical analysis of the tissues after tritiated glucosamine labeling indicated approximately 30% of the label was incorporated into glycoproteins and the remainder into glucosaminoglycans. Of the 70% of the tritiated glucosamine incorporated counts that were present in GAG, we found that the majority of this fraction was in hyaluronate, the next most prevalent material was chondroitin sulfate. Heparan sulfate was the third most prevalent, and dermatan sulfate and/or keratan sulfate were present in the remaining small amounts.

Treatment of the urogenital ridges with testosterone to stabilize the Wolffian ducts and with MIS to cause regression of the Müllerian duct showed that regression was accompanied by a large fall in hyaluronate and

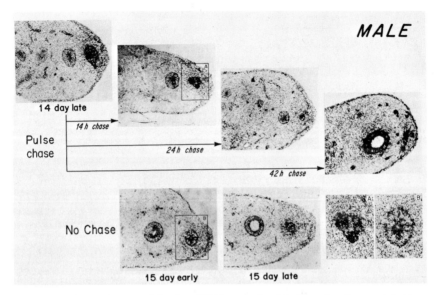

FIG. 21. Autoradiograms following [³H]glucosamine labeling of male gonadal ridges. The upper series demonstrates a pulse-chase experiment in which 14 day ridges were labeled for 6 hours following which they were chased in isotope-free media for the indicated periods of time. Specimens labeled early and late on the fifteenth day of gestation for 6 hours and then fixed immediately are presented in the lower portion of the figure. Higher magnifications of the Müllerian duct in the 14 hour pulse-chase and the 15 day no chase experiments are indicated at the right. All photomicrographs are of unstained preparations. The pronounced labeling of the Wolffian and Müllerian ducts is apparent. In the 42 hour chase specimen note the persistence of label in the distal portion of the ridge despite apparent disappearance of the Müllerian duct. The prominent ductal structure in the 42 hour chase specimen is the Wolffian duct. The two higher magnifications indicate the condensation of the label over the regressing duct and the fragmentation of the labeling at the perimeter of the duct.

heparan sulfate (Fig. 22). Because of the large fall in hyaluronate, we looked for hyaluronidase activity in the tissues by a histochemical procedure using a hyaluronate film. This technique localized the hyaluronidase activity in the periductal region of the regressing Müllerian duct.

Several features of Müllerian duct development which are particularly illuminated by these studies and which probably have bearing on the interaction of the epithelium with its mesenchyme are the condensation of the mesenchyme around the duct prior to its disappearance; the dissolution of the ductal basement membrane; and the persistence of ductal products and possibly ductal cells themselves in the mesenchymal cell population. The collapse of cells around the duct prior to its regression has been noticed in previous morphological studies in this laboratory

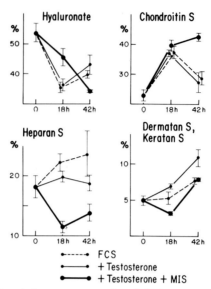

FIG. 22.   Changes in relative percentage of total CPC precipitable radioactivity among the GAG fractions indicated following *in vitro* treatment of agonadal ridges with fetal calf serum (FCS), testosterone, or testosterone plus Müllerian inhibiting substance (MIS). Note that MIS treatment is associated with a suppressed level of hyaluronate and heparan sulfate following 42 hours and an elevated level of chondroitin sulfate.

(Donahoe *et al.*, 1977d; Price *et al.*, 1977, 1979). If hyaluronate is responsible for maintenance of intercellular space, as has been suggested (Trelstad *et al.*, 1967; Fisher and Solursh, 1977), and the removal of hyaluronate by hyaluronidase with the condensation of tissue space (Toole and Trelstad, 1971; Orkin and Toole, 1978; Hayashi *et al.*, 1982) then the condensation of mesenchyme around the Müllerian duct could be explained by the removal of hyaluronate from this region. Our finding that this area is rich in hyaluronate and that it is rapidly degraded by localized hyaluronidase is consistent with this general model (Toole, 1976). The additional information that the basement membrane of the duct disappears at the same time and that the cellular processes in the mesenchyme are found in close opposition to the basement membrane suggests that development of hyaluronidase activity may be one of the early effects of MIS on this system. The cells of origin of this hyaluronidase-like activity remain to be defined; both the mesenchyme and the epithelium are logical candidates (Cohn *et al.*, 1977; David and Bernfield, 1979). The manner in which exogenous agents such as MIS could promote hyaluronidase activity are several, including the stimulation of *de novo* production of the enzyme, activation of a zymogen, or a possible removal of an inhibitor. The possibility that epithelial cells reenter the mesenchymal cell population is suggested by the transmission electron microscopy studies. This phenomenon is not uncommon in embryonic development. Cells of Müllerian origin may persist in the embryo following duct regression and may contribute to other structures in ways not hitherto anticipated.

C. IMMUNOFLUORESCENT LOCALIZATION OF EXTRACELLULAR MATRIX CONSTITUENTS

In an attempt to study specific extracellular matrix constituents important in differentiation of the urogenital ridge we used monospecific antibodies kindly provided by Dr. G. R. Martin, National Institute of Dental Research, NIH, to detect and localize laminin, fibronectin, collagen Type IV, and basement membrane heparan sulfate in rat male and female urogenital ridges during sexual differentiation. The tissues were fixed and processed for immunofluorescence according to the method of Sainte-Marie (1962).

All the above mentioned matrix constituents localized in the basement membrane of Müllerian duct, Wolffian duct, and coelomic epithelium. The immunological staining of Müllerian duct basement membrane by all constituents became irregular and discontinuous in the 15 day male, almost disappearing in 16 days. Fibronectin, which was present in the interstitium, as well as in the basement membranes mentioned above, failed to localize in the condensed mesenchyme in the 15 day male, showing a clear area specifically around the regressing Müllerian duct. Fibronectin was the only one of these four matrix constituents which was affected in the surrounding mesenchyme during Müllerian duct regression.

Fibronectin is a glycoprotein which mediates cell attachment to collagen substrates and is also thought to play a role in cell movements during embryonic development (Ruoslahti, 1981). Therefore, the disappearance of fibronectin from the Müllerian duct periductal mesenchyme may play an important role in promoting mesenchymal transformation and/or reorientation of the regressing Müllerian duct epithelium. It remains unclear, however, whether the disappearance of fibronectin is caused by decreased biosynthesis or by increased rate of proteolytic degradation as in the case of hyaluronate.

VI. The Role of Zinc in Müllerian Duct Regression

Müllerian duct morphology during regression has been studied extensively (Josso et al., 1977; Price et al., 1979; Trelstad et al., 1982), and some light has been shed on the mechanism of action of MIS using the organ-

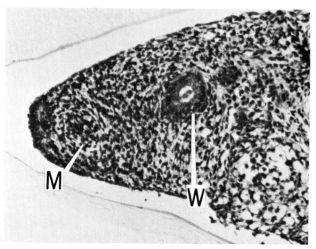

FIG. 23.   Fourteen and one-half day female fetal rat urogenital ridge after incubation with 0.5 m*M* EDTA shows 4–5+ regression of the Müllerian duct. M, Müllerian duct; W, Wolffian duct. ×200.

culture assay. Although this assay is tedious, it is quite reliable, giving few false positive results. We were, therefore, intrigued to find that Müllerian duct regression could be induced by the chelating-agent EDTA (disodium ethylenediaminetetraacetate), which was assayed as a routine check of all agents used during the biochemical purification of MIS. We have subsequently investigated the effects of chelating agents and various cations on Müllerian duct regression and studied their interaction with semipurified preparations of MIS.

The Müllerian duct completely regressed after incubation for 3 days with 0.5 m*M* EDTA (Fig. 23). The histological appearance of the urogenital ridge was very similar to that after exposure to MIS (compare Fig. 3). A dose–response curve was constructed over the range of 0.25 at 0.5 m*M*, as doses of >1 m*M* EDTA were found to be toxic. At doses above 0.3 m*M* there was measurable regression which become complete at 0.45 m*M* (Fig. 24). EGTA [ethylene bis(oxyethylenenitrilotetraacetic acid)] which is a specific chelator for calcium did not cause regression in the organ-culture assay when added in amounts similar to EDTA.

We replaced a number of cations to determine if the EDTA was acting by withdrawing an essential cation from the media or tissue. When 0.5 m*M* EDTA was mixed with 0.5 or 2.5 m*M* Ca^{2+} or Mg^{2+}, there was no inhibition of regression (Fig. 25). By contrast to the inertness of Ca^{2+}, Mg^{2+}, the transition ions, Zn^{2+}, Fe^{2+}, and Fe^{3+} had a profound effect on the Müllerian duct. When 0.5 m*M* EDTA mixed with Zn^{2+}, Fe^{2+}, or Fe^{3+}

M. D. REGRESSION
5
4
3
2
1
0
0
0.1
0.2
0.3
0.4
0.5
[EDTA] mM

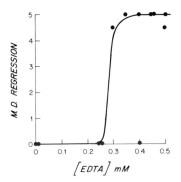

FIG. 24. Regression of the Müllerian duct *in vitro* with increasing concentrations of EDTA. Müllerian duct regression is graded on a semiquantitative scale from 0 to 5. Each circle represents one experiment.

was added to the organ-culture, regression of the Müllerian duct was completely inhibited although none of these cations affected the Müllerian duct when added alone.

After the initial observations demonstrating that Fe^{2+}, Fe^{3+}, or Zn^{2+} could inhibit EDTA-induced Müllerian duct regression, it seemed appropriate to test the effect of cations on the action of MIS directly. When various cations (0.5 mM) were incubated in the presence of partially purified MIS (Fraction WGL-2), only Zn^{2+} blocked regression by MIS

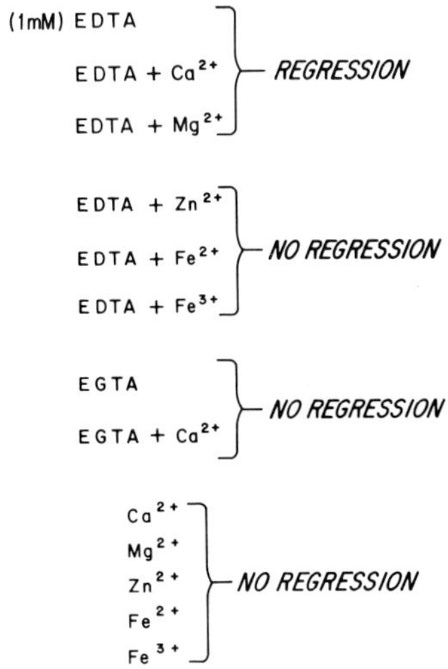

(1mM) EDTA
EDTA + Ca2+
EDTA + Mg2+
REGRESSION
EDTA + Zn2+
EDTA + Fe2+
EDTA + Fe3+
NO REGRESSION
EGTA
EGTA + Ca2+
NO REGRESSION
Ca2+
Mg2+
Zn2+
Fe2+
Fe3+
NO REGRESSION

FIG. 25. Effect of chelating agents and cations on Müllerian duct regression (without MIS).

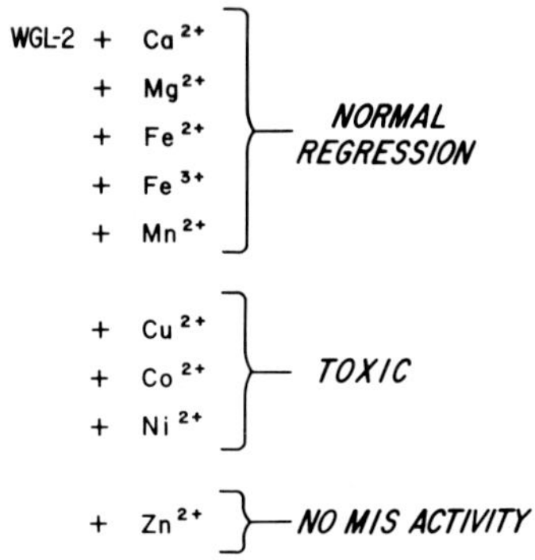

WGL-2 + Ca²⁺ ⎤
       + Mg²⁺ ⎥   *NORMAL*
       + Fe²⁺ ⎬   *REGRESSION*
       + Fe³⁺ ⎥
       + Mn²⁺ ⎦

       + Cu²⁺ ⎤
       + Co²⁺ ⎬— *TOXIC*
       + Ni²⁺ ⎦

       + Zn²⁺ ⎤—*NO MIS ACTIVITY*

FIG. 26. Effect of cations on MIS activity. WGL-2 is a fraction with biological activity for MIS.

(Fig. 26). In most instances, the inhibition of MIS by Zn^{2+} was complete. A dose–response curve for Zn^{2+} against a standard amount of the MIS fraction revealed progressive inhibition of activity above 0.3 mM (Fig. 27).

These results demonstrate that the action of MIS can be imitated by EDTA. The reversal of this effect by Zn^{2+}, along with the inhibition of MIS activity by Zn^{2+}, suggests that this cation is an essential link in the cascade of events leading to Müllerian duct regression.

Zinc is an important constituent in many common enzymes (Riordan, 1976). Zinc deficiency or removal of zinc by chelating agents from those enzymes studied in detail usually leads to enzyme inactivation. Zinc inactivation of MIS-stimulated Müllerian duct regression described in these experiments is different from those previously described, since chelation of zinc duplicates a highly specific protein synthesis dependent regression process (Price *et al.*, 1977). In other words the presence of zinc protects

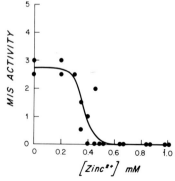

FIG. 27. Effect of increasing concentration of Zn^{2+} on Müllerian duct regression induced by semipurified MIS (WGL-2).

duct integrity or prevents dissolution or migration of the cells. There are only a few reported instances where addition of zinc specifically prevents cellular events. One such event is the inhibition of histamine release from mast cells. Another is the inhibition of macrophage mobility and phagocytosis. Since Müllerian duct regression is characterized by migration of Müllerian duct epithelial cells into the mesenchymal compartment Trelstad *et al.*, 1982), zinc may act by preventing epithelial cell migration. Several membrane-bound enzymes can also be inhibited by zinc, such as ATPase and phospholipase A2 (Chvapil, 1976).

Depletion of zinc from growth media by chelation or zinc deficiency is known to inhibit proliferation of both prokaryotic and eukaryotic cells in culture (Shulman and Dwyer, 1964). However, microscopic examination of histologic sections of urogenital ridges exposed to EDTA does not show such effects, i.e., other cells in the ridge look healthy (Fig. 23). The exact fate of Müllerian duct cells during the regression process is presently unknown. Although cell death apparently plays a role in the regression of the Müllerian duct, it has been suggested that some duct cells may reenter the mesenchymal cell population (Trelstad *et al.*, 1982). Müllerian duct cells may be much more sensitive to the depletion of zinc as compared to the surrounding tissue, thus the addition of EDTA could stimulate epithelial cell migration. A differential sensitivity to zinc deficiency of normal and leukemic lymphoblasts has been noted (Falchuk and Krishan, 1977). While growth of leukemic cells was inhibited at low concentrations by the transition metal chelator, 1,10-phenanthroline, no inhibition of normal lymphoblasts was found at even higher concentrations which were cytotoxic to leukemic cells (Vallee, 1976). Zinc deficiency during pregnancy can also result in congenital malformations of the embryo by causing aberrations in developing organs (Hurley, 1976).

We considered the possibility that MIS might chelate zinc directly, but preincubation of MIS with Zn^{2+} followed by dialysis to remove unbound metal failed to alter the course of regression in the bioassay. Needless to say, these crude experiments do not completely discount the possibility of MIS–zinc binding. However, it appears more likely that zinc is involved in one or more of the subsequent cellular events after MIS triggers the signal for regression such as the hyaluronidase activity observed during duct regression (Hayashi *et al.*, 1982), or the fibronectin depletion seen during specific fluorescent-labeled antibody localization studies during duct regression (Ikawa *et al.*, 1982a).

VII. Avian MIS and Estrogen Receptor Activity

There are intriguing differences between mammals and avian species which have recently thrown some light on the action of MIS. The chick

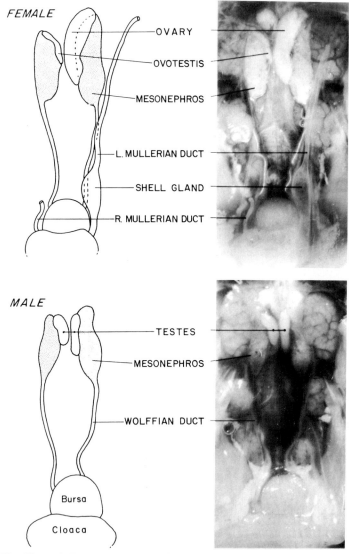

FIG. 28.   Urogenital anatomy of the 19 day female and male chick embryos. In the female embryo both the gonads and Müllerian ducts are asymmetrical.

testis causes regression of the mammalian Müllerian duct, but the mammalian testis does not cause regression of the avian duct (Tran and Josso, 1977). In addition, there is asymmetrical development of the gonads and Müllerian ducts in the female chick which has an ovary and a persistent

Müllerian duct on the left side, and a small ovotestis with an absent Müllerian duct on the right. By contrast the male chick has bilateral testes and no Müllerian ducts after regression (Fig. 28). We originally studied the chick embryo to determine if the right ovotestis of the female chick secreted MIS (Hutson *et al.*, 1981). Chicken gonads were cocultured with the 14.5 day rat urogenital ridge in organ culture (Donahoe *et al.*, 1977a).

To our surprise, we discovered that not only the ovotestis contained MIS, but the left ovary also produced MIS (Fig. 29). This result provided an explanation for unilateral regression of the right Müllerian duct in the female chick, but was puzzling because of the failure of the left duct to regress. We also discovered that MIS was produced by adult fowl gonads,

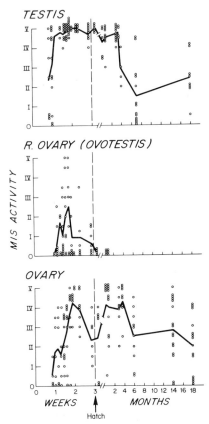

FIG. 29.   MIS activity of chick testis, ovotestis, and ovary from 6 days of embryonic life until 18 months after hatching was graded on a semiquantitative scale of 0–5. The solid line represents the mean of observations at each age. The open circles represent the results of each observation.

both male and female, suggesting that it may have other functions in the adult bird.

Although various hypotheses have been offered to explain regression of the Müllerian ducts in both male and female chick embryos (for a review see Hamilton, 1963), our results suggested that regression can be prevented even in the presence of MIS. Since exogenous estrogens have been shown to cause preservation of the Müllerian ducts in male embryos (Groenendijk-Huijbers, 1962; Scheib and Reyss-Brion, 1979), we considered the possibility that ovarian steroids may inhibit the effect of MIS in the left Müllerian duct. Estrogen receptors have been characterized in the left Müllerian duct of the female chick embryo, and are similar to those found in the adult (Teng and Teng, 1975a). Their number steadily increases from 8 to 12 days, which is the time of sexual differentiation in the chick (Teng and Teng, 1975b). Since only the left duct had been systematically studied for estrogen receptors, it seemed important to determine if there were any differences between the right and left sides, which might be related to the asymmetry of development. Therefore, the content of putative estradiol receptors of right and left Müllerian ducts from 9 day chick embryos was measured using conventional techniques (Anderson et al., 1972; Markaverich et al., 1980). Müllerian ducts were collected onto dry ice and stored at $-80°C$. After a harvest of 100–150 ducts from each site and sex, receptors were analyzed. Estradiol-specific (i.e., diethylstilbestrol displaceable) binding was detected in all cytosol and nuclear preparations examined. The nuclear preparations contained more estradiol binding sites than did the cytosols and when ducts from males and females were examined separately, the levels of estradiol binding were only slightly higher in the males than in the females. In subsequent studies, since no significant difference was seen between males and females, pools of 8 or 9 day right ducts (male and female) were compared to left ducts.

Right Müllerian duct cytosols contained more of the low capacity estradiol-specific binder of the Type I variety than left Müllerian ducts (Fig. 30) (1.5 vs 0.5 fmol/mg duct tissue). The content of nuclear Type I estradiol binder, however, was quite similar on both sides with the left having slightly more (5.3 vs 4.1 fmol/mg duct tissue). The major difference noted in the estradiol binding properties of these ducts was found in the content of nuclear Type II binder. The left ducts, those that are retained in the female, had considerably more Type II binder than the right ducts (22.9 vs 4.3) fmol/mg duct tissue).

The role of low-affinity, high-capacity Type II nuclear binding sites for estrogens is not known, but the presence of such sites may be correlated with an estrogen-induced growth response in the left ducts such as that

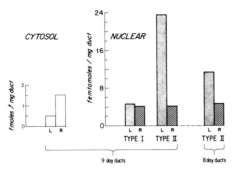

FIG. 30. Levels of estrogen receptors in the cytosol and nucleus (Type I and II) in 8 and 9 day chick Müllerian ducts.

suggested for the uterus by Eriksson *et al.* (1980). This initial screening of estrogen binders in 8–9 day chick embryos provides a clue perhaps to the reason why the left duct in the female is preserved in the presence of sufficient MIS to ablate the right duct.

The biological response of the right and left Müllerian ducts to estrogen may be different since the nuclear content of Type II estrogen binding sites is not the same. The response of the left duct may include molecular events that inhibit or otherwise block MIS activity and allow the duct to develop.

VIII. Steroid Enhancement of Müllerian-Inhibiting Substance

The differences in estrogen Type II nuclear receptors in the left Müllerian duct of the chick led us to study a number of steroid hormones to see if MIS activity could be either inhibited or enhanced. Three hormones are important for male sexual differentiation in the mammalian fetus, testosterone, dihydrotestosterone, and MIS. Testosterone maintains the mesonephric tubules and Wolffian ducts, and stimulates their morphogenesis into epididymis, vas deferens, and seminal vesicles. Moreover, testosterone is a precursor of dihydrotestosterone, which masculinizes the urogenital sinus and external genitalia. MIS, which is produced by Sertoli cells (Josso, 1973), causes Müllerian duct regression. Many *in vivo* (Jost, 1955) and *in vitro* (Josso, 1971) experiments have shown that testosterone and its derivatives have no direct effect on regression of the Müllerian ducts. However, little attention has been given to any potential interaction between testosterone and MIS, although both hormones are produced by the fetal testis.

Despite these considerations, however, serendipity initiated our studies of steroid–MIS interactions. Prompted by the observations of a fall in hyaluronic acid and an increase in hyaluronidase activity during Müllerian duct regression, we studied medroxyprogesterone as a collagenase inhibitor. Instead of the expected inhibition of Müllerian duct regression, enhancement was observed. We reasoned that the enhanced regression may be progesterone mediated. We therefore initiated a study of the effects of various steroids on the action of MIS on Müllerian ducts in organ culture, by comparing the degree of Müllerian duct regression observed after incubation with MIS alone, and after incubation with MIS and steroid together (Ikawa *et al.,* 1982b).

The significance of the data was determined by the null hypothesis, that on average, the differences from control would be zero if no difference existed between the control group (MIS alone) and the MIS + steroid experimental group. The comparison of all of the groups, MIS alone and MIS + steroid doses was simultaneously carried out by means of an analysis of variance (the different preparations forming the blocks for a randomized block design). The comparison of the different MIS + steroid dose groups to the MIS alone group were carried out subsequently ($p <$ 0.05 was considered significant; $p < 0.01$ was considered highly significant).

Neither testosterone, MPA, progesterone, DHT, E_2, corticosterone, or CPA caused Müllerian duct regression when added alone at any dose to the organ culture assay. If the MIS preparation was initially biologically inactive, i.e., Müllerian duct regression = 0, addition of progesterone, MPA, or testosterone never restored biological activity to a fraction which lost or should have been active, or endowed an inactive fraction with activity.

The Mullerian duct regression caused by the semipurified biologically active MIS preparations was enhanced by some steroids, but unaffected by others. Testosterone (Fig. 31), medroxyprogesterone acetate (Fig. 31), and progesterone (Fig. 32) increased the grade of Müllerian duct regression caused by the biologically active MIS preparation. Maximal and statistically significant augmentation by testosterone was observed at $10^{-7} M$ (ΔMIS = + 1.33 ± 0.34, mean effect + standard error, $p < 0.001$) and $10^{-8} M$ (ΔMIS = + 0.96 ± 0.35, $p = 0.009$) (Fig. 31). Marked augmentation was seen also with medroxyprogesterone acetate at $10^{-8} M$ (ΔMIS = + 1.07 ± 0.43, $p < 0.017$) and $10^{-7} M$ (ΔMIS = 1.53 ± 0.36, $p < 0.001$).

Enhancement was also seen with progesterone (Fig. 32) over the same dose range, but statistical significance was achieved only at $10^{-6} M$ (ΔMIS = + 0.89 ± 0.41, $p = 0.05$).

Cyproterone acetate (CPA), a synthetic antiandrogen, caused some en-

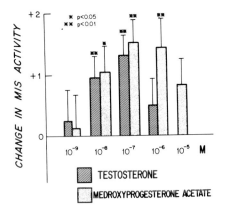

FIG. 31. Effect of testosterone and medroxyprogesterone acetate on MIS-induced Müllerian duct regression. Each bar indicates the change of activity (mean + SE) after incubating with MIS alone, and after incubating with MIS and steroid together, graded on a semiquantitative scale from 0 to 5. Testosterone led to a significant increase of MIS activity at concentrations of $10^{-8}\,M$ ($n = 10$, $p < 0.009$) and $10^{-7}\,M$ ($n = 10$, $p < 0.001$) when compared to MIS alone ($n = 16$). Medroxyprogesterone also significantly increased the activity at $10^{-8}\,M$ ($n = 8$, $p = 0.007$) when compared to MIS alone ($n = 16$). (* = $p < 0.05$; ** = $p < 0.01$.)

hancement of MIS biological activity but did not achieve statistical significance (Fig. 33). Neither dihydrotestosterone, estradiol (Fig. 34), nor corticosterone (not shown) produced any significant effect on MIS activity at the doses tested.

It has been demonstrated clearly that MIS causes Müllerian duct regression and that androgens alone cannot induce regression (Josso, 1971).

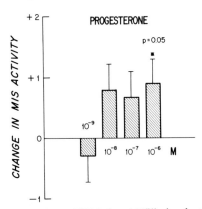

FIG. 32. Effect of progesterone on MIS-induced Müllerian duct regression. Progesterone (10^{-8}, 10^{-7}, and $10^{-6}\,M$) increased the activity of MIS ($n = 6$ control, $n = 4$ experimental at each dose). Significance was achieved only at $10^{-6}\,M$ ($p = 0.05$).

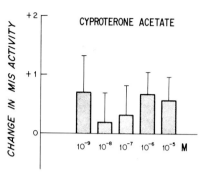

FIG. 33.   Effect of cyproterone acetate on MIS-induced Müllerian duct regression. Cyproterone acetate did not increase the activity of MIS significantly at any of the concentrations under study (n = 6 control, n = 6 experimental at each dose).

However this fact does not imply that androgens have no role in regression of the Müllerian duct. The present study demonstrates that testosterone and/or progesterone derivatives augment the action of MIS. The rat fetal testis is capable of androgen secretion during Müllerian duct regression (Picon, 1967). In the mouse fetus, the testosterone level in the blood rises rapidly to approximately $10^{-8}\,M$ during ductal regression (Pointis, 1979). Wilson *et al.* (1981) measured androgens in the 18 day fetal rabbit testis during the course of Müllerian duct regression. These androgen levels may be sufficient to produce enhancement of MIS activity *in vivo* similar to that observed *in vitro* in the present experiment. Since MIS does not bind to androgens, estrogens, or progestins (MacLaughlin, unpublished data), we assumed that the steroid enhancement effect is mediated through the target organ, either the epithelial cell or the mesenchyme.

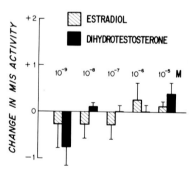

FIG. 34.   Effect of estradiol and dihydrotestosterone and MIS-induced Müllerian duct regression. Neither estradiol (control and experimental number at each dose = 6) nor dihydrotestosterone (control and experimental number at each dose = 4) changed the activity of MIS fraction.

Differentiation of androgen-dependent prostatic epithelium is mediated by mesenchyme (Cunha, 1972), similarly regression of mammary epithelium depends on testosterone stimulation of breast bud mesenchyme (Kratochwil, 1977). Therefore, the potential site of action of testosterone or MPA could be the mesenchymal cells surrounding the epithelial duct cells. Moreover, there are many observations that the extracellular matrix is under hormonal control (Cunha, 1976). Testosterone therefore may modulate the action of MIS by signals from the mesenchymal cells and extracellular matrix of the duct. Testosterone, for example, may pave the way for epithelial migration by changing the mesenchyme and its matrix constituents.

The role of progesterone in regression is unknown, although its presence in the placental circulation throughout embryonic development needs to be considered. The enhancement of regression by CPA appears to be a manifestation of its progestogenic activity rather than antagnonism of androgen receptors. The failure of estrogen to cause inhibition of MIS activity in the mammalian duct contrasts to the inhibition observed in the chick embryo, where E_2 or DES readily feminize Müllerian ducts in males (Teng and Teng, 1979). This suggests that the effects of the steroids in the mammal are different from those seen in nonplacental avians. Whether the effect of androgens and/or progestins is permissive or obligatory for MIS-induced regression has not been determined at this stage. Since the steroids have nuclear receptors and the proteins and glycoproteins have membrane bound receptors, it is possible that the steroid may act as a DNA promoter for another signal initiated by MIS.

IX. Summary

The complexity of the cascade of both molecular and cellular events initiated by fetal inducers and fetal regressor is just beginning to unfold. An indepth study of the developmental events initiated by MIS may provide some insight into the interactions required for normal migration and transformation to occur in the fetus. These events seem intuitively similar to events occurring during changes permissive for carcinogenic transformation. A knowledge of the mechanism involved in the developmental events may have widespread clinical applications to an understanding of developmental malformations and to cancer morphogenesis.

ACKNOWLEDGMENTS

The authors acknowledge helpful discussions and continued interest of Drs. Roy O. Greep, Jesse F. Scott, and David A. Swann. We sincerely appreciate the able technical assistance of Stephen R. Guy, Kimiko Hayashi, Thomas F. Manganaro, Susan M. Powell, and Marcia D. Sullivan, and the editorial assistance of Martha P. Wright, without whom this work could not have been completed.

We are also grateful for support during the course of this work from the American Cancer Society, the Charles A. King Trust, the Hood Foundation, the National Cancer Institute, the National Health and Medical Research Council (Australia), and the Pediatric Surgical Research Fund (Massachusetts General Hospital).

REFERENCES

Alexander, S. A., and Donoff, R. B. (1979). *J. Surg. Res.* **27**, 163.

Alexander, S. A., and Donoff, R. B. (1980). *J. Histotechnol.* **3**, 41.

Anderson, J., Clark, J. H., and Peck, E. J., Jr. (1972). *Biochem. J.* **126**, 561.

Auerbach, R., Morrissey, L. W., and Sidky, Y. A. (1978). *Cancer Res.* **38**, 1739.

Banerjee, S. D., Cohn, R. H., and Bernfield, M. R. (1977). *J. Cell Biol.* **73**, 445.

Blanchard, M., and Josso, N. (1974). *Pediatr. Res.* **8**, 968.

Budzik, G. P., Swann, D. A., Hayashi, A., and Donahoe, P. K. (1980). *Cell* **21**, 909.

Chvapil, M. (1976). *Med. Clin. N. Am.* **60**, 799.

Cohn, R., Banerjee, S. D., and Bernfield, M. B. (1977). *J. Cell Biol.* **73**, 464.

Constantinople, N., and Walsh, P. (1973). *Surg. Forum* **24**, 538.

Cuatrecasas, P., and Parikh, I. (1972). *Biochemistry* **11**, 2291.

Cunha, G. (1972). *Anat. Rec.* **172**, 179.

Cunha, G. (1976). *Int. Rev. Cytol.* **47**, 137.

David, G., and Bernfield, M. B. (1979). *Proc. Natl. Acad. Sci. U.S.A.* **76**, 786.

De St.Groth, S. F., and Scheidegger, D. (1980). *J. Immunol. Methods* **35**, 1.

Donahoe, P. K., Ito, Y., Marfatia, S., and Hendren, W. H. (1976). *Biol. Reprod.* **15**, 329.

Donahoe, P. K., Ito, Y., and Hendren, W. H. (1977a). *Cryobiology* **14**, 534.

Donahoe, P. K., Ito, Y., and Hendren, W. H. (1977b). *J. Surg. Res.* **23**, 141.

Donahoe, P. K., Ito, Y., Morikawa, Y., and Hendren, W. H. (1977c). *J. Pediatr. Surg.* **12**, 323.

Donahoe, P. K., Ito, Y., Price, J. M., and Hendren, W. H. (1977d). *Biol. Reprod.* **16**, 238.

Donahoe, P. K., Swann, D. A., Hayashi, A., and Sullivan, M. D. (1979). *Science* **205**, 913.

Donahoe, P. K., Budzik, G. P., and Swann, D. A. (1981a). "Pediatric Andrology" (S. J. Kogan and E. S. E. Hafez, eds.), pp. 37–46. Martinus Nijhoff, Publishers, The Hague.

Donahoe, P. K., Fuller, A. F., Jr., Scully, R. E., Guy, S. R., and Budzik, G. P. (1981b). *Ann. Surg.* **194**, 472.

Eriksson, H. A., Hardin, J. W., Markaverich, B., Upchurch, S., and Clark, J. H. (1980). *J. Steroid Biochem.* **12**, 121.

Falchuk, K. F., and Krishan, A. (1977). *Cancer Res.* **37**, 2050.

Fisher, M., and Solursh, M. (1977). *J. Embryol. Exp. Morphol.* **42**, 195.

Fuller, A. F., Jr., Guy, S. R., Budzik, G. P., and Donahoe, P. K. (1982). *J. Clin. Endocrinol. Metab.,* in press.

Fuller, A. F., Jr., Budzik, G. P., and Donahoe, P. K. (1982). *Gynecol. Oncol.,* in press.

Fulton, S., and Marois, M. (1980). Dye-Ligand Chromatography-Applications, Method, Theory of Matrex Gel Media. Amicon, Lexington, Massachusetts.

Gottlieb, A. B., Seids, R. K., and Kindt, T. J. (1975). *J. Immunol.* **114**, 51.

Greenwood, F. C., Hunter, W. M., and Glover, J. S. (1963). *Biochem. J.* **89**, 114.

Groenendijk-Huijbers, M. M. (1962). *Anat. Rec.* **142**, 9.

Hamburger, A. W., and Salmon, S. E. (1977). *Science* **197**, 461.

Hamburger, A. W., Salmon, S. E., Kim, M. B., Trent, J. M., Doehnlen, B. J., Alberts, D. S., and Schmidt, H. J. (1978). *Cancer Res.* **38**, 3438.

Hamilton, T. H. (1963). *Proc. Int. Ornithol. Congr. Ithaca* p. 1004.

Hammerling, G. J., Hammerling, U., and Lemke, H. (1979). *Immunogenetics* **8**, 433.

Hayashi, A., Donahoe, P. K., Budzik, G. P., and Trelstad, R. L. (1982). *Dev. Biol.*, in press.

Herlyn, M., Steplewski, Z., Herlyn, D., and Kaprowski, H. (1979). *Proc. Natl. Acad. Sci. U.S.A.* **76**, 1438.

Ikawa, H., Donahoe, P. K., and Trelstad, R. L. (1982a). In preparation.

Ikawa, H., Hutson, J. M., Budzik, G. P., MacLaughlin, D. T., and Donahoe, P. K. (1982b). *J. Pediatr. Surg.*, in press.

Hutson, J. M., Ikawa, H., and Donahoe, P. K. (1981). *J. Pediatr. Surg.* **16**, 822.

Josso, N. (1971). Rev. Eur. *Etud. Clin. Biol.* **16**, 694.

Josso, N. (1972). *Biol. Neonate* **20**, 368.

Josso, N. (1973). *Endocrinology* **93**, 829.

Josso, N., Forrest, M., and Picard, J. Y. (1975). *Biol. Reprod.* **13**, 163.

Josso, N., Picard, J. Y., and Tran. D. (1977). *Recent Prog. Horm. Res.* **33**, 117.

Jost, A. (1946a). *C.R. Soc. Biol.* **140**, 460.

Jost, A. (1946b). *C.R. Soc. Biol.* **140**, 463.

Jost, A. (1947). *C.R. Soc. Biol.* **141**, 135.

Jost, A. (1953). *Recent Prog. Horm. Res.* **8**, 379.

Jost, A. (1955). "Biologie des Androgenes chez l'Embryon," p. 160. IIIe Reunion Endocrinol. Langue Francaise, Paris.

Karnovsky, M. J. (1965). *J. Cell Biol.* **27**, 137A.

Klinman, N. R., Pickard, A. R., Sigal, N. H., Gearhart, P. J., Metcalf, E. S., and Pierce, S. K. (1976). *Ann. Immunol. (Paris)* **127C**, 489.

Kohler, G., and Milstein, C. (1976). *Nature (London)* **256**, 495.

Kohler, G., Howe, C. S., and Milstein, C. (1976). *Eur. J. Immunol.* **6**, 292.

Kratochwil, K. (1977). *Dev. Biol.* **61**, 358.

Laemmli, U. K. (1970). *Nature (London)* **227**, 680.

Littlefield, J. W. (1964). *Science* **145**, 709.

Macieira-Coelho (1973). "Tissue Culture, Methods and Applications" (P. F. Kruse, Jr. and M. K. Patterson, Jr., eds.), pp. 412–422. Academic Press, New York.

Markaverich, B. M., Upchurch, S., and Clark, J. H. (1980). *J. Receptor Res.* **1**, 415.

Marshak-Rothstein, A., Fink, P., Gridley, T., Raulet, D., Beven, M., and Gefter, M. L. (1979). *J. Immunol.* **122**, 2491.

Moore, S., Spackman, D. H., and Stein, W. H. (1958). *Ann. Chem.* **30**, 1185.

Mudgett-Hunter, M., Colligan, J. E., and Kindt, T. J. (1978). *J. Immunol.* **120**, 293.

Mudgett-Hunter, M., Ju, A., Margolies, M. N., and Haber, E. (1980a). In preparation.

Mudgett-Hunter, M., Margolies, M. N., Rosen, E. M., and Haber E. (1980b). *Fed. Proc. Fed. Am. Soc. Exp. Biol.* **39**, 928.

Mudgett-Hunter, M., Budzik, P. G., Sullivan, M., and Donahoe, P. K. (1982). *J. Immunol.* **128**, 1327.

Orkin, R. W., and Toole, B. P. (1978). *Dev. Biol.* **66**, 308.

Peto, R., Pike, M. C., Armitage, P., Breslow, N. E., Cox, D. R., Howard, S. V., Mantel, N., McPherson, K., Peto, J., and Smith, P. G. (1977). *Br. J. Cancer* **34**, 585.

Picard, J. Y., and Josso, N. (1976). *Biomedicine* **25**, 147.

Picon, R. (1967). *Arch. Anat. Microsc. Morphol. Exp.* **56**, 281.

Picon, R. (1969). *Arch. Anat. Microsc. Morphol. Exp.* **58**, 1.

Pointis, G. (1979). *J. Steroid Biochem.* **11**, 1609.

Price, J. M., Donahoe, P. K., Ito, Y., and Hendren, W. H. (1977). *Am. J. Anat.* **149**, 353.

Price, J. M., Donahoe, P. K., and Ito, Y. (1979). *Am. J. Anat.* **156**, 265.

Rheinhold, V. N. (1972). *Methods Enzymol.* **25**, 244.

Riordan, J. R. (1976). *Med. Clin. N. Am.* **60**, 661.

Rosenwaks, Z., Liu, H., Jones, H., Tseng, L., and Stone, M. (1981). *J. Clin. Endocrinol. Metab.* **52**, 817.

Ruoslahti, E. (1981). *Collagen Res.* **1**, 95.

Rygaard, J., and Povlsen, C. O. (1969). *Acta Pathol. Microbiol. Scand.* **77**, 758.

Sainte-Marie, G. (1962). *J. Histochem. Cytochem.* **10**, 250.

Salmon, S. E., and Buick, R. N. (1979). *Cancer Res.* **39**, 1133.

Salmon, S. E., Hamburger, A. W., Soehnlen, B., Durie, B. G. M., Alberts, D. S., and Moon, T. E. (1978). *N. Engl. J. Med.* **298**, 1321.

Scheib, D., and Reyss-Brion, M. (1979). *Arch. Anat. Microsc.* **68**, 85.

Scully, R. E. (1979). "Atlas of Tumor Pathology." Armed Forces Institute of Pathology, Washington, D. C.

Secher, D. S., and Burke, D. C. (1980). *Nature (London)* **285**, 446.

Schieb, D. (1963). "Lysosomes (A. V. S. deReuch and M. P. Cameron, eds.) pp. 264–277. Little, Brown, Boston.

Shulman, A., and Dwyer, F. P. (1964). "Chelating Agents and Metal Chelates" (F. P. Dwyer and D. P. Mellor, eds.), p. 415. Academic Press, New York.

Springer, T., Galfre, G., Secher, D. S., and Milstein, C. (1978). *Eur. J. Immunol.* **8**, 539.

Staehelin, T., Durrer, B., Schmidt, J., Takacs, B., Stocker, J., Miggiano, V., Stahli, C., Rubinstein, M., Levy, W. P., Hershberg, R., and Pestka, S. (1981). *Immunology* **78**, 1848.

Swann, D. A., Sotman, S., Dixon, M., and Brooks, C. (1977). *Biochem. J.* **161**, 473.

Swann, D. A., Donahoe, P. K., Ito, Y., Morikawa, Y., and Hendren, W. H. (1979). *Dev. Biol.* **69**, 73.

Teng, C. S., and Teng, C. T. (1975a). *Biochem. J.* **150**, 183.

Teng, C. S., and Teng, C. T. (1975b). *Biochem. J.* **150**, 191.

Teng, C. S., and Teng, C. T. (1979). "Ontogeny of Receptors and Reproductive Hormone Action" (T. H. Hamilton, J. H. Clark, and W. A. Sadler, eds.), pp. 421–440. Raven, New York.

Tepperman, B. S. (1980). "Actuarial Survival by Lifetable Methods." Texas Instruments Professional Program Exchange.

Tran, D., and Josso, N. (1977). *Biol. Reprod.* **16**, 267.

Toole, B. P. (1976). "Neuronal Recognition." Plenum, New York.

Toole, B. P., and Gross, J. (1971). *Dev. Biol.* **25**, 57.

Toole, B. P., and Trelstad, R. L. (1971). *Dev. Biol.* **26**, 28.

Travis, J., and Pannell, R. (1973). *Clin. Chim. Acta* **49**, 49.

Travis, J., Bowen, J., Tewksbury, D., Johnson, D., and Pannell, R. (1976). *Biochem. J.* **157**, 301.

Trelstad, R. L., Hay, E. D., and Revel, J. P. (1967). *Dev. Biol.* **16**, 78.

Trelstad, R. L., Hayashi, A., Hayashi, K., and Donahoe, P. K. (1982). *Dev. Biol.,* in press.

Vallee, B. L. (1976). "Cancer Enzymology" (J. Schultz and F. Almad, eds.), p. 159. Academic Press, New York.

Wilson, J. D., Griffin, J. E., George, F. W., and Leshin, M. (1981). *Recent Prog. Horm. Res.* **37**, 1–40.

Wood, W. G., and Morton, D. L. (1970). *Science* **170**, 1318.

Yamada, T. (1974). *Keio J. Med.* **23**, 53.

DISCUSSION

E. J. Peck: Pat, thank you for a fine talk. I am interested in your observations on Zn^{2+} and MIS. It is known that the majority of Zn^{2+} is bound *in vivo;* in addition, testes contain a high level of Zn in the bound state. Since MIS is derived from testes, is it possible that MIS is a "sequestrator" of Zn and thus reduces free Zn^{2+} below that required to maintain the duct system?

P. K. Donahoe: Zinc appears to be required to maintain Müllerian duct integrity. Removal of zinc results in Müllerian duct regression. There is no effect on the adjacent Wolffian duct. Zinc also appears to inactivate MIS or prevent MIS from causing duct regression possibly by occupying its zinc binding sites and preventing farther binding of zinc in the tissues. Whether MIS is a zinc sequestrator is not known. This attractive hypothesis needs further testing. It is also possible that zinc may be involved in subsequent epithelial or mesenchymal cellular or extracellular events that occur after MIS triggers the signal for regression. The finding that zinc depletion imitates Müllerian duct regression, however, gives us another piece by which to unlock the puzzle of this interesting developmental event.

J. Shapiro: Did you identify Type IV collagen in the laminar membrane around the Müllerian duct with your antibodies?

P. K. Donahoe: Yes, it localized in the Müllerian duct basement membrane and disappeared when the duct disappeared.

J. Shapiro: Would you care to speculate on the probable proteolytic cascade related to lysis of the laminar membrane or how this could relate to MIS—a large glycoprotein?

P. K. Donahoe: We speculate that MIS membrane bound receptors on either the epithelial or mesenchymal cells trigger stimulation (or inhibitor blockade) of either hyaluronidase or other protease activity, which in turn leads to the consistently observed basement membrane breakdown, mesenchymal condensation, and epithelial migration or transformation.

S. Glasser: Have you ever attempted in the manner of Cunha to dissociate Müllerian duct mesenchyme from epithelium and to reaggregate them in various combinations such as left duct mesenchyme with right duct epithelium? Would such recombinants alter the patterns of duct regression? Second, have you tried to localize and identify the specific cell type associated with steroid hormone receptor by the use of autoradiography controlled for specific hormone binding?

P. K. Donahoe: John Hutson, an Australian MRC Fellow in our laboratory, is now doing mesenchymal epithelial separation and recombination of mesenchyme and epithelial cells in the chick Müllerian ducts. We have not yet done recombination of right and left in the female chick, but those experiments are planned and should yield interesting results. The steroid enhancement and estrogen receptor studies demand steroid autoradiography follow-up. These experiments are planned for the Fall in collaboration with Dr. Jerry Cunha.

S. Glasser: I would like to suggest that if you go back 10 to 12 years and look at the literature of Sandstead and Darby on hypogonadism in clinically zinc-deficient males that there might be some clues related to zinc and cadmium-dependent membrane changes.

L. Bullock: I was interested in your comments, on the interaction of steroids and MIS activity, particularly the effects of testosterone and MPA. You suggested that the effects of steroids may be mediated via androgen receptors in the mesenchyme, because Cunha has shown this tissue is important in regulating differentiation. I am sure you have considered the fact that Müllerian duct regression does occur in the TFM/Y mouse despite the effective absence of androgen receptors. I will admit I do not know if this regression is quantitatively or temporally similar to the normal animal or not. In addition, Cunha has shown that TFM/Y mesenchyme of the urogenital sinus cannot induce prostatic differentiation of normal urogenital epithelium although the converse is true. Would you like to comment on this?

P. K. Donahoe: Certainly in the patients that we've seen with TFM and have explored intraabdominally, there are no remaining Müllerian duct structures. It is not clear in the TFM whether there is complete absence of receptors. In our patients in whom Dr. Charles Eil has measured androgen receptors, there is never complete absence of steroid receptor. Androgen may function at a low but effective level. I cannot answer those questions yet.

J. Larner: I wondered if you had any idea about how this relatively high-molecular-weight glycoprotein interacts with sensitive cells, in other words, do you visualize it as interacting with a cell at its surface, via possibly a receptor, or do you visualize it entering the cell. What is your idea about this?

P. K. Donahoe: We suspect that MIS acts at the cell surface, probably through adenylate cyclase. The carbohydrate moiety may streamline transport of the large molecular weight glycoprotein.

J. K. Findlay: Which cell types make Müllerian inhibiting substance; does it act locally, and can you detect it in the circulation?

P. K. Donahoe: Evidence is strong that Sertoli cells make Müllerian inhibiting substance. Nathalie Josso separated calf interstitial cells from seminiferous tubules and demonstrated that MIS came from the latter, and that the Sertoli cells specifically produced MIS. The present assay is not sensitive enough to detect MIS in serum, urine, or blood. We have not been able to detect MIS except in whole tissues, extracts, or incubates.

J. F. Findlay: Have you used any of your monoclonal antibodies to do immunofluorescent localization?

P. K. Donahoe: Not yet.

M. H. G. Raj: I wasn't sure whether you mentioned that you had a radioimmunoassay for Müllerian inhibiting substance?

P. K. Donahoe: Now that we have been able to obtain a monoclonal antibody, that is next on the agenda. When we obtain a high affinity monoclonal or a library of monoclonals, then we'll tackle the radioimmunoassay.

M. H. G. Raj: I was looking at your bioassays and I thought how tedious and subjective it must be. An assay which would quantitate in microgram amounts as to how much of MIS would be there, would be very useful.

P. K. Donahoe: The assay is certainly tedious, but it is not subjective. Each is read blind by two different observers. We can quantitate the amount of protein in the preparation added but since the preparation is not homogeneous, we cannot yet accurately access the amount of MIS present or the sensitivity of the assay.

M. H. G. Raj: Do you see the same kind of regression all along the Müllerian duct or do you look at a single section?

P. K. Donahoe: We look at the most sensitive part of the duct which is the upper part or the cephalic end of the duct.

M. H. G. Raj: Can you, for example, dissect out the duct and weigh it? Would that give a more quantitative picture? Would the degree of regression be proportional to the weight?

P. K. Donahoe: That approach may be untenable since it would require separation of the Müllerian duct from the Wolffian duct, an impossible dissection even for pediatric surgeons.

H. Papkoff: Your gel patterns indicated a spectrum of proteins, all of which were of fairly high molecular weight, and all of which were glycoproteins. It wasn't entirely clear to me whether one or more of the protein bands was active and if more than one, does this suggest that you may yet find lower molecular species that would be active? Finally, can you say something about the stability of the active material?

P. K. Donahoe: We have not been able to separate and individually test the bands present in the most purified biologically active fraction, which is still heterogeneous. We have not been able to further fractionate those and retain biological activity, so we don't know whether any or all of those bands are the biologically active fractions. The prominent bands stain with PAS and we know we can elute the biological activity from carbohydrate affinity columns. Also there is measurable carbohydrate to 8% in the most active fraction. These findings infer that MIS is a glycoprotein. None of the low-molecular-weight fractions has biological activity in the assay. MIS is relatively unstable. All purification steps have to be done at 4 degrees, and we cannot freeze dry MIS. Josso has demonstrated heat inactivation of the biologically active material and sensitivity to protein inhibitors.

G. P. Budzik: I just wanted to underscore a point about stability. As shown in one of the figures, mercaptoethanol was found in the latter stages of purification to be absolutely essential for maintaining the biological activity through the Matrex Gel Green A chromatography. EDTA also helps, but the mercaptide seems to be more effective.

K. Ahren: Since this factor is produced also in the ovary, have you considered the possibility that it might have an effect also in the ovary. I'm thinking, in particular, of the meiotic divisions at the oocytes which is started already during the embryonic life and then arrested until after puberty. If you have considered it, have you done any experiments?

P. K. Donahoe: We have considered that MIS may function in the ovary as a meiosis inhibitor. The biological assay may be too insensitive to detect MIS in the mammalian ovary. We do, however, detect MIS in the avian ovary using the same assay. Since chickens are continuous ovulators, meiosis inhibition may not be as important in avians as it is in single ovulating mammals. The avian ovary is an enormous organ. We are not certain of the function of MIS in this ovary, but it may become an interesting source for purification of MIS.

H-C. Blossey: The influence of MPA on the Müllerian duct was very interesting. Now, MPA is not only a progestagen but it has also intrinsic androgenic and a very marked glucocorticoid activity. Have you any experience with glucocorticoids on the development of the Müllerian duct?

P. K. Donahoe: Corticosterone and hydrocortisone acetate do not enhance MIS activity in the organ culture assay. Cyproterone acetate which we thought would act as an antiandrogen enhanced biological activity, probably because of its progestational effects.

D. K. Pomerantz: You stated toward the end of the talk when you were predicting usefulness of this material, that you would envision using it in cases of intersex problems. Now it escapes me as to how you're going to do that. It seems to me that Müllerian duct derivatives would already have differentiated at the time you would make the diagnosis and thus MIS would be an unsuitable therapy.

P. K. Donahoe: My interest as a surgeon caring for infants with ambiguous genitalia first led me into an indepth study of MIS. A knowledge of MIS function helps us to understand some of the phenotypic expressions that we see. MIS may eventually be useful as a contraceptive agent, but that is futuristic.

I. Mowszowicz: I would like to make one comment in the line of the steroid–MIS interaction: patients with the testicular feminization syndrome, as you said, have complete Müllerian regression; these patients have high estradiol levels and apparently normal estradiol receptors; this questions the reality of protective effect of estradiol against MIS action that you mentioned. I would also like to ask you a question. I recently heard a talk by Dr. Short in England, and intersex goats in which he reported an inverse correlation between testicular descent and Müllerian regression. Could you comment on this please?

P. K. Donahoe: Roger Short carefully studied the Saanan goat in whom he described retained testes that produce detectable levels of testosterone. If the testes were maldescended, he found retention of the Müllerian duct on the side of the maldescent. We have both raised the question of whether Müllerian inhibiting substance is important to descent of the testes. In other words, this dysgenetic gonad, although it was producing testosterone, was not producing enough Müllerian inhibiting substance to cause regression of the Müllerian duct on that side and in addition the testes had not undergone descent. The evidence is fairly high that testicular descent may be T or DHT related, but both Roger and I wonder whether it might also be MIS related. We've done some studies looking at the 17 day rat gubernaculum which differentiates from myoblast to rhabdomyoblast to striated muscle. Subsequently we attempted to enhance the differentiation schedule with either T, DHT, or MIS. Unfortunately, we could not document enhancement using this system, although I still believe MIS is somehow related to testicular descent.

C. Monder: You indicated in one of your earlier slides that EDTA mimics Müllerian inhibiting substance. Do you have an explanation?

P. K. Donahoe: EDTA chelates zinc which may be required for maintenance of duct integrity. If EDTA is incubated with zinc, but not calcium or magnesium, then the Müllerian duct is preserved. MIS may function as a zinc sequestrator.

C. Monder: When EDTA is incubated in this system along with a number of other divalent cations, they don't influence the EDTA effect. Now, EDTA chelates those ions, so there evidently is something unique about the chelation of EDTA and zinc, because free EDTA and bound EDTA are neither structurally nor electronically the same.

P. K. Donahoe: The biological significance of the EDTA and the Zn^{2+} effects are not known.

S. R. Plymate: Have you tried to determine whether the effect of the testosterone and MPA is to stabilize the protein such as testosterone does to another Sertoli cell, large molecular weight glycoprotein androgen binding protein, as has been shown by Tindall and Means.

P. K. Donahoe: We're not certain whether the steroid effect is on the mesenchyme or epithelial tissue or on the molecule itself.

Z. Rosenwaks: Have you used your monoclonal antibody to neutralize the antitumor effect of the MIS?

P. K. Donahoe: We did a series of experiments using a monoclonal antibody which had shed its kappa chain and had lost its activity. We have not yet repeated those important experiments. Certainly that is important to do.

W. F. Crowley: In following up on the previous question about the descent of the testes being related to MIS, do you need to go as far as an animal model? There is a human intersexual disorder called Hernia Uteri Inguinale in which retained Müllerian elements are present in an otherwise phenotypically normal male. If I'm not mistaken, there is evidence of ipsilateral cryptorchidism in these patients supporting an association between a defect in MIS and testicular descent. Would you comment on this?

P. K. Donahoe: Sloan and Walsh (W. R. Sloan and P. C. Walsh, *J. Urol.* **115**, 459, 1976; C. G. D. Brook, H. Wagner, M. F. Zachman, *et al., Br. J. Med.* **1**, 771, 1973) described kindreds of patients with retained Müllerian ducts. They described them as normal males with retained Müllerian ducts, but each patient had testicular maldescent as well on the side of the retained Müllerian duct. We assayed the testes of one patient with maldescent, and retained Müllerian ducts who was less than 1 year of age. This patient had detectable Müllerian inhibiting substance. Although the Müllerian duct was retained we could detect MIS in the testicular biopsy indicating, as in most other anomalies, that this child may have MIS receptor deficiency.

C. S. Nicoll: In view of your results showing inhibition of growth of the ovarian tumor with the MIS, I wonder if you have tested the substance for inhibition of growth of normal cells from ovaries or the reproductive tract from adult females?

P. K. Donahoe: We haven't. We cannot test them in soft agar in the nude mouse since nontransformed cells will not grow. The unique thing about the ovarian cancer is that it is surface epithelial which is of coelomic derivation, the same cells that invaginate to form the Müllerian duct. The normal ovary does not have the same derivation and therefore may not be sensitive to MIS.

RECENT PROGRESS IN HORMONE RESEARCH, VOL. 38

The Role of Nonsteroidal Regulators in Control of Oocyte and Follicular Maturation

CORNELIA P. CHANNING,* LARRY D. ANDERSON,†
DENNIS J. HOOVER,* JAROSLAV KOLENA,* KEVIN G. OSTEEN,*
SEYMOUR H. POMERANTZ,‡ AND KIYOO TANABE*

*Departments of *Physiology, †Anatomy, and ‡Biological Chemistry,
University of Maryland School of Medicine,
Baltimore, Maryland*

I. Introduction

The ovarian follicle is bathed in a fluid rich in steroid hormones as well as nonsteroidal regulators which interact to serve to control its maturation, responsiveness to gonadotropins, as well as to lead to control of the maturation of its oocyte. The mammalian oocyte remains in the immature dictyate stage of meiosis from shortly prior to or at the time of birth until it matures immediately before ovulation under the influence of the preovulatory gonadotropin surge. Only the oocyte in the preovulatory follicle matures; all of the others remain in the immature dictyate state. Furthermore in the primate only one follicle is chosen to mature and ovulate each menstrual cycle. This particular follicle in the case of monotocous species, or a few follicles in the case of polytocous species, is the only one which increases its ability to secrete estrogen and increase in LH receptors in response to changing serum LH and FSH levels. All of the other smaller follicles outside the ''chosen'' one either stay small and immature or undergo atresia. The mechanisms choosing the selection of the follicle in terms of which one will grow, secrete hormones, and eventually ovulate are most decidedly local since all follicles are exposed to the same serum gonadotropin levels. Changes in follicular fluid levels of a polypeptide substance, oocyte maturation inhibitor (OMI), may play a role in controlling oocyte maturation. It appears that OMI is present in all follicles except the preovulatory ones (and atretic ones). In addition small follicles but not large follicles contain small- and large-molecular-weight polypeptides which inhibit FSH induction of LH receptors and FSH stimulation of progesterone secretion and LH binding to granulosa cells. The inhibitor is replaced by an enhancer of FSH action and granulosa proges-

331

terone secretion. These ovarian regulators as well as changes in follicular inhibin-F secretion occurring throughout the primate menstrual cycle will be discussed in more detail below. The status of the chemistry and physiology of several follicular regulators will also be reviewed. A brief conceptual summary of changes in various follicular functions and levels of some nonsteroidal regulators will be presented first. Data obtained in our laboratory will be discussed in more detail and references to studies of others will be made whenever appropriate. Three books have appeared recently which cover much of the field of nonsteroidal gonadal regulators (Franchimont and Channing, 1981; Channing and Segal, 1981; Fujii and Channing, 1982).

II. Changes in the Porcine Follicle during the Estrous Cycle

As shown in Fig. 1 as the porcine follicle matures and aquires the ability to secrete estrogen there is an accompanying 50-fold increase in LH/hCG receptors (Channing and Kammerman, 1972; Channing et al., 1973) and LH ability to stimulate follicular cyclic AMP and progesterone secretion as well as a gradual decrease in granulosa cell FSH receptors (Nakano et al., 1973) and a decrease in FSH responsiveness in the granulosa cell in terms of ability to accumulate cyclic AMP (Lindsey and Channing, 1979) and secrete progesterone (Thanki and Channing, 1978). Only the so-called dominant follicles undergo these changes; adjacent small follicles fail to undergo these maturational changes (Channing, Brinkley and Young, 1980). In order for the final preovulatory increase in ability to secrete progesterone and ability to luteinize to occur the granulosa cells of the dominant follicle must be exposed to the preovulatory LH surge (Channing, Brinkley and Young, 1980). Mere attainment of a given follicular size is not sufficient to cause eventual luteinization of the dominant follicle.

In order to achieve induction of LH receptors in cultured granulosa cells, small porcine follicles should be exposed to FSH, insulin (I), thyroxine (T), and cortisol (F) (Channing et al., 1980). Estradiol enhances FSH induction of granulosa cell LH/hCG receptors and the ability of LH to stimulate cyclic AMP but prevents induction of the ability of LH to stimulate progesterone secretion (Loeken and Channing, 1981). Upon the arrival of the preovulatory LH surge the estrogen level in large preovulatory follicles rises and then falls and the oocyte matures (Ainsworth et al. 1980).

Following the pattern of follicular maturation follicular fluid levels of nonsteroidal regulators as well as steroids also change (Fig. 2). The role of each follicular nonsteroidal regulator in controlling the maturation process

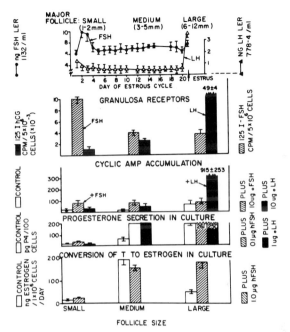

FIG. 1.   Changes occurring in porcine granulosa cells during follicular maturation. Data at the top represent serum FSH and LH levels occurring throughout the porcine estrous cycle. Levels of FSH are adapted from the data of Rayford *et al.* (1974) and levels of serum LH are adapted from the data of Niswender *et al.* (1970). Data on granulosa FSH binding are taken from Nakano *et al.* (1977) and data on HCG binding are taken from Channing and Kammerman (1973). Data represent the mean ± SEM of 6–15 observations. Data on the ability of FSH and LH to stimulate intracellular cyclic AMP accumulation represent the mean ± SE of 6–11 observations and are taken from Lindsey and Channing (1979). Observations on the effect of human FSH 1 μg/ml (LER 1801-3) and 1.0 μg of ovine LH on progesterone secretion are taken from the data of Thanki and Channing (1978) using observations on granulosa cells cultured for 4 days.

will be discussed in more detail below. As a means of introduction the nonsteroidal regulators of interest are summarized in Fig. 2 and include luteinization inhibitor (LI) (Fig. 2a and b, left), luteinization stimulator (LS) (Fig. 2a and b, right), oocyte maturation Inhibitor (OMI) (Fig. 2c), and inhibin-F (Fig. 2d). Additional ovarian nonsteroidal regulators of follicular function which also play a role in follicular function are FSH receptor binding inhibitor (FSHRBI) originally described by Darga and Reichert (1978) and luteinizing hormone receptor binding inhibitor (LHRBI) originally described by Yang *et al.* (1976) and Sakai, *et al.* (1977).

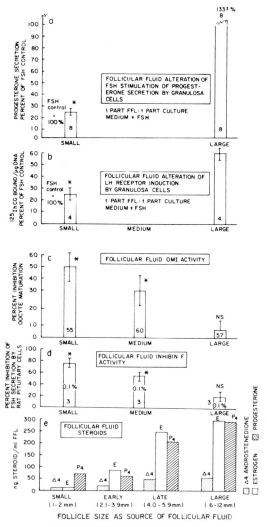

FIG. 2. Changes in levels of follicular fluid nonsteroidal regulators and steroid levels during maturation of the porcine follicle. (e) depicts follicular fluid steroids [Δ4 = Δ⁴-androstenedione; estrogen (E) and progesterone (P)] in follicular fluid and represent data obtained by Ainsworth and his colleagues and Channing *et al.* (1980). (d) depicts inhibin-F levels in porcine follicular fluid as assayed in the rat anterior pituitary cell culture assay and data represent the mean ± SE of 3 determinations (taken from Anderson and DePaolo, 1981 with permission). (c) depicts oocyte maturation inhibitor (OMI) activity of porcine follicular fluid and represent data on follicular fluid freshly collected on ice. Data shown are the percentage inhibition of maturation of cumulus enclosed porcine oocytes cultured for 2 days in 50% porcine follicular fluid. The number of oocytes examined is indicated in the bars. The asterisk indicates $p < 0.01$ vs control oocytes (data taken from Stone *et al.*, 1978, with

III. Purification and Physiology of Oocyte Maturation Inhibitor

Since the initial reports on the presence of an inhibitor of oocyte maturation (OMI) in pig follicular fluid (Tsafriri and Channing, 1975; Tsafriri *et al.*, 1976a,b) several schemes for partial purification have been developed (Stone *et al.*, 1978; Pomerantz *et al.*, 1979). Although we have not yet obtained homogeneous material we will report some additional refinements. Considerable effort has been expended in devising an assay which would parallel OMI activity and yet be easier and faster to execute; some of the results of that effort are summarized here. The assay examines inhibition of granulosa cell clump monolayer formation. The site of synthesis of OMI has also been the subject of detailed study and some of these results pointing to the granulosa cell will be presented.

A. INHIBITION OF OOCYTE MATURATION: PHYSIOLOGICAL CONSIDERATIONS

Although the first maturation division of the mammalian oocyte begins either in prenatal life or in the early postnatal period, the meiotic process is arrested when the germ cell reaches the diplotene or dictyate stage. Meiosis is resumed only shortly before ovulation and this resumption, followed by progress to the second metaphase stage, is termed oocyte maturation. The first (Tsafriri and Channing, 1975) and subsequent studies of this process and its inhibition utilized an *in vitro* system in which isolated cumulus-enclosed oocytes were cultured in a modified medium 199 containing 15% pig serum, insulin, pyruvate, and lactate. These studies showed that a large fraction of oocytes from medium-sized pig follicles or from immature rats (Tsafriri *et al.*, 1977) treated with PMSG would mature spontaneously and reproducibly. This system was then successfully employed to study the effect of added ovarian constituents on oocyte matura-

---

permission). (b) depicts the effect of porcine follicular fluid (50%) on FSH induction of hCG/LH binding sites by cultured porcine granulosa cells. Granulosa cells were harvested from small (1–2 mm) porcine follicles and cultured in TC 199 ± 10% pig serum for 4 days with 0.1 μg human FSH, insulin, thyroxine (10^{-7} M), and cortisol (0.01 μg/ml) and 50% porcine follicular fluid. After 4 days with 1 medium change occurring after 2 days the number of specific binding sites for ^{125}I-labeled hCG was determined. Data are expressed as percentage of control binding observed in the presence of FSH, I, F, T alone and represent the mean ± SE of 6–8 observations (Osteen and Channing, unpublished observations). (a) depicts the ability of the same granulosa cell culture [as were used in (b)] to secrete progesterone into the culture medium after 2 days. It should be noted that small follicular fluid is inhibitory to FSH induction of LH/hCG receptors and FSH stimulation of progesterone secretion whereas follicular fluid from large follicles enhances FSH stimulation of progesterone secretion.

tion (Tsafriri and Channing, 1975; Tsafriri *et al.*, 1976b). Inhibition of oocyte maturation was obtained reproducibly by addition of follicular fluid and coculture of oocytes with granulosa cells. The same oocyte culture system was then utilized to follow the inhibitor (OMI) through various purification steps (Tsafriri *et al.*, 1976a; Stone *et al.*, 1978).

One interesting feature of the assay system was noted by Tsafriri *et al.* (1976b): the inhibition of maturation produced by partially purified fractions of follicular fluid never reached 100%. This was explained by the time sequence of maturation of isolated oocytes (Fig. 3). Already during the first 18–24 hours of the culture period, 30% of the oocytes reached the first anaphase or second metaphase stage, while 70% reached the same stages by 42–46 hours. Hunter and Polge (1966) observed that at least 36 hours are needed for attaining these stages following administration of hCG to pigs. It is likely that the 30% early maturing oocytes were already exposed *in vivo* to a maturing-inducing stimulus, were committed to mature, and were insensitive to the action of OMI.

The activity of OMI was estimated by incubating cumulus-enclosed pig oocytes from medium follicles with an aliquot of the test fraction. The

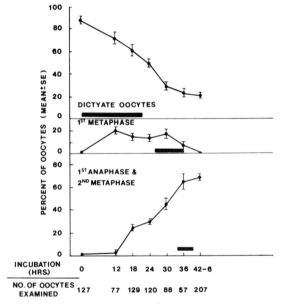

FIG. 3. Time sequence of maturation of isolated porcine oocytes. Maturation of isolated oocytes was measured following the indicated incubation time in medium 199A. For comparison the time interval between hCG administration and degree of maturation *in vivo* is indicated by horizontal lines (Hunter and Polge, 1966). Reprinted from Tsafriri *et al.* (1976b), with permission.

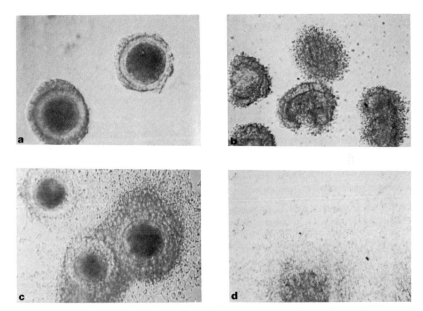

FIG. 4.   Photomicrographs of cumulus enclosed oocytes and granulosa cell clumps before and after culture in Medium 199A for 2 days. (a) Cumulus–oocyte complexes freshly
harvested from medium sized follicles (×200). (b) Granulosa cell clumps freshly harvested
from medium sized follicles (×200). (c) Cumulus oocyte complexes harvested from medium
sized follicles after culture for 2 days (×200). (d) Granulosa cell clumps harvested from
medium sized follicles after culture for 2 days (×200). From Channing *et al.* (1981), with
permission.

appearance of these cumulus-enclosed oocytes before and after culture
for 2 days is shown in Fig. 4. Under control conditions the oocyte under-
goes nuclear maturation and the cumulus cells grow out as a monolayer.
By comparing the percentage maturation obtained in test incubations with
that observed in control cultures containing medium alone, a percentage
inhibition of maturation was calculated for each fraction (Stone *et al.*,
1978). After active fractions from a given procedure were pooled, oocyte
maturation was measured at three to five dilutions. The dilution at which
50% inhibition occurred (defined as 1 unit of OMI) was read from the
dose–response curve.

The physiological significance of OMI was studied in several ways.
Since follicular fluid had always been frozen for several weeks or months
before use we wished to show that the activity was present in fresh follicular fluid that had not been frozen (Stone *et al.*, 1978). The results are seen
in Fig. 2c. Small (1–2 mm), medium (3–5), and large-sized (6–12 mm)
porcine follicles were aspirated at the slaughterhouse, the fluid kept on ice

in sterile tubes, sterilized by filtration, and added to cultures within 3 hours of collection. Significant inhibition of maturation was observed in fluid from both small and medium follicles. A pool of follicular fluid aspirated in the laboratory after harvest from the slaughterhouse and frozen and thawed exerted a 28% inhibition of oocyte maturation. Thus the inhibition of maturation *in vitro* by follicular fluid is not due to artifacts derived from freezing and thawing the fluid.

In order to rule out the possibility that the oocytes were irreversibly damaged by OMI, experiments were conducted by replacing follicular fluid after 20–24 or 28–36 hours with either follicular fluid or control culture medium (Stone *et al.*, 1978). Replacement of follicular fluid at 20–24 hours with control medium led to complete reversal of inhibition (Fig. 5). Similar results were found with a partially purified OMI fraction eluted from a Sephadex G-25 column. Addition of 5 μg/ml ovine LH to the oocytes cultured in follicular fluid also led to reversal of the inhibitory effect of the fluid (Fig. 6; Tsafriri *et al.*, 1976a)

The sensitivity of oocytes from various sized follicles to the action of OMI was also examined. Figure 7a shows data for the inhibition of mat-

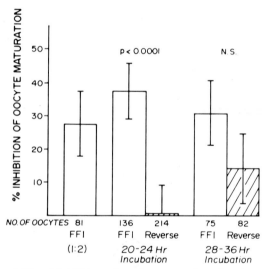

FIG. 5. Reversibility of inhibition of oocyte maturation after 20–24 or 28–36 hours incubation in follicular fluid. After 20–24 or 28–36 hours of oocyte incubation in a 1:2 dilution of follicular fluid the medium surrounding half the oocyte cultures was gently aspirated with a sterile syringe and replaced with freshly prepared inhibitor medium. The other cultures were replenished with noninhibitory control medium. After the change of medium the incubations were continued for an additional 24 hours to allow time for germinal vesicle breakdown. The bars show ± SEM. From Stone *et al.* (1978), reprinted by permission.

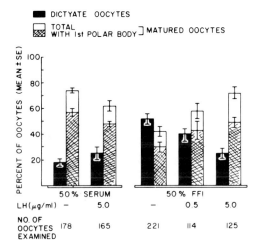

FIG. 6. Ability of LH to overcome the inhibitory action of porcine follicular fluid upon porcine oocyte meiosis. Oocytes were cultured in a mixture of 50% medium 199 and serum or follicular fluid with and without the indicated dose of ovine LH which was added about 2 hours prior to the addition of the oocytes. Bars are ± SEM. From Tsafriri *et al.* (1976a), reprinted by permission.

uration for oocytes from small, medium, and large pig follicles by a low molecular fraction (PM-10; <10,000) of pig follicular fluid. Oocytes from all three sizes of follicles were about equally sensitive to OMI; but in these experiments, which were completed in 1978, the ability of oocytes from small follicles to mature was significantly lower than oocytes from medium and large follicles. At the present time, however, we find that oocytes from small follicles mature at the same rate as those from medium sized follicles. This observation is as yet unexplained.

As shown in Fig. 7b cumulus-enclosed oocyte cultures secrete progesterone, with the amount increasing with the follicle size from which the oocytes are derived. We explain this increase as due to the fact that the oocyte–cumulus complexes from medium and large follicles have responded more to LH and FSH *in vivo* compared to complexes from small follicles (Channing *et al.*, 1981). Figure 7 also demonstrates that considerable inhibition of progesterone secretion is brought about by increased doses of PM-10 filtrate fractions (low-molecular-weight fraction of follicular fluid). Similar inhibitions have been reported by Hillensjö *et al.* (1980) for follicular fluid, PM-10 fraction, and the OMI fraction eluted from a Sephadex G-25 column. The mechanism of the inhibitory action of OMI fractions on the cumulus–oocyte complex cannot be explained at present, although the effects appear to keep the oocyte–cumulus complex in an

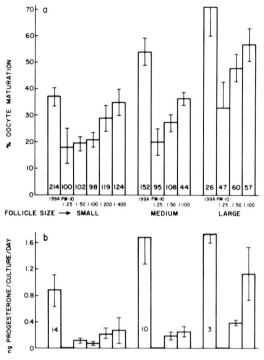

FIG. 7.   Inhibition of maturation of oocytes from small, medium, and large pig follicles by use of a low-molecular-weight fraction of pig follicular fluid (PM-10). Follicular fluid was filtered through an Amicon PM-10 filter, the filtrate was lyophilized to dryness and redissolved in water to give a low-molecular-weight fraction (<10,000) that was 40- to 50-fold concentrated. Oocytes were collected separately from small, medium, and large follicles. (a) shows percentage oocyte maturation (± SEM) after 2 days for oocytes from each follicle size and for several dilutions of PM-10. (b) shows the amount of progesterone secreted/culture/day ± SEM. The numbers within the bars give the number of oocytes cultured (a) or the number of individual cultures (b).

immature state. It is not known whether the reduction in progesterone secretion by the cumulus cells is the result of a decrease in progesterone synthesis or an increase in its rate of metabolism.

B. INHIBITION OF OUTGROWTH OF CLUMPS OF GRANULOSA CELLS: POSSIBLE OMI BIOASSAY?

Hillensjö *et al.* (1980) observed that OMI fractions had another action on the cumulus–oocyte complex: they inhibited cumulus cell outgrowth (monolayer formation). This action apparently represents maintenance of an immature state for the cumulus-enclosed oocyte. The cumulus cells probably mediate the inhibitory action of OMI since both pig and rat oocytes, denuded of cumulus cells, no longer are inhibited from maturation after addition of an OMI preparation (Hillensjö *et al.*, 1979; Channing *et al.*, 1980; Tsafriri *et al.*, 1981).

The behavior of cumulus cells in the presence of OMI led us to investigate the possible parallel behavior in cultured granulosa cell clumps. Both cumulus and granulosa cells have receptors for LH and FSH, although cumulus cells have fewer receptors for each gonadotropin (Channing *et al.*, 1981). Both cell types respond to LH with increased cyclic AMP and progesterone. FSH acts on both cell types to induce receptors for LH. Finally, both cell types increase in responsiveness to LH with increasing size of the follicle (Channing *et al.*, 1981). As shown in Fig. 4b and 4d, clumps of granulosa cells also spread into monolayers when they are incubated in culture medium. For use as an assay for inhibition of monolayer formation granulosa cell clumps are harvested from the follicular fluid by first centrifuging follicular fluid from either small or medium follicles at 1000 g for 5 minutes. The fluid is decanted and the cells are resuspended in wash medium (TC 199 plus 5% pig serum) on a watch glass. Using a binocular dissecting microscope the top layer, consisting of dead cells, debris, and single cells, is aspirated off. Rinsing is continued several more times with clumps of 1000–3000 viable cells finally obtained in a >90% pure preparation. The clumps are suspended in culture medium 199 A (TC 199 + 15% pig serum) and continuously stirred so that about 25 to 40 clumps of cells are present in 0.1 ml. Aliquots of the granulosa cell clump suspension are added to 0.1 ml of test substance in microtest plates. Five to eight wells of clumps are employed for each test. After 24 hours (as shown in Fig. 8) the PM-10 fraction of follicular fluid added to the granulosa cells prevents monolayer formation when compared to the clumps grown in control medium.

Subsequently we utilized inhibition of outgrowth of granulosa cell clumps to assay OMI-containing fractions of porcine follicular fluid in order to determine whether OMI and granulosa cell clump monolayer inhibition activities of porcine follicular fluid copurify.

We first determined that granulosa cells from small follicles responded more rapidly to inhibitory fractions in culture than did cells from medium follicles and that by 24 hours in culture, at least 40% of the clumps obtained from small follicles had developed monolayers (Fig. 9). We also showed (Fig. 9) that at 24 hours, PM-10 fractions of porcine follicular fluid exhibited a greater fractional inhibition of monolayer formation than they did at 48 hours. For this reason we adopted the practice of utilizing granulosa cells from small follicles for routine work. In the routine assay they were incubated 24 hours, then scored for monolayer formation.

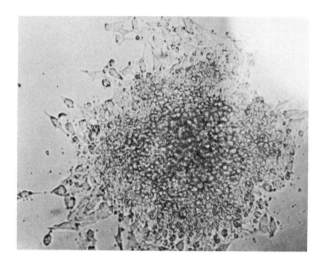

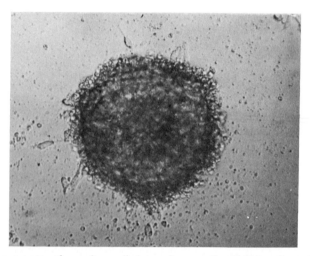

FIG. 8. Appearance of granulosa cell clumps from medium follicles after culture for 48 hours. (bottom panel) In the presence of a PM-10 fraction of OMI (1 : 100 dilution); (top panel) in the presence of control medium.

Figure 10 indicates that pig follicular fluid from small follicles inhibits outgrowth of granulosa cell clumps in a dose-dependent fashion and exhibits a dose–response. On the other hand pig serum at the same dilution is not inhibitory; but rather it actually slightly stimulated outgrowth.

The reversibility of action of OMI on granulosa cell monolayer formation is shown in Fig. 11. In this experiment the medium around the clumps was replaced after 24 hours: control medium was removed and replaced with control medium while OMI-containing medium was replaced with either control or OMI-containing medium. The figure shows that replacement of OMI with control medium led to a reversal of the inhibition by an OMI fraction.

A dose–response curve using inhibition of granulosa cell monolayer formation as an assay can be obtained in the presence of two OMI preparations and is shown in Fig. 12.

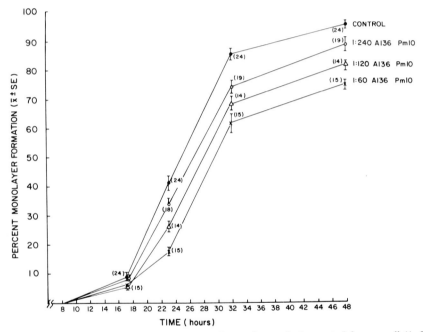

FIG. 9. Monolayer formation by clumps of granulosa cells harvested from small (1–2 mm) porcine follicles. Granulosa cell clumps were harvested by aspiration from small porcine follicles and washed 3–4 times in medium containing 5% pig serum in TC 199. The clumps were aliquoted into small Falcon microtest plate wells in groups of 25–40 clumps/well using 15–24 wells per point. Cultures were all incubated in 0.1 ml of culture 199A (TC 199 + 15% pig serum + 1 μg/ml insulin) plus 0.1 ml of suspension medium containing 10% pig serum + 90% TC 199 plus 50 μg/ml gentamicin. To the cultures various dilutions of low-molecular-weight fraction of porcine follicular fluid (AL36 PM-10) were added to the culture at 0 time. After 8, 18, 23, 32, and 48 hours the number of clumps exhibiting monolayer formation were estimated under an inverted ocular microscope at 100× magnification (cf. Fig. 8 for example). The data are expressed as percentage of clumps showing monolayer formation and represent the average ± SE of the number of observations shown in parentheses. Each observation is for 1 culture well consisting of an average of 25–40 clumps.

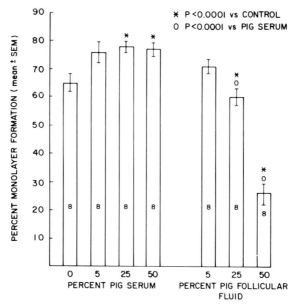

FIG. 10. Effect of pig serum and follicular fluid harvested from small (1–2 mm) pig follicles upon monolayer formation by clumps of granulosa cells harvested from small porcine follicles. Granulosa cell clumps were inoculated in groups of 30–45 in 8 wells of Falcon multiwells in a balance of medium 199A consisting of 15% pig serum in TC 199 + 1 μg/ml insulin and 50 μg/ml gentamicin. To the 199A either pig serum or pig follicular fluid was added to bring the concentration of added serum or fluid to 5, 25, or 50%. The serum and follicular fluid were sterilized by filtration through a 0.22-μm filter prior to addition to the culture. The cells were grown for 27.5 hours and evaluated for monolayer formation. Data were analyzed by χ^2 analysis.

These results have allowed us to measure both inhibition of oocyte maturation (OMI) and inhibition of monolayer formation in parallel during fractionations designed to purify OMI. Our ultimate aim is to determine whether these two activities copurify so that one might use inhibition of monolayer formation as a partial substitute assay for detection of OMI. The granulosa cell clump outgrowth assay is relatively easy to perform and many more samples can be measured in a single assay than in the standard OMI test.

C. OMI: CURRENT STATUS OF PURIFICATION

Pig follicular fluid continues to serve as our primary source of OMI. Since Stone *et al.* (1978) observed that fluid from small and medium follicles contained more OMI activity than did fluid harvested from large follicles most of our subsequent studies on purification of OMI have em-

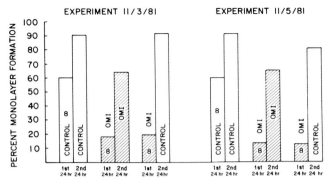

FIG. 11. Reversibility of action of Sephadex G-25 fraction of OMI (#92, AL 52) used at 1:50 dilution upon granulosa cell clump monolayer formation. Granulosa cell clumps were inoculated into 8 wells of (total of 400–500 clumps) 40–50/well in culture medium 199A with or without a 1:50 dilution of Sephadex fraction #92 of OMI from experiment AL 52 originating from porcine follicular fluid. After a 24-hour culture period ¾ of the cultures were replaced by control medium and ¼ were left in the presence of the OMI material. The cultures were then incubated for an additional 24-hour period. Monolayer formation was evaluated after 24 and 48 hours. It is clear that even in the continuous presence of OMI there is still some monolayer formation during the second 24-hour period, but it is significantly less than control culture (control for 48 hours) or OMI first 24 hours followed by control for the second 24 hours ($p < 0.01$, χ^2). OMI replaced by control gave percentage monolayer formation close to control (both 24-hour period control) values.

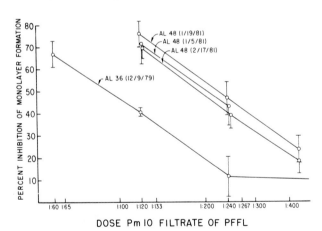

FIG. 12. Dose–response curves of the inhibitory effect of PM-10 filtrates of porcine follicular fluid upon granulosa cell clump monolayer formation. Granulosa cell clumps were harvested from small porcine follicles, washed extensively to remove cellular debris and dead clumps, and inoculated in 0.1 ml TC 199A in groups of 25–40 into Falcon microtest plates. Eight wells of cells were used for each point on the standard curve. Two standard PM-10 fractions of porcine follicular fluid (AL 36 and AL 48) were assayed. At the end of the culture the clumps were scored for monolayer formation and the data expressed as percentage inhibition of monolayer formation. Data from 8 wells per variable were averaged and the mean ± SEM for the 8 wells are shown in the graph. Using χ^2 analysis the 1:60, 1:120, and 1:240 dose of PM-10 filtrate exerted a significant ($p < 0.01$) inhibition of granulosa cell clump monolayer formation.

ployed pools of follicular fluid from small and medium follicles. The observation of this decline in OMI as the follicle matures was confirmed in staged pig ovarian follicular fluid (A. Tsafriri, personal communication). He found, using rat oocytes, that fluid from large follicles of pigs in estrus did not contain OMI. In contrast, fluid isolated from medium follicles before estrus contained significant amounts of OMI activity. This suggests that the concentration of OMI might have regulatory significance since a low level in large follicles at the time of ovulation would permit oocyte maturation to occur.

However, other observations may require revision of this hypothesis. Liebfried and First (1980), Tsafriri (personal communication), and Pomerantz and Channing (unpublished) have found that some samples of pooled pig follicular fluid or the PM-10 fraction contain little or no OMI activity. Also, when we carried out purification of OMI by chromatography on Sephadex G-25 followed by CM-Sephadex (Channing *et al.*, 1981) the total OMI activity was >100% of starting activity (Table I). These results can be interpreted to mean that follicular fluid contains both OMI and a stimulator of oocyte maturation, the stimulator being removed by purification by CM-Sephadex. In support of this concept Atlas and Channing (unpublished experiments), using CM-Sephadex chromatography of conditioned porcine granulosa cell culture medium, have recovered a fraction which stimulates the outgrowth of granulosa cell clumps. These findings mean that even fluid from large follicles may have OMI whose action is masked by stimulators of oocyte maturation. Variable

TABLE I

Recovery of OMI Activity after Chromatography on CM-Sephadex[a]

Experiment	Activity applied (units)	Activity recovered (units)	Recovery (%)
1	590	1300	220
2	510	1000	196
3	475	665	140
4	450	470	104

[a] In each case the activity applied was an OMI fraction from a Sephadex G-25 column. In experiments 1 and 2 the CM-Sephadex (2×37 cm) was suspended in $0.01\ M$ NH_4HCO_3, pH 8, and the sample was eluted with that buffer after about 116 ml had been passed through the column. In experiments 3 and 4, the column (2×50 cm) was suspended in $0.01\ M$ NH_4OAC, pH 5, and the column was eluted in succession with 0.01, 0.05, 0.10, and 0.20 M NH_4OAC. The activity recovered is the sum of three areas of activity.

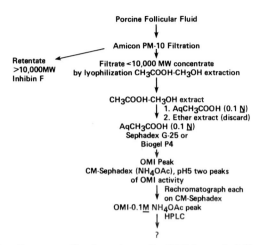

FIG. 13.   Current purification scheme for OMI from pig follicular fluid.

concentrations of stimulators could thus explain the inability of some laboratories to measure OMI in crude samples.

Our current purification scheme is illustrated in Fig. 13. The activity of OMI is now estimated using oocytes from small follicles rather than those from medium follicles. In the past 2 years the pig ovaries from a local meat packing plant contained relatively more small compared to medium follicles. In addition the control maturation rate for the oocytes from small follicles has shifted upward to 50–75% in our laboratory. This makes assay using such oocytes more practical; they are available in greater number and have an adequate maturation rate under control conditions.

If the PM-10 filtrate of porcine follicular fluid is chromatographed on Sephadex G-25 the OMI and granulosa cell clump monolayer inhibitory activity coelute. If this Sephadex Peak A material is applied to CM-Sephadex the elution pattern is shown in Fig. 14. The three peaks of OMI activity, fractions (18–25), (180–199), and (240–280) also have the ability to inhibit the outgrowth of granulosa cell clumps, although the correlation is far from perfect. For example, there is considerable OMI activity but no inhibition of clump monolayer formation in fraction (260–280). Inhibition of monolayer formation is seen in fraction (100–110) but no OMI activity is present. In this experiment we also measured progesterone secretion in the cultures of granulosa cell clumps. With a few exceptions, inhibition of progesterone secretion by these fractions parallels inhibition of clump outgrowth.

When fraction (18–25) of Fig. 14 [OMI(1)] was rechromatographed on CM-Sephadex under roughly the same conditions, the elution diagram

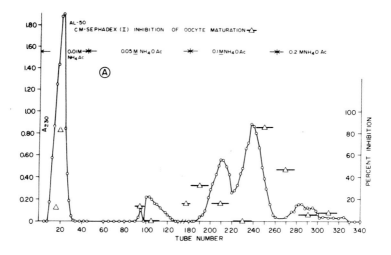

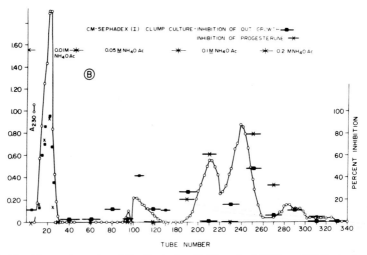

FIG. 14. Chromatography of the Sephadex G-25 peak of OMI on CM-Sephadex. The OMI fraction from a column of Sephadex G-25 (585 units; 0.57 units/mg peptide) was adjusted to pH 5.0 with acetic acid. It was then applied to a column of CM-Sephadex (2 × 50 cm) suspended in 0.01 M NH$_4$OAC, pH 5 and the column eluted as shown in the figures with 0.01, 0.05, 0.10, and 0.20 M NH$_4$OAC, pH 5. Tube volume was 7 ml. Both (A) and (B) show the elution pattern observed at 230 nm. For assay purposes the tubes were combined into 28 fractions, lyophilized to dryness, and dissolved in 2 or 4 ml of water. For OMI (A) 60 μl of each fraction was taken for assay at a final dilution of (1 : 25). (B) shows the inhibition of progesterone secretion and monolayer formation by the granulosa cell clumps for which 30 μl of each fraction was taken for assay at a final dilution of 1 : 200. Granulosa cells were pooled from many small (<2 mm) porcine follicles and washed several times. A large number of clumps were selected, pooled, and stirred in medium 199A, and then dispensed (100 μl) into culture wells containing test fractions, standards, and controls. The results are graphed as percentage inhibition of oocyte maturation and progesterone formation. The span of each bar indicates the tubes within a given fraction.

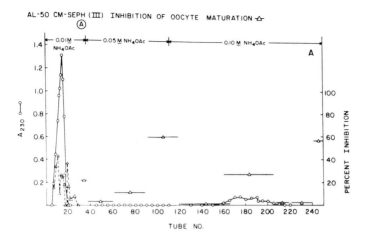

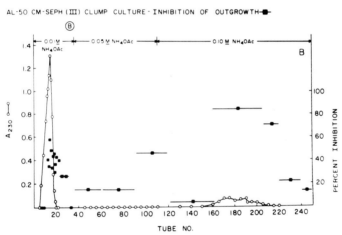

FIG. 15.   Rechromatography of fraction (18–24) of Fig. 14 [OMI(1)] on CM-Sephadex. Fraction (18–24) of Fig. 14 was loaded on a CM-Sephadex column prepared as described in the legend for Fig. 14. The column was eluted as shown in this figure. (A) indicates the OMI activity of various fractions and (B) shows the inhibition of clump culture outgrowth.

shown in Fig. 15 was obtained. Inspection reveals that much of the OMI activity previously eluted with 0.01 M ammonium acetate now elutes with 0.05 M ammonium acetate. Furthermore, there is a wide divergence between OMI and inhibition of clump culture outgrowth. One OMI peak at (90–119) [OMI(2)] does, however, coincide with inhibition of outgrowth of granulosa cells.

Rechromatography of fraction (240–280) of Fig. 14 [OMI(3)] gave the elution diagram in Fig. 16. The bulk of the OMI activity was eluted with

AL-50 CM-SEPH(IV) INHIBITION OF OOCYTE MATURATION -△-

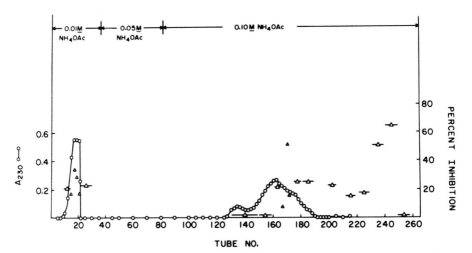

TUBE NO.

FIG. 16.   Rechromatography of fraction (240–260) of Fig. 14 [OMI(3)]. Fraction (240–260) of Fig. 14 was loaded on a CM-Sephadex column prepared as described in the legend for Fig. 14. The column was eluted as shown in this figure. The inhibition of oocyte maturation is shown for various fractions.

0.10 *M* ammonium acetate but there was some activity in the 0.01 *M* ammonium acetate fraction. We do not have data for inhibition of clump culture outgrowth by these fractions.

Our tentative conclusion is that there are probably two, and possibly three, OMI species in follicular fluid. In addition it is likely that there are several compounds which inhibit granulosa cell monolayer formation. While it is possible that one of these compounds is identical with one of the OMI species, the relationship between these two inhibitions remains uncertain and it is not possible to use the clump culture assay as an absolute substitute for inhibition of oocyte maturation except during early stages of the purification.

D. CONTROL OF OMI SECRETION BY GRANULOSA CELLS

Several lines of evidence point to granulosa cells as a source of OMI: Coculture of granulosa cells and oocyte–cumulus complexes (Tsafriri and Channing, 1975; Sato and Ishibashi, 1977) results in inhibition of oocyte maturation; medium conditioned by culture of granulosa cells suppresses oocyte maturation (Tsafriri, 1979) and the inhibitory effect was reversed by LH (Tsafriri and Bar-Ami, 1981); and extracts of granulosa cells (Tsafriri *et al.*, 1976; Sato and Ishibashi, 1977; Centola *et al.*, 1981) also inhibited oocyte maturation. These inhibitory effects were proportional to the number of granulosa cells used (Tsafriri and Channing, 1975; Tsafriri, 1979). Furthermore, granulosa cells from small follicles were more potent than cells from medium and large follicles (Tsafriri and Channing, 1975; Centola *et al.*, 1981). A preliminary characterization of OMI activity in conditioned medium was made by chromatography of the PM-10 fraction of the medium on Sephadex G-25. Three peaks of OMI activity were located, one of which corresponded to that obtained from pig follicular fluid; LH reversed the inhibitory action as it does when added to OMI from follicular fluid (Pomerantz and Channing, unpublished).

Additional studies carried out by Anderson, Stone, and Channing (unpublished) revealed that the potential of granulosa cells to secrete OMI activity into the culture medium was greater in the case of small compared to large follicles (Fig. 17). This is in keeping with the observation of a decline in OMI present in FFI as the follicle enlarges (Stone *et al.*, 1978, Fig. 2).

Anderson and Stone (1980) found that addition of human FSH (1 μg/ml) to suspension cultures of granulosa cells from small and medium follicles stimulated OMI secretion by the cultured cells. Testosterone or dihy-

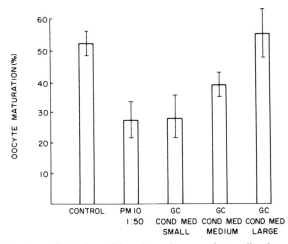

FIG. 17. Inhibitory effect of conditioned porcine granulosa cell culture medium upon porcine oocyte maturation. Porcine granulosa cells from small (1–2 mm), medium (3–5 mm), and large (6–12 mm) follicles were cultured for 48 hours and the conditioned medium filtered through PM-10. The PM-10 filtrate was added to porcine oocytes (50–60/test) and the effect on oocyte maturation determined after 2 days of incubation in media consisting of 1 part conditioned medium and 1 part TC 199A. Data are expressed as the mean $\pm$ SE of 6–8 experiments.

drotestosterone, however, led to decreases, while LH or estrogen had no effect on secretion of OMI by granulosa cell suspensions. Thus, elevated follicular androgens associated with atresia (McNatty *et al.*, 1979a,b) and with the LH/FSH surge (Ainsworth *et al.*, 1980) may play a role in the resumption of oocyte meiosis by causing a decrease in OMI secretion by granulosa cells. Since atresia is associated with oocyte maturation and the death of granulosa cells (Hirschfield and Midgley, 1978; McNatty *et al.*, 1979a,b), atretic follicles may also contain less OMI as a result of granulosa cell death. Human cystic follicles, which contain fewer granulosa cells than normal, do contain less OMI than viable follicles (Channing *et al.*, 1981b).

Recently Channing (unpublished experiments) has shown that ovine prolactin stimulates secretion of OMI from granulosa cells from small and medium follicles. As shown in Fig. 18 addition of 1.0 and 10 but not 0.1 µg

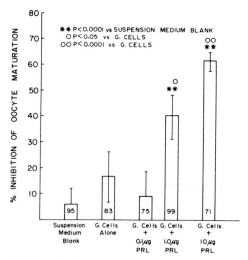

FIG. 18.   Effect of ovine prolactin (oPRL) on porcine granulosa cell secretion of material inhibiting oocyte maturation. Various doses of NIH ovine prolactin (0.1, 1, 10 µg) were added to porcine granulosa cells (1 × 10⁶ ml) obtained from 1–5 mm follicles and the cells were cultured as a suspension in siliconized Packard scintillation vials. Prolactin was also added to blank suspension medium. Cultures were incubated for 48 hours. At the end of the culture period medium was poured off and frozen for further assay. Two oocyte assays were carried out and the entire experiment repeated two more times. For oocyte assay medium was thawed and filtered and added to microtest plates 0.1 ml per well. To that was added 0.1 ml Medium 199 A plus 15 cumulus-enclosed porcine oocytes and the oocytes incubated 2 days. Blank suspension medium was included as a control. Oocyte maturation was evaluated and the percentage maturation was expressed as percentage inhibition of maturation compared to control culture medium 199 A. The number of oocytes is indicated inside bars and the standard error of the mean is indicated as the top of each bar. χ² analysis was used to compare groups.

prolactin/ml to granulosa cell culture brought about significant increases in inhibition of oocyte maturation when this conditioned medium was added to oocyte cultures. This preliminary experiment shows that prolactin may also be involved in control of OMI secretion. Thus, the infertility of hyperprolactinemic patients may be partly due to an overproduction of OMI.

IV. Follicular Control of FSH Induction of Granulosa Cell Maturation

The number of follicles ovulating at maturity differs among various mammals, however, there is a tendency for each species to ovulate approximately the same number of follicles at each estrus. Even though there are obviously differences in the "fine control" of follicular dynamics in different species, many of the factors which affect the maturation of follicles in mammals have been identified. LH and FSH secreted by the pituitary prior to and during puberty and cyclically throughout the adult reproductive life have been shown to be responsible for controlling follicular growth past the antrum stage, maturation of the follicle including estrogen secretion, follicular rupture, and most aspects of corpus luteum growth and function. Other extraovarian hormones including insulin, cortisol, thyroxine, and prolactin also may serve to modulate follicular maturation. Additionally, intraovarian factors are intimately involved in controlling follicular function. Steroids produced by various ovarian compartments (estrogen, progesterone, and androgen) have been shown to have multiple effects involving both intraovarian and extraovarian loci in controlling many aspects of follicular maturation. Less well understood is a group of nonsteroidal regulators present in follicular fluid which have been described though not yet purified to homogeneity. In this section the role of two such follicular fluid components, LI (luteinization inhibitor) and LS (luteinization stimulator), will be discussed in reference to work done in this laboratory and elsewhere. The effects of LI and LS on the *in vitro* maturation of granulosa cells leading to development of LH/hCG receptors and secretion of increased amounts of progesterone both basally and in response to LH/hCG or cAMP will be presented and considered in relation to the modulation of follicular development *in vivo*.

A. LUTEINIZATION INHIBITOR (LI)

Granulosa cells taken from large preovulatory porcine follicles will luteinize spontaneously in culture with a resulting increase in progesterone secretion (Channing, 1970). Ledwitz-Rigby *et al.* (1977) demonstrated that follicular fluid taken from immature (1–2 mm) follicles of the pig will reduce the accumulation of cAMP in response to LH and will decrease the secretion of progesterone when added to cultures of granulosa cells obtained from large follicles. The morphological transformation of these granulosa cells normally seen when luteinization occurs was also blocked by follicular fluid addition. Treatment of follicular fluid with charcoal to remove both estrogen and progesterone did not change the capacity of the fluid to inhibit *in vitro* luteinization (Ledwitz-Rigby, 1981; Osteen and Channing, unpublished observations). Additionally, follicular fluid inhibition of various aspects of granulosa cell luteinization has been reported to occur in several species including bovine (Shemesh, 1979; Bernard, 1973), rat (Lieberman *et al.*, 1973; Amsterdam *et al.*, 1979), porcine (Ledwitz-Rigby *et al.*, 1977; Ledwitz-Rigby and Rigby, 1979), equine (Younglai, 1972; Channing *et al.*, 1980), and human (Kraiem *et al.*, 1978; Hillensjö *et al.*, 1978). The presence of LI activity in follicular fluid from many species supports the concept that this inhibitory activity may be very important physiologically for follicular function. However, follicular fluid obtained from nonatretic preovulatory follicles may not contain significant amounts of LI; in fact, fluid from large porcine follicles appears to be stimulatory of some aspects of granulosa cell luteinization (Ledwitz-Rigby and Rigby, 1979; Kolena and Channing, 1981). The stimulatory activity of granulosa cell maturation found in follicular fluid will be discussed later in this section. LI activity appears to be present mainly in fluid from atretic follicles (Shemesh, 1979; Channing *et al.*, 1980) or fluid obtained from small immature follicles (Ledwitz-Rigby *et al.*, 1977; Ledwitz-Rigby and Rigby, 1981). Loss of LI activity may therefore be a part of the normal maturation process of follicles permitting granulosa cells to develop the necessary capabilities to respond to the ovulatory gonadotropin surges only in mature nonatretic follicles. Evidence for a role of LI in keeping granulosa cells from immature follicles in maturational abeyance may lie partly in the ontogeny of granulosa cell LH receptors.

There are 20- to 50-fold more LH/hCG receptors demonstrable in large porcine follicles (6–12 mm) compared to small (1–2 mm) immature follicles (Channing and Kammerman, 1973; Nakano *et al.*, 1977). The number of binding sites for FSH is, however, much greater in small follicles compared to preovulatory follicles (Zeleznik *et al.*, 1974; Nakano *et al.*, 1977). Cells from large follicles accumulate more cAMP in response to LH than cells isolated from small follicles (Channing, 1973) and demonstrate an increased potential to secrete progesterone (Anderson *et al.*, 1979; Thanki and Channing, 1978). The ability of granulosa cells from follicles of various sizes to luteinize in culture appears to correlate with the acquisition of LH/hCG receptors. Whereas granulosa cells from large preovulatory follicles will spontaneously luteinize in culture, cells obtained from medium sized follicles (2–5 mm) require either LH or FSH in order to mature (luteinize) *in vitro* (Channing, 1970). Granulosa cells from small follicles will not secrete as much progesterone as cells from medium or large follicles even after exposure to appropriate amounts of LH or FSH *in vitro* (Thanki and Channing, 1978). Prior exposure to high levels of LI activity *in vivo* may be involved in the lack of spontaneous luteinization *in vitro* observed with granulosa cells obtained from either small or medium sized porcine follicles. Present studies in this laboratory have investigated the induction of functional LH/hCG receptors in granulosa cells from immature porcine follicles and the effect of follicular fluid components on this induction.

Granulosa cells from small, immature follicles can be cultured for 4 days in the presence of a mixture of hormones which can induce luteinization. Initially Channing *et al.* (1976) reported that in addition to LH and FSH, insulin, cortisol, and thyroxine will increase progesterone secretion in cultured granulosa cells from immature porcine follicles. A 2- to 3-fold increase in LH/hCG receptors was later shown to also be demonstrable when insulin, cortisol, and thyroxine were added to cultures in addition to FSH alone (Channing *et al.*, 1978). Anderson *et al.* (1980) further demonstrated that a dramatic 5- to 10-fold increase in functional LH/hCG receptors can be seen if serum is added to the cultures in addition to FSH. Again, an increase in LH/hCG receptors was measured in cultures containing insulin, cortisol, and thyroxine above the levels present with FSH alone (Fig. 19). Granulosa cells from immature follicles of the pig therefore have the potential to acquire LH/hCG receptors and secrete progesterone when removed from their follicular fluid environment and cultured with appropriate hormones. When follicular fluid obtained from small porcine follicles is added to cultures of granulosa cells from immature follicles a dose-responsive inhibition of LH/hCG receptor induction occurs (Fig. 20), whereas fluid from mature follicles was not inhibitory. Inhibition of progesterone secretion can also be demonstrated when fluid from small follicles is added as opposed to a stimulatory effect of fluid from preovulatory follicles (Fig. 21). Preliminary fractionation of whole follicular fluid from small porcine follicles by Amicon PM-10 filtration revealed that both a high molecular weight component (>10,000 MW) and a low molecular weight component (<10,000 MW) of LI "activity" existed. The high- and low-molecular-weight components when added to cultures of granulosa cells from immature follicles inhibited induction of LH/hCG receptors and progesterone secretion (Figs. 22 and 23). Whether or not a small-molecular-weight inhibitor of FSH binding, reported to exist in follicular fluid by Darga and Reichert (1978), is involved in the

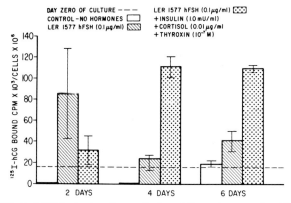

FIG. 19. Effect of FSH plus insulin, cortisol, and thyroxin upon the ability of porcine granulosa cells to bind iodinated hCG. Granulosa cells from small antral follicles of the pig were cultured for 2, 4, and 6 days in medium 199 and 4% pig serum containing either no exogenous hormones (control), hFSH (LER 1577; 0.1 μg/ml), or hFSH (LER 1577; 0.1 μg/ml) + insulin (1 mU/ml), cortisol (0.01 μg/ml), and thyroxine ($10^{-7} M$). At the end of each incubation time the cells were removed from the flasks by scraping with a rubber policeman in physiological saline. Seven aliquots of the cells were taken: five for determination of ^{125}I-labeled hCG bound to the cells (three for specific and two for nonspecific binding), one for cell number, and one for protein by the Lowry assay. The values represent the mean ± SE (n = 4) of two individual experiments. Data shown here represent specific binding of ^{125}I-labeled hCG bound to the cells on the day of collection.

inhibitory activity of the <10,000 MW fraction is not known. However, work is presently underway to purify both the high- and low-molecular-weight components of LI.

B. LUTEINIZATION STIMULATOR (LS)

In sharp contrast to the various inhibitory influences exerted by follicular fluid obtained from small, immature antral follicles, fluid collected from large preovulatory follicles has been shown to be quite permissive of *in vitro* luteinization of granulosa cells from mature follicles and additionally potentiates the effects of LH and FSH on granulosa cells from immature follicles. Younglai (1972) reported stimulation of both progesterone and estrogen synthesis in equine granulosa cell cultures when fluid from large preovulatory equine follicles was added to the medium. None of the inhibitory effects seen when follicular fluid from small porcine follicles was added to porcine granulosa cell cultures was seen when fluid from mature follicles was added (Ledwitz-Rigby et al., 1977). These authors speculated that as the follicle matures it may either lose inhibitory activity or gain a substance that enhances luteinization. Porcine granulosa cells

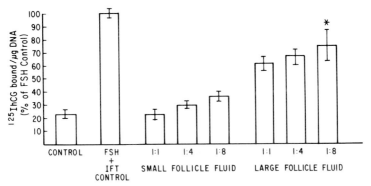

FIG. 20. Effect of various doses of follicular fluid obtained from small (left) or large (right) porcine follicles upon FSH stimulation of LH/hCG receptors in cultured porcine granulosa cells. Granulosa cells from small antral porcine follicles were cultured for 4 days in 0.5 ml TC Media 199 and 10% pig serum containing either no exogenous hormone (control), FSH-IFT (hFSH; LER 8/117; 0.1 μg-ml, 1 mU/ml insulin, 0.01 μg/ml hydrocortisone, $10^{-7} M$ thyroxine), or FSH + IFT with 50, 25, or 12.5% whole porcine follicular fluid replacing part of the culture media. At the end of the culture period, cells were removed from the wells by scraping with a rubber policeman in physiological saline. Aliquots of the cells were taken for determination of ^{125}I-labeled hCG binding and for DNA content. The values represent the mean ± SE for 3 separate experiments (n = 6). It should be noted that all of the cultures except the "control" (far left) contained FSH-IFT.

obtained from preovulatory follicles showed more morphological changes associated with increased steroidogenesis when cultured with follicular fluid from large follicles as opposed to cultures containing follicular fluid from small follicles or serum (Alexander *et al.*, 1978). Serum alone, however, may lack certain factors needed by granulosa cells in culture since fluid from either small or large porcine follicles will support granulosa cells that appear mostly epithelioid, while in serum the cells become largely fibroblastic (Ledwitz-Rigby and Rigby, 1979). Fluid from either immature or preovulatory follicles will also promote increased progesterone secretion in granulosa cell cultures, but compared to fluid from small follicles the fluid obtained from large porcine follicles enhances progesterone secretion more rapidly (2 compared to 4 days) (Ledwitz-Rigby and Rigby, 1979; Ledwitz-Rigby, 1981). Ledwitz-Rigby *et al.* (1981) have demonstrated that fluid from large porcine follicles will also enhance estrogen secretion by cultures of granulosa cells from small, medium, or large follicles when both FSH and androgen precursor is supplied (Table II). One possible role of LS in follicular fluid may involve a synergism with FSH in promoting LH receptor induction in the maturing granulosa cell. The acquisition of LH receptors has been shown to be an integral part of granulosa cell maturation (Channing and Kammerman, 1973; Stouffer *et al.*, 1976; Lee, 1976). This induction is regulated to a large

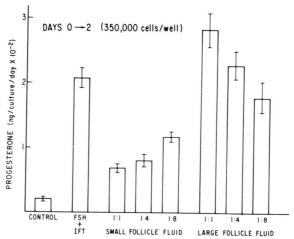

FIG. 21. Effect of follicular fluid from small (left) and large (right) porcine follicles upon FSH stimulation of progesterone secretion by cultured porcine granulosa cells. Granulosa cells from small antral porcine follicles were cultured for 4 days in 0.5 ml TC Media 199 and 10% pig serum containing either no exogenous hormone (control), FSH-IFT (hFSH; LER 8/117; 0.1 μg/ml, 1 mU/ml insulin, 0.01 μg/ml hydrocortisone, $10^{-7}M$ thyroxine), or FSH + IFT with 50, 25, or 12.5% whole porcine follicular fluid replacing part of the culture media. After 2 days of culture, media were changed and the "spent" media assessed for progesterone content by specific radioimmunoassay. The values represent the mean ± SE for 3 separate experiments ($n = 12$). It should be noted that FSH + IFT was present in all the cultures except the "control" (far left).

TABLE II

Influence of Follicular Fluids on Estrogen Secretion by Granulosa Cells from Small, Medium, and Large Follicles[a]

Size of follicles granulosa cells were obtained from	Culture medium	Estrogen secreted/culture (% stimulation over control cultures in 50% serum ± SE; number of experiments given in parentheses)
Small (1–2 mm)	50% SFFl[b]	132 ± 31.7 (3)
	50% LFFl	568 ± 171 (7)
Medium (3–5 mm)	50% SFFl	173 ± 86 (3)
	50% LFFl	261 ± 38 (6)
Large (6–12 mm)	50% SFFl	156 ± 46 (4)
	50% LFFl	331 ± 96 (4)

[a] From Ledwitz-Rigby *et al.* (1981) with permission.
[b] All media contained 2 μg ovine FSH and 0.14 μg testosterone/ml.

extent both *in vitro* and *in vivo* by FSH (Channing *et al.*, 1979; Nimrod *et al.*, 1977; Anderson *et al.*, 1980; May *et al.*, 1980). LS present in follicular fluid could synergize with FSH and/or LH and thus modulate the selection of follicles which will ovulate. Ledwitz-Rigby (1979) demonstrated that either LH or FSH synergized with follicular fluid obtained from large porcine follicles in promoting progesterone secretion by cultures of immature granulosa cells. Studies in our laboratory have shown that immature granulosa cells cultured in the presence of porcine follicular fluid from large preovulatory follicles will promote LH/hCG receptor induction by 2- to 3-fold over the level of induction elicited with comparable amounts of fluid from immature follicles (Fig. 20). Progesterone secretion was also increased in these cultures by greater than 3-fold in the presence of fluid obtained from large follicles as opposed to fluid obtained from immature follicles (Fig. 21). A partial purification of LS activity from large preovulatory porcine follicular fluid has been accomplished in this laboratory by Kolena and Channing (1981). This work demonstrated both an enhancement of LH/hCG receptor induction and stimulation of progesterone secretion in cultured, immature porcine granulosa cells by a Sephadex G-100 fraction of ethanol precipitated fluid (Fig. 24). A further

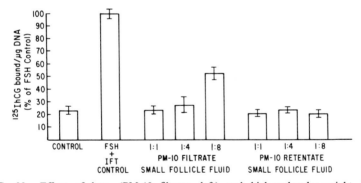

FIG. 22. Effect of low- (PM-10 filtrate—left) and high-molecular-weight (PM-10 retentate—right) fractions of follicular fluid obtained from small porcine follicles upon FSH stimulation of hCG/LH receptors in porcine granulosa cell cultures. Granulosa cells from small antral porcine follicles were cultured for 4 days in 0.5 ml TC Media 199 and 10% pig serum containing either no exogenous hormone (control), FSH-IFT (hFSH; LER 8/117; 0.1 μg/ml, 1 mU/ml insulin, 0.01 μg/ml hydrocortisone, 10^{-7} M thyroxine), or FSH + IFT with 50, 25, or 12.5% PM-10 filtrate ($<$10,000 MW) or retentate ($>$10,000 MW) of whole follicular fluid from small porcine follicles replacing part of the culture media. At the end of the culture period, cells were removed from the wells by scraping with a rubber policeman in physiological saline. Aliquots of the cells were taken for determination of ^{125}I-labeled hCG binding and for DNA content. The values represent the mean $\pm$ SE for 3 separate experiments (n = 6). It should be noted that all of the cultures except the "control" (far left) contained FSH-IFT.

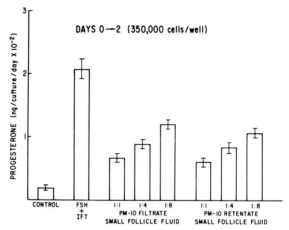

FIG. 23. Effect of low- (left, filtrate) and high- (retentate, right) molecular-weight fractions of follicular fluid upon FSH stimulation of progesterone secretion by cultured porcine granulosa cells. Granulosa cells from small antral porcine follicles were cultured for 4 days in 0.5 ml TC Media 199 and 10% pig serum containing either no exogenous hormone (control), FSH-IFT (hFSH; LER 8/117; 0.1 μg/ml insulin, 0.01 μg/ml hydrocortisone, 10^{-7} M thyroxine), or FSH-IFT with 50, 25, or 12.5% PM-10 filtrate or retentate of whole follicular fluid from small porcine follicles replacing part of the culture media. After 2 days of culture, media were changed and the "spent" media assessed for progesterone content by specific radioimmunoassay. The values represent the mean $\pm$ SE for 3 separate experiments (n = 12). It should be noted that FSH-IFT was present in all of the cultures except the "control" (far left).

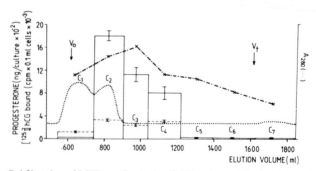

FIG. 24. Gel filtration of LFF on a Sephadex G-100 column. The fractions, after lyophilization and redissolution in water, were tested for effect on both progesterone secretion (n = 7–8) on day 2 (dashed line column) and day 4 (full line column) and binding of ^{125}I-labeled hCG (n = 2) (dot-and-dashed line) to cultures of cells from small porcine follicles. The bars show mean $\pm$ SEM. The absorbency of each fraction of 280 nm is shown by the small dotted line. The full scale for absorbency is 2.0.

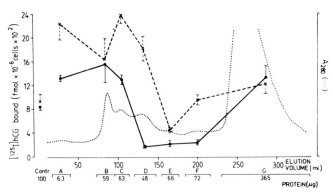

FIG. 25. Gel filtration on a DEAE-Sephacel column (1.5 × 11 cm) of 230 mg protein fraction (P3) from column of Sephadex G-100. Linear gradient 0.05–0.5 M NH$_4$HCO$_3$ (400 ml). Fractions A–G were tested for effect on induction of binding of ^{125}I-labeled hCG to granulosa cells incubated in culture on day 4 (n = 3). Concentration of protein is either indicated in figure (●——●) or is diluted 10 times (×-------×). Controls contained BSA. The bars show mean ± SEM. The absorbency of each fraction at 280 nm is shown by the small dotted line. The full scale for absorbency is 2.0.

purification of the most active fraction from the Sephadex G-100 column on DEAE-Sephacel revealed both a stimulatory and an inhibitory component with respect to FSH induction of LH/hCG receptors in cultures of granulosa cells from immature follicles (Fig. 25). Work in this laboratory is in progress to further investigate the molecular nature of both LI and LS activity in porcine follicular fluid. It now appears that both LI and LS activity are present to some extent in follicles at various stages of maturation. The changing ratio at LS/LI (or lack of a change) may modulate within individual follicles their response to circulating gonadotropin. As a follicle matures, LS may be needed to synergize with both LH and FSH to promote further development of the follicle leading to eventual ovulation. Follicles lacking adequate LS support may be doomed to atresia (Fig. 26). Evidence in favor of this concept was shown by Channing and her col-

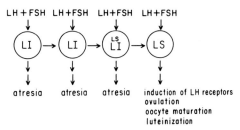

FIG. 26. Diagrammatic representation of the proposed role for LI/LS in the maturational process of the ovarian follicle.

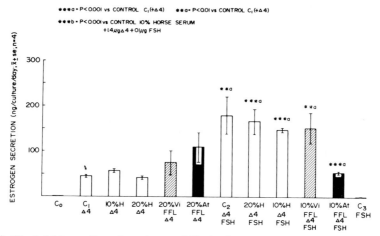

FIG. 27.   Inhibitory effect of atretic mare follicular fluid upon FSH stimulation of porcine granulosa cell conversion of androstenedione ($\Delta 4$, 1.4 μg/ml) to estrogen. C_0, control, no $\Delta 4$; $C_1 \Delta 4$, control + $\Delta 4$; H, horse serum (charcoal treated, CT); ViFFl, mare viable follicular fluid (CT); At FFl, mare atretic follicular fluid (CT); FSH, 0.1 μg/ml Saxena purified hFSH; C_3, control, no $\Delta 4$, + hFSH (0.1 μg/ml). All cultures contained androstenedione substrate except C_0 control and C_3 FSH control. Taken from Channing *et al.* (1981c), with permission.

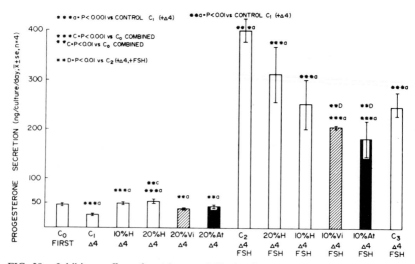

FIG. 28.   Inhibitory effect of atretic mare follicular fluid upon progesterone secretion by cultured porcine granulosa cells (Experiment I). Porcine granulosa cells were cultured for 2 days in TC 199 plus 10% pig serum plus charcoal-treated horse serum or charcoal-treated viable and atretic mare follicular fluid. ** $p < 0.001$ vs viable mare FFl; * $p < 0.005$ vs mare serum. Taken from Channing *et al.* (1981c), with permission.

leagues (Channing *et al.*, 1980) who examined the effect of follicular fluid obtained from atretic and viable large follicles of estrous mares upon cultured porcine granulosa cells. Addition of 10 and 20% charcoal-treated follicular fluid obtained from viable mare follicles stimulated FSH enhancement of estrogen and progesterone secretion by the cultured cells whereas addition of similar amounts of charcoal-treated follicular fluid obtained from atretic mare follicles inhibited their steroidogenic activity (Figs. 27 and 28).

Factors in both atretic and viable follicular fluid markedly affect granulosa cell metabolic activity, however, these factors will have to be purified before any rigorous conclusions can be drawn as to their *in vivo* role in controlling follicular maturation.

V. Role of Inhibin-F in Control of Follicular Maturation

A. BACKGROUND

Studies in the female rat have provided strong evidence pointing to the existence and significance of inhibin-F (folliculostatin or FSH-suppressing substance) in this animal. Although serum LH can be restored to basal levels in ovariectomized rats by steroid injections, the elevated serum FSH which follows ovariectomy cannot be suppressed to basal levels by steroid injections (Campbell and Schwartz, 1979; Chappel and Barraclough, 1977). However, injection of charcoal-treated, porcine follicular fluid (pFFl), a presumed source of inhibin-F, can completely inhibit the postcastrational rise in FSH (Marder *et al.*, 1977). Furthermore, the existence of the secondary rise in serum FSH which occurs during the morning of estrus in the rat does not appear to be satisfactorily explained by a simple steroid feedback mechanism (Campbell *et al.*, 1977; Barraclough, 1981). It is clear that the secondary surge in FSH is mediated by the presence of the ovary, and it has been shown that charcoal-treated pFFl can suppress this surge without altering the normal pattern of LH secretion (Schwartz and Channing, 1977). In addition, the secondary surge in FSH has been shown to coincide with a marked nadir in inhibin-like activity in rat ovarian vein serum (DePaolo *et al.*, 1979b).

From these findings, it appears that inhibin-F may have two roles in the control of FSH secretion in the rodent (and perhaps other polytocous species). (1) Inhibin-F may act throughout most of the reproductive cycle to prevent inappropriately high FSH secretion, thus maintaining the appropriate balance of LH and FSH secretion. (2) Regulation of inhibin-F feedback may also provide the appropriate signal for triggering the sec-

ondary surge in FSH secretion on the morning of estrus. Since maintenance of diestrous tonic levels of FSH and the secondary surge in FSH
have both been shown to be important requirements for normal murine
folliculogenesis (see Schwartz, 1981 and Barraclough, 1981 for review),
inhibin-F control of FSH secretion may play a key role in assuring the
appropriate course of this process in the rat. Various aspects of the study
of inhibin-F in subprimate species are reviewed in detail below (Sections
V,B and C).

For the female primate, the circumstantial evidence for the existence
and significance of inhibin-F has not been as fully developed as in the rat.
In the discussion which follows, consideration will be given to the subject
of serum gonadotropin profiles and how such information may implicate
an ovarian nonsteroidal substance in the control of FSH secretion in the
primate (Section V,D). For background information the endocrine events
occurring during the primate menstrual cycle are shown in Fig. 29. Studies

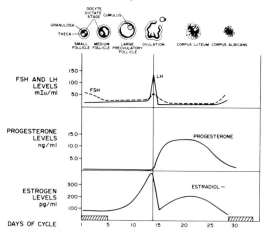

FIG. 29.   Diagrammatic sketch of ovarian and pituitary events occurring during the
human menstrual cycle. The bottom line of the graph shows the days of the menstrual cycle,
with the shaded areas representing menstrual flow. Blood estrogen and progesterone levels
are shown in the bottom and middle panels, respectively. Above these serum follicle-
stimulating hormone (FSH) levels (- - -) and serum luteinizing hormone (LH) levels (——) are
depicted. At the top of the figure the cycle of follicular and luteal development is shown. The
follicle (extreme left) starts out at the beginning of the cycle as a small follicle containing an
oocyte in the immature dictyate state. It grows and matures under the influence of pituitary
FSH and LH and secretes estrogen. Immediately prior to ovulation the preovulatory LH
surge occurs, which acts on the follicle to cause the oocyte to mature and the follicle to
rupture 36–48 hours later. The granulosa and thecal layers transform into a corpus luteum
that secretes principally progesterone and some estrogen. During the nonpregnant cycle the
corpus luteum persists for about 12 days and regresses to a corpus albicans (extreme right).
Taken from Channing et al. (1980), with permission.

aimed at a more direct demonstration of the existence and significance of inhibin-F in the primate will subsequently be reviewed (Section V,E). As background for the discussion of inhibin-F in female primates, the reader is referred to reviews of the work by Hodgen and co-workers (DiZerega and Hodgen, 1981; DiZerega *et al.*, 1981) which discuss the role of FSH in primate folliculogenesis. In brief, from their studies of folliculogenesis in the monkey, this group has concluded that the normal time course of follicular development, and quantitatively normal endocrine function of the follicle, can be supported by maintenance of normal tonic FSH input to the ovary during the perimenstrual period and the follicular phase. However, full development of a functional corpus luteum may require increased FSH input at levels observed during the perimenstrual FSH surge. At the other extreme, the ovary of females in the prime reproductive years is sensitive to supraphysiological FSH input at all times except during the late follicular phase when the dominant follicle appears to be responsible in some fashion for a bilateral ovarian insensitivity to increased FSH levels. These findings may be taken to indicate that control of FSH input to the ovary is important in ensuring normal reproductive function. This proposal is further supported by the finding that spontaneous luteal inadequacy is associated with abnormal FSH secretion in both women (Ross *et al.*, 1970) and monkeys (Wilks *et al.*, 1970).

B. ON THE ROLE OF INHIBIN-F AS A HORMONE *in Vivo* IN THE RAT AND MOUSE

In order for inhibin-F to alter pituitary gland secretion of FSH it must leave the ovary via the venous effluent. An indirect approach to address this question is transplantation of the ovary into the kidney or spleen. Bronson and Channing (1978) have shown that transplantation of a mouse ovary beneath the kidney capsule caused marked suppression of serum FSH even in the presence of 100 μg estradiol, while estradiol alone was unable to depress serum FSH levels (Fig. 30). Similarly, Uilenbroek *et al.* (1978) transplanted an ovary to the spleen in castrated male and female rats. They reasoned that the majority of steroids leaving the ovary would be metabolized once the splenic venous blood passed through the liver, but many of the proteins produced by the ovary would not be metabolized and would enter the peripheral circulation. In ovariectomized rats with intrasplenic-ovarian transplants, LH levels increased whereas FSH levels decreased. In contrast, ovariectomized rats with intrarenal-ovarian transplants both LH and FSH were suppressed to levels present in intact male and female rats. The renal transplants, unlike the spleen transplants, secrete steroids into the bloodstream without apparent further metabolism.

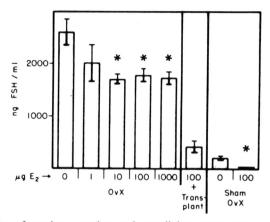

FIG. 30.   Effect of ovarian transplant and estradiol treatment upon serum FSH in the ovariectomized and sham ovariectomized adult female mouse. Serum FSH (nanograms per ml, ± SE) levels were measured in CF-1 females which were ovariectomized and given an ovarian transplant. All females were implanted with Silastic capsules containing nothing or one of several doses of estradiol (E_2) and killed 7 days after surgery ($^*p$ at least < 0.01 when tested against the appropriate control group by Neuman–Keuls tests after an analysis of variance which revealed an overall significance at $p < 0.001$; 8–10 females/treatment). Taken from Bronson and Channing (1978), with permission.

These results suggest that some ovarian moiety other than estradiol or other steroids, possibly a protein such as inhibin-F, is responsible for the suppression of FSH.

However, the concept of inhibin-F regulation of FSH secretion requires that changes in inhibin-F secretion of the intact animal should be accompanied by changes in FSH secretion during the reproductive cycle. More direct evidence for the ovarian secretion of inhibin-F-like material in the rat has been provided by the studies of DePaolo *et al.* (1979b). The amount of FSH-suppressing material present in the ovarian vein plasma (OVP) was bioassayed by its ability to suppress basal FSH secretion from dispersed pituitary cells, *in vitro*. The amount of inhibin-F activity present in the OVP fluctuated depending upon the stage of the estrous cycle and varied inversely with plasma FSH concentrations (Fig. 31). Thus, when OVP inhibin-F activity is high (during diestrous 1, diestrous 2, and proestrous morning), plasma FSH levels are low. During the preovulatory period when there is a proestrous surge of LH and FSH, inhibin-F activity declines rapidly in OVP and is further reduced on estrous morning when plasma FSH is elevated (Fig. 31). In addition, these results suggest that inhibin-F secretion may be regulated directly by gonadotropins.

Previous studies demonstrated that the administration of LH or FSH to phenobarbital-blocked proestrous rats induces a selective rise in en-

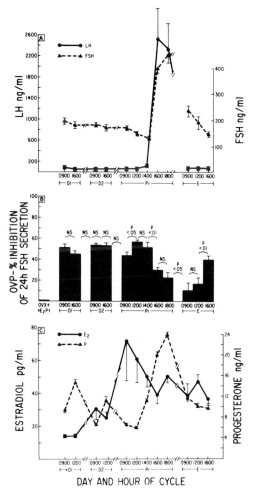

FIG. 31. Changes in peripheral plasma concentrations of FSH, LH, estradiol (E_2), and progesterone (P) during the 4-day rat estrous cycle correlated with changes in inhibin-F activity in ovarian venous plasma (OVP). All OVP and peripheral plasma samples were obtained from the same animals. (A) Plasma LH and FSH concentrations. (B) Changes in percentage of inhibin-F activity during the rat estrous cycle. As the proestrous preovulatory surge in LH and FSH occurs (1400–1800 hours) inhibin-F activity declines significantly ($p <$ 0.01) in OVP. At 0900 hours estrus, peripheral plasma FSH is elevated and inhibin-F activity has further declined. When plasma FSH approaches basal D1 levels, inhibin-F activity again is increased in OVP. (C) Peripheral plasma E_2 and P concentrations during the rat estrous cycle. Plasma E_2 levels increase between D2 and Pr to reach peak concentrations at 0900 hours Pr. Following the preovulatory LH and FSH surge, plasma E_2 declines and P increases in the peripheral circulation. On estrous morning P plasma levels are basal but E_2 values are somewhat elevated above D1 concentrations. Thus, as inhibin-F activity declines in OVP on Pr, E_2 also declines and P rises in peripheral plasma. D1, D2, Diestrous days 1, 2; Pr, proestrous; E, estrous; OVP, ovarian vein plasma. Reprinted with permission from DePaolo *et al.* (1979a).

dogenous FSH similar to that observed on estrus in cycling rats with no changes in LH (Ashiru and Blake, 1979). Using a similar protocol, Shander *et al.* (1980) investigated whether this secondary rise in FSH on 0900 hours estrus (after administration of exogenous FSH or LH to phenobarbital-treated rats on 1300 proestrus) is correlated with the amount of inhibin-F activity present in the ovarian vein at this time period. The results show that while the secondary FSH surge was suppressed by the administration of phenobarbital, the OVP from phenobarbital-treated rats had the highest amount of inhibin-F activity of all the treatment groups. With injection of 1 μg FSH or 8 μg LH, inhibin-F activity was decreased and restored to that observed in untreated control rats (Fig. 32). These results suggest that either gonadotropin can suppress the amount of inhibin-F activity leaving the ovary at 0900 hours on the expected estrus. Furthermore, blocking the endogenous gonadotropin surges on proestrus causes increased inhibin-F secretion on the following day. It remains to be determined whether these actions are direct effects of the gonadotropins or whether other hormones or factors mediate the gonadotropic action on inhibin-F activity.

Indirect evidence reported by Sasamoto and Taya (1980) suggests that LH may indeed be capable of releasing the pituitary gland from the negative feedback action of inhibin-F upon FSH secretion during various reproductive states. A selective surge in serum FSH was observed during the period of ovulation after injection of hCG in rats on day 15 of lactation. Similar surges of FSH were associated with hCG induced ovulation in 29-day-old, immature rats and adult cycling rats on 0900 hours diestrus. In contrast, the same amount of hCG did not induce a selective FSH surge, or ovulation, in 26-day-old, immature rats or on day 3 of lactation. This may suggest that the population of follicles in these nonresponsive rats was not capable of responding to hCG with ovulation or changes in inhibin-F secretion. Perhaps injecting FSH into rats on day 3 of lactation or at 26 days of age might have induced a subsequent selective FSH surge.

Sasamoto *et al.* (1981) also administered bovine follicular fluid (presumably containing inhibin-F activity) to diestrous rats pretreated with hCG. Even though ovulation occurred 1 day later, the selective FSH surge occurring at 0200 hours was suppressed in a dose-dependent manner and delayed from 0500 to 2300 hours. Continued injections of bovine follicular fluid over a longer time period further delayed the FSH surge from 1700 to 1100 hours on the following day.

It is quite possible that FSH and LH may have preferential effects on inhibin-F secretion depending upon the maturational state of the ovarian follicles. In the case of the preovulatory stage, both FSH and LH (hCG) may decrease inhibin-F secretion by causing luteinization of the granulosa compartment and/or ovulation of the preovulatory follicles.

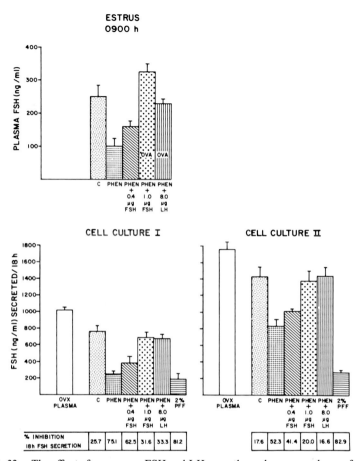

FIG. 32. The effect of exogenous FSH and LH upon the endogenous release of pituitary FSH and the ovarian secretion of inhibin-F in rats. Between 1215 and 1300 hours proestrus all rats were anesthetized with ether and polyethylene cannulas were inserted into the right external jugular veins to the level of the right atria. Immediately after cannula insertion, rats were divided into 5 treatment groups: Group 1 (n = 8) received only 0.9% phosphate-buffered saline (PBS) iv via jugular cannulas, while Groups 2–5 were reanesthetized with phenobarbital at 1245 hours to block the spontaneous FSH and LH surges. At 1300 hours the following substances were injected iv in 0.4 ml of 0.9% PBS: Group 2, PBS only (n = 8); Group 3, 0.4 μg highly purified rat FSH-I_3 (n = 12); Group 4, 1.0 μg highly purified rat FSH-I_3 (n = 17); Group 5, 8.0 μg highly purified rat LH-I_5 (n = 14). Blood samples (0.5 ml) were taken via jugular cannulas from each rat at 1400 and at 1700 hours proestrous and assayed for FSH, LH, and progesterone (data not shown). At 0900 hours estrous all rats were anesthetized with ether, the original cannulas were removed, and new polyethylene cannulas were inserted, via the external jugular veins and vena cava into the left ovarian vein. Ovarian vein blood was collected for 20 min (2.0 ml) after which peripheral blood samples were taken from the inferior vena cava. In all estrous rats the oviducts were removed and examined for the presence of ova. Upper panel represents the concentration of FSH in the peripheral plasma at 0900 hours estrous. Lower panels represent the relative amounts of inhibin-F activity present in the ovarian blood as bioassayed in two separate rat pituitary cell cultures. Reprinted with permission from Shander *et al.* (1980a).

On the other hand, inhibin-F secretion from ovaries containing non-preovulatory follicles may be gradually increased as the follicles mature under the influence of FSH and LH. DePaolo et al. (1981) have made an initial attempt to examine the gonadotropin action on inhibin-F secretion by ovaries having no preovulatory follicles by determining the output of inhibin F activity from the remaining ovary following unilateral ovariectomy (ULO) at diestrous day 1 (DePaolo et al., 1981). Unilateral ovariectomy results in compensatory hypertrophy of the remaining ovary. This has been shown to occur in rats (Welschen et al., 1977, 1978), and in hamsters (Chiras and Greenwald, 1978). The cause of this phenomenon appears to be an acute rise in serum FSH (Bast and Greenwald, 1977; Welschen et al., 1978). Furthermore, both compensatory hypertrophy (Sato and Ishibashi, 1978; Sato et al., 1978, 1980) and the acute rise in FSH (Welschen et al., 1978) following ULO can be suppressed by follicular fluid.

DePaolo et al. (1981) removed one ovary from rats at 0800 hours of diestrous day 1. The remaining ovary was cannulated, and ovarian vein plasma (OVP) was sampled at various time periods postsurgery. In addition, peripheral blood samples were obtained from the abdominal aorta at each time period. The amount of inhibin-F activity present in OVP was assessed by its ability to suppress basal FSH secretion in a pituitary cell culture bioassay system. The results illustrated in Fig. 33 show that plasma FSH concentrations were significantly higher ($p < 0.05$) by 4 hours in rats that underwent ULO at 0800 hours on D1 when compared to FSH levels in sham-operated rats. However, plasma FSH at 4 hours in ULO rats was similar to levels prior to surgery. Peak concentrations of FSH were reached 12 hours after ULO. While plasma levels of FSH declined by 24 hours, they were still significantly elevated ($p < 0.01$) above levels observed in sham-operated rats but not significantly different from values measured before ULO. Interestingly, FSH levels in plasma gradually declined between 0 and 32 hours after sham-ULO such that levels by 12 hours were lower ($p < 0.01$) than levels measured before sham surgery. Like FSH, inhibin-F in ovarian vein plasma significantly increased ($p < 0.05$) between 4 and 12 hours following ULO (Fig. 33). However, in contrast to the decline in FSH levels between 12 and 32 hours after ULO, inhibin-F remained elevated. Changes in steroids in the blood could not account for the changes in FSH occurring after ULO.

These data demonstrate a temporal relationship between FSH and inhibin-F activity in ovarian vein plasma after ULO. This relationship may take the form of an FSH-inhibin-F negative feedback system. Stronger support for the existence of such a feedback system would have required the determination of inhibin-F in peripheral plasma. This necessi-

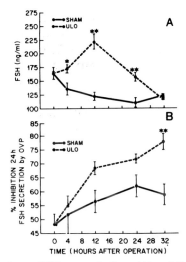

FIG. 33. Changes in plasma FSH concentrations (A) and the percentage inhibition of basal FSH secretion by OVP inhibin-F activity (B) as assessed in a dispersed pituitary cell bioassay system following ULO or sham operation. Whereas both FSH and inhibin-F activity increase between 4 and 12 hours after ULO, FSH declines and inhibin-F activity in OVP remains elevated between 12 and 32 hours after ULO. $*p < 0.05$; $**p < 0.01$ between sham and ULO animals. Reprinted from DePaolo *et al.* (1981), with permission.

tates the development of a highly sensitive RIA or a more sensitive bioassay for inhibin-F, since its activity in rat peripheral plasma is undetectable in our bioassay system (DePaolo *et al.*, 1979b). If inhibin-F could be measured in peripheral plasma, then it is conceivable that ULO may result in a decrease in circulating inhibin-F levels which, in turn, results in increased pituitary FSH secretion.

Interestingly, the increase in FSH levels between 4 and 12 hours after ULO was accompanied by a simultaneous increment of inhibin-F in OVP. Thereafter, inhibin-F activity was maintained at these levels while FSH levels declined. If increased circulating inhibin-F (resulting from increased secretion) is responsible for suppressing plasma levels of FSH, then a lag phase appears necessary for expression of the inhibitory effects of inhibin-F on pituitary secretion of FSH. This finding is in accord with previous reports (Campbell and Schwartz, 1979; DePaolo *et al.*, 1979c; Hoffman *et al.*, 1979) which show a delay of 2 to 5 hours between injection of rats with FFl and inhibition of plasma FSH levels. Alternatively, the initial increase in inhibin-F may have occurred later than 4 hours after ULO since the exact temporal relationship between FSH and inhibin-F during the interval from 4 to 12 hours after ULO could not be determined from the data. Finally, since ovarian rather than peripheral plasma inhibin-F activity was assessed, it is possible that the lag phase may simply reflect the time required to restore peripheral inhibin-F levels in plasma to the threshold concentration sufficient to suppress FSH release.

The decline in plasma FSH concentrations and the increase in inhibin-F in OVP observed between 0800 hours D1 and 0800 hours D2 in sham-operated rats also is an interesting finding. Elevations in FSH levels on the morning of D1 have been previously documented (Butcher et al., 1974; DePaolo et al., 1979a), and it is possible that these high levels may act to increase inhibin-F production by the ovary. Therefore, an FSH-inhibin-F feedback system may operate during diestrus of the rat reproductive cycle as well as during estrus and after ULO. Recently, Lee et al. (1981) have provided further evidence of gonadotropin stimulation of inhibin secretion. This study demonstrated an increase in ovarian vein and peripheral serum inhibin-F following PMSG treatment of immature rats. A decrease in endogenous FSH levels was also observed concomitant with the increase in inhibin.

An alternative approach to the direct assessment of inhibin-F activity in the ovarian vein would be to exogenously administer substances containing inhibin-F activity and monitor its effect upon FSH secretion, in vivo. Using this method, both the primary, preovulatory (Hoffmann et al., 1979; DePaolo et al., 1979c) and secondary (Schwartz and Channing, 1977; De-Paolo et al., 1979a,c, 1981) rise in FSH can be suppressed by the administration of steroid-free, porcine follicular fluid without affecting serum LH levels. Conversely, when hamsters were ovariectomized on diestrous day 1 or 2 and implanted with silastic capsules of estradiol and progesterone a simulated proestrous surge in LH and FSH occurred. However, the extremely high FSH levels seen after ovariectomy were sustained with no suppression seen by the administration of steroids (Chappel, 1980). With the addition of bovine follicular fluid to this steroid regimen, a simulated FSH surge was evoked which strongly resembled the proestrous–estrous FSH surge observed in the intact hamster. A preliminary report by Williams and Lipner (1980) showed that the same type of regulation of FSH occurs in ovariectomized rats given silastic implants of estradiol and progesterone with administration of follicular fluid. Furthermore, additional observations of Rush et al. (1981) show that steroids alone are not able to regulate FSH secretion so as to reproduce the normal pattern of circulating FSH seen throughout the rat estrous cycle. They observed that steroids did not have an additive effect above that of pFFl alone in suppression of the periovulatory FSH surge in intact and phenobarbital-treated rats ovariectomized on proestrus.

All of the above studies indicate that the administration of preparations containing inhibin-F activity at the appropriate time periods could be a useful tool to examine the interplay of inhibin-F and FSH in controlling folliculogenesis in the female rat. Furthermore, when DePaolo *et al.* (1979a) suppressed the proestrus and/or estrus rise in FSH with pFFl injection (at 1100 and 1800 hours proestrus and 0800 hours estrus) and allowed the rats to complete one additional cycle, the plasma LH and FSH concentrations at the next proestrus and estrus were not significantly different among groups regardless of the time follicular fluid was administered in the previous cycle. By histological examination on the morning of proestrus the ovaries of pFFl-treated rats were similar in appearance to the pig serum-injected controls. Furthermore, all animals ovulated a normal complement of ova at the next estrus regardless of whether preovulatory, secondary, or both increases of FSH had been blocked by pFFl treatment during the previous cycle. These results could indicate that increased plasma FSH concentration at proestrus and estrus may not be essential for folliculogenesis and ovulation in the subsequent cycle. However, it is very probable that the characteristic "rebound" of FSH concentrations observed on diestrous day 1 (probably due to waning of the pFFl administered on proestrus and estrus) may be sufficient to provide ovulatory follicles for the next proestrous day.

DePaolo *et al.* (1981) reported a more detailed examination of the events occurring during this "rebound" of FSH on diestrus following pFFl administration. Plasma LH, estradiol, and progesterone concentrations did not differ significantly between pFFl-injected and control rats at any time examined on proestrus, estrus, or diestrous days 1 and 2. As expected, the suppression of pituitary FSH secretion by pFFl on proestrus prevented recruitment of new follicles on estrus (Table III). However, by diestrous day 1 ovaries contained as many nonatretic, large follicles as control ovaries. Furthermore, there was no significant difference in the size of pre-Graafian follicles measured on diestrus 1 and 2 between experimental and control groups. Interestingly, more atretic follicles were observed in ovaries from pFFl-treated rats on estrus. Ovarian vein plasma was also sampled for inhibin-F activity in this study before, during and after the "rebound" of FSH secretion on diestrus 1 (Fig. 34). Inhibin-F activity in OVP was quite low at 1800 hours estrus, perhaps reflecting the fact that the follicular population of the ovary consisted of small follicles, and those follicles ≥ 400 μm were atretic at this time period. However, the peripheral levels of FSH at 1800 hours estrus were at a nadir due to the administration of pFFl at 1200 and 1900 hours proestrus and 0900 hours estrus. Concomitant with the elevated levels of FSH during the "rebound" phase on 1800 hours diestrus 1, inhibin-F activity was also increased over levels observed on estrus (but the amount was not significantly different from that present in OVP from saline-injected rats on diestrus 1). Also at this

TABLE III
Number and Size of Follicles $\geq$ 400 μm at 1800 Hours
after Treatment of Rats with Saline or PFF[a,b,c]

Day	Treatment	Number of follicles[d]	Size (μm)
Estrus	Saline	4.7 ± 1.9	462 ± 19
	PFF	0	
Diestrus 1	Saline	7.3 ± 1.0	458 ± 8
	PFF	6.7 ± 1.0	442 ± 7
Diestrus 2	Saline	6.5 ± 1.8	505 ± 17
	PFF	5.0 ± 2.8	546 ± 20

[a] Ovaries were removed from animals, at the various times indicated (Fig. 34) and fixed in Detrich's solution. Subsequently, ovaries were dehydrated, embedded in paraffin, and sectioned at 8 μm thickness. Serial sections were mounted on slides and stained with Molnar's modification of Mallory's aniline blue collagen stain. Sections from three ovaries from each group were examined beginning on estrus. All follicles greater than or equal to 400 μm in diameter (pre-Graffian) were measured and qualitatively examined for possible signs of atresia as judged by the presence of two or more pyknotic granulosa cells in a single cross section. Saline or PFF (porcine follicular fluid) was injected at 1200 and 1900 hours proestrus and 0900 hours on estrus.

[b] Values are means ± SE of 3 ovaries. PFF, porcine follicular fluid.

[c] From DePaolo et al. (1981), with permission.

[d] Nonatretic, per ovary.

time, the ovary contained antral follicles $\geq$400 μm, suggesting that the elevated levels of FSH of the "rebound" phase recruited these pre-Graffian follicles. These pre-Graafian follicles may have been the principal source of inhibin-F activity present in the OVP at 1800 hours diestrus 1. On diestrus 2, the pFFl-treated rats were indistinguishable from control rats: low peripheral FSH concentrations, high inhibin-F activity in OVP, and normal population of growing follicles.

Hoak and Schwartz (1980) and Schwartz (1981) have studied this phenomenon of FSH rebound further, and have provided conclusive evidence that the post-pFFl treatment rise in FSH is responsible for recruitment of new pre-Graffian follicles destined for the next proestrus. By injecting ovine FSH during the pFFl suppression of endogenous FSH, they observed a restoration of follicular recruitment in a dose-dependent manner. Furthermore, Schwartz (1981) has shown that continued blockage of the FSH rebound on diestrous day 1 results in a normal proestrous surge of

LH, attenuated serum estradiol before the onset of the critical period on proestrus, and lower FSH levels during the secondary surge. This was accompanied by the failure of some animals to ovulate, and those which did ovulate had fewer ova present in the oviducts. These findings have been corroborated by Hirshfield (1981) and Hirshfield and DePaolo (1981).

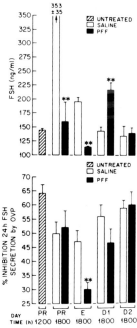

FIG. 34. Effect of treatment of intact rats with porcine FFl at 1200 and 1900 hours proestrus and 0900 hours estrus on ovarian vein inhibin-F and serum FSH. The animals in this study were injected intraperitoneally with either 1 ml pig follicular fluid (PFF; charcoal-treated) or an equal volume of physiologic saline (0.15 M) at 1200 and 1900 hours proestrus and again at 0900 hours estrus. Blood samples were obtained from the abdominal aorta for determination of plasma FSH concentrations using RIA. Ovarian vein blood was collected from the left ovary from various groups (n = 5–7) of saline- and PFF-treated rats at 1800 hours on proestrus, estrus, diestrous day 1 (D1) and diestrous day 2 (D2), and from an additional group of seven untreated rats at 1200-hours on proestrus. Samples of these ovarian vein plasma (100 μl) were added in triplicate to a series of multiwells containing dispersed, rat pituitary cells to quantify the relative amounts of inhibin-F activity by their ability to suppress basal FSH release. Control wells received 100 μl untreated peripheral plasma obtained from diestrous rats castrated 2 hours previously. Values of FSH measured in these control wells represented maximal FSH released by pituitary gonadotropes under our culture conditions. Inhibin-F activity was therefore expressed as percentage inhibition of basal FSH secretion by ovarian vein plasma during a 24-hour culture period compared to control wells. **p < 0.01 between saline- and PFF-treated rats. Reprinted with permission from DePaolo et al. (1981).

C. CONTROL OF OVARIAN INHIBIN-F SECRETION *in Vitro* IN THE PIG AND COW

Hormonal control of inhibin-F secretion is best examined *in vivo*. However, such studies necessitate examining measurements of short-term changes of ovarian inhibin-F secretion in response to various hormones. In the absence of a sensitive radioimmunoassay for inhibin-F the *in vivo* approach is not feasible. It is nevertheless possible to examine hormonal control of inhibin-F secretion using a bioassay to measure inhibin-F production by cultured granulosa cells. Granulosa cells of the rat (Erickson and Hseush, 1978), pig (Channing *et al.* 1980; Anderson and Hoover, 1981), and cow (Franchimont *et al.*, 1981; Henderson and Franchimont, 1981) can secrete inhibin-F activity. In the case of the pig, suspension cultured cells obtained from all sizes of follicles demonstrated potential to secrete inhibin-F with about a 2-fold greater secretory ability in cells obtained from large compared to cells obtained from small and medium sized follicles (Fig. 35). The inhibin-F activity as measured in the rat anterior pituitary cell cultures resided in a molecule >10,000 daltons (Fig. 35) which resembles the behavior of inhibin-F present in porcine follicular fluid (Channing *et al.*, 1981). Large follicular fluid contains a lower amount of inhibin-F compared to small follicular fluid in the pig (Lorenzen *et al.*, 1978 and Fig. 2d) and cow (Franchimont *et al.*, 1981). The difference between the potential of cultured granulosa cells to secrete inhibin-F and FFl levels could be explained by a greater blood flow to large follicles which acts to clear away the inhibin-F more rapidly compared to small follicles. It is also possible that the inhibin-F in large follicular fluid is cleaved by proteases and rendered more easily diffusable from the follicle. Studies on the molecular size of inhibin-F activity in FFl from large follicles compared to FFl from small porcine follicles by Tanabe and his colleagues (unpublished observations) support such a possibility. About 1% of inhibin-F activity in large FFl was <10,000 daltons whereas no inhibin-F activity in small FFl (<0.1%) was <10,000 daltons. Plasminogen activator may be the protease responsible for decreasing the inhibin-F in large follicles since it has been shown by Strickland and Beers (1976) to be elevated in preovulatory rat follicles.

The amounts of inhibin-F secreted into the conditioned granulosa cell medium under basal conditions are less than what is present in follicular fluid (Table IV). This may indicate that (1) conditions in the follicle are more favorable for inhibin-F secretion compared to culture conditions due to a multiplicity of hormones and other factors acting within the follicle and not present in culture, or (2) inhibin-F accumulates in the follicular

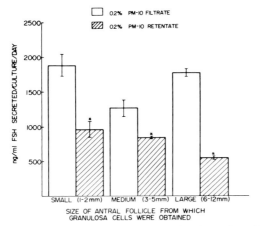

FIG. 35. The effect of PM-10 retentate and filtrate fractions of conditioned media from granulosa cells of various-sized, antral follicles on basal FSH secretion from rat anterior pituitary cells, *in vitro*. Granulosa cells were isolated from small (1–2 mm), medium (3–5 mm), and large (6–12 mm) antral follicles of porcine ovaries obtained at a local slaughterhouse. These granulosa cells were incubated in siliconized glass vials at 37°C in TC 199 + 10% pig serum for 2 days at a concentration of 1×10^6 viable cells/ml of media. Conditioned media were treated with 10% (v/v) activated charcoal and 1% dextran, to remove free steroids, followed by ultrafiltration through an Amicon PM-10 membrane. The high-molecular-weight substances retained by the membrane (>10,000 MW) and filtrates (<10,000 MW) were added at various concentrations to media. These media were then added to anterior pituitary cells (obtained from female, Sprague-Dawley rats) using a primary monolayer system. The data represent the amount of FSH (ng/ml) secreted from triplicate cultures of pituitary cells during a 24-hour period of culture (mean ± SE); *$p < 0.01$ as compared to the PM-10 filtrate additions. The secretion of LH during this time interval was not affected by any additions to the pituitary cell media. Data reprinted from Anderson and DePaolo (1981), with permission.

fluid faster than it can pass through the follicular wall. The latter explanation may involve a requirement for postsecretion processing of inhibin-F to reduce its size to a more permeable form. Interestingly, inhibin-M secretion by Sertoli cell cultures is approximately comparable to that in granulosa cell cultures (Table IV), but inhibin-F activity in FFl is 100-fold greater than inhibin-M levels in rete testis fluid.

In preliminary studies employing suspension type cultures of granulosa cells obtained from small, medium, and large porcine follicles, we have observed that addition of dihydrotestosterone, LH, and FSH appears to stimulate inhibin-F secretion by granulosa cells harvested from large follicles (Anderson and Hoover, 1981). Henderson and Franchimont (1981) have investigated hormonal control of inhibin-F secretion by monolayer

TABLE IV

Inhibin Content of Ovine Testicular Lymph Fluid, Sertoli Cell Conditioned Medium, Porcine Follicular Fluid, and Granulosa Cell Conditioned Medium[a,b]

Preparation and source	Relative potency Scott–Burger assay		Relative potency Hoover–Anderson–Channing assay	
	OTL standard	HSN8-110-0.9P standard	AL36 CTFF1 standard	HSN8 111-0.9P standard
1. Ovine testicular lymph Scott–Burger	1.0 Units/mg	0.0093	227 ± 49 U/mg (105–349)	0.0118
2. Porcine follicular fluid (AL36CT)	—	—	13,889 U/mg	0.72
3. Porcine follicular fluid 90% ethanol ppt of PM-10 retentate fluid HSN-8-110-0.9P (Ward–Channing)	107 Units/mg (83–137)	1.0	19,310 ± 1382 U/mg (15,880–22,700)	1.00
4. Conditioned porcine granulosa cell medium (Channing–Tanabe)	8.4 Units/mg (6.5–10.7)	0.078	1,400 ± 35 U/mg (1,313–1,487)	0.0725
5. Conditioned Sertoli cell pool medium (Pool #24) (SCF + 10% FCS) (3/12/80) (A. Steinberger)	—	—	74.9 U/500 µl (73–76)	—
6. Pool #19 Sertoli cell conditioned medium (A. Steinberger)	—	—	1,310 U/mg (1,270–1,350)	0.0678

378

^{a} The inhibin content of ovine testicular lymph (preparation 1), porcine follicular fluid 90% ethanol precipitate (preparation 3) were assayed by Dr. Burger in the Scott–Burger inhibin assay [*Nature (London)* **285**, 246–247, 1980] [left columns] and by Dr. D. J. Hoover in the Hoover–Anderson–Channing assay (Channing *et al.*, *J. Clin. Endocrinol. Metab.* **52**, 1193, 1981) (right columns). An additional sample of charcoal-treated porcine follicular fluid (AL-36 CT/preparation 2) and Sertoli cell conditioned medium provided by Dr. Anna Steinberger (preparation 5, 6) were assayed by us in the Hoover–Anderson–Channing assay. Potencies in terms of suppression of basal FSH secretion in rat anterior pituitary cell cultures are expressed using either the OTL standard (preparation 1) or the 90% ethanol precipitate of porcine follicular fluid (preparation 3) as standard. It is worth noting that by both assays the porcine follicular fluid contains about 100-fold more inhibin activity compared to the ovine testicular lymph.

^{b} For the Sertoli cell cultures 25- to 26-day-old rats were used as a source of testes cultures grown for 2 days using an initial inoculum of 0.5×10^6 cells/ml. In the case of Pool #24 the cells were grown in 10% fetal calf serum in Eagle's MEM. In the case of pool #19 the Sertoli cells were grown in Eagle's MEM without serum. Both pools of Sertoli cell media were dialyzed and lyophilized prior to assay. In the case of the granulosa cell cultures 10^6 granulosa cells obtained from small and medium sized porcine follicles were grown per ml of TC 199 plus 10% pig serum. The cultures were grown for 2 days and the conditioned medium passed through an Amicon PM-10 membrane. The PM-10 retentate was lyophilized and assayed. Each sample was assayed using 3–4 doses using 3 pituitary cell culture wells per dose. In this case, data are expressed as relative potencies with 95% confidence limits in parentheses. The standard error of the mean potency estimate is also shown ($n = 3$).

cultures of granulosa cells harvested from bovine follicles (Fig. 36). These authors report no effect of LH or FSH, a stimulatory action of testosterone, and a suppressive effect of progesterone upon inhibin-F secretion. We observed no demonstrable effect of progesterone or androstenedione

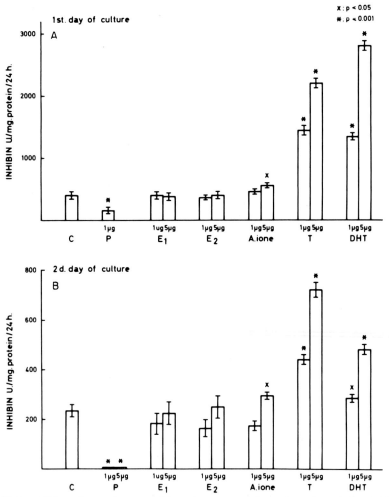

FIG. 36.   Effect of several sex steroids at the concentrations of 1 and 5 μg/ml on inhibin production (expressed in units per mg protein) by cultured bovine granulosa cells. P, Progesterone; E_1, estrone; E_2, estradiol; Aione, androstenedione; T, testosterone; DHT, dihydrotestosterone. Results are given for the first (A) and second (B) day of culture. Each bar represents the mean value $\pm$ SEM calculated from five individual cultures. The stimulatory effect of T and DHT is dose-dependent. C, Control. Taken from Franchimont *et al.* (1981), with permission.

upon inhibin-F secretion. Since we used suspension type cultures and Henderson and Franchimont used monolayer cultures it is difficult to compare the two types of observations. Both groups, however, failed to observe an effect of estradiol upon inhibin-F secretion. Interestingly, Sertoli cell cultures secreted more inhibin-M in response to FSH, testosterone, cyclic AMP, or MIX (Steinberger, 1981).

D. GONADOTROPIN SECRETION PATTERNS IN THE PRIMATE AND POSSIBLE ROLE OF INHIBIN-F IN THEIR CONTROL

1. Effects of Ovariectomy in the Cyclic Adult and Reversal by Ovarian Steroids. Chronic Control of FSH Secretion

Following ovariectomy in women (Yen and Tsai, 1971; Monroe *et al.*, 1972) and adult monkeys (Karsch *et al.*, 1973a) there is an increase in the secretion of both LH and FSH. In monkeys, the postcastrational hypersecretion of gonadotropins is associated with a pulsatile pattern of circulating hormone (Krey *et al.*, 1975), a phenomenon that is apparently not observed in the intact animal (Dierschke *et al.*, 1970). It has also been observed that the postovariectomy rise in serum FSH is more rapid than that of LH in women (Yen and Tsai, 1971; Monroe *et al.*, 1972) and the ratio of serum FSH:LH is higher after ovariectomy (human: Yen and Tsai, 1971; Monroe *et al.*, 1972; monkey: G. D. Hodgen, personal communication) than the range observed in the intact adult (human: Ross *et al.*, 1970; monkey: Wilks *et al.*, 1976).

The effects of ovarian steroids on LH and FSH secretion have been studied following ovariectomy of adult, cyclic women treated postoperatively with an estrogen and a progestogen (given orally) alone and in combination (Wallach *et al.*, 1970). The administration of the estrogen (in unphysiological doses) plus progesterone led to complete suppression of blood LH and FSH levels. However, it should be noted that the progesterone may have acted to block the positive feedback action of the estrogen.

The postovariectomy hypersecretion of LH in the monkey has been shown to be completely suppressable by administration of estradiol at a dose which achieves baseline circulating levels of this steroid (Karsch *et al.*, 1973a). A similar assertion has been made for FSH (Knobil and Plant, 1978), but the only documentation published shows that estradiol and progesterone in combination are required to completely suppress FSH secretion in ovariectomized monkeys, and the authors expressed some reservations on the physiological relevance of these findings to control of FSH secretion in the intact adult (Karsch *et al.*, 1973b). On the other hand injection of a preparation with inhibin-F activity (charcoal-treated porcine follicular fluid) can suppress serum FSH in ovariectomized monkeys (Channing *et al.*, 1981a). Serum LH is apparently not affected by pFFl treatment.

Complex mechanisms involving the characteristics of steroid feedback and releasing hormone signals and the changes in responsiveness of the hypothalamo-pituitary complex (Yen *et al.*, 1977) have yet to be tested before chronic control of FSH secretion can be disassociated, completely or in part, from a steroid feedback mechanism. However, it is interesting to note that though FSH secretion in ovariectomized monkeys is clearly and selectively suppressable by a porcine follicular fluid preparation with inhibin-F activity (Channing *et al.*, 1981a), a seemingly high dose of charcoal-treated pFFl (100 ml) is required to suppress circulating FSH to the range of baseline levels observed in intact adults. In contrast, intact monkeys given as little as 5 ml of charcoal-treated pFFl daily for 3 days during the early follicular phase show suppression of circulating FSH to, or below, the lowest levels observed at any time throughout the menstrual cycle (DiZerega *et al.*, 1981). This result suggests that chronic control of FSH secretion may require both steroid and inhibin-F feedback or that there is a loss of responsiveness of the pituitary gland to inhibin-F after prolonged deprivation of this substance.

2. The Menstrual Cycle

In both humans (Ross *et al.*, 1970) and monkeys (Wilks *et al.*, 1976), the ratio of serum FSH : LH shows a striking decline over the course of the follicular phase, reaching a nadir at the time of the midcycle surge in gonadotropin secretion. In the ensuing luteal phase, the serum FSH : LH ratio increases to its maximum, which occurs around the time of menses and in the early follicular phase (Fig. 29). Another divergence of FSH and LH secretion is seen in the pulsatile nature of LH secretion in women during the luteal phase and early follicular phase while FSH secretion during the menstrual cycle does not show evidence of pulses (Yen *et al.*, 1974). Attention has been focused on a number of possible explanations for these differences in the pattern of FSH and LH secretion: (1) greater sensitivity of FSH secretion to estrogen negative feedback action (Yen *et al.*, 1977; Zeleznik, 1981), (2) actions of other steroids on gonadotropin secretion (Yen *et al.*, 1977), (3) the longer half-life of FSH (Yen *et al.*, 1977; Knobil, 1981), and (4) the differential LH versus FSH responses of the pituitary to changes of releasing hormone secretion (Yen *et al.*, 1977). Yen *et al.* (1977) also suggested that inhibin-F feedback on FSH secretion might be considered as a possible mechanism explaining the divergence of FSH and LH secretion in cyclic women.

One other aspect of the menstrual cycle profiles of serum gonadotropins has been given some attention during the perimenstrual period in women; there is a surge in serum FSH which is more pronounced and discernible than the increase in serum LH (Ross *et al.*, 1970). In the monkey, this perimenstrual, or intercyclic, FSH surge may not be quite as discernibly selective. A more pronounced perimenstrual FSH surge can be seen in individual animal profiles of serum FSH, but it may not always (Knobil, 1974) be seen in profiles of across animal mean serum FSH concentrations. It has been proposed that the perimenstrual FSH surge results from a drop in steroid feedback inhibition associated with luteal regression (Ross *et al.*, 1970), but steroid feedback signals have not been clearly defined as the trigger for the perimenstrual FSH surge. Luteal phase progesterone levels can suppress FSH secretion in a selective fashion in midfollicular phase monkeys (Resko *et al.*, 1981). However, the perimenstrual FSH surge cannot be blocked by administering progesterone to maintain its peak luteal serum concentration (Resko *et al.*, 1974). There is evidence that an ovarian feedback signal other than estradiol or progesterone, which originates in the nonluteal ovary, may participate in the regulation of FSH secretion around the time of menses (Goodman *et al.*, 1979). If a mechanism involving inhibin-F feedback is responsible for triggering the perimenstrual FSH surge, it would serve as an example of inhibin-F actually regulating FSH secretion in a manner similar to that proposed for the secondary surge of FSH secretion in the rat.

3. Age-Related Changes in Gonadotropin Secretion

  a. The Climacteric and Postmenopause. Loss of Chronic Control of FSH Secretion?   As women approach the menopause, there is a striking increase in serum FSH levels throughout most of the menstrual cycle (Sherman *et al.*, 1976; Reyes *et al.*, 1977). Serum LH, on the other hand, has been reported to be stable during aging (Sherman *et al.*, 1976) except perhaps for an increase during the follicular phase in women close to the menopause (Reyes *et al.*, 1977). The age-related elevation in serum FSH is accompanied by a shorter follicular phase which has been attributed to accelerated follicular development (Sherman and Korenman, 1975). In spite of the apparent hyperstimulation of the ovary by FSH, and perhaps LH, serum estrogen is subnormal (Sherman *et al.*, 1976) or steady (Reyes *et al.*, 1977) and luteal phase serum progesterone has been reported to be stable (Sherman *et al.*, 1976) or to decline (Reyes *et al.*, 1977) with age. Limited information available for the rhesus monkey suggests that a similar selective rise in serum FSH is observed in this species during the climacteric (Hodgen *et al.*, 1977).

  After the menopause, secretion of both gonadotropins is markedly elevated (Reyes *et al.*, 1977; Barlow *et al.*, 1979), and FSH secretion, like LH, becomes pulsatile, a phenomenon not clearly evident in the premenopausal women (Yen *et al.*, 1972). The ratio of serum FSH : LH is postmenopausal women appears to be above the range observed in premenopausal women (Ross *et al.*, 1970). Serum estrogens are lower than (estradiol), or in the lower range (estrone) of baseline values observed in premenopausal women, and serum androstenedione is in the range of premenopausal women (Barlow *et al.*, 1979).

Several mechanisms may be, or have been proposed to explain the differential effect of aging on FSH versus LH secretion: (1) the longer half-life of FSH (Ross *et al.*, 1970), (2) the greater sensitivity of FSH, versus LH, secretion to estrogen negative feedback (Yen *et al.*, 1977) resulting in greater pituitary FSH secretion responsivity to LHRH (DeKretser *et al.*, 1978), (3) changes in the operation of steroid feedback mechanisms or the action of other steroids (Sherman and Korneman, 1975) which may become apparent in the absence of cyclic ovarian function, and (4) an age-related decline in inhibin-F feedback (Sherman and Korenman, 1975) that may be associated with the decline in the total number of follicles in the ovary (VanLook *et al.*, 1977).

b. Childhood through Puberty. Restraint of FSH Secretion during Maturation of Endocrine Function of the Reproductive System. During childhood, serum gonadotropins are suppressed (Lee *et al.*, 1970; Winter *et al.*, 1975) to levels far below the range of baseline values of the menstrual cycle (Ross *et al.*, 1970). From published profiles of serum gonadotropins, the serum FSH : LH ratio during this time has been variously reported to be in the range of the menstrual cycle, i.e., less than unity (Faiman and Winter, 1974; Winter *et al.*, 1975; Beck and Wattken, 1980), or greater than unity (Yen *et al.*, 1969; Yen and Vicic, 1970; Penney *et al.*, 1974; Lee *et al.*, 1970). In prepubertal monkeys (Dierschke *et al.*, 1974), serum gonadotropins are apparently also below baseline menstrual cycle levels. Low circulating gonadotropins are maintained until the premenarcheal period of puberty when serum LH and FSH rise (Sizonenko *et al.*, 1970; Lee *et al.*, 1970, 1976) to the baseline levels of the menstrual cycle (Ross *et al.*, 1970). The onset of the pubertal rise in serum gonadotropins has been reported to be fairly consistently associated with the thelarche (Lee *et al.*, 1976). However, by serially monitoring serum FSH it has been reported that increased FSH secretion may appear in prepubertal girls in the form of a circadian rhythm which is characterized by a nocturnal increase in circulating FSH (Lee *et al.*, 1976, 1978; Beck and Wuttke, 1980).

The current paradigm for maturation of endocrine function of the human female reproductive system (Grumbach *et al.*, 1974; Forest *et al.*, 1976) holds that the reduced serum gonadotropins observed in childhood derive from an ovarian inhibition of LH and FSH secretion which is superimposed on a reduced functional capacity of the hypothalamo-pituitary complex. The capability of the ovary to restrain gonadotropin secretion, despite minimal steroid output, has been ascribed to increased sensitivity of the gonadostat mechanism to feedback signals originating in the ovary. (However, it has not yet been established by physiological experiments that steroids can provide adequate restraint of gonadotropin secretion prior to adulthood.) The pubertal changes in gonadotropin secretion have been hypothesized to derive from eventual acquisition of adult competency of the hypothalamo-pituitary complex and the ovary. Maturation of the neuroendocrine control of gonadotropin secretion is said to include a decline in sensitivity of the gonadostat and, in the last (postmenarcheal) phase of maturation, activation of the positive feedback mechanism which controls the cyclic discharge of gonadotropins that is characteristic of the menstrual cycle.

The role of inhibin-F in FSH secretion control before adulthood has not been studied in the primate. It has been shown that castrate infant monkeys respond to injection of charcoal-treated porcine follicular fluid with a selective suppression of serum FSH (Channing *et al.*, 1981a), suggesting that inhibin-F may act before adulthood to restrain FSH secretion. It is possible that the maturation of the gonadostat also involves changes in the sensitivity to inhibin-F feedback. An alternative speculation is discussed in the next section.

4. Speculations on the Role of Inhibin-F in the Primate

By consideration of the similarities of the endocrine and follicular dynamics of the climacteric versus the prepubertal–pubertal period, we have developed some notions on the significance of inhibin-F in the primate (and perhaps other species). In the adult there is an increase in FSH secretion with advancing age and this trend culminates with the hypersecretion of gonadotropins characteristic of the postmenopausal period. Similarly, hypothalamo-pituitary function is restrained during childhood, then at puberty serum gonadotropins rise to levels characteristic of adulthood. The reduced pituitary function of childhood appears to result, at least in part, from an inhibitory influence of ovarian origin. As mentioned above, Van Look *et al.* (1977) have suggested that reduction of the number of follicles in the ovaries is a possible explanation for the loss of ovarian restraint of pituitary function which begins in the climacteric and culminates with menopause. However the loss of ovarian follicles is also occurring in childhood, and in fact follicle wastage occurs at a greater rate at younger ages and declines with advancing age (Peters *et al.*, 1979). Conversely, the number of antral follicles reaching large diameters increases with age. In view of the important role inferred for the primate's quiescent ovary (which contains no preovulatory follicles and no corpus luteum) in regulating FSH secretion (Goodman *et al.*, 1979), it might be hypothesized that restraint of FSH secretion throughout life is a function of the existing number of ovarian follicles of all sizes. Thus restraint of FSH secretion may be closely tied to the number of smaller follicles in the ovary since these are the most numerous. Speculating further that the circulating level of inhibin-F is a function of the total number of follicles of all sizes, it may be hypothesized that inhibin-F feedback acts as the signal to the hypothalamo-pituitary complex indicating the number of follicles remaining in the ovary.

To summarize these speculations, we propose the following hypothesis. Some component(s) of the brain–pituitary gland mechanism which controls gonadotropin secretion monitors the circulating level of inhibin-F as an indication of the number of follicles in the ovaries. The inhibin-F feedback signal is determined in large part by the number of immature follicles remaining in the ovaries. Therefore, in childhood when follicle numbers are high, FSH secretion is strongly inhibited. As follicular wastage proceeds, the peripheral serum levels of inhibin-F begin to decline. This releases the restraint on FSH secretion and causes the appearance of antral follicles of greater diameters. Along with the increased number of more mature follicles, entry of follicles into the proliferating pool is restrained by steroidal or nonsteroidal regulators acting at the intraovarian level. The influence of this restraint becomes stronger with the appearance of the cyclic structure associated with the menstrual cycle, thus preventing increased folliculogenesis in response to the higher basal circulating gonadotropins seen in adulthood. In turn, reduction of the rate of follicular wastage halts the decline in circulating inhibin-F and thereby stabilizes FSH secretion to the adult pattern until later in life when the population of follicles has been so reduced that FSH secretion can no longer be restrained. It is also possible that the cyclic structures of the ovary act to acutely regulate inhibin-F secretion so as to facilitate the normal physiological events of the menstrual cycle.

E.   DIRECT EVIDENCE FOR THE EXISTENCE AND ROLE OF INHIBIN-F IN THE PRIMATE

1. Selective Inhibition of FSH Secretion in Monkeys by Charcoal-Treated Porcine Follicular Fluid (ct-pFFl)

Channing and co-workers (1979) first demonstrated that injection of ct-pFFl could selectively suppress FSH secretion in ovariectomized and intact monkeys. They went on to show that suppression of FSH is dose dependent (Channing *et al.*, 1981a) (Fig. 37). FSH secretion is also selectively suppressed by ct-pFFl treatment during the follicular phase of the menstrual cycle (DiZerega and Hodgen, 1981; Channing *et al.*, 1981a) (Fig. 38), but both FSH and LH secretion are inhibited by injection of ct-pFFl during the midcycle gonadotropin surge, or during gonadotropin surges induced by injecting follicular phase monkeys with estradiol (Channing *et al.*, 1981a). This lack of selectivity of inhibin-F action may be due to the apparent capability of inhibin-F preparations to suppress both LH and FSH secretion that is LHRH induced (Shander *et al.*, 1980). On the other hand, it appears that the majority of gonadotropin secretion capability in monkeys is dependent on LHRH stimulation (Knobil, 1981). Hence, considerations presently unknown may be responsible for the differing responses to ct-pFFl injected at different times of the menstrual cycle. For instance, the sensitizing action of estrogen on LH response to LHRH at midcycle may be responsible for the action of ct-pFFl on LH secretion at this time. In studies of FSH secretion in response to ct-pFFl treatment of intact monkeys, it is not possible at this time to rule out

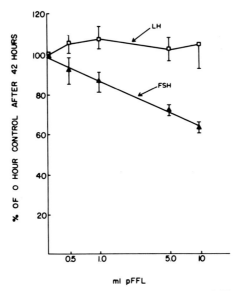

FIG. 37. Effect of various doses of charcoal-treated porcine follicular fluid upon serum LH and FSH levels in castrate female monkeys. The follicular fluid was administered sc at time 0 and the serum FSH and LH measured 42 hours later. Each point is the mean percentage suppression of serum FSH or LH of 3 monkeys. Taken from Channing *et al.* (1981a), with permission.

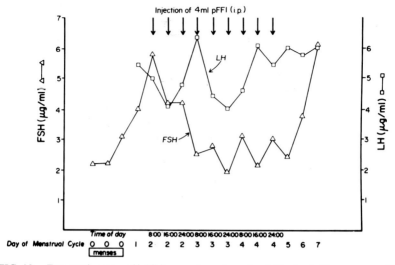

FIG. 38. Temporal course of inhibitory action of porcine follicular fluid upon serum FSH and LH in a rhesus monkey given porcine follicular fluid every 8 hours for 4 days during the early follicular phase of the menstrual cycle. Taken from Channing *et al.* (1981a), with permission.

action of some component of follicular fluid directly on the ovary which alters steroid feedback signals and thereby affects FSH secretion.

As discussed above, studies by Hodgen and co-workers (DiZerega and Hodgen, 1981) have shown that suppression of FSH secretion by administration of ct-pFF1 can drastically deter follicular development and endocrine function of the follicle and the corpus luteum derived from it. These observations have been extended by Channing *et al.* (1981a) who reported that early follicular phase treatment with ct-pFFl results in smaller diameter follicles containing fewer granulosa cells at day 10 of the menstrual cycle when compared to control monkeys injected with charcoal-treated pig serum. These pFFl treated monkeys had atretic follicles as evidenced by the tendency of the recovered oocyte to degenerate in culture and by the poor ability of granulosa cells obtained from FFl-treated monkeys to secrete progesterone and estrogen in culture compared to cells from control, serum-treated monkeys (Fig. 39).

2. Follicular Fluid Inhibin-F Activity

There are reports of the detection of inhibin-F activity in the follicular fluid of primates (Chari *et al.*, 1979; Channing *et al.*, 1980), but there are limited data on the pattern of follicular fluid inhibin-F activity occurring during follicular development in the primate ovary.

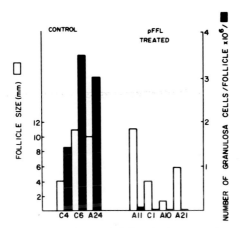

FIG. 39. Effect of treatment of intact adult female rhesus monkeys with porcine follicu-lar fluid on days 1–4 of the menstrual cycle and control serum (pig serum treated) on the follicle size and number of granulosa cells of the dominant follicle present on day 12 of the menstrual cycle. Taken from Channing *et al.* (1981a), with permission.

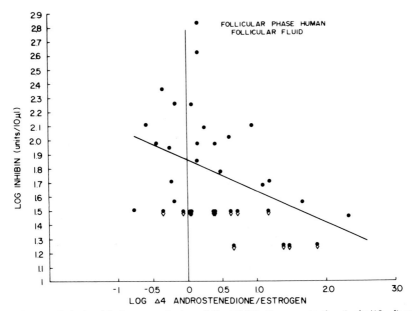

FIG. 40. Relationship between the log of the inhibin-F concentration (units/10 μl) and the log of the Δ⁴-androstenedione/estrogen ratio of samples of human follicular fluid obtained during the follicular phase of the cycle. More atretic follicles have a higher Δ⁴-androstenedione/estrogen ratio (McNatty *et al.*, 1980) and also have a lower inhibin-F con-tent. Inhibin-F was assayed as detailed in the legend for Fig. 41. Data taken from Channing *et al.* (1981d), with permission.

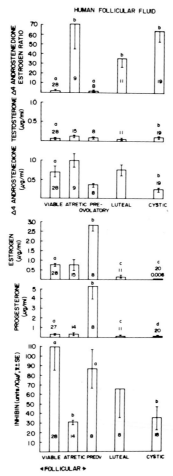

FIG. 41. Changes in inhibin-F levels in human follicular fluid throughout the human menstrual cycle. Follicular fluid was added at a concentration of 10 μl to rat pituitary cell culture and data expressed as percentage suppression of FSH. A standard curve consisting of charcoal-treated porcine follicular fluid was (shown in Fig. 42) run and data expressed in terms of inhibin units which are equivalent to nanoliters of standard porcine follicular fluid. Data reprinted with permission from Channing *et al.* (1981d).

For the human, Chappel *et al.* (1980) have reported that antral fluid from follicular phase follicles contains more inhibin-F activity than the fluid collected from luteal phase follicles. Human FFl inhibin-F activity has been studied in more detail by Channing *et al.* (1981d). FSH-suppressing activity measured by pituitary culture bioassay was related to steroid levels in follicular fluid from 72 follicles at various stages of development.

Inhibin-F activity was highest in viable follicular phase and preovulatory follicles. No evidence was obtained on the changes in FFl inhibin-F activity during normal follicular maturation. However, atretic follicular phase follicles (as classified by a androstenedione : estrogen ratio > 10) had significantly less FFl inhibin activity (Figs. 40 and 41). Cystic follicles (large fluid volume; low estrogen and no recoverable granulosa cells) had inhibin-F levels equal to atretic follicular phase follicles, and in confirmation of earlier work luteal phase FFl had reduced inhibin-F levels perhaps reflecting the poor viability of luteal phase follicles (androstenedione : estrogen ratio > 10). An example of an inhibin-F bioassay is shown in Fig. 42.

3. Ovarian Vein Serum Inhibin-F Activity

DePaolo *et al.* (1979b) have demonstrated the endocrine nature of inhibin-F in the female rat by detecting inhibin-F activity in ovarian vein serum (OVS), but not peripheral serum, using a bioassay based on suppression of basal FSH secretion of rat pituitary cells in primary culture. Channing and co-workers have attempted to perform a similar study in the monkey with only limited success (Channing, Anderson, Hodgen, and Hoover, unpublished, Fig. 43). The pituitary culture bioassay for inhibin-F activity was

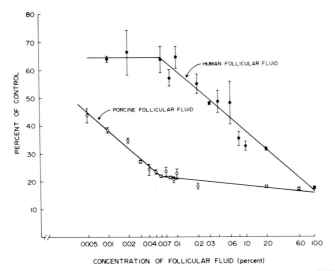

FIG. 42. Effect of various doses of charcoal-treated human and porcine follicular fluid upon FSH secretion of dispersed rat anterior pituitary cells in primary culture. Data are expressed as percentage FSH secretion observed in untreated control cultures and are the mean ± SE of 3 observations per dose of follicular fluid. The follicular fluid was present for a 24 hour period. Taken from Channing *et al.* (1981), with permission.

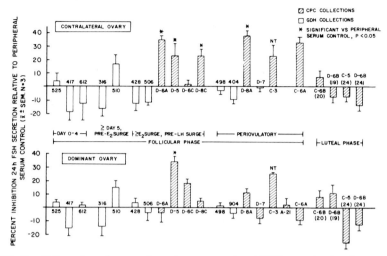

FIG. 43. Effect of monkey ovarian vein serum on basal FSH secretion by dispersed rat anterior pituitary cells in primary, monolayer culture. The basic pituitary culture procedure is detailed in Channing *et al.* (1981d). Monkey serum samples from the femoral vein (peripheral) and both ovarian veins were collected by venipuncture at laparotomy at the various menstrual cycle stages shown in the figure. The dominant ovary was identified by the presence of a preovulatory follicle or a corpus luteum or by asymmetry in steroid concentrations in the ovarian vein serum. In addition to the collections performed by us (designated CPC collections in the figure), additional ovarian vein and peripheral serum samples were provided by Dr. G. D. Hodgen of the Pregnancy Research Branch of the N.I.C.H.H.D. Sera were assayed (without charcoal treatment) in triplicate wells in the pituitary culture at a dose of 20% (100 μl). For statistical analysis, a one-way analysis of variance and, when appropriate, Duncan's new multiple range test were applied within each animal to FSH concentration in conditioned media (after 24-hour incubation). For each animal, data are expressed in the figure as percentage inhibition relative to mean FSH secretion in wells containing the simultaneously collected peripheral serum.

also employed in this study to measure FSH-suppressing activity in noncharcoal-treated OVS (dose 20%) and simultaneously collected peripheral serum. Suppression of basal FSH secretion was assessed in OVS by comparison to cultures containing an equivalent amount of peripheral serum. In three of six monkeys sampled during the period of the follicular phase estrogen surge, prior to the midcycle gonadotropin surge, inhibin-F activity was detected in the venous effluent of the ovary contralateral to the dominant follicle. One of these six monkeys also showed inhibin-F activity in OVS collected from the dominant follicle containing ovary. In 9 monkeys sampled at other times during the early follicular and luteal phase, no inhibin-F activity was detected in the OVS collected for either ovary (Fig. 43). The consistently low levels observed during the early follicular and luteal phase could have some relation to the perimenstrual FSH surge.

During the periovulatory period at the time of the LH surge, the vein draining the dominant follicle containing ovary had low or nondetectable levels of inhibin-F activity (7 monkeys) whereas three of these monkeys had inhibin-F activity in the vein draining the contralateral ovary. A possible explanation for these findings is that in the monkey inhibin-F levels are low and the variability is due to the fact that the levels are near the sensitivity of the assay or that inhibin-F could be secreted in a pulsatile fashion such as the case for parathyroid hormone (Fox *et al.*, 1981). Since blood samples were obtained acutely (within 1–2 minutes) it would have been impossible to evaluate them for pulsatile secretion. Resolution of this must await the development of a sensitive radioimmunoassay for inhibin F.

4. Inhibin-F Activity in Culture Medium Conditioned by Incubation with Ovarian Cell Types

Culture medium conditioned by incubation with rat (Erickson and Hsueh, 1978), pig (Anderson and Hoover, 1981), and bovine (Henderson and Franchimont, 1981) granulosa cells has been shown to possess

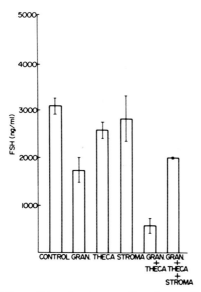

FIG. 44. Effect of 2% conditioned culture medium from cultured human ovarian cell types upon rat pituitary FSH secretion. Each point is the mean ± SE of 4 replicate pituitary cultures. Statistical analysis using Duncan's multiple range test indicated that FSH inhibition by media conditioned by granulosa, granulosa + theca, and theca + stroma were significant vs control. Various human ovarian cell types were cultured for 2 days and the conditioned medium at a concentration of 2% was added to rat anterior pituitary cultures and the mixture incubated for 24 hours. Cell types from 6 pairs of ovaries were grown for 2–8 days and the conditioned media pooled. Taken from Channing *et al.* (1981), with permission.

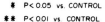

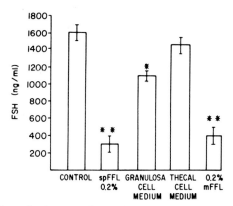

FIG. 45.   Effect of culture media conditioned by incubation with monkey ovarian cell types on FSH secretion by rat anterior pituitary cell in primary monolayer culture. The follicle was obtained from a monkey on day 10 of the menstrual cycle and granulosa cells and 1 mm^3 thecal explants were cultured in TC 199 + 10% monkey serum for 48 hours in 5% CO_2 in humidified air. The conditioned media (dose of 20% by volume) or monkey follicular fluid (dose 0.2% by volume) was added in triplicate to the pituitary cultures. Standard charcoal-treated porcine follicular fluid (spFFl) (0.2%) was added as a reference inhibin-F preparation.

inhibin-F activity by *in vitro* bioassays, thus establishing the granulosa cell as a source of inhibin-F. Channing and co-workers using the pituitary cell culture bioassay have reported preliminary findings which indicate that both human (Channing *et al.*, 1981b) and monkey (Channing and Anderson, unpublished) granulosa cells release inhibin-F activity in culture, but theca cells do not (Figs. 44 and 45). Though work has begun in subprimate species (Henderson and Franchimont, 1981; Anderson and Hoover, 1981) on the changes in granulosa cell potential for inhibin-F secretion, which occur during follicular maturation and as a result of hormone treatment, this area has yet to be investigated in primates.

VI. Summary and Conclusions

The orderly maturation of an ovarian follicle and its oocyte is controlled by pituitary LH and FSH in concert with local intrafollicular regulators. The principal nonsteroidal follicular regulators are an oocyte maturation inhibitor (OMI), a luteinization inhibitor (LI), a luteinization stimulator (LS), FSH receptor binding inhibitor (FSHRBI), and inhibin-F (FSH suppressing substance). The presence of these ovarian regulators within the

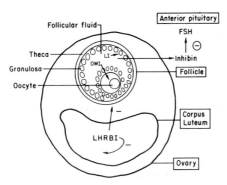

FIG. 46.   Diagrammatic representation of a mammalian ovary along with its nonsteroidal regulators. Besides the ones shown there is an FSH RBI which is found in follicular fluid (Darga and Reichert, 1978).

follicle is pictured diagrammatically in Fig. 46. OMI is a polypeptide <2000 daltons and is elevated in small and medium sized follicles and declines in the follicle under the influence of the preovulatory LH/FSH surge. The decline of OMI immediately prior to ovulation might be responsible in part for oocyte maturation. The action of FSH upon the granulosa cell to stimulate accumulation of LH receptors and stimulate progesterone secretion is inhibited by a low- and high-molecular-weight luteinization inhibitor which is present in greater amounts in small compared to large follicular fluid. Conversely, as the follicle enlarges a luteinization stimulator appears which enhances these actions of FSH upon the granulosa cell.

The follicle also secretes inhibin-F which reaches the ovarian venous blood and acts upon the pituitary to selectively inhibit FSH secretion. Inhibin-F is a large protein >10,000 daltons and is secreted by the granulosa cell. In the rat, FSH enhances the small diestrous follicle to secrete inhibin-F which in turn inhibits FSH secretion is a closed loop feedback system. Inhibin-F in rat ovarian vein blood is elevated up until the afternoon of proestrus at which time it declines and stays low until the afternoon of estrus. The decline in inhibin-F at estrus is responsible for the secondary FSH surge. Changes in follicular inhibin-F (along with ovarian steroids) might play a role in modulating the change in FSH secretion at puberty, at menopause, and at selected times during the menstrual cycle.

ACKNOWLEDGMENTS

The original work carried out here was supported in part by grants from the National Institute of Child Health and Human Development, USPHS [HD 08834 (CPC), HD 12003

(CPC), and HD 14696 (SHP)], a grant from the USDA-BARD project No. 1-112-79 (CPC), a grant from the Rockefeller Foundation (LDA), a postdoctoral fellowship from the USPHS (DJH), and the Rockefeller Foundation (KT). We thank Dr. Leo Reichert for a supply of purified human FSH. Some of the porcine follicular fluid used here was the generous gift of the NICHHD. The able collaboration of Dr. Gary Hodgen in many of these studies is acknowledged. We thank Ms. Pat Gagliano, Mrs. Valerie Evans, Mr. Timothy Conn, Mr. David Wetherell, Mr. Jack Vallejo, and Mr. Dave Shurkin for their dedicated assistance. The expert typing by Ms. Gail Williams is gratefully acknowledged.

REFERENCES

Ainsworth, L., Tsang, B. K., Downey, B. R., Marcus, G. J., and Armstrong, D. T. (1980). *Biol. Reprod.* **23,** 621.

Alexander, J. S., Rigby, B. W., and Ledwitz-Rigby, F. (1978). *Biol. Reprod.* **19,** 693.

Amsterdam, A., Riesel, R., Mintz, Y., Shemesh, M., and Salomon, Y. (1979). *Biochem. Biophys. Res. Commun.* **87,** 505.

Anderson, L. D., and DePaolo, L. V. (1981). *In* "Intragonadal Regulation of Reproduction" (P. Franchimont and C. P. Channing, eds.), p. 343. Academic Press, New York.

Anderson, L. D., and Hoover, D. J. (1981). *In* "Intraovarian Control Mechanisms" (C. P. Channing and S. Segal, eds.). Plenum, New York (in press).

Anderson, L. D., and Stone, S. L. (1980). Abstract No. 358, Annual Meeting of the Endocrine Society, Washington, D.C., June 18–20.

Anderson, L. D., Schaerf, F. W. and Channing, C. P. (1979). *In* "Ovarian Follicular and Corpus Luteum Function" (C. P. Channing, J. Marsh, and W. D. Sadler, eds.), p. 187. Plenum, New York.

Anderson, L. D., Schaerf, F. W., Osteen, K. G., Reichert, L. E., and Channing, C. P. (1980). *In* "Functional Correlates of Hormone Receptors in Reproduction" (V. B. Mahesh, T. G. Muldoon, B. B. Saxena, and W. A. Sadler, eds.), p. 557. Elsevier, North Holland, Amsterdam.

Ashiru, O. A., and Blake, C. A. (1979). *Endocrinology* **105,** 1162.

Barlow, D. H., Macnaughton, M. C., Mowat, J., and Coutts, J. R. T. (1979). *In* "Functional Morphology of the Human Ovary" (J. R. T. Coutts, ed.), p. 223. MTP, Lancaster, England.

Barraclough, C. A. (1981). *In* "Nonsteroidal Regulators in Reproductive Biology and Medicine" (T. Fujii and C. P. Channing, eds.). Pergamon, Oxford (in press).

Bast, J. D., and Greenwald, G. S. (1977). *Endocrinology* **100,** 955.

Beck, V., and Wuttke, W. (1980). *J. Clin. Endocrinol. Metab.* **50,** 635.

Bernard, J. (1973). *C.R. Seances Soc. Biol. Fil.* **167,** 880.

Bronson, F. H., and Channing, C. P. (1978). *Endocrinology* **103,** 1894.

Butcher, R. L., Collins, W. E., and Fuge, N. W. (1974). *Endocrinology* **94,** 1704.

Campbell, C. S., and Schwartz, N. B. (1977). *J. Toxicol. Environ. Health* **3,** 61.

Campbell, C. S., and Schwartz, N. B. (1979). *Biol. Reprod.* **20,** 1093.

Campbell, C. S., Schwartz, N. B., and Firlit, M. G. (1977). *Endocrinology* **101,** 162.

Centola, G. M., Anderson, L. D., and Channing, C. P. (1981). *Gamete Res.* **4,** 451.

Channing, C. P. (1970). *Endocrinology* **87,** 156.

Channing, C. P. (1973). *In* "IV International Congress of Endocrinology, Washington, D.C." (E. Scow, ed.), p. 914. North-Holland, Amsterdam.

Channing, C. P., and Kammerman, S. (1973). *Endocrinology* **92,** 531.

Channing, C. P., Tsai, V., and Sachs, D. (1976). *Biol. Reprod.* **15,** 235.

Channing, C. P., Anderson, L. D., and Batta, S. K. (1978). *In* "Clinics in Obstetrics and Gynecology" (T. Tyson, ed.), Vol. 5, p. 375. Saunders, London.

Channing, C. P., Anderson, L. D., and Hodgen, G. D. (1979). *In* "Ovarian Follicular and Corpus Luteum Function" (C. P. Channing, J. Marsh, and W. A. Sadler, eds.), p. 407. Plenum, New York.

Channing, C. P., Anderson, L. D., and Hodgen, G. D. (1980a). Abstracts 6th International Congress of Endocrinology.

Channing, C. P., Anderson, L. D., Schaerf, F., Brinkley, H. J. and Young, E. P. (1980b). *In* "Endocrinology 1980, Proceedings of the VI International Congress of Endocrinology, Melbourne, Australia, Feb. 10–16, 1980" (I. A. Cumming, J. W. Funder, and E. A. O. Mendelsohn, eds.), p. 430. Australian Academy of Science, Canberra.

Channing, C. P., Anderson, L. D., Hoover, D. J., Gagliano, P., and Hodgen, G. D. (1981a). *Biol. Reprod.* **25**, 885.

Channing, C. P., Schaerf, F. W., Anderson, L. D., and Tsafriri, A. (1980c). *In* "Reproductive Physiology III. International Review of Physiology" (R. O. Greep, ed.), Vol. 22, p. 117. University Park Press, Baltimore.

Channing, C. P., Anderson, L. D., Stone, S. L., and Batta, S. K. (1981b). *In* "Reproductive Processes and Contraception" (K. W. McKerns, ed.), p. 619. Plenum, New York.

Channing, C. P., Batta, S. K., Condon, W., Ganjam, V. K., and Kenney, R. M. (1981c). *In* "Dynamics of Ovarian Function" (N. B. Schwartz and M. Hunzicker-Dunn, eds.), p. 73. Raven, New York.

Channing, C. P., Gagliano, P., Hoover, D. J., Tanabe, K., Batta, S. K., Sulewski, J., and Lebech, P. (1981d). *J. Clin. Endocrinol. Metab.* **52**, 1193.

Channing, C. P., Pomerantz, S. H., Bae, I.-H., Evans, V. W., and Atlas, S. J. (1981e). *In* "Intraovarian Control Mechanisms" (C. P. Channing and S. Segal, eds.). Plenum, New York (in press).

Chappel, S. C. (1980). *Biol. Reprod.* **22**, 798.

Chappel, S. C., and Barraclough, C. A. (1977). *Endocrinology* **98**, 927.

Chappel, S. C., Holt, J. A., and Spies, H. S. (1980). *Proc. Soc. Exp. Biol. Med.* **163**, 310.

Chari, S., Hopkinson, C. R. N., Daume, E., and Sturm, G. (1979). *Acta Endocrinol.* **90**, 157.

Chiras, D. D., and Greenwald, G. S. (1978). *J. Reprod. Fertil.* **52**, 221.

Darga, N. C., and Reichert, L. E. (1978). *Biol. Reprod.* **19**, 235.

DeKretser, D. M., Burger, H. G., and Dumpys, R. (1978). *J. Clin. Endocrinol. Metab.* **46**, 227.

DePaolo, L. V., Hirshfield, A. N., Anderson, L. D., Barraclough, C. A., and Channing, C. P. (1979a). *J. Endocrinol.* **83**, 355.

DePaolo, L. V., Shander, D., Wise, P. M., Channing, C. P., and Barraclough, C. A. (1979b). *Endocrinology* **105**, 647.

DePaolo, L. V., Wise, P. M., Anderson, L. D., Barraclough, C. A., and Channing, C. P. (1979c). *Endocrinology* **104**, 402.

DePaolo, L. V., Anderson, L. D., and Hirshfield, A. N. (1981). *Am. J. Physiol.* **240**, E544.

Dierschke, D. J., Bhattacharya, A. N., Atkinson, L. E., and Knobil, E. (1970). *Endocrinology* **87**, 850.

DiZerega, G. S., and Hodgen, G. D. (1981). *Endocrinol. Rev.* **2**, 27.

DiZerega, G. S., Stouffer, R. L., and Hodgen, G. D. (1981). *In* "Intragonadal Regulation of Reproduction" (P. Franchimont and C. P. Channing, eds.), p. 9. Academic Press, New York.

Erickson, G. F., and Hsueh, A. W. (1978). *Endocrinology* **103**, 1960.

Faiman, C., and Winter, J. S. D. (1974). *In* "Control of the Onset of Puberty" (M. M. Grumbach, G. D. Grave, and F. E. Mayer, eds.), p. 32. Wiley, New York.

Forest, M. G., DePeretti, E., and Bertrand, J. (1976). *Clin. Endocrinol.* **5,** 551.

Fox, J., Offord, K. P., and Heath, H. (1981). *Am. J. Physiol.* **241,** E171.

Franchimont, P. Henderson, K., Verhoeven, G., Hazee-Hagelstein, M.-T., Charlet-Renard, C., Demoulin, A., Bourguignon, J.-P., and Lecomte-Yerna, M.-J. (1981). *In* "Intragonadal Regulation of Reproduction" (P. Franchimont and C. P. Channing, eds.), p. 167. Academic Press, New York.

Goodman, A. L., Nixon, W. E., and Hodgen, G. D. (1979). *Endocrinology* **105,** 69.

Grumbach, M. M., Roth, J. C., Kaplan, S. L., and Kelch, R. P. (1974). *In* "Control of the Onset of Puberty" (M. M. Grumbach, G. D. Grave, and F. E. Mayer, eds.), p. 115. Wiley, New York.

Henderson, K. M., and Franchimont, P. (1981). *J. Reprod. Fertil.* (in press).

Hillensjö, T., Batta, S. K., Schwartz-Kripner, A., Wentz, A. C., Sulewski, J., and Channing, C. P. (1978). *J. Clin. Endocrinol. Metabol.* **47,** 1332.

Hillensjö, T., Schwartz-Kripner, A., Pomerantz, S. H., and Channing, C. P. (1979). *In* "Ovarian Follicular and Corpus Luteum Function" (C. P. Channing, J. M. Marsh, and W. Z. Sadler, eds.), p. 283. Plenum, New York.

Hillensjö, T., Pomerantz, S. H., Kripner, A. S., Anderson, L. D., and Channing, C. P. (1980). *Endocrinology* **106,** 584.

Hirshfield, A. N. (1981). *In* "Dynamics of Ovarian Function" (N. B. Schwartz and M. Hunzicker-Dunn, eds.), p. 79. Raven, New York.

Hirshfield, A. N., and Midgely, A. R., Jr. (1978). *Biol. Reprod.* **19,** 606.

Hoak, D. C., and Schwartz, N. B. (1980). *Proc. Natl. Acad. Sci. U.S.A.* **77,** 4953.

Hodgen, G. D., Wilks, J. W., Vaitukaitis, J. L., Chen, H.-C., Papkoff, H., and Ross, G. T. (1976). *Endocrinology* **99,** 137.

Hodgen, G. D., Goodman, A. L., O'Connor, A., and Johnson, D. K. (1977). *Am. J. Obstet. Gynecol.* **127,** 581.

Hoffman, J. C., Lorenzen, J. R., Weil, T., and Schwartz, N. B. (1979). *Endocrinology* **105,** 200.

Karsch, F. J., Dierschke, D. J., Weick, R. F., Yamaji, T., Hotchkiss, J., and Knobil, E. (1973a). *Endocrinology* **92,** 799.

Karsch, F. J., Weick, R. F., Hotchkiss, J., Dierschke, D. J., and Knobil, E. (1973b). *Endocrinology* **93,** 478.

Knobil, E. (1974). *Rec. Prog. Horm. Res.* **30,** 46.

Knobil, E. (1981). *Biol. Reprod.* **24,** 44.

Knobil, E., and Plant, T. M. (1978). *In* "Frontiers in Neuroendocrinology" (W. F. Ganong and L. Martini, eds.), Vol. 5, p. 249. Raven, New York.

Kolena, Y., and Channing, C. P. (1981). *Biol. Reprod.,* submitted.

Kraiem, Z., Druker, B., and Lunenfield, B. (1978). *J. Endocrinol.* **78,** 161.

Krey, L. C., Butler, W. R., and Knobil, E. (1975). *Endocrinology* **96,** 1073.

Ledwitz-Rigby, F., and Rigby, B. (1979). *Molec. Cell Endocrinol.* **14,** 73.

Ledwitz-Rigby, F., and Rigby, B. (1981) *In* "Intragonadal Regulation of Reproduction" (P. Franchimont and C. P. Channing, eds.), p. 97. Academic Press, New York.

Ledwitz-Rigby, F., Rigby, B. W., Long, S. Y., Stewart, L., and McLean, M. (1981). *In* "Intraovarian Control Mechanisms" (C. P. Channing and S. Segal, eds.). Plenum, New York (in press).

Ledwitz-Rigby, F., Rigby, B. W., Gay, V. L., Stetson, M., Young, J., and Channing, C. P. (1977). *J. Endocrinol.* **74,** 175.

Lee, C. Y. (1976). *Endocrinology* **99,** 42.

Lee, P. A., Midgley, A. R., and Jaffe, R. B. (1970). *J. Clin. Endocrinol. Metab.* **31,** 248.

Lee, P. A., Plotnick, L. P., Steele, R. E., Thompson, R. G., and Blizzard, R. M. (1976a). *J. Clin. Endocrinol. Metab.* **43**, 168.

Lee, P. A., Xenakis, T., Winer, J., and Matsenbaugh, S. (1976b). *J. Clin. Endocrinol. Metab.* **43**, 775.

Lee, P. A., Plotnick, L. P., Migeon, C. J., and Avinoam, A. (1978). *J. Clin. Endocrinol. Metab.* **46**, 488.

Lee, V. W. K., McMaster, J., Quigg, H., Findlay, J., and Leversha, L. (1981). *Endocrinology* **108**, 2403.

Lindsey, A. M., and Channing, C. P. (1979). *Biol. Reprod.* **20**, 473.

Lorenzen, J. R., Channing, C. P., and Schwartz, N. B. (1978). *Biol. Reprod.* **19**, 635.

McNatty, K. P., Makris, A., Degrazia, C., Osathanondh, R., and Ryan, K. J. (1979a). *J. Clin. Endocrinol. Metab.* **49**, 987.

McNatty, K. P., Smith, D. M., Makris, A., Osathanondh, R., and Ryan, K. J. (1979b). *J. Clin. Endocrinol. Metab.* **49**, 851.

Marder, M. L., Channing, C. P., and Schwartz, N. B. (1977). *Endocrinology* **101**, 1639.

May, J. V., McCarty, K., Jr., Reichert, L. E., Jr. and Schomberg, D. W. (1980). *Endocrinology* **107**, 1041.

Monroe, S. E., Jaffe, R. B., and Midgley, A. R. (1972). *J. Clin. Endocrinol. Metab.* **34**, 420.

Nakano, R., Akahori, T., Katayoma, K., and Tujo, S. (1977). *J. Reprod. Fertil.* **51**, 23.

Nillius, S. J., and Wide, L. (1971). *Acta Endocrinol.* **67**, 362.

Nimrod, A., Tsafriri, A., and Linder, H. R. (1977). *Nature (London)* **267** (5612), 632.

Niswender, G. D., and Spies, H. G. (1973). *J. Clin. Endocrinol. Metab.* **37**, 326.

Niswender, G. D., Reichert, L. E., and Zimmerman, D. R. (1970). *Endocrinology* **87**, 576.

Penny, R., Olambiwonnu, N. O., and Frasier, S. D. (1974). *J. Clin. Endocrinol. Metab.* **38**, 320.

Peters, H., Byskov, A. G., and Grinsted, J. (1979). *In* "Functional Morphology of the Human Ovary" (J. R. T. Coutts, ed.), p. 26. MTP Press, Lancaster, England.

Rayford, P. L., Brinkley, H. J., Young, E. P., and Reichert, L. E. (1974). *J. Anim. Sci.* **39**, 348.

Resko, J. A., Norman, R. L., Niswender, G. D., and Spies, H. G. (1974). *Endocrinology* **94**, 128.

Resko, J. A., Ellinwood, W. E., and Knobil, E. (1981). *Am. J. Physiol.* **240** (*Endocrinol. Metab.* 3), E489.

Reyes, F. I., Winter, J. S. D., and Faiman, C. (1977). *Am. J. Obstet. Gynecol.* **129**, 557.

Ross, G. T., Cargille, C. M., Lipsett, M. B., Rayford, P. L., Marshall, J. R., Strott, C. A., and Rodbard, D. (1970). *Rec. Prog. Horm. Res.* **26**, 1.

Rush, M. E., Ashiru, O. A., Lipner, H., Williams, A. T., McRae, C., and Blake, C. A. (1981). *Endocrinology* **108**, 2316.

Sarkar, D. K., Chiappa, S. K., Fink, G., and Sherwood, N. M. (1976). *Nature (London)* **264**, 461.

Sasamoto, S., and Taya, K. (1980). *J. Endocrinol.* **86**, 489.

Sasamoto, S., Otani, T., and Shirota, M. (1981). *J. Endocrinol.* **89**, 205.

Sato, E., and Ishibashi, T. (1977). *Jpn. J. Zootech. Sci.* **48**, 22.

Sato, E., and Ishibashi, T. (1978). *Jpn. J. Zootech. Sci.* **49**, 313.

Sato, E., Miyamoto, H., Ishibashi, T., and Iritani, A. (1978). *J. Reprod. Fertil.* **54**, 263.

Sato, E., Ishibashi, T., and Iritani, A. (1980). *Fert. Steril.* **34**, 55.

Schwartz, N. B. (1981). *In* "Intraovarian Control Mechanisms" (C. P. Channing and S. Segal, eds.). Plenum, New York (in press).

Schwartz, N. B., and Channing, C. P. (1977). *Proc. Natl. Acad. Sci. U.S.A.* **74**, 5721.

Shander, D., Anderson, L. D., and Barraclough, C. A. (1980). *Endocrinology* **106**, 1047.

Shemosh, M. (1979). *J. Endocrinol.* **82**, 27.

Sherman, B. M., and Korenman, S. C. (1975). *J. Clin. Invest.* **55**, 699.

Sherman, B. M., West, J. H., and Korenman, S. C. (1976). *J. Clin. Endocrinol. Metab.* **42**, 629.

Sizonenko, P. C., Burr, I. M., Kaplan, S. L., and Grumbach, M. M. (1970). *Pediat. Res.* **4**, 36.

Steinberger, A. (1981). *In* "Intragonadal Regulation of Reproduction" (P. Franchimont and C. P. Channing, eds.), p. 283. Academic Press, New York.

Stone, S. L., Pomerantz, S. H., Schwartz-Kripner, A., and Channing, C. P. (1978). *Biol. Reprod.* **19**, 585.

Stouffer, R. L., Tyrey, L., and Schomberg, D. W. (1976). *Endocrinology* **99**, 516.

Strickland, S., and Beers, W. H. (1976). *J. Biol. Chem.* **251**, 5694.

Thanki, K. H., and Channing, C. P. (1976). *Endocrine Res. Commun.* **3**, 319.

Thanki, K. H., and Channing, C. P. (1977). *Endocrinology* **103**, 74.

Tsafriri, A. (1979). *In* "Ovarian Follicular and Corpus Luteum Function" (C. P. Channing, J. Marsh, and W. J. Sadler, eds.), p. 269. Plenum, New York.

Tsafriri, A., and Channing, C. P. (1975). *Endocrinology* **96**, 922.

Tsafriri, A., Pomerantz, S. H., and Channing, C. P. (1976a). *Biol. Reprod.* **14**, 511.

Tsafriri, A., Pomerantz, S. H., and Channing, C. P. (1976b). *In* "Proceedings of a Serono Symposium on Ovulation in the Human" (V. Crosgini, ed.), p. 31. Academic Press, New York.

Tsafriri, A., Channing, C. P., Pomerantz, S. H., and Lindner, H. R. (1977). *J. Endocrinol.* **75**, 285.

Uilenbroek, J. T. J., Tiller, R., DeJong, F. H., and Vels, F. (1978). *J. Endocrinol.* **78**, 399.

VanLook, P. F. A., Lothian, H., Hunter, W. M., Michie, E. A., and Baird, D. T. (1977). *Clin. Endocrinol.* **7**, 13.

Wallach, E. E., Root, A. W., and Garcia, C.-R. (1970). *J. Clin. Endocrinol. Metab.* **31**, 376.

Welschen, R., Hermans, W. P., Dullaart, J., and DeJong, F. H. (1977). *J. Reprod. Fertil.* **50**, 129.

Welschen, R., Dullaart, J., and DeJong, F. H. (1978). *Biol. Reprod.* **18**, 421.

Wilks, J. W., Hodgen, G. D., and Ross, G. T. (1976). *J. Clin. Endocrinol. Metab.* **43**, 1261.

Williams, A. T., and Lipner, H. (1980). Abstract No. 620, Annual Meeting of Endocrine Society, Washington, D.C., June 18–20.

Winter, J. S. D., Faiman, G., Hobson, W. C., Prasad, A. V., and Reyes, F. I. (1975). *J. Clin. Endocrinol. Metab.* **40**, 545.

Yen, S. S. C., and Vicic, W. J. (1970). *Amer. J. Obstet. Gynecol.* **106**, 134.

Yen, S. S. C., and Tsai, C. C. (1971). *J. Clin. Invest.* **50**, 1149.

Yen, S. S. C., Vicic, W. J., and Kearchner, D. V. (1969). *J. Clin. Endocrinol. Metab.* **29**, 382.

Yen, S. S. C., Tsai, C. C., Naftolin, F., VandenBerg, G., and Ajabor, L. (1972). *J. Clin. Endocrinol. Metab.* **34**, 671.

Yen, S. S. C., VandenBerg, G., Tsai, C. C., and Parker, D. (1974). *In* "Biorhythms and Human Reproduction" (M. Ferin, F. Halzberg, R. M. Richart, and R. L. VandeWiele, eds.), p. 203. Wiley, New York.

Yen, S. S. C., Hoff, J. D., Lasley, B. L., Rakoff, L. J., and Lein, A (1977). *In* "Hypothalamic Peptide Hormones and Pituitary Regulation" (J. C. Porter, ed.), p. 253. Plenum, New York.

Younglai, E. V. (1972). *J. Reprod. Fertil.* **28**, 95.

Zeleznick, A. J. (1981). *Endocrinology* **109**, 352.

Zeleznik, A. J., Midgley, A. R., Jr., and Reichert, L. E., Jr. (1974). *Endocrinology* **96**, 818.

DISCUSSION

R. Jewelewicz: Thank you for a very nice paper. I have one brief question. You showed that FSH will increase OMI and inhibin, however, this doesn't fit with clinical facts. If you treat anovulatory patients with gonadotropins where you inject LH and FSH, you get a very high incidence of multiple ovulations as evidenced by multiple corpora lutea and by the high incidence of multiple pregnancies which is as high as 20%, so how do you explain this discrepancy?

C. Channing: Your observations are not inconsistent with the existence of inhibin in the human. You gave *exogenous* FSH (LH) which would take the place of the FSH which the inhibin would inhibit. Furthermore according to the observations of Hodgen and Dizerega the injection of FSH in the monkey can well induce formation of additional follicles if given prior to choice of a dominant follicle (but not afterward). This is possible because the other follicles are still sensitive to FSH (and are not atretic or have elevated FSHRBI?). In the case of control of OMI biosynthesis FSH enhancement of its synthesis may decline as the follicle matures and luteinizes because the granulosa cells harvested from large porcine follicles have fewer FSH receptors compared to cells from smaller follicles (Nakano *et al.*, 1975). All of our studies on the effects of FSH on OMI secretion were done in cells from small and medium sized immature follicles (porcine). We have not added FSH to cells from large follicles and examined its effect on OMI secretion. I am willing to predict that it would not alter OMI secretion in the mature large follicle.

G. A. Hedge: In your *in vitro* study of LH receptor binding you showed a stimulatory effect of FSH in the presence of a cocktail of cortisol, thyroxin, and insulin. However, it was not completely clear to me that the FSH was even necessary. What does this cocktail do on its own, and within this group of 3 hormones is one of these a prime player?

C. Channing: First of all an addition of the cocktail consisting of I, F, and T alone produces only a small transient increase in receptor which is very small compared to when FSH is present. The endocrine cocktail appears to enhance the ability of the FSH to achieve induction of receptors. We have not studied the role of each hormone alone in the cocktail in FSH induction of receptors. However we have studied the roles of individual hormones in this "endocrine cocktail" on progesterone secretion in the cultured porcine and monkey granulosa cells (*Biol. Reprod.* **15**, 235, 1976). The mixture of all of them enhances basal and LH and FH stimulated progesterone secretion better than either one by itself. In the absence of insulin neither cortisol (0.01 μg/ml) nor thyroid hormone (10^{-7} M) works to enhance progesterone secretion.

G. A. Hedge: Does the FSH at any dose have an effect on its own?

C. Channing: There is a small enhancing effect of FSH alone on LH receptor induction. It should be remembered that all of the induction experiments were in the presence of 10% adult pig serum which contains some of these hormones. Other studies with defined medium have to be done further to rigorously examine the exact role of each hormone on induction of LH receptor. This presents a problem since porcine granulosa cells without serum grow poorly and die after 2–4 days.

J. K. Findlay: Dr. Victor Lee in our laboratory has examined the hypothesis that FSH is involved in the stimulation of inhibin from the ovary, which in turn has a feedback effect on endogenous FSH (V. W. K. Lee, J. McMaster, H. Quigg, J. K. Findlay, and L. Leversha, *Endocrinology* **108**, 2403, 1981). Various doses of PMSG were injected into immature rats and 64 hours later, inhibin content of the ovary and the inhibin and FSH concentration in peripheral blood were measured. Inhibin activity was measured in the bioassay of R. S. Scott, H. G. Burger, and H. Quigg (*Endocrinology* **107**, 1536, 1980) which is an FSH cell content assay. Very strict controls were maintained in the *in vitro* bioassay by monitoring nonspecific effects of toxic factors which can be present in serum and using parallel-line assay statistics. In our experience, just charcoal treating the serum samples is insufficient to remove the highly toxic material, so we have to resort to polyethylene glycol (M. Dobos, H. Quigg, and H. G. Burger, *Proc. Endocrine Soc. Aust.* **24**, 88, Abstr., 1981). The data in Table A show a dose-dependent increase in ovarian and blood inhibin and a concomitant decrease in the peripheral FSH level. This supports the hypothesis that FSH stimulates ovarian inhibin production and release. We have examined the time course of this effect at 6, 24, and 64 hours, comparing a saline treated group and a PMSG-treated group at each time point (V. W. K. Lee and J. K. Findlay, *Proc. Reinier de Graaf Symp.* **4**, in press, 1982). There was a time-dependent increase in inhibin in both the ovary and serum (Fig. A). What we think is particularly interesting and important is that there was an increase in inhibin in blood by 6 hours corresponding to a significant decrease in FSH by 6 hours. We believe these data support the hypothesis that FSH stimulates ovarian inhibin production and secretion which in turn can feedback on the hypothalamic pituitary unit to suppress FSH release. We have now been able to confirm these studies using ovine FSH rather than PMSG (V. W. K. Lee, J. McMaster, H. Quigg, and L. Leversha, *Proc. Endocrine Soc. Aust.* **24**, 88, Abstr., 1981).

C. Channing: You presented some elegant data which very nicely confirm our enhancing effect of FSH on inhibin secretion in the rat and lead to the strengthening of the hypothesis that there is a closed loop feedback system between inhibin secretion and serum FSH.

R. R. Grady: Neena Schwartz and I have data which I would like to present to you which supports Dr. Channing's observations that inhibin levels change within follicles at different times of the cycle. Jim Ireland and Andrea Qurato at Michigan State University collected follicular fluid from bovine ovaries at different cycle stages, estrus, early luteal, and mid-luteal. We compared inhibin (folliculostatin) activity in this bovine follicular fluid to porcine follicular fluid in our *in vivo* bioassay. Since Dr. Schwartz will be speaking about the *in vivo* bioassay, I won't go into the assay details during this discussion. We have plotted percentage serum FSH suppression versus dose of these follicular fluids. You will notice that there is a parallel response of all four follicular fluids tested and that the bovine fluids (bFF) are more potent than porcine follicular fluid. The point is that the 3 bFF preparations are not equipotent. Early luteal phase bovine follicular fluid has a much greater potency, that is, activity per milligram of protein, than fluid collected during estrus or the mid-luteal phase of the estrous cycle. We believe that these data support Dr. Channing's conclusions in the monkey and the human. It appears that in the cow, as well, inhibin concentrations change with the reproductive cycle.

TABLE A

Changes in Ovarian Inhibin and Serum FSH and Inhibin in Immature Rats 64 Hours after Treatment with Varying Doses of PMSG[a]

Dose of PMSG (IU)	n	Ovarian inhibin (U/ovary)[b]	Serum inhibin (U/ml)[c]	Serum FSH (ng/ml)[b]
0	5	42 ± 7	<4	417 ± 54
10	5	347 ± 59	208 (174 ± 247)	56 ± 3
20	6	1344 ± 179	452 (380 ± 535)	68 ± 10
40	5	1452 ± 384	674 (555 ± 815)	70 ± 10

[a] From Lee *et al.* (1981).

[b] Values represent mean ± SEM.

[c] Values represent potency (95% CL), index of precision of assay (λ) = 0.1.

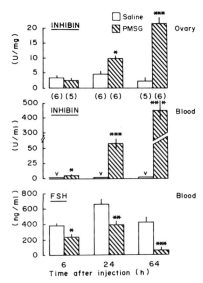

FIG. A.   The time course of changes in ovarian inhibin and peripheral serum FSH and inhibin in immature female rats treated with saline or 20 IU PMSG. $*p < 0.05$; $**p < 0.01$; $***p < 0.001$ versus saline control. From Lee and Findlay (1982).

C. Channing: Thank you, that is nice work.

U. Zor: Thank you Cornelia for the excellent presentation. I have only one comment in regard to the inhibitory effect of the crude small follicular fluid on the stimulatory effect of FSH on LH receptor induction or progesterone production. It is quite possible in regard to the recent study of Schomberg (*Science*, 1981) that the follicular fluid contained an EGF-like activity, other growth factors, or GnRH-like activity which may originate either from the theca layer or from the granulosa cells and may prevent FSH action. In our case at least, exogenous addition of GnRH-analog to granulosa cells inhibits the FSH-induced increase in plasma membrane microviscosity and desensitization (Strulovici *et al.*, *Biochim. Biophys. Acta*, 1981). So it may be possible that in the crude follicular fluid you used at least two factors, one which has OMI activity and then another that inhibits the effect of FSH on progesterone stimulation or on LH-receptor induction, and may have similar biological activity as GnRH.

C. Channing: Thank you for calling our attention to these observations. We are currently trying to purify the inhibitor of FSH induction of LH receptors to see if it is separable from OMI and LHRH activity. Such a purification could resolve some of these questions.

P. J. Olsiewski: Have you compared the OMI concentration of large preovulatory follicles to that of large nonpreovulatory follicles?

C. Channing: Yes. Van deWiel, Bar-Ami, and de Jong (in preparation) using staged pigs have carried out this type of study. Once the large follicle has been exposed to LH the OMI decreases in the follicular fluid. They also measured inhibin concentration in the follicular fluid of the same staged pigs and also found that inhibin decreased as well. So it would appear that exposure to the LH surge and accompanying luteinization may be responsible for the decline of the synthesis of OMI and inhibin F. The granulosa cell appears to decrease its ability to secrete some proteins and increase its steroidogenic potential as it luteinizes.

K. Ahren: You mentioned that the OMI inhibits the monolayer formation of the cumulus cells and also of the mural granulosa cells. What about the specificity of these effects? Have you tested this on other cells, particularly on some cells from the testis? Another question; you mentioned that you had no OMI-like effect in pig serum. If I remember right, you reported in an early publication an OMI-like effect of some sera in your test system. Is it now clear that serum has no OMI-like effect?

C. Channing: Let me answer on the effects of serum on oocyte maturation first. The low-molecular-weight fraction of 500 ml of porcine serum was obtained by Amicon filtration and applied to a Sephadex G-25 column and eluted as described by Stone *et al.* (1978). There was no OMI activity in the region corresponding to that which would be found in follicular fluid. In regard to the specificity in monolayer formation by granulosa cell clumps we are currently carrying studies out with other cell lines to see if monolayer formation can be inhibited by crude and purified fractions of OMI. If some thecal cells are added to the granulosa cell cultures their outgrowth appears not to be inhibited; more studies are in progress on specificity of the clump culture. At the moment inhibition of granulosa cell monolayer formation is used primarily as a screening method. There is activity in inhibiting monolayer formation present in native porcine follicular fluid which is absent in pig serum up to doses of 50% by volume. Details of the clump culture assay can be found in the text.

J. H. Oppenheimer: Just a small point. I was intrigued by your study on the effect of thyroxin and cortisol on the granulosa cell. The gonads are not supposed to be responsive to thyroid hormones, at least as far as O_2 consumption is concerned. In fact we have shown that the testes are almost completely devoid of T3 nuclear receptors. Have you had any opportunity to look for receptors in the granulosa cells?

C. Channing: Yes, that is an obvious question. Earlier we observed that T3 and T4 had definitive enhancing effects on progesterone secretion when insulin was also present. These data are published (*Biol. Reprod.* **15**, 235 1976). It also enhances the stimulatory effect of LH and FSH on progesterone secretion in the ovary. Perhaps some members of this audience will want to look for receptor for thyroid hormone in granulosa cells.

J. H. Oppenheimer: Would you also postulate on the conversion of T4 to T3?

C. Channing: We have found that T3 is about 10-fold more active than T4 in enhancing LH and FSH to stimulate progesterone secretion in porcine granulosa cells grown in serum-free medium with BSA added as a supplement.

H. Papkoff: Is there any evidence for a pituitary OMI or inhibin? I ask this because I recently ran across a paper by Herbert Evans and colleagues in 1936 which described a substance in the pituitary, separable from gonadotropin, which would antagonize the action of gonadotropin on the ovary.

C. Channing: We have not examined pituitary extracts for OMI or inhibin activity. We have examined adrenal and liver extracts and found that they did not contain OMI activity (Centola *et al., Gamete Res.,* in press). We have not examined pituitary or hypothalamus. Of interest is the finding by Jesse Roth that many organs have potential to make a number of hormones but only those "customary endocrine organs" can accumulate enough hormone and store it so that the hormone can be secreted. It is the "one experiment too many" to examine unusual sources of OMI and inhibin. We would like to think that OMI is a local regulator that works within the ovary to act where it is needed.

J. E. Tyson: In an androgen-dominated microenvironment such as may exist in polycystic ovarian disease, have you identified OMI and is its concentration decreased?

C. Channing: We have not measured OMI in polycystic ovarian disease (PCO) follicular fluid but we have measured inhibin levels in PCO follicular fluid and the data are shown in Table B.

TABLE B

Inhibin-F and Steroid Contents of Follicular Fluid Obtained from Viable and Atretic Follicular Phase and Cystic Follicles of Normal Human Ovaries as Well as from Small Follicles of Patients with PCO Disease[a]

	n	Mean	SE
Follicular phase follicles (viable)			
E	23	273.71	37.99
Δ^4	23	619.68	90.00
Δ^4/E	23	3.58	0.64
Inhibin	23	313.14	32.10
Follicular phase follicles (atretic)			
E	14	65.86	11.94
Δ^4	14	1017.56	167.26
Δ^4/E	14	23.38	7.82
Inhibin	14	118.88	29.36
Cystic follicles			
E	5	14.40	8.57
Δ^4	4	494.38	311.80
Δ^4/E	4	48.75	43.57
Inhibin	5	64.00	24.70
PCO follicles			
E	14	221.2	36.5
Δ^4	14	2533.5	383.2
Δ^4/E	14	15.89	3.45
Inhibin	14	328.3	12.8

[a] Steroid contents (ng/ml) as well as inhibin-F activity (units/10 μl) were determined as detailed previously (*J. Clin. Endocrinol. Metab.* **52**, 1193, 1981). E, Estrogen; Δ^4, androstenedione (Tanabe, Nakamura, Fortuny, and Channing, unpublished observations).

In studies in collaboration with Dr. Nakamura from Keio University in Tokyo, and with Dr. Tanabe in our laboratory we measured inhibin activity in small PCO follicles and compared levels to normal viable follicles obtained from the follicular phase of the menstrual cycle. The follicular fluid samples from the normal patients were obtained from Dr. Fortuny of Barcelona. We observed that PCO patients had normal levels of inhibin or slightly elevated levels compared to normal follicles. The question is what do you use for a control? We are going to measure the OMI and luteinization inhibitor in the same follicles. In Fig. B I have taken the liberty to speculate upon a possible role of inhibin in the etiology of PCO disease. Since nobody knows the mechanism of PCO, I think that I can be free to speculate. It has been shown that LH is elevated in PCO disease and it could act upon the theca and stimulate

(1)   ↑ serum LH ⟶ thecal hypertrophy ↑ thecal androgens
  ⟶ granulosa cell inhibin secretion ↑ ⟶ serum FSH ↓
  poor granulosa cell maturation and inability to luteinize.

(2)   ↑ accumulation of follicular luteinization inhibitor
  ⟶ inhibit FSH induction of LH receptors
  granulosa cells fail to respond to LH and FSH, stay
  immature and secrete inhibin instead of maturing
  and luteinizing ↑ inhibin ⟶ ↓ serum FSH
  ovarian estrogen ↓ because of lower FSH and
  luteinization inhibitor ⟶ ↑ thecal androgens
  ⟶ ↑ inhibin secretion by granulosa etc.

FIG. B.   Two possible causes of polycystic ovarian disease involving ovarian inhibin.

androgen biosynthesis. Thecal hypertrophy is common in PCO disease. The elevated androgens may stimulate inhibin secretion. Subsequently there are normal or low levels of FSH preventing the follicle from maturing properly. Another possibility in PCO disease is that maybe the granulosa cell is inhibited by a local follicular luteinization inhibitor which prevents it from making receptors for LH, therefore it can't luteinize. Instead it stays immature and secretes inhibin instead of progesterone. This further contributes to the immaturity or ultimate demise of this follicle. The theca can probably secrete progesterone which contributes to some of the circulating levels of progesterone.

J. E. Fortune: Like Dr. Ahren, I am also interested in your clump inhibition assay. I noticed that when you were looking for OMI activity secreted by granulosa cells, you used inhibition of oocyte maturation as your bioassay and I wondered whether granulosa cells also secrete a clump inhibiting activity.

C. Channing: Yes. Dr. Atlas in our laboratory has shown that granulosa cells do secrete granulosa cell clump monolayer formation inhibiting activity in significant amounts. Interestingly we found that some pools of follicular fluid have low clump inhibiting as well as low OMI activity indicating that maybe there is a stimulator or masker of OMI in some pools of follicular fluid, and we subsequently observed that cultured granulosa cells may secrete a stimulator as well as an inhibitor of granulosa clump monolayer formation. The stimulator will be further purified.

J. E. Fortune: Do you think the two activities are identical, i.e. that they are the same molecule?

C. Channing: No, they (the stimulator and inhibitor of granulosa cell clump outgrowth) seem to be separable on the basis of size but we really have to purify them further to say much more about them.

M. B. Nikitovitch-Winer: Nina, congratulations on a very lovely paper and I want to wish you luck with your protein machine so that you can continue your work and supply us with various ovarian inhibitors. I would like to make a comment and ask a question. As many people working with inhibiting factors, we are also thinking of a possible usage of these factors as nonsteroidal contraceptives. We reasoned that if a substance like inhibin were to be used for this purpose, it should be proven that it remains active after prolonged administration. A graduate student in my laboratory, Mr. Carl Thomas, has been investigating the effects of continuous infusion of charcoal extracted porcine follicular fluid (PFF) on acutely or chronically castrated female rats and he finds that he can inhibit FSH secretion very rapidly and maintain this inhibition for the duration of infusion of 10–12 days. At the end of infusion, the pituitary concentration of FSH is 2–5 times lower than in control animals. After cessation of infusion of PFF the plasma levels of FSH returned to control levels within 24 hours. My question is, do you think that our experimental design is the right approach to use to examine possible contraceptive properties of PFF? In light of your work, should one infuse PFF only at certain times of the cycle in females and over a prolonged period of time in males?

C. Channing: As far as female reproduction is concerned probably one should give inhibin very early in the menstrual cycle and give just enough to inhibit some granulosa cells from growing and to inhibit FSH induction of LH receptors. This could permit follicular luteinization without follicular rupture and allowance of normal levels of progesterone so that no abnormal bleeding should occur. The decrease of serum FSH should deprive the early follicle of FSH which is needed to induce LH receptors. This is the ideal; however, it would be necessary to administer a small molecular weight fragment of inhibin because in the monkey Hodgen, Tanabe, and I (submitted) have observed that porcine follicular fluid administration brings about antibodies against the inhibin. Oocyte maturation inhibitor has not been tested *in vivo* yet. An alternate approach is to administer substances which alter OMI or inhibin secretion. The small molecular weight inhibitor of FSH induction of LH receptor also has potential as a contraceptive.

K. Yoshinaga: I am interested in your observation on the decreased secretion of inhibin by the rat ovary in the afternoon of proestrus. I wonder whether it is correct to assume that the FSH increase at this stage of the cycle may be due to the decreased secretion of inhibin which was caused by follicular alteration. We observed an increase of FSH level on day 4 of pregnancy in the rat. Since the ovarian function at this stage of pregnancy is entirely different from that at the proestrus afternoon, luteinization of follicles may not be the only cause that results in an increase in FSH secretion. Have you measured inhibin during pregnancy?

C. Channing: In the case of the afternoon of proestrus it is possible that the preovulatory surge of FSH and LH may act on the follicule and cause it to luteinize and then secrete less inhibin. Alternately there may be some intrinsic mechanism that decreases inhibin secretion on the afternoon of proestrus which in turn allows FSH to rise. In the case of the secondary FSH surge in the rat this rise in FSH secretion is due to a lack of inhibin. This will be discussed more by Dr. Schwartz.

K. Yoshinaga: Yes, I asked this question because we have observed FSH increase 4 days later when the rats become pregnant. So there is no ovulation, the ovaries have functional corpora lutea secreting progesterone, and the FSH secretion increases on day 4 of pregnancy.

C. Channing: We have never measured inhibin levels in ovarian vein blood during pregnancy. Such measurements could answer this question. It has been shown by Franchimont and his colleagues that addition of progesterone to cultures of bovine granulosa cells (1, 5 μg/ml) brings about a marked decrease in inhibin secretion. This could explain your observation. We are also testing the effects of progesterone on inhibin secretion but have no answer yet.

D. K. Pomerantz: I would like to challenge your contention that the circulating levels of inhibin play a role in the regulation of the menstrual cycle in the monkey. You showed data today concerning estimations of inhibin activity in ovarian vein plasma. I think the largest changes you observed were roughly 15% during the menstrual cycle, now that 15% change of inhibin activity in the venous fluent is going to be diluted by the cardiac output and I would think the pituitary then would be seeing changes in inhibin levels of tenths of a percent. Based on your own data where you injected the monkeys with inhibin preparations, I would predict that the changes in circulating levels of inhibin which occur during the menstrual cycle would not alter FSH secretion.

C. Channing: In the primate it may be that small changes in inhibin are needed to control

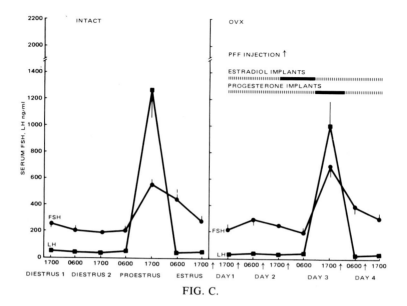

FIG. C.

FSH. Rigorous analysis of this problem must await a radioimmunoassay that is more sensitive. The inhibin levels in monkey ovarian vein are near the lower limits of the sensitivity of the rat pituitary cell culture bioassay. The experiments on lutectomy in unilateral castrate monkeys indicate a role for inhibin in control of FSH in the monkey. Data in the rat are more convincing since the rat appears to make more inhibin then the monkey, perhaps because they have more antral follicles to make it. (This problem is addressed in more detail in the text.)

H. Lipner: These results are from a study performed by Dr. T. Williams in my laboratory. Figure C shows a normal intact animal estrous cycle (left panel) a simulated estrous cycle (right panel) generated in ovariectomized rats bearing implants of estrogen and progesterone. The solid line shows the high level estrogen or progesterone implant and the dashed line low levels. We injected pFF twice a day (indicated on the abscissa). One can simulate the entire gonadotropin secretory pattern of the estrous cycle by using a combination of steroids and porcine follicular fluid. Note that to control the intensity of the FSH surge one has to drop out 1 pFF injection at 0600 hours giving rise to a normal level surge. On the other hand, if you maintain the pFF injections in the absence of steroid implants then the gonadotropin surge is blocked. If you just administer steroids only a runaway FSH surge occurs. We conclude that the steroids regulate the timing of gonadotropin secretion and pFF regulates the intensity of the FSH surge.

C. Channing: Your data are indeed most convincing and I cannot help agreeing with you that inhibin is extremely important in the control of FSH secretion in rat probably more so than in primate. It could be that inhibin is more important in an animal with multiple ovulations and less important in animals with only one ovulation.

Characterization of the FSH-Suppressing Activity in Follicular Fluid

ROSEMARY R. GRADY, M. CRISTINE CHARLESWORTH, AND
NEENA B. SCHWARTZ

*Department of Neurobiology and Physiology, Northwestern University,
Evanston, Illinois*

I. Introduction

For many years, the interactions between the ovary and the pituitary gland were thought to encompass only the stimulatory effects of gonadotrophic hormones on ovarian morphology and secretion, and the inhibitory and stimulatory feedback effects of ovarian steroid hormones on the pituitary (Schwartz, 1969). Even after the two gonadotrophic hormones LH and FSH were separated (Schwartz, 1974), there was no strong incentive to search for differential feedback regulation of these two pituitary hormones. There are probably several reasons for this. First, strong evidence exists in favor of a single hypothalamic releasing hormone, GnRH, which is proposed to regulate both LH and FSH (Guillemin, 1978). Furthermore, since estradiol replacement therapy suppresses both LH and FSH, at least to some extent, there appeared to be no need to search for additional feedback regulators from the ovary. Finally, in a self-confirming prophecy, investigators have routinely measured only serum LH as an indicator of pituitary function in many experiments. It is assumed either that serum LH will be entirely reflective of change in pituitary secretion of FSH, or that a change in serum FSH will be too sluggish to be of interest (Savoy-Moore and Schwartz, 1980).

The present article begins with a description of recent experiments which make it obvious that estradiol could not be the sole negative feedback signal for FSH secretion. We then summarize the experimental evidence that the ovary, particularly ovarian follicular fluid, contains a nonsteroidal substance which selectively suppresses pituitary FSH secretion both *in vivo* and *in vitro*. In the following section, we briefly divert our attention to some evidence which suggests that this substance, which we have named folliculostatin, is a hormone (see Channing's article in this volume which also addresses this issue). We then discuss the selection of

409

an appropriate bioassay system for purification of folliculostatin. This section is included because we feel that the failure to select a valid and reliable assay and use it consistently was a major impediment to the isolation of inhibin, the putative FSH-suppressing hormone, from testicular sources. In the final section, we describe the current status of the chemical characterization of the FSH-suppressing activity in follicular fluid.

II. Inadequacy of Estradiol as a Negative Feedback Signal for the Regulation of Serum FSH

In every species tested, removal of the ovaries eventually leads to an elevation in serum levels of both LH and FSH. In the rat, serum FSH rises during the first 24 hours after ovariectomy on proestrus, even though serum estradiol levels do not differ from those in intact controls (Fig. 1). Circulating estradiol levels are maintained in these ovariectomized animals by adrenal secretion of estradiol (Campbell *et al.*, 1977). Also, following unilateral ovariectomy, serum FSH rises in the face of unchanged estradiol levels (Butcher, 1977; Welschen *et al.*, 1978) (Fig. 2). On the other hand, serum LH levels in these experiments are unchanged. Serum LH does not show a reliable rise until 3 or 4 days postbilateral ovariectomy (Brown-Grant and Greig, 1975). These acute FSH changes in re-

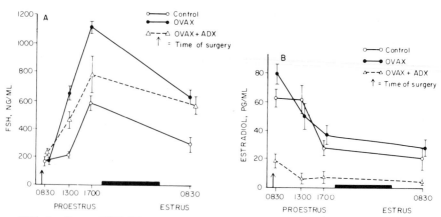

FIG. 1. Serum FSH (RP1) (A) and estradiol (B) levels in adult female rats ovariectomized (OVAX), ovariectomized and adrenalectomized (OVAX + ADX), or unoperated (Control) on proestrus. Surgery was performed at 0800 hours. Shown is average ± SEM. Serum FSH levels rise prior to a significant fall in serum estradiol levels in ovariectomized rats. Circulating estradiol levels are maintained in these animals due to adrenal secretion of estradiol (compare OVAX and OVAX + ADX groups). These data are redrawn from Campbell *et al.* (1977).

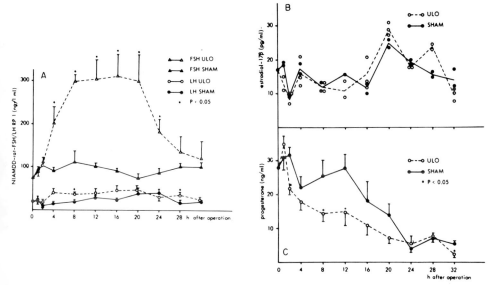

FIG. 2.   Serum levels of FSH and LH (A), estradiol-17β (B), and progesterone (C) in adult female rats 0–32 hours after removal of the left ovary or after sham-ovariectomy performed at 0900 hours on diestrus-2. Serum FSH, LH, and progesterone data are average ± SEM; estradiol-17β was determined in two or three different volumes of pooled plasma. $N = 5$–6 rats/group. These figures are reproduced with permission from Welschen *et al.* (1978).

sponse to alterations in ovarian feedback in the rat argue against the hypothesis that estradiol is the sole negative feedback signal for FSH.

Similar evidence comes from other species as well. Unilateral ovariectomy in the monkey (di Zerega and Hodgen, 1981) also leads to an elevation of serum FSH without an alteration in circulating levels of LH or estradiol. In perimenopausal women (Sherman and Korenman, 1975), serum FSH begins to rise before estradiol levels fall, while serum LH rises only after steroid levels decline.

Steroid replacement therapy is not adequate to reverse the elevation in serum FSH which accompanies removal of one or both ovaries. Estrogen injections will not suppress the rise in serum FSH seen in the unilaterally ovariectomized rat (Fig. 2; Butcher, 1977). Even though serum progesterone in these rats falls, due to a temporary reduction in the number of corpora lutea, injection of progesterone does not lower FSH (Welschen *et al.*, 1978). In the bilaterally ovariectomized rat, immediate replacement with a Silastic capsule which produces physiological levels of estradiol does not restrain serum FSH within cyclic range even after a week has elapsed (Campbell and Schwartz, 1977, 1979) (Fig. 3). The failure of es-

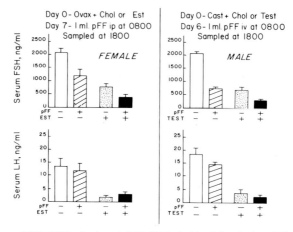

FIG. 3.   Serum FSH (RP1—top) and LH (S16—bottom) levels in adult female (left) and male (right) rats, gonadectomized, and given a Silastic capsule of cholesterol or steroid (estrogen, females; testosterone, males) on day 0. Average + SEM is plotted. On day 6 or 7, animals received 1.0 ml of either porcine serum (pS) or porcine follicular fluid (pFF) at 0800 hours. Blood samples were taken 10 hours postinjection. Steroid replacement alone returned LH, but not FSH, to basal levels in both male and female rats. These data are replotted from Campbell and Schwartz (1979) and Summerville and Schwartz (1981).

tradiol to suppress serum FSH, relative to its effectiveness in suppressing serum LH, has been reported in the mouse (Bronson and Channing, 1978), rabbit (Dufy-Barbe et al., 1978), heifer (Roche and Ireland, 1981), and ewe (Goodman et al., 1981).

In addition to the obvious situations just cited, another experimental and natural paradigm is relevant to the issue of gonadal regulation of FSH. Following the natural preovulatory LH and FSH surges on the afternoon of proestrus in the rat, there is a prolonged elevation of serum FSH in the presence of falling or low LH levels (Savoy-Moore et al., 1980a). If the primary LH and FSH surges are prevented by barbiturate treatment, this secondary FSH rise does not occur (Schwartz and Talley, 1978; Ashiru and Blake, 1980). It can be stimulated in such barbiturate-blocked rats by exogenous LH, FSH, or GnRH (Schwartz and Talley, 1978; Ashiru and Blake, 1980), but not by exogenous progesterone (Schwartz and Talley, 1978). Moreover, elevating serum levels of testosterone, estradiol, or progesterone does not *prevent* the naturally occurring secondary FSH rise (Ashiru and Blake, 1980; Welschen et al., 1980). Evidence accumulates that this rise may be independent of hypothalamic or, at least, GnRH control (Rush et al., 1980; Elias and Blake, 1980). The secondary FSH surge is yet another example of incongruent changes in circulating FSH and LH levels, which cannot be accounted for by changes in steroid hormone levels.

We have cited evidence against the hypothesis that estradiol is the sole regulator of serum FSH levels. Ovarian steroids (estrogen, progesterone, testosterone) do not serve as good suppressing agents for FSH. This led us to search for other negative feedback signals from the ovary which could exert a specific suppression of FSH secretion with no, or minimal, suppression of LH.

III. Specific Suppression of FSH Secretion by Ovarian Follicular Fluid

A. *In Vivo* STUDIES

The first two studies investigating the effects of follicular fluid on serum FSH and LH started from different vantage points. De Jong and Sharpe (1976) utilized bovine follicular fluid (bFF) to suppress selectively serum FSH levels in castrated male rats. They were searching for inhibin, analogizing the granulosa cell to the Sertoli cell. We have since confirmed their findings in the male rat, using porcine follicular fluid (pFF) (Lorenzen *et al.*, 1981). At the same time, we hypothesized that the preovulatory LH surge elicited the secondary FSH surge by suppressing the secretion of a negative feedback signal for FSH from the ovary (Schwartz and Talley, 1978). As pointed out above, this negative feedback signal did not appear to be a steroid. The preovulatory LH surge also causes resumption of oocyte meiosis (Ayalon *et al.*, 1972), and Tsafriri *et al.* (1977) had shown that pFF contained a substance which could inhibit resumption of meiosis *in vitro*. We reasoned that pFF might also contain a substance which could inhibit the secondary FSH surge. We obtained pFF from Cornelia P. Channing to test this hypothesis (Schwartz and Channing, 1977). Figure 4 illustrates the effect of pFF on the LH-induced secondary FSH surge. The results were unequivocal; there was a spectacular suppression of serum FSH. These results have been confirmed by Welschen *et al.* (1980).

We, and others, have since discovered a wide variety of circumstances in which follicular fluid can selectively suppress FSH secretion. This activity is not due to a steroid, since the follicular fluid was charcoal-extracted before injection to remove more than 95% of the steroids (Schwartz and Channing, 1977; Marder *et al.*, 1977). Since the FSH-suppressing activity in bFF or pFF is lost after treatment with pepsin or trypsin (de Jong and Sharpe, 1976; Lorenzen *et al.*, 1978), it is believed to be proteinaceous in nature. We named the activity folliculostatin, since it suppresses FSH secretion (Schwartz and Channing, 1977). Others have

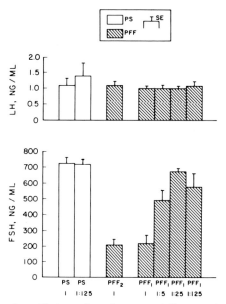

FIG. 4. Effect of various dilutions of porcine serum (pS) or porcine follicular fluid (pFF) on LH (S16) and FSH (RP1) serum levels at 0400 hours on the day of estrus. All rats were injected with pentobarbital at 1330 and 1500 hours, and LH at 1530 hours on the day of proestrus. The dilutions of porcine serum and porcine follicular fluid (pFF₁ or pFF₂) are indicated on the bottom of the figure; these substances were injected (0.5 ml/inj) at 1545 and 1830 hours. Rats exhibiting 4-day estrous cycles were used; three rats were used in each treatment group except the pFF₂-treated group, which contained five rats. SEM is indicated above each bar. These data originally appeared in Schwartz and Channing (1977).

called it ovarian inhibin or inhibin-F (see Franchimont and Channing, 1981).

Folliculostatin is effective in suppressing serum FSH on each day of the estrous cycle in intact animals (Figs. 5 and 6) (Marder *et al.*, 1977; Hoffmann *et al.*, 1979; Grady *et al.*, 1981). As can be seen in Fig. 6, folliculostatin administered early on proestrus suppresses the primary surge of FSH, without altering the secretion of serum LH, estradiol, or progesterone. Suppression of the primary FSH surge does not block ovulation, the secondary FSH surge, or follicular recruitment (Hoffmann *et al.*, 1979; Hoak and Schwartz, 1980). We will return to this point below.

Folliculostatin can also suppress serum FSH in the acutely ovariectomized metestrous rat (Fig. 5). It does so in a dose-dependent manner (Fig. 7). These studies show that pFF exerted its effects within 5.5 hours following intraperitoneal or intravenous administration. To determine how rapidly this effect could be manifested, we measured the latency of suppression following intravenous injection of a large dose of pFF (Savoy-Moore *et al.*, 1980b) (Fig. 8). The regression lines describing FSH levels in the porcine serum (pS) controls and the pFF-injected rats intersect at 1.4 hours after injection. Since the initial half-life of circulating FSH following hypophysectomy is about 120 minutes (Gay *et al.*, 1970), it appears that pFF begins to suppress FSH secretion within minutes following injection.

The chronically ovariectomized rat also shows FSH-suppression following folliculostatin administration (Fig. 3). Maximum suppression is seen 10 hours following injection in either ovariectomized (Campbell and Schwartz, 1979) or orchidectomized (Lorenzen *et al.*, 1981) rats. By 24

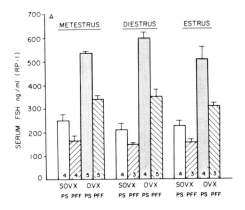

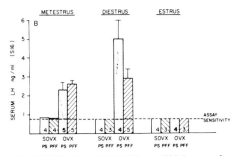

FIG. 5. Serum levels of FSH (A) and LH (B) at 1700 hours of metestrus, diestrus, or estrus following surgery and injection that morning. Surgery was performed at 0800 hours. SOVX, Sham-ovariectomy; OVX, ovariectomy. Either porcine serum (pS) or porcine follicular fluid (pFF) (62.5 μl) was injected iv at 1130 hours, 5.5 hours before sacrifice by decapitation. The number of rats per group is shown at the bottom of each bar. Group means plus standard errors are depicted. LH assay detectability was 0.75 ng/ml; FSH assay detectability was 130 ng/ml. Only serum FSH was suppressed by pFF. These data are taken from Grady *et al.* (1981), reproduced by permission.

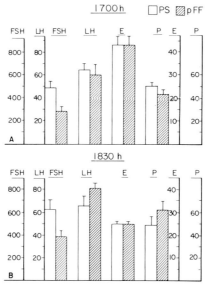

FIG. 6.   Serum levels of FSH (ng/ml—RP1), LH (ng/ml—S16), estradiol (pg/ml), and progesterone (ng/ml) at 1700 hours (A) or 1830 hours (B) of proestrus in animals which had received 1 ml of either porcine serum (pS) or porcine follicular fluid (pFF) earlier that day. Injections were given intraperitoneally at 1200 hours. Only serum FSH levels were reduced by pFF; other hormone levels remained unchanged. These data appeared in another form in Hoffmann *et al.* (1979).

hours after injection, the effect on serum FSH has subsided. No suppression of LH is seen at any time in males (Lorenzen *et al.*, 1981) or females (Campbell and Schwartz, 1979). We have recently conducted a study, using cannulated rats, which followed the detailed time course of both serum FSH and LH after three doses of pFF (Grady, Charlesworth, and Schwartz, unpublished observations). The reasons for carrying out this compulsive "pharmacological" study were (a) to examine the duration and intensity of FSH suppression as a function of intravenous dose and (b) to test the effect on serum LH in a recipient with high LH levels during a prolonged time interval after treatment. Serum gonadotrophin levels in four rats, each treated with a different pFF dose, are depicted in Fig. 9. Serum FSH was suppressed in proportion to pFF dose, and duration of suppression was proportional to dose in these and the other rats in the study. Serum LH showed some variation with time [probably due to the circhoral LH oscillations observed in ovariectomized rats (Gay and Sheth, 1972)], but no consistent changes occurred related to dose of pFF.

Finally, the singular rise in serum FSH, which occurs after unilateral ovariectomy (Fig. 2) and is not suppressible by progesterone or estradiol

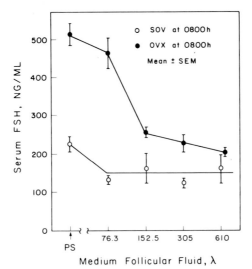

FIG. 7. Serum FSH levels (RP1) at 1700 hours metestrus following surgery and injection that morning. Surgery was performed at 0800 hours. SOV, Sham-ovariectomy; OVX, ovariectomy. Animals received an intraperitoneal injection at 1130 hours of either porcine serum (PS) or various doses (λ or μl) of follicular fluid harvested from medium-size follicles. Means ± SEM are shown; $N = 4$ rats per point. FF caused a dose-dependent decrease in serum FSH levels. This figure is reproduced from Marder *et al.* (1977) by permission.

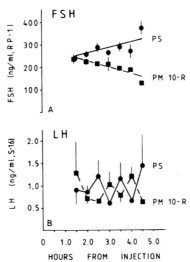

FIG. 8. Serum levels of FSH (A) and LH (B) in rats, which were ovariectomized at 0800 hours and received 0.5 ml porcine serum (pS) or the >10,000 MW fraction of pFF (PM 10-R) at 1130 hours on metestrus. Animals were sacrificed by decapitation 1.5–5.5 hours following injection. Group averages ± SEM are depicted. These data were presented in abstract form at the Society for the Study of Reproduction Meetings, Ann Arbor, MI, 1980 (Savoy-Moore *et al.*, 1980b).

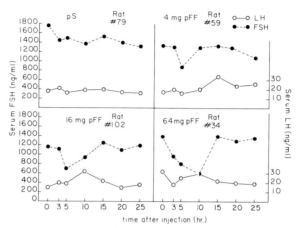

FIG. 9. Serum FSH (RP1) and LH (S16) levels in four chronically ovariectomized (14 days) female rats, 0–25 hours after receiving porcine serum (pS) or 4, 16, or 64 mg protein of porcine follicular fluid (pFF) at 0800 hours. Illustrated are values for one representative animal in each treatment group (Grady, Charlesworth, and Schwartz, unpublished observations).

(Butcher, 1977; Welschen *et al.*, 1978), is suppressible by bFF (Welschen *et al.*, 1978). Furthermore, bFF blocks compensatory testicular hypertrophy (Hopkinson *et al.*, 1977), which is assumed to result from the FSH elevation which follows unilateral castration (Ramirez and Sawyer, 1974).

Follicular fluid or ovarian extracts have also been shown to suppress serum FSH levels in the monkey (di Zerega and Hodgen, 1981), hamster (Chappel, 1979), mouse (Bronson and Channing, 1978), and horse (Miller *et al.*, 1979). Follicular fluid or ovarian derivatives from the following species have been shown to be active in suppressing FSH secretion: pig (vide supra), cow (de Jong and Sharpe, 1976), human (Chappel *et al.*, 1980), hamster (Chappel, 1979), mouse (Bronson and Channing, 1978), rat (Erickson and Hsueh, 1978), and horse (Miller *et al.*, 1979). We are, in fact, unaware of any reports of follicular fluid from any species failing to suppress FSH selectively in a female recipient.

To summarize the characteristics of the *in vivo* action of folliculostatin from follicular fluid:

1. Follicular fluid from many mammalian species suppresses FSH secretion significantly and selectively when injected intraperitoneally or intravenously in intact, bilaterally ovariectomized or unilaterally ovariectomized recipients.

2. The degree of FSH suppression is proportional to the dose administered whether or not the ovaries are present in the recipient (Figs. 7 and 9)

(Schwartz and Channing, 1977; Campbell and Schwartz, 1979; Grady *et al.*, 1981).

3. The latency for FSH suppression by pFF administered intravenously is only 1.4 hour (Fig. 8), close to the half-life of serum FSH (Gay *et al.*, 1970). The duration of action of a single high dose, injected intraperitoneally into a gonadectomized recipient, is between 14.5 and 24 hours (Campbell and Schwartz, 1979; Lorenzen *et al.*, 1981). The duration of action after intravenous injection is shorter, but is equally dose-dependent (Fig. 9).

4. Highly significant suppression of serum FSH levels is possible following follicular fluid injection without any significant change in serum LH (Figs. 3, 4, 5, 6, 8, and 9). A few studies, however, have demonstrated a shift in serum LH as well. Repeated high doses of pFF given to rats at proestrus (De Paolo *et al.*, 1979b; Rush *et al.*, 1981) or diestrus (Schwartz, 1981), can partially suppress LH levels. In pFF-treated gonadectomized rats, we have sometimes seen a slight rise in serum LH above pS-control levels after the FSH suppression has ended, but the effects on LH are not statistically significant (Campbell and Schwartz, 1979; Lorenzen *et al.*, 1981). Equine FF sometimes causes an elevation of serum LH (Miller *et al.*, 1979). No consistent effect of FF on serum LH levels can be demonstrated, while overwhelming evidence points to a highly significant and selective suppression of serum FSH levels.

B. *In Vitro* STUDIES

In elegant studies, the Steinbergers first demonstrated that cocultures of Sertoli cells and anterior pituitary cells resulted in selective suppression of FSH synthesis and secretion (Steinberger and Steinberger, 1976; Chowdhury *et al.*, 1978). Follicular fluid (porcine or bovine) has also been shown to suppress FSH secretion in primary pituitary cell cultures derived from rat pituitaries (Lagacé *et al.*, 1979; de Jong *et al.*, 1979a; De Paolo *et al.*, 1979a). Similarly, human follicular fluid suppresses FSH secretion by hamster pituitary cells (Chappel *et al.*, 1980), and medium from rat or porcine granulosa cell cultures inhibits the pituitary secretion of FSH (Erickson and Hsueh, 1978; Anderson and De Paolo, 1981).

The effect of follicular fluid has been tested on both basal cell cultures and GnRH-challenged cultures. These two test systems show differences with respect to folliculostatin's specificity. Two such published studies are illustrated in Figs. 10 and 11. In both studies the <10,000 MW and the >10,000 MW fractions of follicular fluid, separated by ultrafiltration, were tested. Whole follicular fluid or the >10,000 MW fraction causes a highly specific suppression of FSH secretion in basal cell cultures; there is either

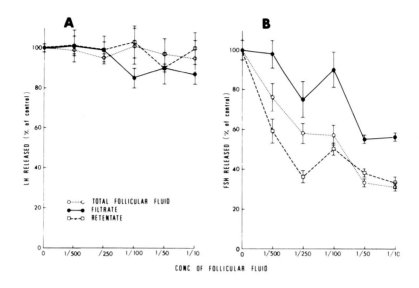

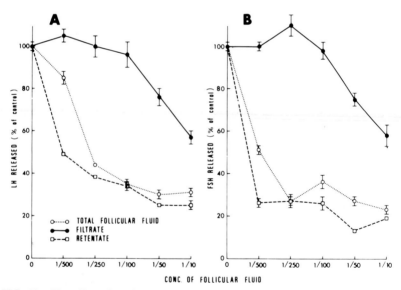

FIG. 10. The effect of total porcine follicular fluid, the <10,000 MW fraction (filtrate), and the >10,000 MW fraction (retentate) of follicular fluid on LH (A) and FSH (B) release from pituitary cell cultures. Results are shown for both basal cultures (top panel) and cultures treated with 0.3 nM GnRH (bottom panel). These data are reprinted from Legacé *et al.* (1979) by permission.

no suppression of LH (Fig. 10), or an enhancement of LH secretion (Fig. 11). On the other hand, crude and fractionated FF suppress both LH and FSH secretion in GnRH-stimulated cultures. Recall that the <10,000 MW fraction of pFF (Lorenzen *et al.*, 1978) or bFF (de Jong and Sharpe, 1976) is essentially without effect on LH or FSH secretion *in vivo*, and LH suppression or enhancement is rare *in vivo* (vide supra). Therefore, the results obtained in the basal cell culture appear to reflect the *in vivo* situation more closely than do those of GnRH-challenged cultures.

It would be instructive at this point to examine a detailed study, which was carried out by Scott and Burger (1981), on the effects of ovine testicular lymph inhibin (Fig. 12). In pituitary cell cultures, under basal conditions, testicular inhibin suppresses FSH secretion specifically, while both LH and FSH secretion are suppressed in GnRH-stimulated cultures. As can be seen in Fig. 12, inhibin lowers cell content of FSH, implying an effect on FSH synthesis, as well as secretion. Chowdhury *et al.* (1978) demonstrated this directly, using Sertoli cell factor to inhibit the incorporation of labeled leucine into FSH. Testicular inhibin does not alter LH content (Fig. 12). Scott and Burger (1981) feel that the effect on cell content of FSH is the most specific "inhibin" action measurable *in vitro*.

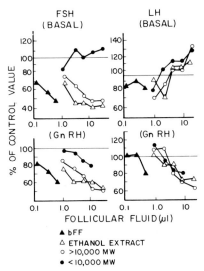

FIG. 11. The effects of whole bovine follicular fluid (bFF), an acid-ethanol extract of bFF, and the <10,000 MW and >10,000 MW fractions derived from the acid-ethanol extract of bFF, on FSH (right) and LH (left) release from pituitary cell cultures. Results are shown for both basal cultures (top panel) and cultures treated with 50 ng GnRH (bottom panel). These data are redrawn, with permission, from de Jong *et al.* (1979a).

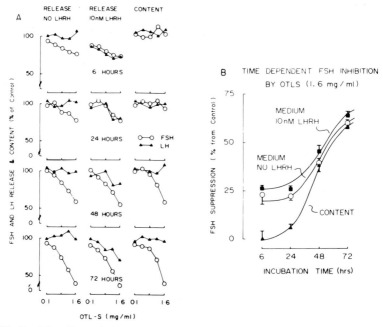

FIG. 12. The effects of ovine testicular lymph (OTL-S) on FSH and LH release and cell content in pituitary cell cultures, incubated with or without 10 nM LHRH, 6, 24, 48, and 72 hours after the addition of OTL-S. These data are reprinted, with permission, from Scott and Burger (1981).

C. DOES FOLLICULOSTATIN AFFECT LH SECRETION?

As reviewed above, follicular fluid is remarkably specific in suppressing serum FSH without altering serum LH (Figs. 3, 4, 5, 6, and 8). The following study clearly illustrates this fact. In a large series of experiments, we showed that pFF significantly suppressed serum FSH in intact male rats or in males which had been castrated 17 hours or longer (Lorenzen *et al.*, 1981). Serum LH values (group means) of pFF-treated animals are plotted against those of the corresponding pS-treated control group in Fig. 13. As can be seen, group means in individual experiments may fall well above or below the line of equality, suggesting "enhancement" or "suppression" of LH by pFF. The regression line describing the correlation between LH values in pFF and pS-treated groups, however, does not deviate from equality.

Follicular fluid also elicits a specific FSH suppression *in vitro* when basal conditions are used (Figs. 9 and 10). GnRH treatment may render the pituitary cells less selective in their response to folliculostatin per se,

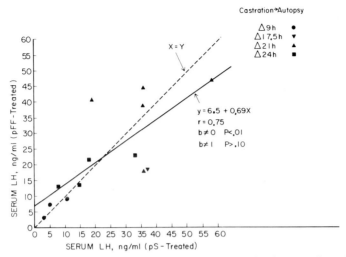

FIG. 13. The correlation between average serum LH levels (S16) in pS- and pFF-treated orchidectomized male rats. Injections were made intraperitoneally 5.5 to 16 hours before autopsy. Animals were sacrificed 9, 17.5, 21, and 24 hours after orchidectomy. The dashed line indicates theoretical equality ($X = Y$). The solid line is the regression line calculated from the data. The slope of this regression line is not significantly different from 1, but it is significantly greater than zero. These data appeared in another form in Lorenzen *et al.* (1981).

or more prone to other, possibly toxic, substances in the impure follicular fluid.

A paradox is thus apparent between the *in vivo* and *in vitro* experiments. *In vivo* secretion of both LH and FSH is considered to be under GnRH control, yet folliculostatin selectively affects FSH *in vivo*. At present, the paradox is unresolved. The few reported cases of follicular fluid-induced LH suppression *in vivo* result from the use of high doses which may contain more nonspecific "contaminating" substances. Alternatively, LH suppression *in vivo* may occur only on a background of high GnRH levels, such as at proestrus (De Paolo *et al.*, 1979b; Rush *et al.*, 1980). Additionally, however, it must be pointed out that several experiments have suggested that *in vivo*, the secretion of FSH is less critically dependent than is LH on the minute to minute secretion of GnRH (Kawakami and Higuchi, 1979; Elias and Blake, 1980). Therefore, "basal" or low GnRH-challenged cultures may more accurately reflect the usual situation *in vivo*.

IV. Should Folliculostatin Be Awarded the Status of a Hormone?

There are four kinds of evidence suggesting that the substance in follicular fluid which causes specific FSH suppression *in vivo* and *in vitro* may

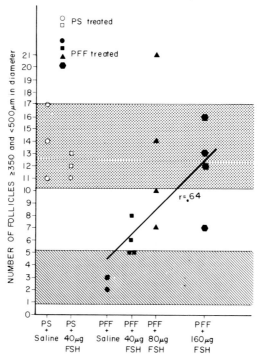

FIG. 14.   Follicular recruitment after treatment with exogenous FSH and pS (open symbols) or pFF (solid symbols). The 95% confidence intervals for all follicles 350–500 μm in diameter (in one ovary at 1100 hours estrus) is represented for pS-treated animals (stippled area) and for pFF-treated animals (hatched area) from a preceding study in which FSH replacement therapy had not occurred. The number of follicles 350–500 μm in diameter from one ovary of each individual animal in the treatment groups in this study is plotted as individual points. This figure is reprinted from Hoak and Schwartz (1980).

be a hormone. The first line of evidence has already been presented. Estradiol is not an adequate candidate as the sole negative feedback signal for FSH control in intact animals. Estradiol administration fails to suppress FSH as effectively as LH in animals lacking ovaries. On the other hand, follicular fluid serves as excellent replacement therapy to suppress serum FSH in the acutely (Fig. 7) or chronically ovariectomized rat (Fig. 3; Campbell and Schwartz, 1979). Follicular fluid also suppresses the already low serum FSH values seen in intact females (Fig. 7) and males (Lorenzen *et al.*, 1981). Since follicular fluid contains many substances which have local ovarian effects in addition to FSH-suppressing activity, questions have been raised about ovarian effects of pFF injection. We have demonstrated, in the rat, that the recruitment of a new cohort of follicles by the morning of estrus can be prevented by pFF-induced suppression of the secondary FSH surge (Hoak and Schwartz, 1980). This effect of pFF can be reversed by simultaneous treatment with exogenous FSH, a powerful argument against this ovarian effect being due to a factor other than folliculostatin activity or a toxic effect (Fig. 14).

The second line of evidence, more direct, is the changes in concentration of folliculostatin activity in follicular fluid or ovarian extracts which occur with changes in follicle size or cycle stage. (It is necessary to recognize, of course, that change in gland content of a substance cannot be used as direct evidence for parallel or inverse change in secretion rate.) The concentration of folliculostatin in pFF (slaughterhouse material) is lower in large (10 mm) follicles than in medium or small follicles (Lorenzen *et al.*, 1978). Follicular fluid collected during the human menstrual cycle shows the highest concentration of folliculostatin activity during the follicular, rather than the luteal, phase (Chappel *et al.*, 1980). Fluid collected from bovine ovaries during the early luteal phase contains more folliculostatin than during mid-luteal or estrous phases (Ireland, personal communication; Fig. 15). Fluid collected from equine ovaries has less folliculostatin activity when taken from atretic than from healthy follicles (Channing *et al.*, 1981).

A third line of evidence on the possible hormonal nature of folliculostatin comes from measurements of FSH-suppressing activity in periph-

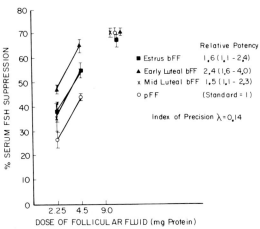

FIG. 15. The *in vivo* FSH-suppressing activity of bovine follicular fluid (bFF) collected at three different ovarian cycle stages, compared against that of porcine follicular fluid. See text for details of our bioassay. $N = 4$ rats/recipient group. Slaughterhouse bovine ovaries were classified estrus, early luteal, or mid-luteal on the basis of ovarian morphology (Ireland, 1981). All preparations had parallel effects. All three bFF preparations had significantly more activity/mg protein than pFF. "Early luteal" bFF was significantly more potent than bFF collected from mid-luteal or estrus ovaries (Ireland, unpublished data).

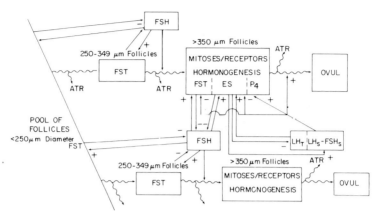

FIG. 16. Model of regulation of FSH secretion during sequential cycles in the rat. FST, Folliculostatin; ES, estradiol; P_4, progesterone; LH_T, tonic LH secretion; LH_S and FSH_S, primary surges of the gonadotrophins; ATR, atresia. Reprinted by permission from Schwartz (1981).

From left to right, horizontally, a cohort of follicles is traced as it is recruited from the pool of ovarian follicles <250 μm in diameter. As one moves down vertically, the drawing shows the secondary FSH surge of the last cycle to the present cycle, and then the recruitment of follicles is shown for the next cycle. Folliculostatin is hypothesized to be secreted by granulosa cells of follicles of all sizes. A cohort of a particular follicular size secretes folliculostatin in proportion to its total number of cells, which is proportional to its total volume. In rats with both ovaries intact, there appears to be no variation in number of cells or volume across the cycle, in the pool of follicles under <349 μm in diameter, except for the primordial follicles which, of course, decline slowly in numbers with age. This slow decline is not reflected in elevated serum FSH values until very late in reproductive life (Sherman and Korenman, 1975), since large follicles contribute most of the folliculostatin (Schwartz, 1981).

The secondary FSH surge of the previous cycle recruits the cohort of follicles (diameter above 350 μm; Fig. 4), which will provide the major contribution to estradiol and folliculostatin secretion for the next cycle. Once estradiol has reached a sufficient level to trigger the preovulatory surges of LH and FSH, germinal vesicle breakdown occurs, estradiol and folliculostatin secretion cease, progesterone secretion starts, and the secondary FSH surge recruits the cohort of follicles for the next cycle. The drop in folliculostatin secretion after the primary surge was predicted by Schwartz and Talley (1978) and confirmed by Shander *et al.* (1980). Atresia occurs in all of these classes of follicles.

The model accounts for a number of experimental findings. The data on unilateral ovariectomy and follicle counts indicate that the largest cohort of follicles (>350 μm) in the remaining ovary is brought up to the volume equal to that normally found in two ovaries when serum FSH returns to normal [28 hours postunilateral ovariectomy, Welschen *et al.* (1980)]. The responsiveness of serum FSH secretion to shifts in ovarian negative feedback is postulated to be due to tight negative feedback control by follicular secretion of folliculostatin, in proportion to numbers of granulosa cells in the ovary. Serum FSH rebounds after the primary surge (producing the secondary surge) or after exogenous folliculostatin, because growth of granulosa cells and follicles is initially suppressed. This results in lack of endogenous feedback and leads to increased FSH secretion and follicular stimulation. FSH can be eral or ovarian vein blood. Basal cell pituitary cultures have been used to assay the activity. Lee *et al.* (1981) have demonstrated a rise in peripheral plasma folliculostatin activity following PMSG treatment in immature female rats. In order to run a valid bioassay, they had to pool serum at each time point following PMSG treatment, thus losing any individual variation in circulating activity. Another series of papers has appeared in which folliculostatin activity in ovarian vein plasma in the rat has been measured at only one dose of test substance. During the estrous cycle, the FSH-suppressing ability of ovarian vein plasma changes only late in proestrus, after the primary gonadotrophin surges (De Paolo *et al.*, 1979a). This decrease is prevented by barbiturate and can be overcome by injection of LH or FSH (Shander *et al.*, 1980). Unilateral ovariectomy leads to an increase in folliculostatin activity in ovarian vein plasma (Anderson and De Paolo, 1981). While these data on blood levels of folliculostatin are preliminary, they do suggest an inverse correlation between serum levels of FSH and of folliculostatin activity. We have presented a general theory of folliculostatin secretion (Schwartz, 1981); a brief summary of that theory can be found in Fig. 16 and the legend to that figure.

A fourth line of evidence comes from an intriguing article by Uilenbroek *et al.* (1978). These authors transplanted ovaries to the kidney or spleen of adult ovariectomized rats. Ovarian transplants to the kidney suppress both serum LH and FSH. However, ovarian transplants to the spleen, which do not restore peripheral estrogen levels due to clearance of steroidal products by the liver (Greep and Jones, 1950), restore serum FSH levels to low tonic values, while serum LH rises even further! These data strongly suggest that the ovary secretes a hormone, at least when it is in the splanchnic circulation, which can suppress FSH without suppressing LH.

Thus, there is evidence that the ovary may secrete a circulating hormone with the characteristics we have observed for folliculostatin following its injection *in vivo*. Of course, the substance may have important local functions as well.

---

suppressed at any time of the cycle in the intact animal (Figs. 5, 6, and 7), the bilaterally ovariectomized rat (Figs. 2, 7, and 9), and the unilaterally ovariectomized rat by pFF (Welschen *et al.*, 1978). Thus, the effect of folliculostatin in suppressing FSH can be expressed regardless of the point in the cycle at which follicle growth exists.

For further elucidation of the data which underlie this model, see the original article (Schwartz, 1981) and experimental observations in Anderson and De Paolo (1981), Ashiru and Blake (1980), Ayalon *et al.* (1972), De Paolo *et al.* (1979b), Erickson and Hsueh (1978), Hoak and Schwartz (1980), Lee *et al.* (1981), Ramirez and Sawyer (1974), Schwartz and Channing (1977), Schwartz and Talley (1978), Shander *et al.* (1980), Sherman and Korenman (1975), Uilenbroek *et al.* (1978), and Welschen *et al.* (1978, 1980).

V. Criteria for a Bioassay for Folliculostatin

The purpose of this section is to evaluate the bioassays which have been used in attempts to characterize folliculostatin. It seems worthwhile to review this material because of the hitherto unsuccessful search for an FSH-suppressing substance from the testes for more than 50 years. In fact, not all are persuaded that such a hormone actually exists. A number of recent reviews have discussed a probable cause of the slow progress in purifying testicular inhibin—i.e., the failure to use a valid assay which is reliable, specific, and quantitative. First-rate reviews of the subject are by Baker *et al.* (1981), de Jong (1979), de Jong *et al.* (1979b), Hudson *et al.* (1979), and Franchimont *et al.* (1979). Accordingly, it is important to launch the field of folliculostatin purification with attention to this issue.

Figure 17 summarizes the arguments for and against utilization of four classes of bioassays which have been employed for purification of ovarian or testicular FSH-suppressing substance. *In vivo* bioassays are those in which folliculostatin is injected into a test animal and serum FSH is measured directly by radioimmunoassay, or indirectly, by *in situ* tissue "assays" for FSH actions. The *in vitro* assays utilize dispersed pituitary cells in primary culture, and the effect of folliculostatin on FSH secretion is assessed under basal conditions or during a GnRH challenge.

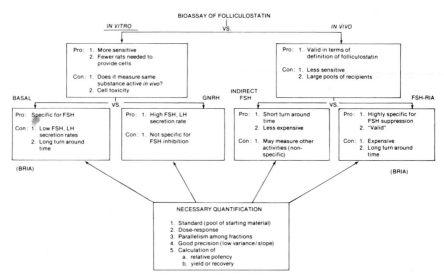

FIG. 17. Summary of the kinds of bioassays proposed and used for purification of folliculostatin (and testicular inhibin). As the figure illustrates, two general kinds of assays have been carried out—*in vivo,* shown on the right, where animals are directly injected with ovarian derivatives, or *in vitro,* shown on the left, where pituitary cells are exposed to ovarian derivatives. Other points shown in the figure are discussed in the text.

Before discussing the four basic types of assays, a major caveat should be stated. Regardless of the bioassay system which is selected for following the purification of folliculostatin, quantification of the results is essential. Besides the monitoring of biological activity during purification, the relative specific activity of the resulting fractions and yield of activity need to be calculated. The failure to quantify bioassay results adequately has probably contributed to the failure, thus far, to purify inhibin from testicular sources.

We have been using a direct FSH-RIA *in vivo* bioassay for several years to characterize folliculostatin from porcine follicular fluid. The assay is a modification of that previously published (Marder *et al.*, 1977; Lorenzen *et al.*, 1978). On a day of metestrus, the recipient rat is ovariectomized at 0800 hours, and the test material is injected intravenously (tail vein) at 1130 hours, 3.5 hours following ovariectomy. At 1700 hours, 5.5 hours after injection, the female is decapitated and serum FSH measured in trunk blood by the standard 7-day equilibrium assay. Figure 18 displays several recent dose–response curves. There is a slight loss of folliculosta-

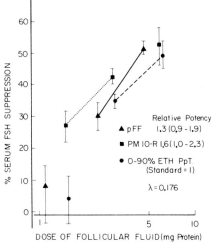

FIG. 18. Percentage serum suppression of FSH in our *in vivo* bioradioimmunoassay. Three doses of each protein were injected, but only two doses of each were on the linear portion of the curve. Percentage FSH suppression is calculated in this assay, and in other assays summarized in this review (Figs. 15, 19, 21, 22, 23, and 24), for each rat given test material in comparison to the average serum FSH value for the pS-treated controls within the assays. All injected fluids had been charcoal extracted to remove steroids. PM10-R is the retentate (>10,000 MW) remaining after Amicon filtration, using a PM-10 membrane. The 0–90% ethanol precipitate used PM10-R fluid as starting material. Protein concentration in injected materials was 75.4, 189.7, 142.4 (mg protein/ml fluid) in pFF, PM10-R, and ethanol precipitate, respectively. The data were analyzed at two doses of standard and test substances, using standard statistical procedures, according to Bliss (1968).

tin activity when it is precipitated with 90% ethanol, but this powder is a very convenient laboratory standard. The index of precision (λ) of this particular assay was 0.176, which is adequate for quantification.

The *in vivo* assay is highly specific for FSH-suppression (Figs. 5 and 8), and thus appears to be a valid assay. It is expensive, owing to the large pool of rats which must be followed for a metestrous vaginal smear, and the FSH-RIA. There is also a long turnaround time between a given purification step and availability of final serum FSH values. Most of this time is consumed by the FSH radioimmunoassay itself. Our standard FSH-RIA is 7 days in length. On day 1, cold FSH and FSH antibody (NIH-anti-rat) are added; 24 hours later, ^{125}I-labeled FSH is added; 48 hours later, second antibody is added; and 48 hours later, samples are centrifuged and counted. In order to shorten the turnaround time, we have tested a 48-hour nonequilibrium FSH assay performed at room temperature (i.e., a "miniassay"). A comparison of the results obtained on the same serum samples with the two radioimmunoassays for FSH is seen in Fig. 19. Serum from rats injected with pFF fractions from a Sephacryl S-300 column was measured by both RIAs. As can be seen from the top panel of Fig. 19, the miniassay overestimated serum FSH levels by about 100 ng/ml. Relative potency calculated from a three-point assay of the fractions was proportional between the two assays, although the absolute value of relative potency was underestimated by the miniassay. We find the miniassay useful to reduce overall assay time and to obtain a preliminary estimate of fraction potencies, but run a backup equilibrium assay on the serum samples.

Several investigators employ an "indirect" *in vivo* bioassay for folliculostatin, utilizing suppression of ovarian compensatory hypertrophy (Sato *et al.*, 1978), or a "reversed Steelman–Pohley type" assay (Chari *et al.*, 1976, 1978; Sato *et al.*, 1980) which measures ovarian or uterine weight in rats or mice injected with hCG plus the test fraction. These indirect assays of suppression of endogenous FSH release are less expensive than the direct FSH *in vivo* assay (Fig. 18) and have a shorter turnaround time. Why not use them?

The basic problem, we believe, lies in the large number of factors present in follicular fluid. In addition to steroids, proteoglycans, and many proteins (Edwards, 1974), a number of factors have been identified which can *directly* alter gonadal and pituitary function (see Franchimont and Channing, 1981). Follicular fluid can inhibit the binding of LH (Yang *et al.*, 1976) and FSH (Darga and Reichert, 1978) to receptors in ovarian membranes. It can enhance or inhibit luteinization (Ledwitz-Rigby *et al.*, 1977). It can prevent resumption of meiosis in cultured oocytes (Tsafriri *et al.*, 1976). Follicular fluid also contains substances which compete for

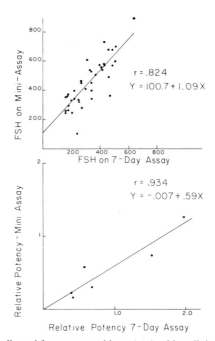

FIG. 19. Serum, collected from rats used in an *in vivo* bioradioimmunoassay of fractions from a Sephacryl S-300 column, was measured for FSH concentration on the standard 7-day RIA and on the 2-day miniassay RIA described in the text. The upper graph depicts the regression analysis of the FSH values obtained on each sample by the two RIA techniques. The lower graph depicts the regression between the estimates of relative potency obtained by the two assays.

GnRH ligand (Ying *et al.*, 1981a), and substances which can enhance LH or FSH secretion as well as inhibit it (Ying *et al.*, 1981b). In the presence of these substances, can one afford to measure folliculostatin or inhibin activity using indirect criteria for FSH such as decreases in ovarian or uterine weight?

The problem can be visualized by examining a pair of papers from the laboratory of Sato (Fig. 20). Sato *et al.* (1978) carried out a series of purification steps of folliculostatin activity in porcine follicular fluid. They employed the suppression of compensatory ovarian hypertrophy (COH) as a bioassay. Presumably, the sequence of events which leads to hypertrophy of the remaining ovary after unilateral removal are (a) a reduction in a negative feedback signal from the ovary (not estradiol, Fig. 2), which (b) induces an elevation in serum FSH, which (c) causes ovarian growth (i.e., follicle recruitment; see Schwartz, 1981). [Probably LH is also necessary for this ovarian growth, since estradiol can prevent the compensatory

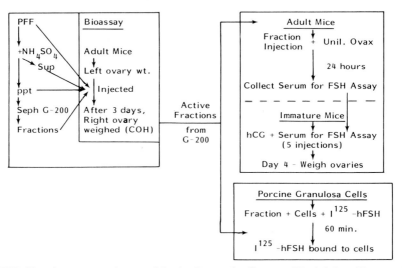

FIG. 20. A summary of two articles by Sato and colleagues. The left box (Sato *et al.*, 1978) depicts their purification scheme for pFF, and also summarizes the indirect FSH bioassay used—compensatory ovarian hypertrophy (COH) in adult mice. The right boxes (Sato *et al.*, 1980) summarize the assays used to test further the active fraction from the G-200 column. In the upper box, it can be seen that adult mice, which had been unilaterally ovariectomized, were injected with the test substance, and after 24 hours, serum was removed and tested in a Steelman–Pohley type bioassay for FSH. In the bottom right box, the test for FSH-binding inhibition ability of the fraction is summarized.

hypertrophy without blocking the elevation of FSH (Ramirez and Sawyer, 1974).] In any case, the "active" fraction from a Sephadex G-200 column was then tested (Sato *et al.*, 1980) in two systems simultaneously—an *in vitro* granulosa cell culture to measure interference with labeled FSH binding and an *in vivo* system again to measure the folliculostatin or inhibin activity. In the latter system (Fig. 20, top right panel), the fraction was injected into unilaterally ovariectomized mice, and serum was collected from the recipient mice 24 hours after injection. This serum was, in turn, injected into hCG-treated immature mice, and ovarian weight was measured 3 days after injection (a Steelman–Pohley type bioassay for FSH). This "active" fraction caused serum from recipient mice to inhibit ovarian weight growth in hCG-treated immature mice. It also inhibited binding of FSH to granulosa cells, as pointed out by Sato *et al.* (1980). Since ovarian weight was used in the initial COH assay for following purification steps, the initial fraction purified could have included a FSH receptor binding inhibitor (Darga and Reichert, 1978) in addition to a substance which directly suppresses FSH secretion. Furthermore, serum FSH, at least in the rat, is no longer elevated 24 hours postunilateral ovariectomy (see Fig. 2), the time when serum was collected from FF fraction recipients for FSH bioassay (Fig. 20). Sato *et al.* (1980) conclude "this inhibitor from porcine follicular fluid may act in the following two ways: suppression of FSH levels in the serum and inhibition of FSH binding to the receptor." Present information suggests that the FSH binding inhibitor found in pFF is under 10,000 MW (Darga and Reichert, 1978), but that the FSH suppressing activity is over 10,000 MW, whether tested *in vitro* (Figs. 10 and 11) or *in vivo* (de Jong and Sharpe, 1976; Lorenzen *et al.*, 1978). Use of an indirect assessment of FSH suppression leaves open the question of what is actually being measured. Alterations in the end-point, which is ovarian function in the test animal, may reflect effects other than the direct suppression of FSH secretion.

Using the direct *in vivo* assay (Fig. 16), we avoid, at least to an extent, the issue of contaminants in pFF. We have shown that pFF does not interfere with the radioimmunoassay for FSH (Table I), and does not contain neuraminidase activity (which might cause enhanced FSH clearance from the blood) (Ward *et al.*, 1981). In addition, follicular fluid does

TABLE I

Recovery of FSH in Rat Serum in the Presence of Porcine Serum or Follicular Fluid[a]

Test porcine solution (μl)	Rat serum pool (150 μl)	FSH (RP-1) measured (ng)	Rat FSH recovered (ng)	Percentage recovery
None	+	28.6 ± 0.7 (191 ng/ml)	—	—
Porcine serum				
450	−	97.4	—	—
50	−	12.2	—	—
50	+	42.5	30.3	106
5	+	29.3	29.3	102
Porcine follicular fluid #1				
450	−	26.8	—	—
50	−	0[b]	—	—
50	+	30.4	30.4	106
5	+	27.9	27.9	98
Porcine follicular fluid #2				
450	−	19.1	—	—
50	−	0[b]	—	—
50	+	31.1	31.1	109
5	+	31.4	31.4	110

[a] Serum and pS or pFF were added together and then a regular FSH RIA was carried out. $N = 9$ for rat serum pool; $N = 3$ for all other measurements.

[b] Binding > 90% in RIA.

not alter estradiol or progesterone secretion by the *in situ* ovary, when given in a single injection in intact rats on any day of the cycle (Fig. 6, Table II). Because of the high steroid content in follicular fluid, steroids should be removed before injection. We have shown that charcoal extraction removes most of the steroids without inactivating folliculostatin activity (Fig. 21). Incidentally, Fig. 21 demonstrates that ether extraction to remove steroids interferes with folliculostatin activity. The effect of ether-extracted pFF did not parallel the effect of the starting material. Note that this finding would not have been possible if only one dose of ether-extracted pFF had been tested.

Let us now return to Fig. 17 and examine the *in vitro* bioassays proposed for folliculostatin and inhibin activity. They are certainly more sensitive than the *in vivo* technique. Two milligrams of protein of unpurified pFF (about 30 μl of original fluid) is necessary to obtain significant suppression *in vivo*, while 16 μg (0.15 μl) is adequate *in vitro* (Jansen *et al.*,

TABLE II

Serum Estradiol and Progesterone in Intact and Ovariectomized Rats following Treatment with Porcine Follicular Fluid[a,b]

	Estradiol (pg/ml)	Progesterone (ng/ml)
Metestrus		
SOVX + pS (4)	14.3 ± 1.8	43.5 ± 5.4
SOVX + pFF (4)	14.4 ± 0.8	33.1 ± 3.6
OVX + pS (5)	8.8 ± 0.1	11.9 ± 5.0
OVX + pFF (5)	12.7 ± 0.9	19.6 ± 6.2
Diestrus		
SOVX + pS (4)	20.6 ± 0.7	23.5 ± 5.4
SOVX + pFF (4)	13.0 ± 0.8	13.7 ± 3.3
OVX + pS (5)	9.6 ± 0.3	6.4 ± 1.3
OVX + pFF (6)	12.2 ± 1.4	10.6 ± 2.3
Estrus		
SOVX + pS (4)	9.3 ± 0.2	20.4 ± 3.3
SOVX + pFF (4)	14.1 ± 2.4	15.7 ± 2.9
OVX + pS (5)	9.5 ± 0.5	19.0 ± 6.6
OVX + pFF (6)	10.6 ± 0.5	10.1 ± 2.7

[a] Rats were ovariectomized (OVX) or sham-ovariectomized (SOVX) at 0800 hours on 3 days of the estrous cycle. At 1130 hours they received 62.5 μl of pS or pFF and were sacrificed at 1700 hours.

[b] $\overline{X}$ ± SEM. Values in parentheses are number of animals per group.

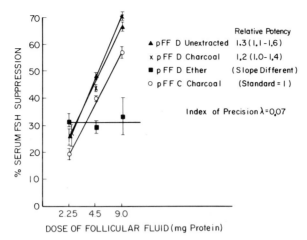

FIG. 21. The *in vivo* bioradioimmunoassay of two batches of pFF (C and D) tested at three doses of protein, after charcoal or ether extraction. The standard solution, C, had been charcoal extracted. Pool D was more potent than C, whether or not steroids were removed by charcoal, but ether extraction of steroids destroyed the dose dependency of D. Steroid and protein concentrations of the porcine serum and pFF D used in the assay are summarized below:

Source	Extraction	Estradiol (pg/ml)	Progesterone (pg/ml)	Testosterone (pg/ml)	Protein (mg/ml)
Porcine serum	None	20.3	3,900	80	—
	Charcoal	10.0	1,330	30	108
Porcine follicular fluid (Pool D)	None	20,800	255,000	32,200	88.8
	Charcoal	51.5	1,430	100	75.4
	Ether	149.0	2,480	130	91.7

1981). Thus, the *in vitro* system is about 100 times more sensitive. It is somewhat less expensive per fraction tested than the *in vivo* bioassay, because one rat can serve as a donor for about four wells of pituitary cells at 250,000 cells/well (Vale *et al.*, 1972). The turnaround time is about the same because the RIA for FSH in the medium is the same as that used for serum FSH. A possible drawback to use of the *in vitro* assays is the possibility that whatever suppresses FSH secretion (or cell content) *in vitro* is not the same substance as that which suppresses FSH secretion *in vivo*, but this seems unlikely. It should be pointed out, however, that inhibin from a testicular source can suppress FSH secretion after injection through the third ventricle (Lumpkin *et al.*, 1981). Also, exposure of pituitary cells to steroids *in vitro* does not yield the same results on rates of LH and FSH secretion as injection of steroids *in vivo* (Labrie *et al.*, 1978). Another possible drawback to the *in vitro* system is the susceptibility of cells to possible toxic substances in the impure fluids being tested (Baker *et al.*, 1981).

The basal cell culture seems more valid as an assessment for FSH-suppressing activity because it matches the effect seen *in vivo*, as was pointed out above. The GnRH-stimulated culture shows increases or decreases in both LH and FSH in response to FF in various hands (Ying *et al.*, 1981b; Sairam, 1981; Figs. 10, 11, and 12). The GnRH-stimulated system is more enticing to use, however, because of the low rate of FSH secretion under basal conditions. Basal FSH production, after 6 hours, is so low that it is not easy to detect a suppression of FSH in response to a test substance (Savoy-Moore, unpublished observations). Usually, in the basal cell culture, assay cells are exposed to medium containing test substance for 48 or 72 hours (de Jong *et al.*, 1979a; Scott and Burger, 1981; Baker *et al.*, 1981) to subvert this problem.

It appears to us that both the basal cell culture and the *in vivo* direct assays are specific, reliable, and adequate for quantification of FSH-suppressing activity in ovarian or testicular sources. We have called these "bioradioimmunoassays" (BRIA). We feel that the basal *in vitro* culture system shouid be used for routine testing of fractions, with a backup test *in vivo* as purification proceeds. In the following section, we will discuss the preliminary characterization–purification studies which have been carried out using the *in vivo* or *in vitro* BRIA.

VI. Purification and Characterization of Folliculostatin

The literature is replete with contradictory schemes on the purification of the FSH-suppressing activity found in ovarian and testicular sources. In the preceding section, we have discussed how indirect and unquantitative bioassays may have contributed to this confusion. Another problem with purification may be the wide variety of source materials studied. These include sperm (Lugaro *et al.*, 1973), seminal plasma (Chari *et al.*, 1978), rete testis fluid (Baker *et al.*, 1978), testicular lymph (Baker *et al.*, 1980), and testicular homogenates (Nandini *et al.*, 1976), as well as ovarian follicular fluid and ovarian extracts (vide infra). We will focus our discussion on the work performed in our laboratory, in collaboration with Darrell Ward and his colleagues, and by others on the purification and characterization of the FSH-suppressing activity derived from ovarian sources. For a comprehensive review, see the recent paper by de Jong *et al.* (1981).

Folliculostatin is not a steroid. In our hands, charcoal extraction of follicular fluid does not diminish folliculostatin activity. On the other hand, ether treatment to remove steroids may damage the molecule (Fig. 21). De Jong and Sharpe (1976) reported no differences in *in vivo* FSH-suppressing activity between whole bovine FF, ether-extracted FF, and charcoal-extracted FF, tested at one dose. Miller and co-workers (1979) reported a reduction in FSH-suppressing ability of equine FF tested in ovariectomized mares when the steroids were removed by ether or charcoal extraction procedures. No decrease in FSH levels was found following administration of an ether-soluble fraction of FF, however (Miller *et al.*, 1979), suggesting that the ether did not "extract" folliculostatin activity. Precipitation of FF with ethanol yields a product which is almost equipotent to starting material (Fig. 18). This also indicates that folliculostatin is not a steroid.

A plethora of data indicates that folliculostatin is proteinaceous in nature. Trypsin, pepsin, and papain have been used to destroy the FSH-suppressing activity derived from numerous testicular sources (see de Jong *et al.*, 1981). Lorenzen and co-workers (1978) showed that the activity in pFF was trypsin sensitive. While Hermans *et al.* (1980) could not destroy the folliculostatin activity in bFF with trypsin, the authors could digest the activity by pronase treatment. Folliculostatin appears to tolerate moderate elevations in temperature (55–60°C, 20–30 minutes), but is destroyed by higher temperatures (80–100°C, 30 minutes) (Lorenzen *et al.*, 1978; de Jong *et al.*, 1981).

Actually, folliculostatin activity appears to be quite stable in follicular fluid (Ward *et al.*, 1981). In the frozen state, activity is retained for at least 1 year. At 4°C, the activity is unchanged for at least 2 months, and at room temperature for at least 4 days. Results of pH stability studies indicate that folliculostatin is stable at pH 4–9.6.

Numerous investigators have asked, "What is the molecular weight of inhibin?" Answers obtained have ranged from 1500 to 160,000 (see Ward *et al.*, 1981). These widely ranging estimates probably arise from the variety of bioassays used to detect activity as well as the various source materials studied. Let us focus on the molecular weight estimates of the FSH-suppressing activity derived from follicular fluid and ovarian extracts.

Most of the studies in which FF is subjected to ultrafiltration and dialysis indicate that the active principle has a molecular weight of >10,000. This is true for FF of bovine (de Jong and Sharpe, 1976; de Jong *et al.*, 1981), porcine (Lorenzen *et al.*, 1978; Legacé *et al.*, 1979), hamster (Chappel *et al.*, 1979), and human (Batta *et al.*, 1978) origin. As mentioned previously, the <10,000 MW fraction of FF does not suppress FSH secretion either *in vivo* (de Jong and Sharpe, 1976; Lorenzen *et al.*, 1978) or *in vitro* in basal pituitary cell cultures (Legacé *et al.*, 1979; de Jong *et al.*, 1979b) (Figs. 11 and 12). The release of both LH and FSH in

GnRH-stimulated cultures is inhibited by high doses of the <10,000 MW fraction of FF (Legacé et al., 1979; de Jong et al., 1979b), but this could reflect susceptibility of this particular assay system to nonspecific toxic effects (Baker et al., 1981).

Several reports in the literature suggest that the molecular weight of folliculostatin might be between 10,000 and 35,000. Williams et al. (1979) subjected pFF to gel filtration on a Sephadex G-150 column. Using the acutely ovariectomized rat as a bioassay model, they reported that the active fraction was found in the range of 10,000 to 35,000. Chari et al. (1979) found that folliculostatin activity in human follicular fluid passed through an Amicon CF 25 filter, indicating a molecular weight less than 25,000. SDS–PAGE gave an estimate of 23,000. It should be noted, however, that an indirect bioassay was used by these authors to monitor biological activity. Chappel et al. (1979) studied folliculostatin activity in charcoal-treated hamster ovarian extracts. Molecular sieving of the ≥10,000 MW fraction of this material on Sephadex G-75 gave a molecular weight estimate of <30,000. GnRH-stimulated hamster pituitary cell cultures were used as the bioassay for activity. Jansen et al. (1981) recently reported that gel filtration of bFF on Sephadex G-75 gave rise to two active fractions, one at 75,000–35,000 MW range, the other at 35,000–14,000, when tested in basal cell cultures. SDS–PAGE of more purified fractions showed a strong band at 65,000, which gave rise to a 32,000 band after lyophilization or iodination. The biological activity of these bands was not tested, however.

With this cited literature in mind, we have performed an extensive series of experiments in collaboration with Darrell Ward and his colleagues to estimate the molecular weight of folliculostatin in pFF. All of our experiences to date, however, have indicated that we are dealing with a much larger molecule than is generally reported. To summarize experiments conducted over a 2.5-year period (Ward et al., 1981), the ≥10,000 MW fraction of pFF (PM 10 Retentate; PM 10-R) was initially subjected to molecular sieving on a BioGel P-30 column. All of the activity appeared to be in the higher molecular weight fraction. A BioGel P-60 column was used next; all of the activity was found at the front of the chromatogram on this column as well. Gel filtration on Sephadex G-100 and Sephadex G-200 was then performed, and the results indicated that folliculostatin has a high molecular weight.

Figure 22 illustrates our experience with gel filtration. The 90% ethanol precipitate of pFF was subjected to molecular sieving on a Sephacryl S-300 column (2.5 × 90 cm). The relative potencies of the collected fractions were estimated in our in vivo bioassay ($\lambda = 0.118$) in comparison to the starting material. Relative specific activity (mg/mg protein) was high-

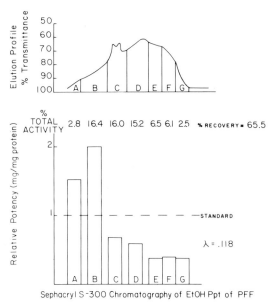

Sephacryl S-300 Chromatography of EtOH Ppt of PFF

FIG. 22. Sephacryl S-300 chromatography of the 90% ethanol precipitate (EtOH Ppt) of porcine follicular fluid (pFF). Shown are the elution profile (top), percentage of total activity in each fraction and percentage total recovery of activity (middle), and the relative potency of each fraction (bottom). EtOH Ppt (250 mg) was chromatographed on a 2.5 × 90 cm Sephacryl S-300 column. There was a 99% recovery of protein. Fractions were tested for folliculostatin activity in our *in vivo* BRIA (see text for bioassay details), and relative potency was calculated against two doses of EtOH Ppt as standard (standard activity = 1 mg/mg protein). The index of precision (λ) for this assay was 0.118.

est in the two fractions at the front of the chromatogram. However, relative potency was not greatly enhanced (only 2-fold), and recovery of activity was poor. Jansen *et al.* (1981) have reported similar results with chromatography of bFF on Sephadex G-75. These authors suggest that their poor recovery of activity could be attributed to interaction between the active protein and other proteins in the follicular fluid, or irreversible interaction of activity with the column material.

Since molecular exclusion procedures appear unable to provide a reliable estimate of molecular weight, we attempted to achieve this using radiation inactivation. Odell and colleagues (Odell *et al.*, 1964; Odell and Paul, 1965) used this technique to estimate accurately the molecular weight of the pituitary glycoprotein hormones prior to their purification and characterization.

The theoretical basis of the radiation inactivation technique is as follows (see Kempner and Schlegel, 1979, for a more extensive discussion of this methodology). It is assumed that any ionizing radiation which strikes a biologically active molecule will cause its inactivation (single hit theory). It is also assumed that the probability of a hit is a function of the target volume which, in turn, is a function of the molecular weight of the protein involved. The basic equation relating these variables is:

$$A = A_0 e^{-kD}$$

The activity (A) after a given dose of radiation (D in rads) is related to the initial activity (A_0) and the constant (k) in the exponent, which is related to the target size. The constant, k, can be experimentally estimated from the radiation required to reduce the biological activity to 37% of A_0. Kempner and Macey (1968) evaluated k based on determinations of enzyme or hormonal activities of known molecular weight substances and produced the following empirical formula:

$$\text{Molecular weight} = (6.4 \times 10^{11})/D_{37}$$

where D_{37} is the dose of radiation in rads required to reduce biological activity to 37% of A_0. Thus, molecular weight is inversely proportional to D_{37}.

An additional requirement for the single hit theory to remain valid is that the protein being tested must be in a dried form. Therefore, we used our 90% ethanol precipitate of pFF, which was lyophilized prior to irradiation, for this purpose.

We have performed this experiment several times. For our first attempt, we assumed a molecular weight of 20,000–30,000, and irradiation doses were chosen accordingly. The results obtained were reminiscent of our experiences with gel filtration. Even at the lowest radiation dose, folliculostatin activity was almost completely inactivated, thus suggesting a larger molecular weight than was anticipated. Therefore, the irradiation treatment periods were shortened in our second attempt (Fig. 23). In this experiment, we were able to estimate a D_{37} of 3.5×10^6 rads for folliculostatin inactivation and a molecular weight of 182,000 (Ward et al., 1981). We have repeated this experiment and subsequent results have corroborated the findings reported here. These data are being prepared for publication by Ward and co-workers.

These results indicate that the biological activity we measure in our in vivo bioassay, and refer to as folliculostatin, is associated with a large molecule. This does not preclude the possibility that folliculostatin is composed of subunits or has some other type of aggregated structure. These results do indicate, however, that the entire complex or "functional unit" is required for biological activity.

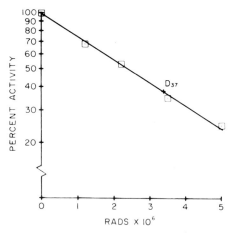

FIG. 23. Radiation inactivation curve for folliculostatin. Irradiation was delivered from a ^{137}Cs source, generating a dose of 5490 rads/minute. Aliquots (100 mg) of the 90% ethanol precipitate of pFF were irradiated at each dose of radiation. Samples were tested for folliculostatin activity in our *in vivo* BRIA (see text for bioassay details), and potency calculated against two doses of nonirradiated ethanol precipitate. See text for a discussion of the theory underlying radiation inactivation and the equations for calculation of molecular weight. These data are reprinted with permission from Ward *et al.* (1981).

The results of the radiation inactivation studies have been corroborated by the results of sucrose gradient ultracentrifugation of the ethanol precipitate of pFF (EtOH Ppt) (Fig. 24). The EtOH Ppt was layered on a 5–25% sucrose gradient (pH 7.4). A mixture of known molecular weight markers was treated similarly. After ultracentrifugation (200,000 g for 8 hours), fractions were tested in our *in vivo* bioassay ($\lambda = 0.189$) against EtOH Ppt as standard. All of the measurable activity was found in the bottom two fractions (#9 and #10), again indicating a very large molecular weight for folliculostatin.

While our results on molecular weight appear to be in conflict with many of those in the literature, Cahoreau *et al.* (1979) reported retention of FSH-suppressing activity from ovine rete testis fluid by an Amicon XM-100 filter, which has a cutoff point at 100,000 MW. These authors used castrated rams to monitor biological activity *in vivo,* and also reported that their active G-200 column fractions had a high molecular weight ($\geq 160,000$). Their low-molecular-weight fractions did not show any activity.

There are some data which suggest that folliculostatin is an acidic molecule. Williams *et al.* (1979) reported an isoelectric point of pH 5.0–5.8 after preparative isoelectrofocusing of pFF. We have shown that FSH-

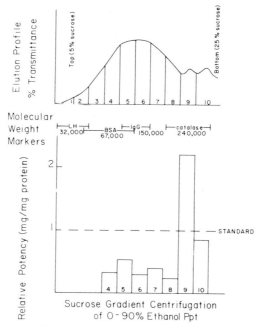

FIG. 24. Sucrose gradient ultracentrifugation of the 90% ethanol precipitate of pFF. Shown are the distribution profile (top), pattern of known molecular weight markers (middle), and the relative potency of each fraction (bottom). The fractions were pooled from five ultracentrifugation runs using a 5–25% sucrose gradient. Each tube contained 40 ml of sucrose solution in phosphate buffer at pH 7.4 to which 40 mg of EtOH Ppt was added. Thus, a total of 200 mg EtOH Ppt was run. Samples were centrifuged at 200,000 g for 8 hours. A mixture of known molecular weight markers was treated similarly. Folliculostatin fractions were tested for activity in our *in vivo* BRIA (see text for bioassay details), and relative potency was calculated against two doses of EtOH Ppt as standard (standard activity = 1 mg/mg protein). The index of precision for this assay was 0.189.

suppressing activity precipitates at pH 4–5.4, suggesting an isoelectric point in this range (Ward *et al.*, 1981). The results of Jansen *et al.* (1981) also indicate an isoelectric point in this range. They found that folliculostatin activity in bFF was not absorbed by CM-cellulose at pH 5.7, but was retained at pH 5.0. A similar isoelectric point for ovine rete testis fluid was suggested by the pH precipitation studies of Baker and co-workers (1978).

Ion-exchange chromatography has been used in the purification of folliculostatin, but the results obtained have been inconsistent. Chappel *et al.* (1979) were unable to observe binding of folliculostatin activity from hamster ovarian extracts to a DEAE column (pH not reported). The activity in bFF has been reported to bind to DEAE at pH 7.5 (Jansen *et al.*,

1981). Similar results have been reported by Chari et al. (1979), who observed absorption of activity in human FF to DEAE at pH 5.2.

Our preliminary results, and those reported by others, indicate that ion-exchange chromatography leads to active fractions with only moderate increases in specific activity and poor recovery of activity (Jansen et al., 1981). Therefore, this technique appears not to be particularly useful for the purification of folliculostatin.

Since the conventional methods discussed have not greatly advanced the purification of folliculostatin, so far, many investigators have turned to less conventional methods, particularly affinity techniques. Williams et al. (1979) used Affi-gel blue to remove 60–80% of the serum proteins in pFF. Further gel filtration and incubation with polymerized antiserum against barrow serum reduced the protein concentration to very low levels while still maintaining biological activity. While this appears to be a unique and profitable approach to purification, the true merit of this technique cannot be judged, due to the authors' failure to calculate specific activity and recovery of activity.

Jansen and co-workers (1981) recently reported exciting results using affinity matrices for the purification of the FSH-suppressing activity in bFF. (These authors utilize a quantitative bioassay, the basal pituitary cell culture, and meticulous "bookkeeping" of relative specific activity and yields.) Folliculostatin in bFF bound to a Matrex Gel Red A column at pH 7.0, and could be eluted with 1.2 M KCl. There was a 90% recovery of activity with a purification factor of 20–25 times. The active fraction was then transferred to phenyl sepharose. Activity was eluted with 8 M urea. This step did not seem particularly useful, however, since there was no increase in relative specific activity, and the recovery was only 63.5%. The authors have since used a less hydrophobic column (de Jong et al., 1981), but observed no binding of activity at pH 8.0. The phenyl sepharose column active fraction was next bound to an ω-aminohexyl agarose and could be eluted with 0.25 M NaCl. This step gave a 3- to 5-fold purification over the previous step and overall recovery of 39.5%. The final step to the purification scheme involved chromatography on a concanavalin A column. While a small portion of the activity was found in the void volume, most was bound to the column and could be eluted with 0.3 M α-methyl-D-mannoside. The final product had a specific activity of 81 relative to the original follicular fluid preparation. Overall recovery was 13.6%.

The results of Jansen et al. (1981) with regard to concanavalin A binding suggest that the FSH-suppressing activity in bFF is associated with a glycoprotein. This is in contrast to the report of Chappel et al. (1979), who found no binding of folliculostatin from hamster ovarian extracts to concanavalin A. This discrepancy may be due to differences in purity of the materials placed on the column.

The affinity techniques described by Jansen *et al.* (1981) may serve as important keys to unlocking the purification of the FSH-suppressing activity found in the female and, perhaps, in the male.

VII. Summary

A concise and consistent description of the chemical characteristics of folliculostatin obviously awaits further purification. However, several points can be derived from the work performed by us and others.

1. Folliculostatin is not a steroid.

2. Folliculostatin is probably an acidic protein with a molecular weight >10,000.

3. There are several reports that folliculostatin has a molecular weight of 10,000–30,000. Our work and that of Jansen *et al.* (1981) indicate a much larger molecular weight. This discrepancy suggests several possibilities: (a) folliculostatin is composed of subunits, or (b) it can exist in several polymerous forms, or (c) it is associated specifically or nonspecifically with other (carrier?) proteins. Whichever of these possibilities is correct, our irradiation studies indicate that the entire complex is required for biological activity *in vivo*.

4. Classical biochemical techniques, such as molecular sieving and ion-exchange chromatography, have been of limited value in the purification of folliculostatin.

5. Affinity techniques hold great methodological promise for the isolation of purified folliculostatin.

6. This field will advance only if specific, quantitative bioassays are used consistently and changes in relative specific activity and yield of activity are carefully monitored.

ACKNOWLEDGMENTS

The authors gratefully acknowledge the support of grants from the National Institutes of Health (2 R01 HD-07504 to N.B.S.; 1 F32 AM-06129 to R.R.G.; 1 T32 HD-07068 to N.B.S.) and the Northwestern University Cancer Center. Unpublished observations presented herein were carried out with the excellent technical assistance of William L. Talley, Brigitte R. Mann, and Sheri Veren. In addition, we wish to thank the NIH Endocrinology Study Section for the ovine LH used as the standard in the LH RIA, and the FSH kits used for the FSH RIA; Dr. L. E. Reichert, Jr., for the ovine LH used for radioiodination, and Dr. G. D. Niswender for the antisera to LH and estradiol, testosterone, and progesterone, used in RIAs. We would like also to thank Dr. Gabe Bialy, of NIH, for supplies of pFF. Finally, we wish to express gratitude to Dr. Ruth Savoy-Moore (Henry

Ford Hospital, Detroit) and Drs. Darrell Ward and Steve Glenn (University of Texas, Houston), who permitted us to cite unpublished data resulting from collaborative experiments.

REFERENCES

Anderson, L. D., and De Paolo, L. V. (1981). *In* "Intragonadal Regulation of Reproduction" (P. Franchimont and C. P. Channing, eds.), p. 343. Academic Press, New York.

Ashiru, O. A., and Blake, C. A. (1980). *Biol. Reprod.* **22**, 533.

Ayalon, D., Tsafriri, A., Lindner, H. R., Cordova, T., and Harell, H. R. (1972). *J. Reprod. Fertil.* **31**, 51.

Baker, H. W. G., Burger, H. G., de Kretser, D. M., Eddie, L. W., Higginson, R. E., Hudson, B., and Lee, V. W. K. (1978). *Int. J. Androl. Suppl.* **2**, 115.

Baker, H. W. G., Eddie, L. W., Higginson, R. E., Hudson, B., Keogh, E. J., and Niall, H. D. (1981). *In* "Intragonadal Regulation of Reproduction" (P. Franchimont and C. P. Channing, eds.), p. 193. Academic Press, New York.

Batta, S. K., Wentz, A. C., and Sulewski, J. M. (1978). *Biol. Reprod. Suppl.* **1**, 45A.

Bliss, C. I. (1968). "Statistics in Biology." McGraw-Hill, New York.

Bronson, F. H., and Channing, C. P. (1978). *Endocrinology* **103**, 1894.

Brown-Grant, K., and Greig, F. (1975). *J. Endocrinol.* **65**, 389.

Butcher, R. L. (1977). *Endocrinology* **101**, 830.

Cahoreau, C., Blanc, M. R., Dacheux, J. L., Pisselet, Cl., and Courot, M. (1979). *J. Reprod. Fertil. Suppl.* **26**, 97.

Campbell, C. S., and Schwartz, N. B. (1977). *J. Toxicol. Environ. Health* **3**, 61.

Campbell, C. S., and Schwartz, N. B. (1979). *Biol. Reprod.* **20**, 1093.

Campbell, C. S., Schwartz, N. B., and Firlit, M. G. (1977). *Endocrinology* **101**, 162.

Channing, C. P., Batta, S. K., Condon, W., Ganjam, V. K., and Kenney, R. M. (1981). *In* "Dynamics of Ovarian Function" (N. B. Schwartz and M. Hunzicker-Dunn, eds.), p. 73. Raven, New York.

Chappel, S. C. (1979). *Biol. Reprod.* **21**, 447.

Chappel, S. C., Acott, T., and Spies, H. G. (1979). *In* "Ovarian Follicular and Corpus Luteum Function" (C. P. Channing, J. M. Marsh, and W. A. Sadler, eds.), p. 361. Plenum, New York.

Chappel, S. C., Holt, J. A., and Spies, H. G. (1930). *Proc. Soc. Exp. Biol. Med.* **163**, 310.

Chari, S., Duraiswami, S., and Franchimont, P. (1976). *Horm. Res.* **7**, 129.

Chari, S., Duraiswami, S., and Franchimont, P. (1978). *Acta Endocrinol.* **87**, 434.

Chari, S., Hopkinson, C. R. N., Daume, E., and Sturm, G. (1979). *Acta Endocrinol.* **90**, 157.

Chowdhury, M., Steinberger, A., and Steinberger, E. (1978). *Endocrinology* **103**, 644.

Darga, N. C., and Reichert, L. E., Jr. (1978). *Biol. Reprod.* **19**, 235.

De Jong, F. H. (1979). *Mol. Cell. Endocrinol.* **13**, 1.

De Jong, F. H., and Sharpe, R. M. (1976). *Nature (London)* **263**, 71.

De Jong, F. H., Smith, S. D., and van der Molen, H. J. (1979a). *J. Endocrinol.* **80**, 91.

De Jong, F. H., Welschen, R., Hermans, W. P., Smith, S. D., and van der Molen, H. J. (1979b). *J. Reprod. Fertil. Suppl.* **26**, 47.

De Jong, F. H., Jansen, E. H. J. M., and van der Molen, H. J. (1981). *In* "Intragonadal Regulation of Reproduction" (P. Franchimont and C. P. Channing, eds.), p. 229. Academic Press, New York.

De Paolo, L. V., Shander, D., Wise, P. M., Barraclough, C. A., and Channing, C. P. (1979a). *Endocrinology* **105**, 647.

De Paolo, L. V., Wise, P. M., Anderson, L. D., Barraclough, C. A., and Channing, C. P. (1979b). *Endocrinology* **104**, 402.

Di Zerega, G. S., and Hodgen, G. D. (1981). *Endocrine Rev.* **2**, 27.

446   ROSEMARY R. GRADY ET AL.

Dufy-Barbe, L., Dufy, B., and Vincent, J. D. (1978). *Biol. Reprod.* **18**, 118.
Edwards, R. G. (1974). *J. Reprod. Fertil.* **37**, 189.
Elias, K. A., and Blake, C. A. (1980). *Life Sci.* **26**, 749.
Erickson, G. F., and Hsueh, A. J. W. (1978). *Endocrinology* **103**, 1960.
Franchimont, P., and Channing, C. P., eds. (1981). "Intragonadal Regulation of Reproduction." Academic Press, New York.
Franchimont, P., Verstraelen-Proyard, J., Hazee-Hagelstein, M. T., Renard, Ch., Demoulin, A., Bourguignon, J. P., and Hustin, J. (1979). *Vitam. Horm.* **37**, 243.
Gay, V. L., and Sheth, N. A. (1972). *Endocrinology* **90**, 158.
Gay, V. L., Midgley, A. R., Jr., and Niswender, G. D. (1970). *Fed. Proc. Fed. Am. Soc. Exp. Biol.* **29**, 1880.
Goodman, R. L., Pickover, S. M., and Karsch, F. J. (1981). *Endocrinology* **108**, 772.
Grady, R. R., Savoy-Moore, R. T., and Schwartz, N. B. (1981). In "Bioregulators of Reproduction" (G. Jagiello and H. J. Vogel, eds.), p. 359. Academic Press, New York.
Greep, R., and Jones, C. (1950). *Recent Prog. Horm. Res.* **5**, 197.
Guillemin, R. (1978). *Science* **202**, 390.
Hermans, W. P., van Leeuwen, E. C. M., Debets, M. H. M., and de Jong, F. H. (1980). *J. Endocrinol.* **86**, 79.
Hoak, D. C., and Schwartz, N. B. (1980). *Proc. Natl. Acad. Sci. U.S.A.* **77**, 4953.
Hoffmann, J. C., Lorenzen, J. R., Weil, T., and Schwartz, N. B. (1979). *Endocrinology* **105**, 200.
Hopkinson, C. R. N., Daume, E., Sturm, G., Fritze, E., Kaiser, S., and Hirschhauser, C. (1977). *J. Reprod. Fertil.* **50**, 93.
Hudson, B., Baker, H. W. G., Eddie, L. W., Higginson, R. E., Burger, H. G., de Kretser, D. M., Dobos, M., and Lee, V. W. K. (1979). *J. Reprod. Fertil. Suppl.* **26**, 17.
Ireland, J. J., Murphee, R. L., and Coulson, P. B. (1980). *J. Dairy Sci.* **63**, 155.
Jansen, E. H. J. M., Steenbergen, J., de Jong, F. H., and van der Molen, H. J. (1981). *Mol. Cell. Endocrinol.* **21**, 109.
Kawakami, M., and Higuchi, T. (1979). *Acta Endocrinol.* **91**, 616.
Kempner, E. S., and Macey, R. I. (1968). *Biochim. Biophys. Acta* **163**, 188.
Kempner, E. S., and Schlegel, W. (1979). *Anal. Biochem.* **92**, 2.
Labrie, F., Lagacé, L., Ferland, L., Kelly, P. A., Drouin, J., Massicotte, J., Bonne, C., Rynaud, J.-P., and Dorrington, J. H. (1978). *Int. J. Androl. Suppl.* **2**, 81.
Lagacé, L., Labrie, F., Lorenzen, J., Schwartz, N. B., and Channing, C. P. (1979). *Clin. Endocrinol.* **10**, 401.
Ledwitz-Rigby, F., Rigby, B. W., Gay, V. L., Stetson, M., Young, J., and Channing, C. P. (1977). *J. Endocrinol.* **74**, 175.
Lee, V. W. K., McMaster, J., Quigg, H., Findlay, J., and Leversha, L. (1981). *Endocrinology* **108**, 2403.
Lorenzen, J. R., Channing, C. P., and Schwartz, N. B. (1978). *Biol. Reprod.* **19**, 635.
Lorenzen, J. R., Dworkin, G. H., and Schwartz, N. B. (1981). *Am. J. Physiol.* **240**, E209.
Lugaro, G., Carrea, G., Casellato, M. M., Mazzola, G., and Fachini, G. (1973). *Biochim. Biophys. Acta* **204**, 719.
Lumpkin, M., Negro-Vilar, A., Franchimont, P., and McCann, S. (1981). *Endocrinology* **108**, 1101.
Marder, M. L., Channing, C. P., and Schwartz, N. B. (1977). *Endocrinology* **101**, 1639.
Miller, K. F., Wesson, J. A., and Ginther, O. J., (1979). *Biol. Reprod.* **21**, 867.
Nandini, S. G., Lipner, H., and Moudgal, N. R. (1976). *Endocrinology* **98**, 1460.
Odell, W. D., and Paul, W. E. (1965). *J. Biol. Chem.* **240**, 2043.

Odell, W. D., Swain, R. W., and Nydick, M. (1964). *J. Clin. Endocrinol. Metab.* **24**, 1266.

Ramirez, V. D., and Sawyer, C. H. (1974). *Endocrinology* **94**, 475.

Roche, J. F., and Ireland, J. J. (1981). *Endocrinology* **108**, 568.

Rush, M. E., Ashiru, O. A., and Blake, C. A. (1980). *Endocrinology* **107**, 649.

Rush, M. E., Ashiru, O. A., Lipner, H., Williams, A. T., and Blake, C. A. (1981). *Endocrinology* **108**, 2316.

Sairam, M. R. (1981). *In* "Intragonadal Regulation of Reproduction" (P. Franchimont and C. P. Channing, eds.), p. 251. Academic Press, New York.

Sato, E., Miyamoto, H., Ishibashi, T., and Iritani, A. (1978). *J. Reprod. Fertil.* **54**, 263.

Sato, E., Ishibashi, T., and Iritani, A. (1980). *Fertil. Steril.* **34**, 55.

Savoy-Moore, R. T., and Schwartz, N. B. (1980). *In* "Reproductive Physiology III" (R. O. Greep, ed.), p. 203. Univ. Park Press, Baltimore, Maryland.

Savoy-Moore, R. T., Schwartz, N. B., Duncan, J. A., and Marshall, J. C. (1980a). *Science* **209**, 942.

Savoy-Moore, R. T., Grady, R. R., and Schwartz, N. B. (1980b). *Biol. Reprod.* **22** (Suppl. 1), 49A.

Schwartz, N. B. (1969). *Recent Prog. Horm. Res.* **25**, 1.

Schwartz, N. B. (1974). *Biol. Reprod.* **10**, 236.

Schwartz, N. B. (1981). *In* "Intra-Ovarian Control Mechanisms" (C. P. Channing and S. Segal, eds.). Plenum, New York, in press.

Schwartz, N. B., and Channing, C. P. (1977). *Proc. Natl. Acad. Sci. U.S.A.* **74**, 5721.

Schwartz, N. B., and Talley, W. L. (1978). *Biol. Reprod.* **18**, 820.

Scott, R. S., and Burger, H. G. (1981). *Biol. Reprod.* **24**, 541.

Shander, D., Anderson, L. D., and Barraclough, C. A. (1980). *Endocrinology* **106**, 1047.

Sherman, B. M., and Korenman, S. G. (1975). *J. Clin. Invest.* **55**, 699.

Steinberger, A., and Steinberger, E. (1976). *Endocrinology* **99**, 918.

Summerville, J. W., and Schwartz, N. B. (1981). *Endocrinology* **109**, 1442.

Tsafriri, A., Pomerantz, S. H., and Channing, C. P. (1976). *Biol. Reprod.* **14**, 511.

Tsafriri, A., Channing, C. P., Pomerantz, S. H., and Lindner, H. R. (1977). *J. Endocrinol.* **75**, 285.

Uilenbroek, J. Th. J., Tiller, R., de Jong, F. H., and Vels, F. (1978). *J. Endocrinol.* **78**, 399.

Vale, W., Grant, G., Amoss, M., Blackwell, R., and Guillemin, R. (1972). *Endocrinology* **91**, 562.

Ward, D. N., Nahm, H. S., Shalek, R. J., Schwartz, N. B., Lorenzen, J. R., Moore, R. B., Grady, R. R., and Channing, C. P. (1981). *In* "Bioregulators of Reproduction" (G. Jagiello and H. J. Vogel, eds.), p. 371. Academic Press, New York.

Welschen, R., Dullaart, J., and de Jong, F. H. (1978). *Biol. Reprod.* **18**, 421.

Welschen, R., Hermans, W., and de Jong, F. H. (1980). *J. Reprod. Fertil.* **60**, 485.

Williams, A. T., Rush, M. E., and Lipner, H. (1979). *In* "Ovarian Follicular and Corpus Luteum Function" (C. P. Channing, J. M. Marsh, and W. A. Sadler, eds.), p. 429. Plenum, New York.

Yang, K. P., Sanraan, N. A., and Ward, D. N. (1976). *Endocrinology* **98**, 233.

Ying, S., Ling, N., Bohlen, P., and Guillemin, R. (1981a). *Endocrinology* **108**, 1206.

Ying, S., Ling, N., Bohlen, P., and Guillemin, R. (1981b). *In* "Bioregulators of Reproduction" (G. Jagiello and H. J. Vogel, eds.), p. 389. Academic Press, New York.

DISCUSSION

K. Savard: I'd just like to contribute a little bit of historical steroid chemistry which might allay your perplexity as to why you get skewed response curves with ether extracted follicular fluid, and not with the charcoal-treated fluid. The original process for making Premarin, that was developed in Montreal at the Ayerst Company, used charcoal which simultaneously absorbed both conjugated steroids and free steroids; ether of course extracts only free steroids. So you might have a clue as to the possible presence of conjugated steroids in your follicular fluid preparations.

N. B. Schwartz: The ether extracted 99% of the measurable steroids. We assume it changed the molecule in some way so that pFF was no longer parallel to the charcoal-extracted or untreated pFF.

B. Hudson: Thank you for a helpful review on assays for inhibin. I described the first approach to an inhibin assay using dispersed pituitary cells at this conference in 1975 (Baker *et al., Recent Prog. Hormone Res.* **32,** 429, 1976). This assay incorporates all the essential features for a parallel line bioassay and depends upon measuring the suppression of GnRH stimulated secretion of FSH after the cells have been incubated for 3 days with inhibin-containing materials. We normally use 3–5 dose levels of standard and 3 dose levels of several unknowns. We have described the details of this assay elsewhere (Eddie *et al., J. Endocrinol.* **81,** 49, 1979). We have used this assay over the past 5 years and the mean λ value for the last 180 assays is 0.078, with an interassay coefficient of variation of $\pm 11\%$. It is true that at high dose levels of inhibin we see suppression of LH secretion but this suppression is less steep and is not parallel to the suppression of FSH. I have also reviewed the available assays for inhibin (Hudson *et al., J. Reprod. Fertil.* Suppl. **26,** 17, 1979). We acknowledge that inhibin assays which use pituitary cell cultures are tedious and time consuming with a turnaround time of at least 7 days. A valid bioassay such as this, however, is essential if the yields of different steps used in the purification of inhibin and changes in the specific activity are to be measured.

From the outset we made a policy decision to purify inhibin rather than to undertake a number of obvious physiological studies. This was done because we did not have a simpler and more sensitive assay, such as a radioimmunoassay. We have found this to be a difficult task, and I would agree with Dr. Schwartz that this will not be easily achieved by conventional procedures. As our starting material we have used ovine rete testis fluid. You can see from Table A that despite four or five different steps we have only achieved a 30-fold purification with an overall yield of 4%. This is fairly typical of the several conventional approaches to purification used by ourselves and others.

We have some other information about the nature of testicular inhibin. First, we find the molecular weight to be 90,000 or more, on the basis of gel filtration in neutral or basic

TABLE A

Purification of Inhibin from Ovine Rete Testis Fluid (RTF)

Step	Protein (mg)	Specific activity (U/mg)	Purification (fold)	Yield (%)
RTF	2850	200	1	100
Diafiltration lyophilization	1518	370	1.8	98
BioGel P-60, 1 *M* acetic acid	407	510	2.6	36
CM-Cellulose	76	940	4.7	12
Con A-Sepharose	3.7	6100	30	4

buffers. However, when chromatographed in 1 M acetic acid on BioGel P-60, the apparent molecular weight is lower and is about 30,000 on SDS–polyacrylamide gel electrophoresis. We find that inhibin is an acidic protein with an isoelectric point between pH 5 and 5.5 as determined by isoelectric focusing. The question has frequently been raised as to whether inhibin is a glycoprotein. This is suggested by its bindings affinity for Con A-Sepharose and wheat germ lectin Sepharose. When treated with neuraminidase, however, there is no loss of activity and only a minor change in charge. The point remains unresolved; however, inhibin may be a glycoprotein or be bound to one.

Our findings are in general agreement with those of de Jong's group (Jansen *et al.*, *Mol. Cell Endocrinol.* **21**, 109, 1981) but are in sharp contrast to those reported by Sairam *et al.* (*Mol. Cell Endocrinol.* **22**, 231, 1981) who describe inhibin as a basic protein and by Franchimont *et al.* (*Int. J. Androl.* Suppl **2**, 69, 1978) and by Sheth *et al.* (*J. Reprod. Fertil.* Suppl. **26**, 71, 1979) who describe much lower molecular weights for inhibin.

We have tried to raise antibodies to inhibin but without success. An antibody could be of great potential help in two ways: for purification using immunoaffinity chromatography and for the development of a radioimmunoassay. I was most interested to hear that Dr. Channing has at least one monkey with antibodies to inhibin. Has the antiserum been characterized to any extent? And, if so, will it neutralize inhibin activity or bind inhibin specifically? I believe these would be important studies to pursue.

N. B. Schwartz: To those of you who do not know Dr. Hudson's work, there is no question in my mind that the testicular inhibin field gained a real boost when he entered it with a quantitative assay. We have produced four different hyperimmune sera but cannot reduce the bioassay activity in our folliculostatin with it.

G. B. Cutler: I'd like to ask your thoughts about the physiological role of inhibin in the male. A couple of years ago, Marshall Decker, Lynn Loriaux, and I attempted to modify the *in vivo* bioassay for inhibin. Our strategy was to remove the source of inhibin by castration but to try to avoid interfering with the sex steroids by replacing testosterone with Silastic capsules. To our surprise, no matter what size capsule we chose, we were never able to get a selective rise in FSH. As soon as the capsule was large enough to return testosterone to normal levels, FSH and LH in the male rat invariably became normal. Thus, it appeared to us that, at least in the male rat, testosterone alone or its metabolites were able to account for all of the FSH-suppressing activity of the testes without any need to postulate a physiological role for inhibin. It seems to me that a critical question is whether this biological activity, which is clearly there, gets out into the circulation in a large enough amount that it can get to the pituitary and exert its presumed physiological effect.

N. B. Schwartz: John Summerville and I have a paper (*Endocrinology* **109**, 1442, 1981) which is supportive of that. Males were castrated and examined sequentially over a 12-day period. They were implanted with two different levels of testosterone, one of them chosen to mimic normal average levels, another a lower dose of testosterone which was calculated to be the near-threshold dose for LH suppression. With the higher dose we obtained exactly the same thing that you did: FSH suppression was just as good as the LH suppression. With the threshold dose, the same thing was true; that is if the dose of testosterone in a given male was good enough to get the LH down, it lowered the FSH. If it did not suppress the LH, it did not suppress the FSH. Nevertheless, we were able to show, using our female-derived folliculostatin, a good suppression of the FSH (60%) regardless of what testosterone background was. I do not know what that means physiologically.

G. A. Hedge: In presenting your *in vitro* cell incubation data, you compared the GnRH stimulated case to the basal state (presumably zero GnRH) and you favored the latter because you could distinguish between LH and FSH. Does it not disturb you that these cells are obviously exposed to GnRH *in vivo*?

N. B. Schwartz: I knew that somebody here was going to pick up what we call the "GnRH paradox." Let me restate what you just said if I may. In a bioassay, I think it is crucial to define an endpoint that is specific, if you've defined the substance which you are looking for as specific. That is the reason we choose the basal assay over the GnRH challenge, since the material appears to exert a specific suppression of FSH as in the *in vivo* assay. The paradox is that it is assumed that FSH and LH are both GnRH dependent *in vivo*. Yet when we give follicular fluid *in vivo* we very specifically suppress FSH and not LH. However, when we establish a GnRH dependency *in vitro* we lose the specificity. We are occupying a lot of our time with that paradox. I'll give you a couple of ideas. One is that the basal cell culture may be somewhere in between an *in vivo* situation where there is no hypothalamic function and a challenge with exogenous GnRH *in vivo*. It is possible that the GnRH challenge *in vitro* is really an over challenge; that is one possibility. Another issue is that there is evidence *in vivo* that FSH secretion is not as GnRH-dependent as LH secretion. Mike Rush has some evidence on that, which has been recently published—maybe he would like to tell you about it. GnRH antiserum does a much better job of suppressing LH *in vivo* than it does of suppressing FSH.

G. A. Hedge: It might be worth considering the fact that these cells are also divorced from their normal *in vivo* steroid environment.

N. B. Schwartz: Yes.

G. V. Callard: It would seem that the rather subtle physiological effects of folliculostatin that you see in estrous and menstrual cycles might be very greatly magnified in species which regularly alternate between periods of reproductive activity and inactivity, i.e., seasonal breeders. Do you have any data of your own or knowledge of any information in the literature that would relate to this point? Also, would you comment on a possible function of folliculostatin during pregnancy?

N. B. Schwartz: I have not seen anything. The one model that I have seen looked at extensively is Fred Turek's stuff on seasonal testicular collapse in the male hamster. He has measured both FSH and LH, but never seen a discrepancy between FSH and LH in his male hamsters, whether the hamster is going into a short photoperiod and is collapsing or whether it is undergoing recrudescence at the end of seasonal infertility. At least at the beginning and end of that one seasonal shift situation there is no reason to believe that there is a discrepancy between the FSH and LH regulation. Furthermore, in terms of Gordon Cutler's question, testosterone feedback, as Turek has demonstrated, is equally good in suppressing the FSH or LH rise. So at least in the male hamster there is no reason to think that there is a discrepancy between FSH and LH regulation. I do not know about pregnancy.

P. K. Siiteri: I am troubled by the same observation that Dr. Savard was and would like to probe a little bit further about the difference between ether extraction and charcoal extraction. The problem is complex because, depending upon the actual method of charcoal extraction, you may or may not remove steroid from high affinity binding sites such as CBG or SHBG. Can you rule out the possibility that this material in fact is a high affinity steroid binding protein which carries the steroid specifically to the appropriate cell in the hypothalamus or the pituitary. The reason I ask this is because in my presentation I will propose that the active forms of steroids in general are the bound forms.

N. B. Schwartz: I doubt that that is true but what we have measured (after ether extraction before steroid RIA) are the steroids that we know about and the ones that we know about are reduced by 99%. If there is a high affinity binding site for some other steroid or even for estradiol, we have not investigated it.

P. K. Siiteri: Are you sure you are taking it out?

N. B. Schwartz: I am not sure that I am taking out something that I am not measuring, no.

P. K. Siiteri: The point is that if you use the ordinary charcoal extraction procedure as you would, say, in a radioimmunoassay, you cannot extract all of the steroid unless you let it sit around for many days. If you want to remove a specifically bound steroid, you have to go to something like 5% charcoal with no dextran and elevate the temperature before you are sure you have removed all the steroid.

N. B. Schwartz: We do the charcoal extraction at low temperature but overnight with a large amount of charcoal. I cannot deny that there may be a mysterious steroid or binding protein in there that has an incredible FSH suppression activity and doesn't suppress LH. I might be just as happy if we discovered a steroid which was specifically suppressing FSH and not suppressing LH as discovering a peptide which was doing the same thing!

C. W. Beattie: I would like to follow up on George Hedge's question. Given that you seem to have specific suppression of basal FSH over LH and given that the specificity seems to be lost following GnRH, what I would like to know is whether in your dose–response curves with the porcine follicular fluid, you changed the concentration of GnRH to see if the differential block of FSH was the result of one particular dose of GnRH. Have you or has anyone else looked to see whether this material will inhibit the binding of a GnRH analog to the pituitary and even if the answers to these questions are yes or no, would you care to speculate on the mechanism of pFF action.

N. B. Schwartz: In the GnRH stimulated culture we use a level of GnRH that gives us a 50% rise in LH secretion rate. I think everybody is using a similar concentration. We have not in an *in vitro* situation used more than that one dose of GnRH. We have picked it for obvious reasons, as the point where we could either see an enhancement of LH and FSH or a suppression. With respect to the issue of whether this pFF is interfering with the GnRH receptor, we have not tested it as yet. I do not think that FF interferes with the binding of GnRH to its receptor because it is not influencing LH. In general all of the *in vitro* data using either agonists or antagonists of GnRH have shown a similar effect on LH and FSH. I do not know the mechanism of FF action. We have been pursuing the GnRH paradox by doing GnRH experiments *in vivo* now. Our prediction was that if we really pushed the system with very high levels of GnRH we would lose the specificity for FSH *in vivo,* and it would then become like the *in vitro* model. The experiments that we have done used two doses of pFF, one moderate and one very high, and two doses of GnRH. For the FSH regardless of the dose of GnRH and regardless of the pFF dose, we were able to overcome the GnRH influence. With respect to LH, at the low dose of pFF using a high dose of GnRH, we enhanced the LH response to GnRH and at the high dose of pFF we suppressed it slightly. We are doing the experiment over again.

H. Papkoff: I have been asked to say a few words on behalf of Dr. N. R. Moudgal (Bangalore) and his work on inhibin over the past few years. Dr. Moudgal has measured the suppression of uterine weight in hCG-treated mice as a test for inhibin and has reported (*Biol. Reprod.* **20,** 831, 1979) on the characteristics and validity of this assay. Despite the fact that this is an indirect assay and may be responsive to other factors, Dr. Moudgal and his colleagues have shown that the purification of inhibin from extracts of ram testes can be effectively monitored as evidenced by constantly increasing specific activities. Indeed, a several thousand-fold purification is indicated. This has been achieved by a series of steps involving $MnSO_4$ precipitation to remove nucleoproteins, a heat treatment ($60°C$), fractionation with $(NH_4)_2SO_4$, gel filtration on Sephadex G-75, and chromatography on DEAE- and CM-cellulose. My input has been to provide a final purification step using sulfoethyl- or sulfopropyl-Sephadex chromatography. I have independently fractionated a batch of ram testes with minor modifications and obtained a highly purified material in a yield of 6.4 mg/kg of testes. The product shows a single, stained band at pH 4.5 and pH 8.5 by conventional disc gel electrophoresis, and a single band in SDS–urea buffers. Comparison with known standards indicate a molecular weight of 10,000–10,500. It has a single amino-terminal amino acid, lysine, and consists of approximately 100 amino acid residues. Noteworthy is the absence of cystine (and probably tryptophan) and the low content of proline and methionine. Whether or not this material represents the long sought after and elusive inhibin, or another equally interesting peptide, remains to be established in the coming months. Fortunately, there is no dearth of investigators, both at this meeting and elsewhere, who are eager to test this material.

N. B. Schwartz: I will make the same comment that I made to Dr. Moudgal when he visited our laboratory. He might be purifying an FSH binding inhibitor. I think he showed that hCG causes a brief pulse of FSH 1 hour after the hCG injection and then FSH drops. Some hours later he looks at uterine weight as an indirect measure of estrogen and estrogen as an indirect measure of FSH's effect on the ovary.

C. Channing: I enjoyed your presentation. Dr. Mougdal recently came and gave a seminar in our department also and presented data using both a more direct inhibin bioassay as well as his indirect assay to follow his testicular inhibin purification. He obtained similar types of data with both assays. In support of the charcoal procedure for removing steroids we have done extensive studies on this procedure. We have added a series of labeled steroid sulfate-free steroids, nucleotides, and prostaglandins to the follicular fluid prior to charcoal treatment and observed that the charcoal treatment removed >99% of these tracers. In the procedure we mix 10% by volume per volume of charcoal with follicular fluid and carry out the extraction overnight. Inhibin may decrease 10% with treatment. If a second charcoal treatment is carried out significant inhibin activity remains but virtually no steroids remain. We have also done a 90% ethanol precipitation which removed all sorts of steroids and all the inhibin activity of the original fluid was retained. The 90% ethanol precipitate is further washed with acetone and there still is retention of inhibin activity. Data using ether extraction should be intrepreted with caution since the ether may well bring about extensive denaturation of the inhibin. A comment on the role of LHRH and the FSH-suppressing activity of inhibin. Wise and her colleagues found that if you take a phenobarbital-blocked proestrus rat and infuse her with a very low dose of LHRH and then give charcoal-treated porcine follicular fluid it was possible to inhibit FSH release while not altering LHRH stimulation of LH release (*Endocrinology* **104**, 402, 1979).

N. B. Schwartz: Indeed ether is changing the activity. Had we only measured the ether-extracted follicular fluid at one dose, we would have seen a good 35% suppression. It was only because we used a dose–response range that we saw that there was no parallelism between standard and ether-extracted FF.

C. S. Nicoll: We have done quite a bit of work with hemi-pituitary and explant incubations in connection with control of prolactin and growth hormone secretion. In our experience when toxic materials are present in the medium they cause the hemi-pituitaries or explants to "dump" both hormones into the medium. This response could be used as an index of toxicity. Have you thought about using explants of pituitaries from castrated male rats in short-term incubations to assay for inhibin? You could use release of LH or some other hormone as an indicator of toxic effects.

N. B. Schwartz: Dr. Hudson and colleagues recently wrote a first rate review in which they reviewed the toxicity material on the *in vitro* assay. I think there are a couple of ways of avoiding the toxicity. You can look at your cells at the end of the experiment and make sure that they have not all fallen away from the plate. When Scott and Burger (1981) withdrew the medium and put in fresh medium after suppressing with their testicular inhibin, they were able to see the FSH secretion come back which I think is sort of a bottom line against the toxicity theory.

C. S. Nicoll: The comment that I have to make is related to the question of selective control of FSH secretion. One of my graduate students, Mr. Davie Wei, became interested in reexamining the evidence for short-loop feedback of the gonadotropins at the hypothalamic level. We decided to repeat some of the studies that were done mainly in L. Martini's laboratory in Milan during the late 1960s. However, we used much more highly purified preparations of ovine LH and FSH that were obtained from Dr. H. Papkoff. Mr. Wei found that implants of LH in cocoa butter into the anterior hypothalamus had no effect on either LH or FSH secretion in castrated male rats. In contrast, implants of FSH in the same region selectively inhibited FSH secretion—LH secretion was not affected. It is difficult to explain these results on the basis of a single GnRH.

N. B. Schwartz: I think the single GnRH may be vanishing within the next 5 years.

H. Lipner: I want to comment about the relationship between estrogen and inhibin. The data I am presenting are derived from experiments by Dr. A. T. Williams in my lab. This study was performed on rats that had been ovariectomized 8 days earlier. The effect of the administration of inhibin from days 15 through 21 on FSH serum levels is indicated in Fig. A by the hatched line (width indicates the standard error of the mean) (A). The FSH levels drop from 1600 to about 600 ng/ml. Implantation of an estrogen-containing Silastic capsule on day 15 causes the FSH levels to achieve the basal levels seen in diestrus. LH (B) is uneffected by the pFF but suppressed from castration levels to diestrus levels by the estrogen implant. (C) shows the level of estrogen in the plasma. In the presence of inhibin only the LH is uneffected and the FSH is depressed 50%. In the presence of 30 pg/ml of estrogen and 1 ml per 24 hour injection of pFF, FSH is depressed to diestrous levels.

Figure B shows an elution pattern of pFF from a Sephacryl S-300 column. The dimensions and characterization of the column are indicated on the figure. Biological activity of the active fraction was determined in a dispersed pituitary cell culture bioassay. Note that the molecular weight is about 115,000. Figure C is an elution pattern of pFF performed on a smaller column and performed in an 8 M urea containing phosphate-buffered medium. The molecular weight derived from this column is between 25,000 and 30,000 in agreement with that reported by Dr. Hudson. I think the variability of reported molecular weight is a function of the source of the material and the tendency of the molecule to aggregate either with other proteins or with itself.

J. M. Nolin: We've been looking for the mechanism, or mechanisms of action of prolactin for a number of years now. In connection with this, we believe, on the basis of several lines of evidence, that the oocyte maturation inhibitory peptide is a fragment of prolactin processed by the granulosa cell. I was just wondering how you would feel about entertaining the possibility that inhibin is a piece of FSH?

N. B. Schwartz: I do not think there is any evidence to think that it is a piece of FSH. How big a piece? I do not have any evidence that it is FSH. It does not interfere with the radioimmunoassay for FSH.

J. M. Nolin: Would you admit that it still might be a possibility?

N. B. Schwartz: Sure.

G. T. Campbell: As one who routinely measures serum FSH in female rats, I know of three things which elevate the serum FSH to LH ratio: one being the lack of inhibin, another being androgens under certain conditions, and the third being a very low frequency of LHRH stimulation. With regard to the first two, I would like to ask you a question concerning the second phase of FSH release during the rat estrous cycle. Vernon Gay published data several years ago on administration of antitestosterone antiserum and blockade of that second phase. Since I'm a little unclear as to whether a relationship exists between androgens and the possible secretory rate of pFF, could you help me out a little bit?

N. B. Schwartz: What Vernon Gay showed some years ago was that if he gave an antiserum to testosterone just before the secondary surge of FSH, he could block that rise. It is possible to infer, as I think you are, that implies a testosterone signal. Vernon inferred in

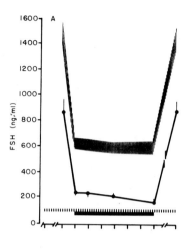

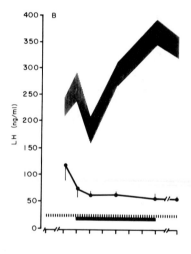

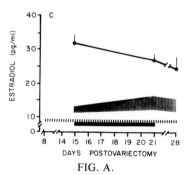

FIG. A.

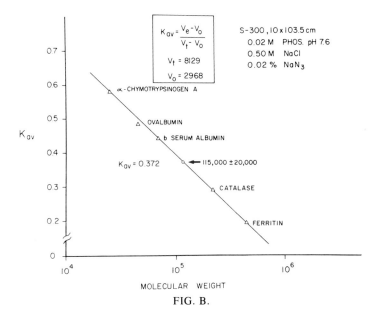

$$K_{av} = \frac{V_e - V_0}{V_t - V_0}$$

$V_t = 8129$

$V_0 = 2968$

S-300, 10 x 103.5 cm
0.02 M PHOS. pH 7.6
0.50 M NaCl
0.02 % NaN$_3$

α-CHYMOTRYPSINOGEN A

OVALBUMIN

b SERUM ALBUMIN

$K_{av} = 0.372$ ← 115,000 ± 20,000

CATALASE

FERRITIN

K_{av}

MOLECULAR WEIGHT

FIG. B.

his paper in *Science* that he was blocking a testosterone signal which was inducing FSH rise. Recently Welshen *et al.* in the *Journal of Endocrinology* has reexamined that hypothesis. They gave testosterone implants and were not able to change the FSH rise. So we can make an interpretation then of Vernon's data. It is possible that what Vernon was doing with the

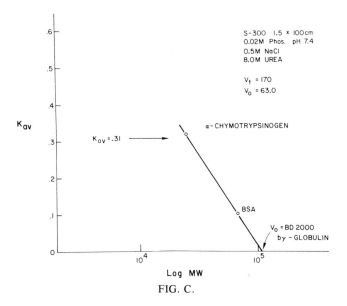

S-300 1.5 x 100 cm
0.02M Phos. pH 7.4
0.5M NaCl
8.0M UREA

$V_t = 170$
$V_0 = 63.0$

α-CHYMOTRYPSINOGEN

$K_{av} = .31$ ⟶

BSA

$V_0 = BD\ 2000$
b γ-GLOBULIN

K_{av}

Log MW

FIG. C.

antiserum was influencing a local ovarian event. Let us say, if the LH surge as I've suggested really does turn off folliculostatin, that that is what causes FSH to rise, then maybe the antitestosterone was influencing the intermediary steps between the LH surge and the folliculostatin.

M. Rush: We have looked at the separability of FSH and LH secretion during the periovulatory period in the 4-day cycling rat. When we made retrochiasmatic cuts, hypothalamic islands, or medial basal hypothalamic lesions at 1200 hours on the day of proestrus, both the LH and FSH surges were abolished as was the subsequent ovulation. When we made any of these lesions at 2000 hours on proestrus, the estrous phase of FSH secretion was unaffected, in amplitude or duration, as compared to the appropriate controls. At 1000 hours on estrus, we administered an iv bolus of GnRH, which induced significant elevations in plasma levels of LH and FSH. These data strongly suggest that hypothalamic GnRH is not necessary for the estrous phase of FSH secretion to occur. Presently we are using the hypothalamic lesioned rat to test further the effects of inhibin and steroids on FSH release. Other experiments are in progress to examine the question of separability of LH and FSH secretion.

Also, I would like to address Dr. Campbell's last point. Dr. Charles Blake and I examined the role of testosterone in the control of the estrous phase of FSH release. Using several different antisera to testosterone, Dr. Blake was unable to duplicate Dr. Gay's work. Using the (pentobarbital) delayed ovulation rat of Dr. Roy Butcher and testosterone implants at various times during the delay, we obtained equivocal results. We have repeated this experiment and are presently analyzing the data.

N. B. Schwartz: Did you use the same antiserum that they used? I think that that is a crucial thing.

M. Rush: I do not know which antisera were used.

J. K. Findlay: I think it is appropriate that the last comment addresses toxicity, because this is a major problem in using an *in vitro* cell culture system. I think it was Dr. Nicoll who has already mentioned the possibility of using the measurement of LH or other pituitary hormones to assess toxicity. You also mentioned the morphologic assessment. Dr. David Robertson in our laboratory has done a nice study to show that chromium release from pituitary cells in culture is also a good way of assessing toxicity. We would urge anyone who is going to try and measure bioactivity in any sample to first of all test out the toxic effects.

The Serum Transport of Steroid Hormones[1]

PENTTI K. SIITERI, JAMES T. MURAI, GEOFFREY L. HAMMOND,[2]
JEFFREY A. NISKER,[3] WILLIAM J. RAYMOURE, AND ROBERT W. KUHN

*Reproductive Endocrinology Center, Department of Obstetrics,
Gynecology and Reproductive Sciences, University of California,
San Francisco, San Francisco, California*

I. Introduction

Steroid hormones are extensively bound to plasma proteins including albumin, corticosteroid binding globulin (CBG or transcortin), and sex hormone binding globulin (SHBG, SBP, or TeBG). While an extensive literature concerning the chemical and physiologic aspects of both CBG and SHBG in many species has accumulated since their discovery in human plasma, their true function is still unclear. Many excellent reviews of this subject are available (Westphal, 1971; Rosner, 1972a, 1976; Anderson, 1974; Ballard, 1979; Bardin *et al.*, 1981). The affinities of physiologically important steroids for CBG or SHBG are 2–3 orders of magnitude higher than those for albumin. Nevertheless, because of its high concentration, albumin binding is important in determining the magnitude of the nonprotein bound or free fraction of a steroid in plasma. Based upon a variety of both experimental and clinical observations it is generally held that only the latter is available to target tissues. According to this view, the level of CBG or SHBG regulates the free hormone concentration and CBG or SHBG bound steroid constitutes a pool of readily available hormone. The role of albumin bound steroid is less clear although it has been suggested that it may supplement the free pool of hormone within tissues because of the rapid dissociation of steroids from albumin. Early studies of steroid hormone kinetics in blood were directed toward quantifying rates of metabolism and production without particular regard to mechanism of action. The important effect on plasma binding in protecting

[1] This investigation was supported in part by USPHS, NIH Grant Awards HD 10328, CA 27702, and a grant from the Andrew W. Mellon Foundation.
[2] Current Address: Department of Medicine, University of Manchester, Manchester, England.
[3] Current Address: University of Western Ontario, Victoria Hospital-South Street, Colborne 3, London, Ontario N6B 1B9, Canada.

steroids from metabolism was recognized more than 20 years ago but has attracted little attention since the advent of the steroid receptor concept. The generally accepted model of steroid hormone action suggests that free steroid (in equilibrium with circulating binding proteins) diffuses passively through target cell membranes and binds to a soluble intracellular receptor. The steroid–receptor complex apparently moves into the nucleus where it modifies the chromatin transcriptional activity which results in, among other things, altered levels of protein synthesis. This receptor dogma so dominates steroid biochemistry that most investigators have ignored the function of plasma steroid binding proteins even though they have been found in many tissues.

In this article we will review our recent studies which were directed initially to an assessment of the availability of estrogens in human plasma. One of our goals was to develop a convenient, physiologically relevant method for measurement of the percentage of unbound steroid in small plasma samples. We soon realized that much additional information was obtainable using the isodialysis technique that evolved. The method has been used to determine the percentage distribution of a steroid between free, albumin bound, and CBG or SHBG bound fractions and also its association constant of binding to both classes of proteins. From studies of various clinical conditions, it became apparent that neither the free nor albumin bound concentration of estradiol in human plasma is sufficient to saturate the estrogen receptors in target cells except during pregnancy. In marked contrast, we have found that the apparent plasma concentrations of free cortisol and testosterone in New World monkeys greatly exceeds that found in other primates including humans.

These results prompted us to reconsider the possibility that plasma binding proteins, particularly CBG, may participate in the uptake of steroids by target cells. Using immunocytochemical methods we have demonstrated the intracellular presence of CBG in many rat tissues in which others have found "transcortin-like receptor" binding. Furthermore, direct evidence for cellular uptake of the corticosterone–CBG complex both *in vivo* and *in vitro* has been obtained. Taken together, the results of our studies suggest that plasma steroid binding proteins may play an essential role in steroid hormone action.

II. Methods

A. MEASUREMENT OF CBG AND SHBG BINDING CAPACITY

A variety of methods for measurement of CBG and SHBG in plasma, based upon their ability to bind radioactive steroids, have been described.

We have employed modifications of two basic methods: the ammonium sulfate precipitation technique of Rosner (1972b) and the DEAE filter disc assay initially described by Mickelson and Petra (1974). Several aspects of the latter method deserve comment. As originally described, these authors applied a correction for assay efficiency to account for loss of bound radioactivity that occurs during the separation of bound and free hormone. While some loss occurs, it is much less than Mickelson and Petra estimated. They chose to determine the efficiency as first described by Yarus and Berg (1970) and subsequently adapted by Santi *et al.* (1973) for measurement of glucocorticoid receptors with DEAE filter discs. In each instance, these workers chose conditions for establishing assay efficiency in which the concentration of binding sites greatly exceeded that of the radiolabeled ligand. Any difference between the total amount of radioactivity added and that lost during the procedure was ascribed to dissociation of the bound ligand during washing. However, this approach is valid only if applied to a solution of pure binding protein. The presence of a large excess of low affinity binding sites such as albumin in plasma significantly reduces the amount of ligand bound to the high affinity sites. We have addressed this problem in a different way, as illustrated in Fig. 1. By actually determining the amount of radioactivity bound after different numbers of washes, the true loss of specifically bound radioactivity is obtained by extrapolation to zero washes. As shown in Fig. 1A, the loss of bound radioactive DHT after 10 1-ml washes is 2% as compared to a loss of 25% estimated by Mickelson and Petra (1974) using the identical procedure. Rosner recognized this problem in his description of a DEAE filter assay for CBG and fortified diluted serum with pure CBG in order to estimate the assay efficiency. However, the value obtained (75%) is not comparable with the data shown in Fig. 1B (96%), since his assay was carried out at ambient temperature (Rosner *et al.*, 1976).

In early experiments with diluted human plasma, we obtained dissociation constants (K_D) of about 0.2–0.5 nM for DHT and 1 nM for cortisol binding at 4°C. We therefore selected a concentration of 10 nM [³H]DHT for measurement of SHBG binding capacity and varied the plasma dilution in order to assure saturation of binding sites. Similar experiments using [³H]cortisol (20 nM) and diluted plasma are shown in Fig. 2A. The fact that linear plots with the predicted slope of -2 were obtained with both ligands suggested that the assays were valid and furthermore that they could be applied to serum from other species if both criteria, i.e., satisfactory efficiency and linearity with dilution, were satisfied. The use of high serum dilutions also obviates the need for removing endogenous steroids prior to assay of binding capacity (Fig. 2B). However, it soon became apparent that the values obtained for both SHBG and CBG binding capacities were considerably lower than those reported in the litera-

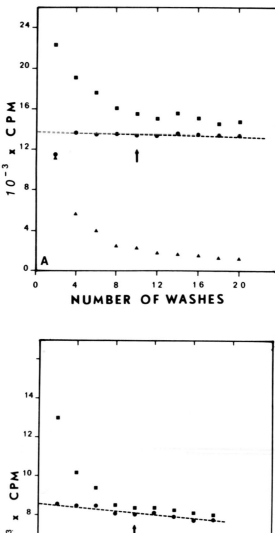

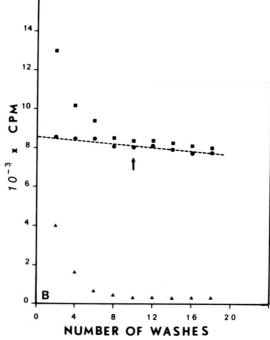

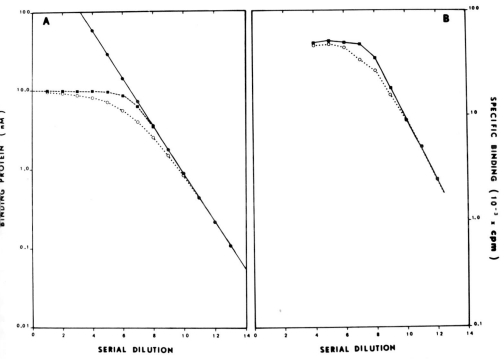

FIG. 2. Effect of endogenous steroid on a typical dilution assay. (A) Results of a theoretical assay assuming 1000 nM initial CBG, $K_D = 1$ nM, and a [³H]cortisol concentration of 10 nM. Closed squares represent the expected curve if no endogenous steroid is present. The open circles illustrate the expected behavior if the initial CBG solution contained 1000 nM radioinert cortisol. Closed circles represent expected levels from extrapolation of the linear portion of the curve. (B) Effect of stripping serum prior to assay. Closed squares are for a charcoal-extracted sample while open circles are results for an untreated sample.

ture. After extensive examination of our assay conditions, we concluded that the only significant difference was that we used higher dilutions of plasma or serum than those used by previous workers. We then examined the effect of dilution on the value of K_D and much to our surprise found the results shown in Fig. 3. As can be seen, the value of K_D for cortisol binding is highly dependent upon the plasma dilution, decreasing nearly 10-fold from 2×10^{-9} at 1:16 to 3.5×10^{-10} at 1:1024. At present, we

FIG. 1. Determination of DEAE-filter assay efficiency. The assays are performed at a serum dilution of 1:256 using 10 nM [³H]DHT (A) or 10 nM [³H]cortisol (B). Data presented are total counts (squares), nonspecific counts (triangles), and specific counts (circles). Efficiency was determined by dividing the number of specific counts after 10 washes by the number with no washes as determined by extrapolation.

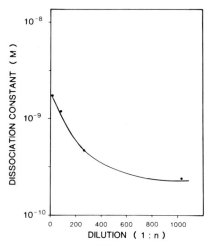

FIG. 3.   Effect of dilution on the dissociation constant for the binding of [³H]cortisol to CBG in diluted human plasma. Dissociation constants were determined by Scatchard analysis of DEAE filter saturation assays at the following dilutions of human serum: 2^4 (1:16), 2^6 (1:64), 2^8 (1:256), and 2^{10} (1:1024).

have no explanation for this behavior. It may be noted, however, that Westphal (1971) observed a similar phenomenon for the binding of polar steroids to pure albumin solutions. Serum dilutions of 1:50 or 1:100 and 100 nM [³H]DHT and [³H]cortisol have been used for DEAE filter assay of SHBG and CBG, respectively.

B. MEASUREMENT OF PERCENTAGE FREE STEROID IN UNDILUTED PLASMA

At present, none of the conventional methods of measuring steroids, including radioimmunoassay, is sensitive enough to conveniently quantitate free steroids in blood samples. Various attempts have therefore been made to estimate the amount of free steroid in blood by determining the percentage of total steroid that is free, after addition and equilibration of a known amount of the radioactive steroid to serum or plasma samples (Westphal, 1971). Numerous methods have been developed for separation of bound and free steroids, including equilibrium dialysis (Forest et al., 1968; Vermeulen et al., 1971; Chopra et al., 1972; Kley et al., 1977a), flow dialysis (Moll and Rosenfield, 1977), ultrafiltration through a dialysis membrane (Plager et al., 1964), zonal chromatography (DeMoor et al., 1962), and steady-state gel filtration (Burke, 1969; Greenstein et al., 1977). Although it has been demonstrated that similar results may be obtained by several of these methods (Kley *et al.*, 1977b), each has one or more draw-backs, including large sample requirement, correction for variable increases in sample volume which occur during the course of dialysis, or the collection and measurement of radioactivity in numerous fractions for each sample. Moreover, alterations in the concentrations of low-molecular-weight constituents relative to the serum proteins are inherent in most of these methods. Such changes may obscure important low affinity interactions with the binding system under study. Therefore, we developed a rapid and convenient method for the estimation of the percentage of various free steroids in small volumes of undiluted serum, under conditions which mimic the *in vivo* situation (Hammond *et al.*, 1980).

In brief, 450-μl samples of plasma or serum are preequilibrated with the tritium-labeled steroid of interest and carbon-14 labeled glucose at 37°C. Duplicate aliquots of 200 μl are placed in a small tube which is closed at one end with Visking dialysis tubing. The tubes are placed within minicounting vials which have three pads of filter paper at the bottom. After capping, the vials are centrifuged at 3000 rpm for 1 hour at 37°C. The inner tube is removed, 500 μl water added, and scintillation fluid added to the minivial. A 30-μl aliquot of the remaining serum is prepared similarly and both vials counted. The percentage of free steroid is obtained simply by dividing the ratio $^3H/^{14}C$ measured outside the membrane by that observed for the serum sample following centrifugation.

In our evaluation of the method, we have shown that there is no adsorption or other loss of radiolabeled compounds during analysis. We have also demonstrated the importance of performing the estimations of percentage of free steroid at physiologic temperature. In addition, our experimental data demonstrated that at 37°C the percentage of free steroid is not influenced by varying the sample volume, the centrifugal force, or the time of centrifugation, all of which determine the volume of ultrafiltrate and the degree to which serum proteins are concentrated. These results can only be obtained if equilibrium exists between free steroid on both sides of the membrane and the serum binding components under the experimental conditions. Thus, centrifugal ultrafiltration-dialysis appears to be ideally suited for studies of ligand–protein interactions in complex biological mixtures, since the sample composition is altered minimally. This is of crucial importance in physiological studies of steroids, such as estradiol, which compete for the same binding site on SHBG with more abundant and higher affinity androgens. Thus, the percentage of free estradiol may either be elevated by a decrease in SHBG concentration or an increase in competing steroids or other substances that interact directly or indirectly with SHBG or albumin. In addition to these theoretical considerations, the technique offers several practical advantages over other methods in current use. In comparison with other methods which utilize undiluted samples, the technique enables the duplicate determination of free steroids in smaller sample volumes (450 μl), a feature which is particularly important when dealing with clinical material or samples from small animals. Moreover, the number of samples which can be assayed at the same time is only limited by the capacity of the centrifuge. During equilibrium dialysis a variable dilution occurs which necessitates corrections that are both tedious and prone to error (Kley *et al.*, 1977a; Moll and Rosenfield, 1978). In contrast, the present technique avoids these problems and no volume measurements are necessary. While the flow dialysis technique described by Colowick and Womack (1969) and recently adapted for measurement of percentage of free testosterone (Moll and Rosenfield, 1977) provides similar theoretical advantages, it is cumbersome and requires 10 ml of sample.

C. ESTIMATION OF THE BINDING AFFINITIES AND DISTRIBUTION OF A STEROID IN PLASMA

As indicated above, much attention has been directed toward developing experimental methods for estimating the free fraction of a steroid hormone in plasma because of its presumed biological importance. In parallel studies, mathematical treatments of complex binding equilibria were also developed as reviewed by Tait and Burstein (1964). These authors presented general equations for estimating the free steroid hormone concentration from experimentally determinable binding parameters for low affinity, high capacity (albumin) and high affinity, low capacity (e.g., CBG) proteins in plasma. Having developed a convenient and accurate method for estimating the percentage of any steroid that is not bound to proteins in plasma, it became apparent that the equations of Tait and Burstein (1964) could be used to obtain direct estimates of the affinity constants of a steroid for albumin, CBG, and SHBG at 37°C. In addition, we were interested in developing a simple method for determining the distribution of a steroid in diluted plasma at 37°C among the free, albumin bound, and CBG or SHBG bound fractions. Many approaches to this problem have been used in the past including the classical method of equilibrium dialysis. For example, Vermuelen (1977) used equilibrium dialysis of 1 : 5 diluted plasma at 37°C to estimate the distribution of testosterone in male and female plasma. While many nonequilibrium methods involving separation of bound and free radioactive hormone have been described for CBG and SHBG bound steroids, they are restricted to studies of high affinity ligands at reduced temperatures. Early methods for separation included variants of the gel filtration technique described for

CBG by DeMoor *et al.* (1962). An interesting improvement was described by Igbal and Johnson (1977) in which a two-tier column was used to remove albumin prior to separation of bound and free hormone by gel filtration on LH-20. Most recently, Dunn *et al.* (1981) devised an equilibrium method suitable for both SHBG and CBG bound steroids based upon the ability of Con A-sepharose to bind both glycoproteins. They estimated the values of K_D at 37°C for various steroids from competitive binding relative to testosterone and cortisol for SHBG and CBG, respectively. Together with literature values for binding affinities to albumin, steroid, and protein concentrations, these workers developed a computer model to estimate the unbound fraction of 21 steroids in human plasma. The results obtained are in excellent agreement with values obtained by our isodialysis method. The important influence of physiologic changes in plasma SHBG or CBG concentrations on the distribution of steroids in plasma was also clearly illustrated by this indirect approach (Dunn *et al.*, 1981).

By taking advantage of the fact that both SHBG and CBG are heat labile (Westphal, 1971; Rosner, 1972b), we have devised simple, direct methods for estimating the extent to which a steroid is bound and its affinity for albumin, CBG, or SHBG under physiologic conditions. Measurement of the percentage free steroid in separate aliquots of a plasma sample with and without prior heating at 60°C for 30 minutes allows estimation of the fractional distribution as determined by the following relationships.

$$\text{native serum} \quad 1 = B + A_n + F_n \tag{1}$$
$$\text{heated serum} \quad 1 = A_H + F_H \tag{2}$$

where B equals the fraction of steroid bound to CBG or SHBG, A_n and A_H equal the fractions of steroid bound to albumin, and F_n and F_H equal the fractions of steroid not bound to proteins in the native and heated serum, respectively. As pointed out by several authors, the distribution of a steroid between albumin and the free fraction is independent of the presence of either CBG or SHBG. Therefore

$$(A_n/F_n) = (A_H/F_H) = (1 - F_H)/F_H$$

Dividing Eq. (1) by F_n and rearranging yields:

$$B = 1 - F_n(A_H/F_H + 1) \tag{3}$$

Which can also be written as

$$B = 1 - F_nN \tag{4}$$

where $N = A_H/F_H + 1$.

The fraction of steroid bound to albumin in native serum, A_n, is then obtained by inserting the values of B and F_n into Eq. (1). The value of A_H/F_H is a direct measure of the binding affinity of the steroid for albumin since $A_H[S]/F_H[S] = nK_A$ where n is the concentration of albumin binding sites and [S] is the total concentration of steroid. If one binding site per molecule is assumed then n is the molar concentration of albumin.

Equation V-79 from Tait and Burstein (1964) can be rewritten for any steroid, S, as follows:

$$F_n[S] = [S]/[N + K_B(C_B - S_B)] \tag{5}$$

where K_B equals the association constant for S binding to CBG or SHBG, C_B equals the total binding capacity of CBG or SHBG, and S_B equals the concentration of S that is bound to CBG or SHBG, and F_n, [S], and N are as before. Rearrangement and simplification of Eq. (5) yields:

$$K_B = B/[F_n(C_B - S_B)] \tag{6}$$

which defines the relationship between the ratio of CBG or SHBG bound to free steroid (B/F_n), and the concentration of unoccupied CBG or SHBG binding sites in plasma $(C_B - S_B)$.

While Eq. (6) implies that the value of K_B may be estimated without knowledge of the total steroid concentration, this is not possible for whole plasma in which more than one steroid may bind with high affinity to either CBG or SHBG. Therefore, in order to obtain precise estimates of K_B, whole plasma was treated with 5% charcoal at room temperature for 2 hours in order to remove both free and bound endogenous steroids. Radiolabeled steroids were then added to approximate physiologic concentrations (e.g., 200 nM [³H]cortisol) prior to determining F_n and F_H as described above. We have ignored binding to α-1-acid-glycoprotein since its concentration in plasma is very low compared to albumin, whereas its affinity for steroids is of the same order of magnitude. Furthermore, we are forced to ignore the problem of steroids binding to both CBG and SHBG. However, this does not introduce serious errors. For example, in the case of T, only 2–3.5% is bound to CBG in the plasma of normal women and men (Dunn et al., 1981). This new approach to estimating binding affinities under physiologic conditions has been particularly valuable in studies of steroid binding in plasma of nonhuman primates as discussed below.

Estimates of the distribution of steroids in plasma according to Eq. (4) have been made with and without prior charcoal extraction. Comparison of results obtained following removal of endogenous steroids can determine if an unusually high free F_n value is due to the presence of high endogenous steroid levels.

III. Distribution of Steroids in Plasma and Relationship to Their Metabolic Clearance Rates

Beginning around 1955 when isotopically labeled steroids became commercially available, much attention was directed to studies of cortisol metabolism *in vivo* (for reviews see Tait and Burstein, 1964; Gurpide, 1975; Peterson, 1977). The theoretical concepts of metabolic clearance (MCR) and production rates (PR), and experimental methods for their estimation, were established and the important effect of CBG binding on the MCR of cortisol was quickly recognized. Subsequent studies in many laboratories have shown that, in general, the MCR of most steroids is inversely related to their binding affinity for either CBG or SHBG. This relationship is exemplified by the sex steroids DHT, T, and E_2, but exceptions occur as in the case of progesterone, which binds to CBG with nearly the same affinity as cortisol but has an MCR approximately 10-fold higher. Throughout this work, it has been tacitly assumed that the MCR of a steroid is related to the free or nonprotein bound steroid concentration in blood. This notion stems from the early proposal of Robbins and Rall (1957) based on their *in vivo* kinetic studies of thyroxine metabolism. Reasonably good correlations of MCR values with estimates of the free concentrations of steroids have strengthened this opinion. Uncertainty concerning the fate of albumin bound steroid can be ascribed in part to the lack of methods for easily obtaining direct estimates of the albumin bound fraction of steroid hormones in plasma. We have for the first time developed a direct method for this purpose.

Figure 4 illustrates the increase in the free percentage for several important steroid hormones following heat denaturation of SHBG and CBG. The increase is small for steroids such as E_2, T, and progesterone whereas it is much larger for others such as DHT and cortisol. This difference in behavior reflects varying affinities for albumin, the former being more avidly bound than the latter. For example, the nearly 10-fold difference in values of F_H for cortisol and progesterone reflect the much higher affinity of albumin for progesterone. Calculated values for the distribution of 4 hormones in plasma from a normal female are presented in Fig. 5. In general, our values are in good agreement with those recently published by Dunn *et al.* (1981). Significant differences can be noted, however. Dunn *et al.* (1981) estimated that only 21% cf aldosterone is bound to CBG in plasma compared to our value of 35%. Furthermore, their estimates of the fractions of E_2 (37.3%) and T (66.0%) that are bound to SHBG are also

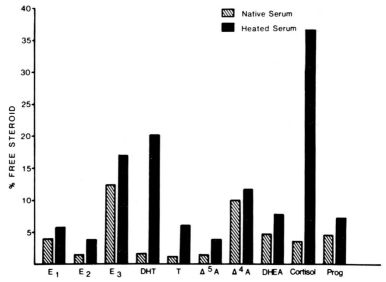

FIG. 4.   Change in percentage of free steroid caused by heating serum from a normal female at 60°C for 30 minutes. Percentage of free steroid was measured in undiluted serum at 37°C by isodialysis as described in Section II.

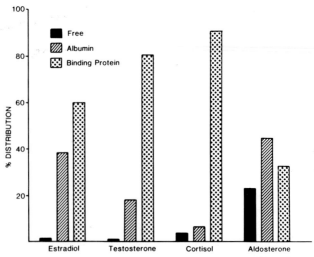

FIG. 5.   Distribution of steroids in normal female plasma at 37°C estimated from measurements of percentage of free steroid in native and heat-treated plasma as described in Section II.

lower than those shown in Fig. 5. This is probably due to their unusually low mean binding capacity of SHBG (37 nM) for normal women, since most investigators report values of 50–60 nM (Anderson, 1974; Rosner, 1972).

Table I presents the binding parameters obtained as described earlier for 6 hormones in normal male plasma. Again, the agreement between our results and those of Dunn *et al.* (1981) is remarkably good for the distribution of steroids and for values of the association constants (K_B). The small differences in K_B may be due to the fact that Dunn *et al.* (1981) assumed values for SHBG, CBG, albumin, and plasma steroid concentrations, whereas our estimates are independent of these variables, except for CBG and SHBG binding capacities which were measured as described earlier. The binding affinities of steroids for albumin (nK_A) are also in good agreement with the available data assembled by Westphal (1971). Figure 6 illustrates the relationship between the percentages of steroid that are bound to either SHBG or CBG and their MCR values in men or women taken from the literature. Since the range of MCR values reported for a given steroid within and between different studies is fairly large, we have used weighted mean values for this analysis. The remarkably good linear relationship between MCR and percentage bound shown in Fig. 6 contrasts with that shown in Fig. 7, where the free percentage of 9 steroids measured by isodialysis is plotted against MCR values. These results suggest that both the free and albumin bound fractions are irreversibly cleared from blood and contribute to the MCR, whereas the SHBG or CBG bound fractions do not. Furthermore, the limiting value of about

TABLE I

Binding Parameters for Hormones in Normal Male Plasma[a]

| Steroids | Binding capacity (nM) | Percentage | | | nK_A $M^{-1} \times 10^{-4}$ | K_B $M^{-1} \times 10^{-8}$ |
		Free	Albumin	CBG or SBG		
Testosterone	39	2.6	30.4	67	1.1 (1.8)	7.6 (16)
Estradiol	39	2.2	72.8	35	2.8	4.5 (6.8)
Cortisol	416	5.1	11.9	83	0.21 (0.3)	0.79 (0.76)
Corticosterone	416	5.1	23.2	71.7	0.36	0.76 (0.76)
Deoxycorticosterone	416	4.2	35.8	60	0.8	0.65 (0.45)
Aldosterone	416	28.2	41.8	30	0.15 (0.17)	0.035 (0.019)

[a] Binding parameters estimated from a charcoal-extracted pool of heparinized plasma obtained from normal young men as described in Section II. The concentration of albumin was 4.6 gm% (0.77 mM). The values for K_B shown in parentheses are those obtained by Dunn *et al.* (1981) and for nK_A from Westphal (1971).

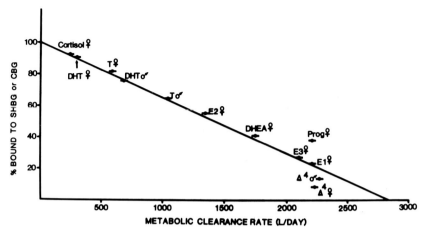

FIG. 6.   Correlation between the percentages of steroids bound to either SHBG or CBG in undiluted serum at 37°C and their metabolic clearance rates (MCR). Values of MCR were obtained from the literature.

2800 liters/day of plasma (Fig. 6), which is roughly twice the rate of splanchnic plasma flow, is in agreement with actual measurements. We interpret this relationship to mean that in the absence of CBG or SHBG, all steroids would be rapidly and irreversibly removed from the circulation by both hepatic and extrahepatic metabolism. As pointed out previ-

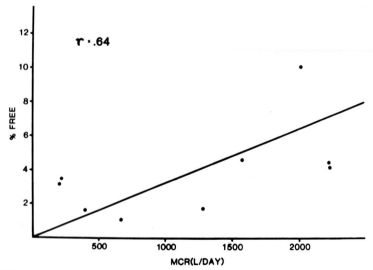

FIG. 7.   Correlation between the percentages of free steroids in undiluted plasma at 37°C and mean values of their MCRs obtained from the literature.

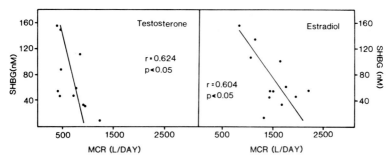

FIG. 8. Correlation between the serum SHBG binding capacity and the MCR of testosterone and estradiol measured by the constant infusion method in postmenopausal women.

ously by many others, the presence of specific high affinity binding proteins in blood appears to protect steroid hormones from rapid metabolism.

A further implication of the results shown in Fig. 6 is that the MCR of a particular steroid in different individuals is a function of the plasma concentration of CBG or SHBG. We have examined this possibility for T and E_2. With the generous assistance of Dr. Howard Judd, we have measured the SHBG levels and the distribution of both hormones in plasma samples from postmenopausal women in whom the MCR had been determined by the constant infusion method. Statistically significant ($p < 0.05$; $r = 0.6$–0.7) correlations between MCR and percentage of T or E_2 bound to SHBG were found (data not shown). The correlations between the SHBG binding capacity and values of MCR for both T and E_2 are shown in Fig. 8. As can be seen, the MCR for both steroids is inversely related to SHBG binding capacity in these individuals. It should be noted that the plasma samples had been stored frozen for 3–5 years prior to our analyses. Nevertheless, these observations suggest that both the clearance (MCR) and production rates (PR = MCR × C) of a steroid hormone may be estimated with reasonable accuracy from a single small sample of blood. This would be invaluable in many situations which preclude the use of radioisotopic methods such as during pregnancy and the neonatal period. Of course these estimates are invalid in abnormal situations such as cirrhosis.

IV. Availability of Estradiol in Human Plasma

A. EVIDENCE FOR ESTRADIOL BINDING TO SHBG

Many reports have demonstrated the importance of SHBG binding of androgens in the plasma of humans and other species (Anderson, 1974; Vermeulen, 1977). Indeed, one of the strongest arguments in support of the concept that only the unbound hormone is biologically active arises from the correlation of free testosterone (or total 17-β-hydroxy androgen) levels with the degree of virilization in abnormal conditions such as polycystic ovarian disease (Anderson, 1974). Little attention has been given to similar relationships for estradiol (E_2). This stems at least in part from the lower affinity of E_2 for SHBG and the greater difficulty in estimating its free concentration. Indeed, one group of workers concluded that binding of E_2 to SHBG was negligible *in vivo* (Vigersky *et al.*, 1979). However, Anderson (1974) provided strong evidence for the important influence of variations in SHBG concentration on the percentage of free E_2 in undiluted plasma. More recently, Wu *et al.* (1976) have also demonstrated an inverse relationship between percentage free E_2 and plasma SHBG levels. In preliminary experiments, we obtained additional direct evidence for binding of E_2 to SHBG under physiologic conditions. As shown in Fig. 9 the addition of nonradioactive steroids to normal female plasma causes an increase in the percentage of free E_2 that is proportional to their known affinities for SHBG. Testosterone (T) and dihydrotestosterone (DHT) are more effective competitors than androstenedione (A) or estrone (E_1). These results indicate that E_2, T, and DHT compete for the same binding site in whole plasma. Figure 10 illustrates the changes in percentage free E_2 that occur when plasma is diluted and/or heated to 60°C for 30 minutes to destroy the SHBG binding activity. The percentage free E_2 increases dramatically upon dilution of plasma but increases still further if the sample is heated before analysis. It should be noted that many

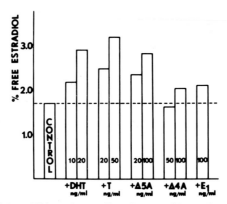

FIG. 9.   Effect of the addition of nonradioactive steroids on the percentage of free estradiol measured in undiluted normal female serum at 37°C by isodialysis. Steroid solutions in alcohol were added to test tubes to achieve the final concentrations indicated and the alcohol was evaporated prior to addition. T, Testosterone; DHT, dihydrotestosterone; Δ5A, androst-5-ene-3,17β-diol; Δ4A, androstenedione; E_1, estrone.

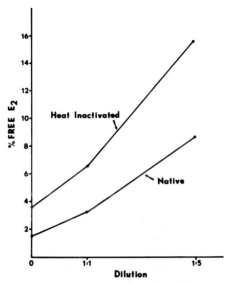

FIG. 10. Effect of dilution and heat inactivation of SHBG on percentage of free estradiol (E_2) measured in undiluted serum at 37°C by isodialysis. Normal male serum was diluted with 0.01 M Tris, pH 7.4 buffer with or without prior heating at 60°C for 30 minutes.

previous workers have used 1 : 5 dilutions of plasma in steroid binding studies. Figure 11 illustrates the relationship between percentage free E_2 and T and SHBG levels found in pregnant women, nonpregnant women, and men. It is apparent that the percentage free E_2 parallels that of T and is inversely related to the SHBG binding capacity as expected. Taken together, these results leave little doubt that binding of E_2 to SHBG occurs under physiologic conditions and that changes in SHBG levels play an important role in the distribution and transport of E_2.

B. NORMAL MENSTRUAL CYCLE

In agreement with previous reports (Wu *et al.*, 1976), we have found no consistent variation in plasma SHBG binding capacity during the normal menstrual cycle. Consequently, the percentage of free E_2 shows no significant pattern. For example, the mean values of percentage free E_2 in 2 normal young women, sampled at 2–3 day intervals during the menstrual cycle, were 1.59% ± 0.09 (n = 9) and 2.11 ± 0.16 (n = 8). The variation observed is no greater than the reproducibility of the assay (CV = 7%). The failure to observe an increase in SHBG levels when E_2 levels are elevated may be due to a counteracting effect of luteal phase proges-

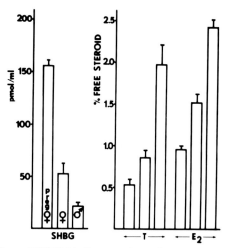

FIG. 11.   Comparison of SHBG binding capacity and percentage of free T or E_2 in serum from pregnant or nonpregnant women, and men. SHBG binding capacity was measured by the DEAE filter assay. Percentages of free T and E_2 were measured by isodialysis in undiluted serum at 37°C. The percentage free values for T and E_2 for the different sera are shown in the same order from left to right as the SHBG values.

terone, since some reports suggest that synthetic progestin administration suppresses SHBG binding capacity (Anderson, 1974). Changes in percentage free E_2 due to competition by serum androgens is not observed because of the high SHBG binding capacity relative to the total concentration of steroids that bind in the plasma of normal women.

C. OBESITY AND ENDOMETRIAL CANCER

Continuing our long standing interest in possible abnormalities of estrogen production or metabolism that might predispose women to cancer of the reproductive tract, we studied plasma binding of E_2 in postmenopausal women with and without endometrial cancer (Nisker *et al.*, 1980; Davidson *et al.*, 1981). In agreement with the early report of DeMoor and Joosens (1970), we found that SHBG levels were depressed in obese subjects and, as a consequence, the percentage free E_2 was increased markedly as shown in Fig. 12. However, the linear regression lines relating plasma SHBG binding capacity and percentage of free estradiol were very similar for the patients with endometrial carcinoma and normal weight-matched postmenopausal women, thus indicating that there was no difference in the SHBG–E_2 interaction in these subject groups. Although previous studies have suggested that increased peripheral production of estrogen in obese subjects may account for the relationship between obesity and endometrial cancer (Siiteri and MacDonald, 1973), no difference in either the extent of conversion of androstenedione to estrone (MacDonald *et al.*, 1978) or serum estrone and estradiol levels (Judd *et al.*, 1976) has been found between patients with endometrial carcinoma and weight-matched controls. Similarly, no differences have been found in plasma free E_2 levels (Davidson *et al.*, 1981). The mean values in the cancer and weight matched controls were 0.35 and 0.31 pg/ml, respectively. Nevertheless, the values are about twice those found in normal weight postmenopausal women with and without hip fractures (Davidson *et al.*, 1981). Thus, obesity appears to augment estrogen availability through both increased production and a decrease in serum SHBG capacity, which increases the percentage of free estradiol.

The seemingly paradoxical decrease in plasma SHBG binding capacity in obese postmenopausal subjects is difficult to explain. Estrogen administration is known to elevate SHBG levels (Anderson, 1974). In addition to obesity, hyperandrogenism and hypothyroidism are known to be associated with depressed serum SHBG binding capacity (Anderson, 1974). There is little evidence to suggest that the production of androgens is elevated in obese postmenopausal women. Similarly, abnormalities in the production or action of thyroid hormone have not been discerned in obesity, despite extensive investigations. However, it is possible that reduced hepatic SHBG synthesis reflects a defect in the action of thyroid hormone in the liver that is not detected by the usual tests of thyroid function. Thus, measurement of serum SHBG capacity may serve as an exquisitely sensitive indicator of thyroid hormone function. Furthermore, some of the observed interactions between thyroid and sex steroid hormones may be mediated by changes in serum SHBG binding capacity rather than at the

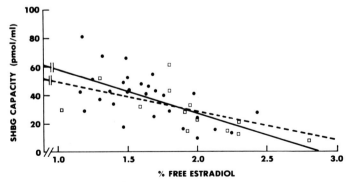

FIG. 12. Correlation of SHBG binding capacity and percentage of free estradiol in serum of postmenopausal women with (□) and without (●) endometrial cancer.

cellular level. For example, the clinical observation that administration of thyroid hormone to women with menorrhagia often eliminates the impact of excessive estrogen on the endometrium could be explained by a decrease in the percentage of free estradiol, as a result of increased SHBG levels. It should be pointed out, however, that measurements of binding capacity may not reflect the actual SHBG protein level in all situations.

D. BREAST CANCER

Previous studies, using equilibrium dialysis of diluted serum (Wang and Bulbrook, 1969; Kirschner et al., 1978), failed to detect differences in free steroids, including E_2, in breast cancer patients. We have compared the percentage of free estradiol in women with breast cancer and controls who were matched for weight and menopausal status. In a pilot study, we found that the mean values in a group of 17 breast cancer patients was significantly higher (2.15 ± 0.09) than in the control group (1.52 ± 0.07; Siiteri, 1981). Of particular interest was the fact that neither the body weight nor the SHBG binding capacity was different in the two groups. This raised the possibility that the percentage of free E_2 might be elevated by factors other than reduced SHBG binding capacity. Possible explanations for the elevated free E_2 that we observed include competition by steroids or other substances for E_2 binding to SHBG, or an abnormal steroid binding site. Despite the fact that we have confirmed our original observations with nearly identical results in a much larger study of nearly 100 patients (Moore et al., 1981), we have thus far not been able to identify the abnormality responsible for elevated percentage free estradiol in plasma of women with breast cancer. Nonetheless, we are continuing to study E_2 binding in plasma from breast cancer patients.

E. POLYCYSTIC OVARIAN DISEASE

In other studies (Nisker et al., 1980) we have measured the percentage of free E_2 in women with polycystic ovarian disease (PCOD). As shown in Fig. 13, we found that plasma SHBG binding capacity is reduced to normal male levels in PCOD patients, in agreement with previous reports (Anderson, 1974). The depressed levels of SHBG are independent of body weight and presumably due to increased androgen production which depresses hepatic SHBG synthesis. As is the case for T, the percentage of free E_2 is also elevated in PCOD. As shown in Fig. 14, the mean level of free E_2 in the 11 PCOD patients was 1.5 pg/ml as compared with 0.5 pg/ml in normal women during the early follicular phase of the menstrual cycle. These observations suggested to us that an increased concentration of free

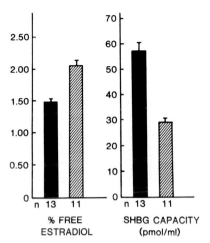

FIG. 13. Percentage of free estradiol and SHBG binding capacity in serum from 13 normal young women during the early follicular phase of the menstrual cycle (solid bars) and 11 women with polycystic ovarian disease (hatched bars).

estradiol, despite normal total levels, might be important in the development of PCOD. Depressed SHBG binding capacity due to hypersecretion of androgens by either the ovaries and/or adrenals, with or without obesity, might indirectly result in a chronic hyperestrogenic effect on the pituitary. Since it is well established that estrogens increase the sensitivity

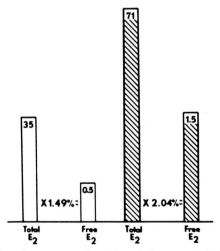

FIG. 14. Mean values for concentrations of total plasma estradiol (E_2), percentage free E_2, and free E_2 in normal women during the early follicular phase of the menstrual cycle (open bars) and women with PCOD (see Fig. 13).

of the pituitary to GnRH (Young and Jaffe, 1976), this could explain the hypersecretion of LH which drives the ovaries to excessive androgen production. A similar proposal was put forth by Mishell and his co-workers subsequently (Lobo *et al.*, 1981).

It is apparent from the above studies that the percentage of free E_2 in human plasma is small and only varies about 1–3%. However, the percentage of E_2 bound to albumin is much larger and varies from about 20 to 90% depending upon the SHBG level. Alterations in the sum of free and albumin-bound (available) estradiol under various conditions are illustrated in Fig. 15. In normal women with SHBG binding capacity in the range of 40–80 nM, about 50–70% of E_2 is potentially available to target cells. In pregnant and hyperthyroid women the fraction is reduced to about 20%, whereas in obese, hypothyroid, and hyperandrogenic women, it is elevated to 80–90%. Thus, for a given level of total plasma E_2 the amount bound to SHBG can vary 4- to 5-fold. We have previously suggested that this neglected aspect of estrogen availability may contribute to a "silent" hyperestrogenic milieu that may underly risk factors such as obesity, hypothyroidism, and hyperandrogenism that have been associated with endometrial and breast cancer (Nisker and Siiteri, 1981; Siiteri, 1981; Siiteri *et al.*, 1981).

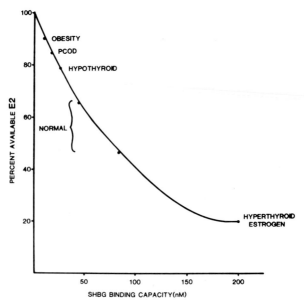

FIG. 15. Variation of percentage available E_2 (percentage free plus percentage albumin bound E_2) with SHBG binding capacity in women.

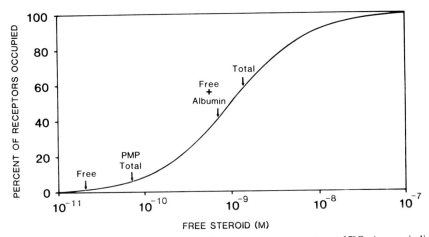

FIG. 16. Theoretical saturation plot for human estrogen receptor at 37°C. Arrows indicate approximate percentages of receptor occupancy for free and free plus albumin bound estradiol concentrations when the total estradiol level is 400 pg/ml and the SHBG binding capacity is 60 nM. Cellular entry of estradiol is assumed to occur by simple diffusion from blood.

F. IS THE PLASMA-FREE HORMONE CONCEPT CONSISTANT WITH STEROID HORMONE ACTION?

During the course of the above studies it became apparent that the actual concentrations of unbound estradiol in the plasma of women were extremely low. For example, the mean concentration of plasma free E_2 (0.35 pg/ml) in postmenopausal women with endometrial cancer, all of whom had associated endometrial hyperplasia, corresponds to a molar concentration of about $1 \times 10^{-12}\ M$, which is far below the value of $1 \times 10^{-9}\ M$ estimated for the dissociation constant (K_D) of the human estrogen receptor at 37°C.[4] Even the maximum free estradiol concentrations observed during the normal menstrual cycle ($1.5\% \times 400$ pg/ml, or about $2 \times 10^{-11}\ M$) would permit only fractional saturation of cellular estrogen receptors as illustrated in Fig. 16. Thus simple diffusion of plasma E_2 into target cells cannot account for its biological activity. At least two alternative possibilities could explain these discrepancies: (1) as suggested by the recent studies of Pardridge (1981), the much larger albumin bound fraction of a steroid in plasma may also be available to target tissues, or (2) one or more mechanisms independent of receptor binding may operate to increase the intracellular concentration of hormone. As shown in Fig. 16,

---

[4] Since we were unable to find a value for the dissociation constant for estrogen binding to the human estrogen receptor at 37°C, we have assumed the value to be similar to that reported for the rat uterine receptor at 37°C (1.3 nM, Anderson *et al.*, 1972).

even if both free and albumin bound fractions of plasma E_2 were available to receptors, the peak concentration in cycling women would be about $5 \times 10^{-10} M$ E_2. Moreover, only about $3 \times 10^{-11} M$ E_2 would be available in the plasma of obese postmenopausal women, even after taking into consideration the depressed SHBG levels. Thus it would appear that biologically effective levels of plasma estradiol saturate estrogen receptors by mechanisms other than simple diffusion of free and albumin bound hormone. A similar problem exists for other steroid hormones that are present in low concentrations in plasma such as aldosterone (free concentration is ca. $10^{-10} M$). The disparity is not as great in the case of cortisol. Using our estimate of 3.5% for unbound cortisol, the normal range of plasma free cortisol is about 5–15 nM whereas the K_D of binding to the glucocorticoid receptor is estimated to be about 10 nM at 37°C (P. Ballard, personal communication). It is often stated that steroid binding to tissue receptors is of higher affinity than to serum binding proteins. Our estimate of the value of K_D for cortisol binding to CBG at 37°C (12 nM, Table I) shows that this is not the case.

Thus it would appear that a mechanism must exist for enriching the intracellular estradiol concentration since much evidence suggests that full biological response requires full receptor occupancy (Clark and Peck, 1979). This may occur simply by nonspecific binding to lipid containing membranes or other cellular components as commonly observed in tissue binding studies or by processes involving specific binding to nonreceptor proteins. For example, Clark and his associates have described specific Type 2 binding sites in rat uterus that have a somewhat lower affinity for E_2 than the classical estrogen receptor (Clark and Peck, 1979). Neither the function nor the origin of these Type 2 binders is known, however. Many reports have described the presence of "transcortin-like" binding proteins in tissues that contain glucocorticoid or progesterone receptors (see below). While these findings raise the possibility that CBG may serve a transport function in cellular uptake of steroids, most studies directed to this question have reached the opposite conclusion (for review see Ballard, 1979).

A considerable body of evidence recently reviewed by Giorgi (1980) suggests that steroids enter cells by simple diffusion. For example, Giorgi and Stein (1980) have recently studied uptake of many steroids by several cell lines and concluded that free diffusion alone is important. However, some evidence has been presented for mediated transport systems. Milgrom et al. (1973) and his co-workers studied E_2 and DES uptake by isolated endometrial cells in the presence and absence of various inhibitors and concluded that receptor binding alone could not account for the rate of steroid uptake. More recently, Szego and Pietras (1981) have presented strong evidence for the presence of E_2 binding sites on the surface of plasma membranes of both rat uterine and liver cells. Although it was suggested that these binding sites may be involved in cellular uptake of estrogen, the possibility that they may arise from serum binding proteins was not considered. It is of interest in this regard that Gurpide *et al.* (1971) found that uptake of estradiol by human endometrial tissue was markedly reduced by albumin but unchanged or increased by partially purified SHBG when both were added to perfusion buffers. Recent studies with a pituitary tumor cell line (AtT-20/D-1) have led Harrison and his co-workers to propose that these cells contain membrane transport systems for glucocorticoids (Harrison *et al.*, 1974, 1975, 1977; Harrison and Yeakley, 1979; Svec *et al.*, 1980; Yeakley *et al.*, 1980). Using [^{3}H]triamcinolone acetonide they found that pretreatment of cells with neuraminidase, phospholipase A, ethanol, or dimethyl sulfoxide greatly reduced uptake by whole cells without affecting binding capacity of the cytosol receptor. In other experiments, these workers found a striking temperature effect on both the rate and extent of steroid uptake by intact cells. Greatly reduced amounts of steroid were taken up at 4°C compared with 25°C and further study revealed a biphasic temperature response with a break at 16°C. Although other interpretations are possible, these authors suggested that the temperature dependence of triamcinolone uptake by AtT-20/D-1 cells reflects a membrane transport system. CBG participation in such a transport system seems to be ruled out by its low binding affinity for synthetic glucocorticoids. However, it has recently been reported by Do and Feldman (1980) that bovine serum contains a high affinity binder for triamcinolone acetonide. Rao *et al.* (1976) studied cortisol uptake by freshly prepared intact liver cells and concluded that uptake at low hormone concentrations was due to a high affinity carrier process whereas simple diffusion occurs at high steroid concentrations. However, the possibility that CBG binding was involved at low steroid concentrations was not investigated. As discussed below, we have obtained new evidence for cellular uptake of CBG–steroid complexes.

V. Comparative Studies of Plasma Steroid Binding in Primates

The presence of CBG has been demonstrated in virtually all species examined although its plasma concentration varies widely (Seal and Doe, 1966). Of interest was the apparently low CBG binding observed in New World monkeys. Certain New World primates such as the squirrel monkey and marmoset are known to have unusually high blood concentrations of steroid hormones. Reichlin and his associates found cortisol levels in squirrel monkeys that are 20- to 50-fold higher than those found in human plasma (Brown *et al.*, 1970). Furthermore, plasma testosterone levels in males during the breeding season are also much higher than those found in men (Coe *et al.*, 1981). In view of our concern that insufficient plasma free steroid is available to saturate tissue receptors in the human, these findings suggested that the opposite situation may occur in other species. For this reason, we have compared the binding of cortisol and DHT in plasma of Columbian squirrel monkeys, rhesus monkeys, and humans. Figure 17 shows the percentage of free cortisol and the fraction that is bound to CBG in these three species. As can be seen, the percentage of free cortisol in the rhesus monkey is 2-fold higher than in humans whereas the value for squirrel monkeys is 5- to 10-fold higher. As a consequence, only about 15–40% of cortisol is bound to CBG in squirrel monkey plasma as compared to about 90% in humans. If we take into consideration the total cortisol levels, it appears that there is 50–400 times more free cortisol in the plasma of squirrel monkeys (ca. 1–4 μM) than in human plasma (ca. 10 nM). As can be seen in Fig. 17, the percentage of free cortisol in squirrel monkey plasma is more variable than in plasma of humans and rhesus monkeys. Presumably, this reflects the much broader range of CBG binding capacity (DEAE filter assay) found in squirrel monkeys. The cortisol binding capacity ranged from 20 to 4700 nM in 35 separate pools of squirrel monkey plasma. Mean values for females (1192) exceeded that of males (602) and cortisol binding capacity is highly correlated with cortisol levels. The calculated binding affinity of cortisol for CBG from squirrel monkey plasma ($K_A = 3.1 \times 10^6 M$) is considerably lower than

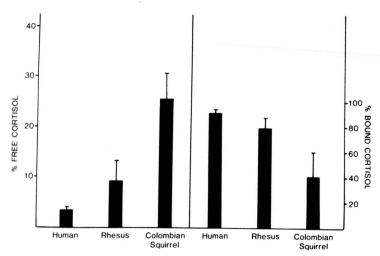

FIG. 17.   Percentage of free and CBG bound cortisol in undiluted plasma (37°C) of three primates. Bars indicate standard errors of the mean.

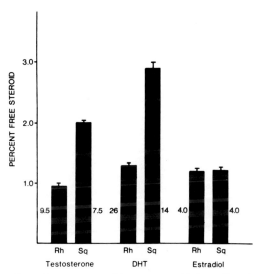

FIG. 18. Comparison of percentages of free sex steroids in undiluted male plasma (37°C) from rhesus (Rh) and squirrel (Sq) monkeys. The numbers beside each bar indicate the percentage free value following heat inactivation of SHBG.

that found for rhesus monkeys ($K_A = 3.5 \times 10^7$) which is consistent with the higher percentage of free cortisol.

Thus, the squirrel monkey adrenal glands appear to secrete enormous quantities of cortisol which results in extraordinarily high free cortisol levels in blood. This situation may represent a condition of severe glucocorticoid resistance analogous to androgen insensitivity found in rodents and humans. At present we can only speculate upon the nature of this apparent resistance to cortisol. On the basis of the free hormone concept of biological activity, one might predict that the tissue glucocorticoid receptors have a markedly reduced affinity for cortisol which would require high steroid levels for occupancy and function. Interestingly, a less severe form of cortisol insensitivity has been described in two related human subjects (Vingerhoeds et al., 1976). Both had high total and free 24 hour mean plasma cortisol, and high ACTH levels without any of the stigmata of Cushing's syndrome. Further study of these subjects revealed that the glucocorticoid receptors in white cells and fibroblasts were reduced in number and had lower than normal affinity for dexamethasone (Chrousos et al., 1981). We have not as yet had an opportunity to completely study the glucocorticoid receptors in the squirrel monkey but such studies are under way.

Figure 18 shows a comparison of the percentages of free E_2, T, and DHT in squirrel and rhesus monkey plasma. As can be seen, the values for both androgens in squirrel plasma are about twice those found in rhesus plasma whereas the percentage free E_2 is the same. Binding studies using the DEAE filter assay at $4°C$ revealed that the K_D for DHT in squirrel monkey plasma (K_D = 10 nM) is about 8-fold lower than in rhesus plasma (K_D = 1.2 nM). Furthermore, comparison of the dissociation rates for DHT revealed that the $t_{1/2}$ obtained for squirrel monkey plasma is about one-twentieth of that found in the rhesus. These results are of special interest because the plasma concentration of T is extremely high (20–50 ng/ml) in males during the breeding season whereas plasma E_2 levels in females during the menstrual cycle are within the range found in other primates (Coe et al., 1981). At present, we can only speculate on the significance of these unusual findings. They suggest that the binding affinities of SHBG for various ligands may vary independently. If this were true, then the possibility is raised for cellular recognition of different forms of the SHBG molecule depending upon whether androgens or estrogens are bound. In any event, it will be of great interest to compare receptor affinities for sex steroids as well as cortisol in these species.

VI. Binding of Steroids in Other Body Fluids

Most studies of extracellular steroid binding proteins have been confined to blood although the presence of CBG in human lymph has been noted (Sandberg et al., 1960). Several studies indicating its presence in human milk, based largely on the similarity of affinities of many steroids to milk and plasma binders, have been reported (Rosner et al., 1976; Payne et al., 1976). CBG identified in guinea pig milk also has steroid affinities similar to plasma CBG (Raymoure and Kuhn, 1980). We were motivated to examine normal human breast fluid for steroid binding because of reports indicating the presence of high concentrations of estrogens in this fluid (Wynder and Hill, 1977). The binding capacity of "SHBG" in breast fluid (55 ± 8 nM, n = 8) is slightly lower than that found in normal female serum, whereas cortisol binding was only 10–20% of that obtained in serum. Since we had no assurance that the binding measured with [^{3}H]DHT and [^{3}H]cortisol was due to SHBG or CBG, we pooled small samples of breast fluid and compared the specificity of binding with that found in serum by the usual method of adding varying levels of nonradioactive steroids. To our surprise, the results indicated unusual specificity of [^{3}H]cortisol binding. In Fig. 19 it can be seen that the synthetic glucocorticoids dexamethasone and triamcinolone as well as E_2 and DHT competed as effectively as cortisol in breast fluid. The expected pattern of competition for cortisol binding to CBG in serum is shown in Fig. 20. Although this experiment has been repeated several times with

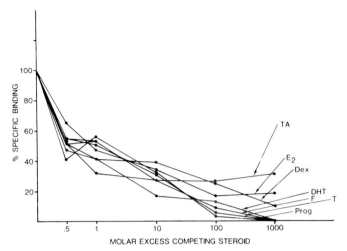

FIG. 19. Competition by steroids for [³H]cortisol binding in normal human breast fluid using a DEAE filter assay at 4°C. Diluted (1 : 160) breast fluid was incubated at 4°C with 20 n*M* [³H]cortisol for 2 hours and the indicated molar excess of various steroids. Total specific binding (5200 cpm) was estimated as the difference between samples containing 20 n*M* [³H]cortisol with and without a 1000-fold excess of nonradioactive cortisol. Values shown are the mean of duplicate assays. TA, Triancinolone acetonide; Dex, dexamethasone; F, cortisol; Prog, progesterone; E₂, estradiol; T, testosterone; DHT, dihydrotestosterone.

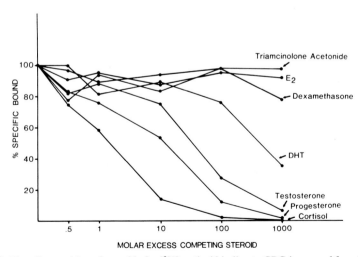

FIG. 20. Competition of steroids for [³H]cortisol binding to CBG in normal female serum diluted 1 : 20 as determined by the DEAE filter assay. See Fig. 19 for details.

essentially the same results, the significance of these findings is unclear. The specificity of binding observed in breast fluid is somewhat similar to that observed for glucocorticoid receptors except for the displacement of cortisol by E_2 and DHT. The origin of normal breast fluid is unclear although it seems likely that sloughing and breakdown of breast epithelial cells contributes to the variety of substances found (Petrakis, 1981). Therefore it is possible that intracellular receptors may escape in the fluid. On the other hand, it seems likely that the fluid arises at least in part by transudation from blood capillaries into ductules. Studies are continuing in order to elucidate this phenomenon further.

VII. Plasma Binding Proteins (CBG and SHBG) in Tissues and Cells

CBG has classically been differentiated from intracellular glucocorticoid and progesterone receptors by its inability to bind synthetic glucocorticoids and progestins. Using this technique of differential binding, transcortin-like binding has been observed in numerous tissues including the uterus (Milgrom and Baulieu, 1970; Guériguian et al., 1974; Al-Khouri and Greenstein, 1980), the kidney (Feldman et al., 1973; Funder et al., 1973; Weiser et al., 1979), muscle (Mayer et al., 1975), lung (Giannopoulos, 1976), liver (Koblinsky et al., 1972; Litwack et al., 1973; Amaral et al., 1974; Suyemitsu and Terayama, 1975; Weiser et al., 1979), lymphocytes (Werthamer et al., 1973; Amaral and Werthamer, 1974), and the brain and pituitary (Koch et al., 1976; DeKloet and McEwen, 1976; Al-Khouri and Greenstein, 1980). Using autoradiography, the CBG-like glucocorticoid binders, called type III, were further localized to the collecting tubules in the outer medulla and cortex of the rat kidney (Strum et al., 1975).

Al-Khouri and Greenstein (1980) examined the nature of the progesterone receptor from rat pituitary, midbrain, hypothalamus, and uterus. Essentially, all of the progesterone receptor in the uterus was transcortin-like in that corticosterone was as effective as progesterone and much more effective than R5020 in displacing [^{3}H]progesterone. Further characterization revealed the presence of a single precipitin line between cytosol and antiserum raised against whole rat serum. Although the techniques employed were relatively crude, the findings led the authors to suggest that CBG may act as a carrier for corticosterone during uptake by cells.

In addition, CBG-like binding activity has been found on plasma membranes prepared from liver (Suyemitsu and Terayama, 1975) and anterior pituitary cells (Koch et al., 1981). Direct evidence for the intracellular presence of plasma steroid binding proteins also has been obtained by immunofluorescence studies. Using an antibody to human SHBG, Bordin and Petra (1980) have obtained evidence suggesting the presence of SHBG in prostate and other cells from the rhesus monkey. They also demonstrated that human mammary tumor cells (MCF-7) apparently take up SHBG. Werthamer and co-workers (Werthamer *et al.,* 1973; Amaral *et al.,* 1974) have presented evidence that human lymphocyte cytoplasm and liver nuclei contain CBG antigens which can be detected with fluorosceinated antibodies prepared against human CBG. They also found that a component of chromatin interacts with CBG to restore cortisol binding activity and change its sedimentation characteristics. They further suggested (Werthamer and Amaral, 1973) that their antibody preparation could prevent binding of [^{3}H]dexamethasone or [^{3}H]cortisol in liver cytosol. While these studies are very intriguing, a sufficient number of critical controls are missing so that the interpretation of the data is open to serious question.

As can be seen from the preceding discussion, many investigators have described the presence of "transcortin-like" binders in a variety of tissues in levels greater than could be accounted for by serum contamination. This led us to ask whether these binders were in fact transcortin or were receptors with similar binding characteristics. To approach this problem, we purified rat CBG to homogeneity utilizing ammonium sulfate fractionation followed by affinity and hydroxylapatite chromatographies essentially as previously described (Mickelson and Westphal, 1979; Raymoure and Kuhn, 1982). Purity of the final preparation was demonstrated by its migration as a single band during polyacrylamide gel electrophoresis under both denaturing (SDS gels) and nondenaturing conditions (Raymoure and Kuhn, 1982). Furthermore, the results of amino acid analysis of the purified protein are in excellent agreement with previously published values (Chader and Westphal, 1968).

This preparation of CBG was used to elicit antibodies in rabbits utilizing the procedure of Vaitukaitis *et al.* (1971). The resulting antiserum was found to be both high in titer and specific fo. rat CBG; no cross-reactivity with other rat serum proteins nor with serum from 6 other species could be detected (Raymoure and Kuhn, 1982).

This antiserum was used for the immunocytochemical detection of CBG in rat tissues utilizing the peroxidase–antiperoxidase technique (Sternberger, 1979). Intact adult male rats were perfused with 1 liter of saline prior to removal of tissues in order to eliminate contamination by plasma CBG. In studies to be reported elsewhere, we found that a number of tissues contained cells which stained positively for CBG. Figure 21 shows the results for five of these tissues. In the liver (Fig. 21A and B) most hepatocytes showed positive staining for CBG. This result was expected as the liver is known to be the site of synthesis for CBG (Wolfe *et*

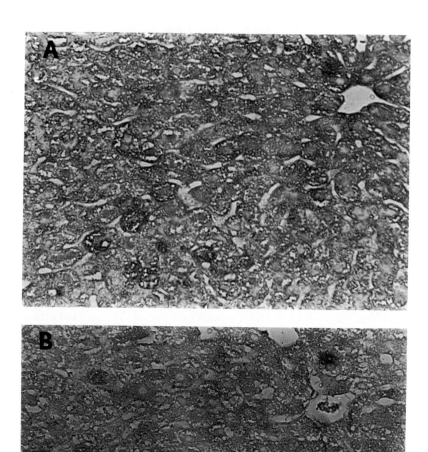

FIG. 21. Immunocytochemical localization of CBG in rat tissues. Adult Sprague–Dawley female rats were extensively perfused with first PBS and then Zamboni's fixative, tissues were removed, fixed, sectioned, and stained for CBG by the peroxidase–antiperoxidase technique (Sternberger, 1979). Experimental tissues were stained with antiserum to rat CBG. Controls were treated with the same antiserum following removal of anti-CBG antibodies by passage over a Sepharose column containing immobilized rat CBG. (A) Liver, ×144; (B) control staining of liver, ×144; (C) kidney, experimental, ×300; (D) kidney, control, ×300; (E) pituitary, experimental (i, intermediate lobe; p, posterior lobe), ×225; (F) pituitary, control, ×225; (G) spleen, experimental, ×176; (H) spleen, control, ×176; (I) uterus, experimental, ×63; (J) uterus, control, ×63.

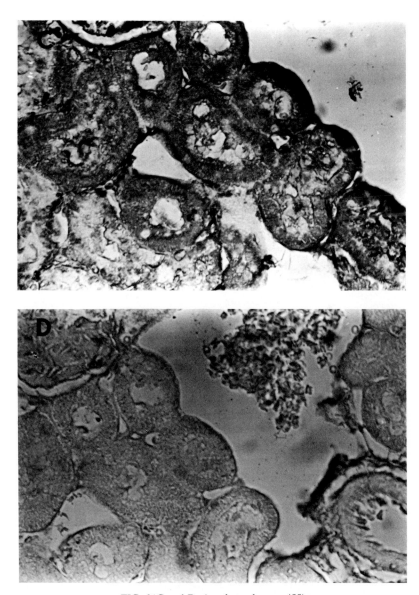

FIG. 21C and D (see legend on p. 488).

al., 1981; Weiser *et al.*, 1979; Perrot-Applanat and Milgrom, 1979). CBG was also found to be present in some cells of the kidney (Fig. 21C and D). It appears to be present in either the distal or collecting tubules; the exact identification is currently under investigation. These results are of particular interest in view of the autoradiographic localization by Strum *et al.*

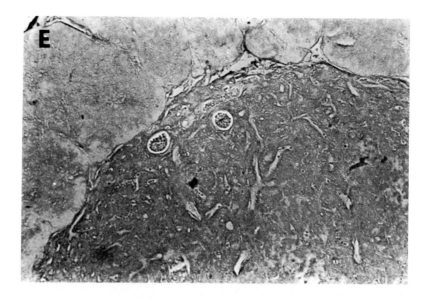

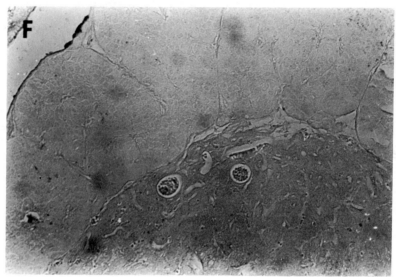

FIG. 21E and F   (see legend on p. 488).

(1975) of type III (or transcortin-like) glucocorticoid receptors in the collecting tubules of the rat kidney. Our results suggest that type III binders are not only "transcortin-like" by steroid binding characteristics, but are also antigenically similar to CBG. Positive staining was also observed in

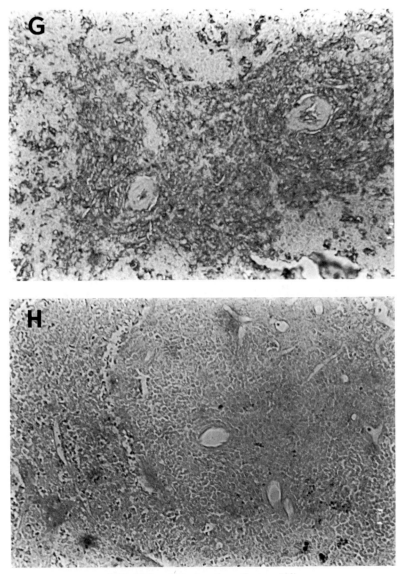

FIG. 21G and H   (see legend on p. 488).

the pituitary gland (Fig. 21E and F). Scattered cells in the anterior pituitary were positively stained, in agreement with previous observations of transcortin-like binding sites in this area (Koch *et al.*, 1976, 1981; Al-Khouri and Greenstein, 1980; Sakly and Koch, 1981). No staining was

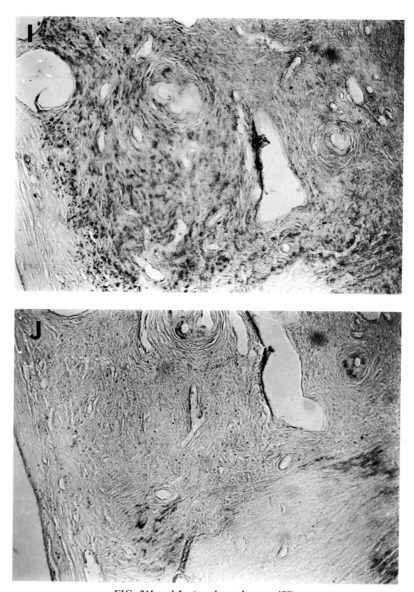

FIG. 21I and J   (see legend on p. 488).

present in the intermediate lobe. Particularly interesting, however, was the dark staining in the posterior lobe. In view of evidence attributing CRF activity to vasopressin (Krieger and Zimmerman, 1977; Zimmerman *et al.*, 1977), which is secreted from the posterior pituitary, it is tempting to speculate that CBG may play a role in the modulation of ACTH secretion.

The spleen (Fig. 21G and H) showed particularly heavy staining in the white pulp regions with little or no staining in the red pulp. The white pulp consists largely of a recirculating pool of lymphocytes. The presence in and uptake of CBG by peripheral human lymphocytes has been previously demonstrated by Werthamer and his colleagues (Werthamer *et al.*, 1976; Amaral and Werthamer, 1976). Our results suggest that recirculating lymphocytes present in the rat spleen contain this protein as well.

The uterus also contained cells which stained positively for rat CBG (Fig. 21I and J). These cells appear in a band along the edge of the myometrium. The finding of cells containing CBG in the uterus is of particular interest in view of the description of "transcortin-like" progesterone receptors in that organ (Milgrom and Baulieu, 1970; Gueriguian *et al.*, 1974; Al-Khouri and Greenstein, 1980), and our finding of steroid dependent uptake of ^{125}I-labeled rat CBG (see below).

In preliminary experiments, the antiserum against rat CBG was also used to immunoprecipitate transcortin-like binding sites from cytosols prepared from rat pituitary and uterus. The extent to which [^{3}H]cortisol binding was eliminated by the addition of 1000-fold excess unlabeled cortisol or dexamethasone was examined in pituitary cytosol before and after immunoprecipitation with anti-rat CBG. The antibody removed binding activity that was blocked by cortisol but not by dexamethasone. Since dexamethasone binds to glucocorticoid receptors and not CBG, these data suggest that the transcortin-like sites previously found in the pituitary are antigenically similar to CBG. Identical studies were carried out with uterine cytosol by displacing [^{3}H]progesterone, which also binds to CBG, with either unlabeled progesterone or R-5020 (a synthetic progestin which binds to progesterone receptors but not CBG). The antibody removed only the binding activity which was not displaced by R-5020, suggesting that the transcortin-like binders previously observed in the uterus are antigenically similar to CBG.

These results clearly demonstrate that a number of tissues contain proteins which are antigenically similar to and have identical steroid binding characteristics as CBG. Their presence could result from *de novo* synthesis, uptake of circulating CBG, or a combination of both processes. To test whether tissues were capable of sequestering circulating CBG, we injected adrenalectomized, ovariectomized rats with ^{125}I-labeled CBG alone or together with 100 μg of corticosterone. After 30 minutes, the rats were killed and extensively perfused with PBS. Tissues were removed, and the uptake of ^{125}I-labeled CBG determined. Nearly all tissues examined showed some uptake of CBG. When the steroid dependence of uptake was examined, certain tissues were found to accumulate more ^{125}I-labeled CBG if corticosterone was administered. Figure 22 shows the ratio of uptake in the presence of steroid to that in the absence of steroid in several tissues. As can be seen liver uptake is increased slightly by steroid administration whereas a greater increase was observed in uptake by the spleen. Both kidney and uterus showed large steroid-dependent increases in uptake. The kidney levels are particularly noteworthy as this organ shows the greatest level of uptake on a per gram basis either in the presence or absence of steroid. The failure to observe a steroid-induced increase in uptake by the liver may be due to the presence of asialoglycoprotein receptors which bind desialated CBG prior its metabolism (Hossner and Billiar, 1979, 1981).

We then asked whether the uptake of CBG by mammalian cells could be directly visualized using purified rat CBG labeled with fluorescein isothiocyanate. Rat pituitary tumor GH₃ cells were plated onto polylysine-coated coverslips, exposed to the labeled CBG, washed, fixed, and examined microscopically under UV light. Figure 23 shows the re-

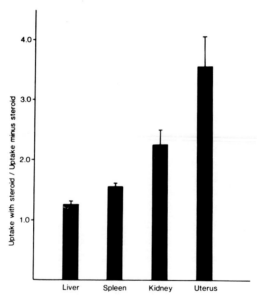

FIG. 22.   Steroid dependence of tissue uptake of ^{125}I-labeled rat CBG. Ovariectomized, adrenalectomized adult rats were injected with ^{125}I-labeled rat CBG and either control vehicle or 100 μg of corticosterone in PBS containing 10% ethanol. After 30 minutes, the animals were extensively perfused with PBS, organs removed and weighed, and the organ content of ^{125}I-labeled CBG determined. The data are expressed as the ratio of uptake in the presence of steroid to that in its absence after normalization for body weight, tissue weight, and initial dose of ^{125}I-labeled CBG injected.

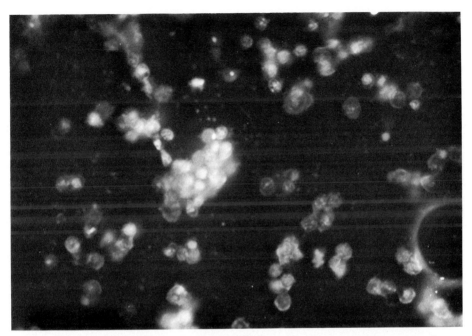

FIG. 23.   Uptake of fluorosceinated rat CBG by GH$_3$ cells. GH$_3$ cells were plated on polylysine-coated coverslips. A solution of corticosterone and fluorosceinated rat CBG in PBS was applied and the cells incubated for 1 hour at 23°C. The cells were then washed with PBS, fixed with 1% paraformaldehyde in phosphate buffer, and viewed under the microscope with fluorescence optics. ×63.

sults that were obtained when these cells were exposed to CBG for 1 hour at 23°C. As can be seen, essentially all cells took up CBG with most displaying a marked nuclear concentration of the protein with some cytoplasmic and peripheral staining noted as well. Preliminary experiments suggest that the rate and degree of uptake is strongly influenced by temperature and the presence or absence of steroid. Similar results have been obtained using freshly isolated rat liver cells and splenic lymphocytes. This uptake process is currently under investigation.

VIII. Summary and Hypothesis

The development of new methods for directly estimating important binding parameters for steroid hormones in plasma has brought new insight to the question of the true function of steroid binding proteins. The ability to easily determine the distribution of a steroid in plasma between the free, albumin bound, and CBG or SHBG bound fractions has permitted a much more penetrating analysis of plasma hormone levels in many physiologic situations. Neither the free nor the free plus albumin bound levels of estradiol in human plasma are sufficient to saturate cellular estrogen receptors by free diffusion alone in conditions where the uterus is markedly stimulated. In contrast, analysis of cortisol and androgen binding in plasma of the squirrel monkey reveals that free hormone levels are much higher than required for both types of hormone if their receptors function as in other species. These studies led to a reinvestigation of the possibility that CBG serves as a mediator of glucocorticoid uptake in rodents. Immunocytochemical localization studies showed that CBG is found within cells of tissues previously identified by others as having CBG-like receptors. Both tissue and cellular specificity was observed thus ruling out a phenomenon of generalized uptake of serum proteins. Direct evidence for uptake of ^{125}I-labeled CBG by rat tissues which is variably enhanced in different tissues by coadministration of corticosterone suggests that cellular uptake of the steroid–CBG complex may occur *in vivo*. Supporting evidence was obtained from experiments using fluorescein-labeled CBG where uptake by rat GH_3 cells *in vitro* was enhanced by addition of corticosterone. These results suggest but certainly do not prove that CBG may be involved in steroid uptake by cells.

Can these observations be reconciled with the large body of evidence supporting the plasma free hormone concept of steroid action? Two major points must be reconciled. First, virtually all *in vitro* studies (summarized by Ballard, 1979) have shown that addition of CBG (or albumin) to various test systems reduces the effectiveness of a given amount of steroid. Second, a large number of experiments have shown that synthetic steroids which appear not to bind to serum proteins are active both *in vitro* and *in vivo*. It is not surprising that the addition of albumin or high affinity binding proteins reduces the free hormone concentration in various bioassay systems just as it does in plasma. Therefore, experiments with broken cell preparations (e.g., reduction of substrate availability to an enzyme) have little physiologic significance. Experiments in which serum or purified proteins are added to cells in culture also must be interpreted carefully in light of our results. In their oft quoted study, Lippman and Thompson (1974) examined the effect of added serum upon glucocorticoid induction of tyrosine amino transferase (TAT) activity in HTC cells adapted to serum-free medium. They found that addition of rat serum increased the amount of cortisol required to induce TAT activity while reducing cell uptake of the steroid. Since a lesser inhibitory effect was observed when dexamethasone was the inducer, they concluded that CBG binding reduces the bioactivity of cortisol. Reduced potency of both steroids compared to serum free conditions was attributed to a nonspecific toxic effect of the added rat serum. However, addition of 20% fetal calf serum to wild type HTC cells also appeared to greatly inhibit the response to dexamethasone. Furthermore, maximal response to cortisol was never achieved despite the addition of levels of steroid far in excess of the CBG binding capacity of the serum added to both cell types. Thus a major decrease in enzyme inducibility appears to have been produced by the addition of serum independent of its steroid binding properties. Therefore, the interpretation of their results is open to serious question. If serum binding proteins are taken up by cells as we have shown for CBG, then the simple act of washing cells with serum free buffers prior to testing the effect of added CBG or serum can yield misleading results. Cells must be maintained in serum free conditions for a sufficient period of time to allow turnover of intracellular or membrane bound CBG. Interestingly, when this has been done, loss of intracellular receptors is a common occurrence (Soto and Sonnenschein, 1979).

In contrast to such *in vitro* studies, *in vivo* studies have suggested an active role for CBG in glucocorticoid action. Keller *et al.* (1969) measured alanine amino transferase (AAT) induction by corticosterone in rat liver, a tissue with a protein-permeable vascular bed, and pancreas, which has a relatively impermeable vascular bed. They found that corticosterone could induce AAT in both liver and pancreas under normal conditions. When CBG binding capacity was increased by estrogen treatment, corticosterone could still induce AAT in liver but was ineffective in the pancreas. These results suggested that tissues with protein-permeable vascular beds can respond to steroid–protein complexes as well as to free hormone.

Rosner (1972a) injected rats with saline, cortisol alone, or cortisol plus purified rat CBG and then determined liver TAT activity and peripheral blood lymphocyte levels as a function of time. Both the degree and time course of induction of TAT activity were identical for animals treated with cortisol alone or with cortisol bound to CBG when compared to saline controls. Similarly decreased lymphocyte counts were also observed.

Clinical observations also suggest that CBG-bound glucocorticoids may be biologically active. Much discussion has concerned the issue of elevated cortisol and CBG levels found in pregnant women and whether or not they experience hypercortisolism. Our results (unpublished) indicate that the percentage free cortisol is reduced during pregnancy as expected from the increased CBG levels. Therefore the free cortisol concentration shows little change. The question of whether or not cortisol activity is enhanced during pregnancy is not easily answered although a teleologic argument can be made that the energy needs of the growing fetus requires increased metabolic action of glucocorticoids on specific maternal tissues.

Perhaps more informative is the observation that the dosage of cortisol or prednisolone (which binds to CBG) required for treatment of chronic inflammatory conditions in humans could be reduced 3- to 20-fold by concurrent administration of estrogens (Spangler *et al.*, 1969). Although the type and dose of estrogen used in these studies varied, CBG levels increased 2- to 3-fold in all nine subjects studied. While these dramatic results may have been due to some unknown antiinflammatory effect of estrogens, they are consistent with biological activity of CBG bound but not free cortisol.

The results of our studies in monkeys deserve further comment. The binding affinity of plasma SHBG for testosterone is about 8-fold higher in the rhesus than in the squirrel monkey. The plasma testosterone levels are similar in males of both species during the nonbreeding season. Testosterone rises during breeding in both species but the levels reached during breeding are 5- to 10-fold higher in squirrel (100–200 nM) than in rhesus monkeys (Mendoza *et al.*, 1978). The free hormone concept predicts that the opposite should be the case. Although other factors appear to be involved, it is tempting to speculate that the increased squirrel monkey body weight, testicular volume, and onset of active spermatogenesis observed during the breeding season may be the consequence of unusually high testosterone levels which result in higher effective levels of plasma SHBG–testosterone complexes. It is possible that squirrel and similar New World monkeys have adapted to the presence of a low affinity plasma binding protein by increasing their capacity to produce testosterone. The situation appears to be more complex in the case of CBG. Although more extensive studies are needed, it appears at present that variable levels of CBG with low binding affinity are found in squirrel monkeys as compared with rhesus monkeys or humans. In any event, the free cortisol levels are much higher than those found in other species. It will be of interest to determine the binding affinity of tissue glucocorticoid receptors for squirrel monkeys. If they are also lower than those found in other species, as expected, then interesting questions are raised concerning the evolution of the two classes of steroid binding proteins.

Our present working hypothesis is illustrated in Fig. 24. Steroid hormones complexed with high affinity binding proteins in blood such as CBG, SHBG, progesterone binding globulin (PBG) in the guinea pig, or androgen binding protein (ABP) are recognized and bound by the outer surface of the plasma membranes of their target cells. The bound complex is then internalized by one of several possible mechanisms. By way of illustration, a mechanism analogous to that described for cholesterol containing lipoprotein complexes by Goldstein and Brown (1977) may be suggested. Only meager evidence is available at present but we further

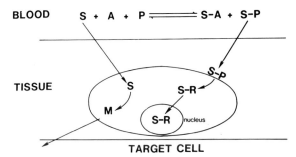

FIG. 24.   Alternative model for steroid hormone action. Steroid is present in the blood as free hormone (S), bound to albumin (S-A), or complexed with specific binding proteins (S-P). S can enter the target cell by diffusion where it is converted by enzymes into inactive metabolites (M) which subsequently diffuse from the cell. S-P complexes bind to specific sites on the cell membrane and are subsequently internalized. These complexes either supply the hormone to classical intracellular receptors or are converted by an unknown process into such receptors. Receptor–steroid complexes (S-R) enter the nucleus, bind to chromatin, and modify transcriptional patterns which results in altered cell function. In the case of androgen action the conversion of S (testosterone) to S′ (dihydrotestosterone) may occur at any stage.

suggest that this internalized complex is then distributed into various subcellular compartments, the nucleus being prominent among these. The consequences of such movement of extracellular steroid binding protein complexes into cells is completely unknown at present. However, the analogy with current views of steroid–receptor movement is obvious. Whether there is a structural relationship between the external binders (CBG etc.) to intracellular "receptors" is also not known although a considerable body of indirect evidence suggests that there is not. However, changes in physicochemical antigenic or binding properties of the extracellular protein during or following internalization would hardly be surprising. For example, the removal of carbohydrates from glycoproteins might be expected. In contrast, the steroid moiety would be protected from metabolism by enzymes that are present in many if not all steroid hormone target cells.

Contrary to popular belief, mature rats have in their circulation both androgen (ABP; Gunsalus *et al.*, 1978) and estrogen (α-fetoprotein; Linkie and LaBarbera, 1979) binding proteins. We therefore believe that the scheme shown in Fig. 24 may be applicable to rodents as well. This is important since the extensive work of Szego and Pietras (1981) has led them to suggest a somewhat similar model based upon estradiol recognition sites in plasma membranes prepared from rat uterus and liver. Membrane-bound serum binding proteins could explain their findings as well as those of Harrison *et al.* (1975) since the latter workers used bovine serum in their cell culture studies.

The scheme shown in Fig. 24 is not only consistent with many experimental observations but leads to some interesting predictions. Current models of steroid hormone action provide no explanations for resistance that develops following prolonged administration of steroids such as estrogen. The presence of a finite number of recognition sites on the cell surface for steroid–protein complexes could provide a mechanism for down regulation analogous to loss of membrane receptor sites for protein hormones. Finally, it should be pointed out that the clinical correlations of increased biological activity with increased plasma free hormone concentrations, due to low levels of plasma binding proteins, may be explained by increased uptake of complexes (e.g., SHBG-testosterone in PCOD) rather than depressed synthesis of the binding protein as currently believed.

We fully recognize that our hypothesis represents a radical departure from those currently under investigation. Nevertheless, we firmly believe that provocative ideas and concepts are essential to progress toward a true understanding of the mechanism of steroid hormone action.

ACKNOWLEDGMENTS

We gratefully acknowledge the expert assistance of Ms. Alyce Green, Barbara Vince, and Laura Stachel, and Mssrs. Jimmy Louie Choy, Joseph Steinberger, and Gregg Garbin in the performance of these studies. We thank Ms. Claudia Bello and Mr. Brian Baskerville for assistance in typing the manuscript. We also wish to thank Drs. Howard Judd, Naguib Samaan, Marvin Kirschner, and Nicholas Petrakis for providing biological samples.

REFERENCES

Al-Khouri, H., and Greenstein, B. D. (1980). *Nature* (*London*) **287**, 58.
Amaral, L., and Werthamer, S. (1974). *Ann. Clin. Lab. Sci.* **4**, 435.
Amaral, L., and Werthamer, S. (1976). *Nature* (*London*) **262**, 589.
Amaral, L., Kobkul, L., Samuels, A. J., and Werthamer, S. (1974). *Biochim. Biophys. Acta* **362**, 332.
Anderson, D. C. (1974). *Clin. Endocrinol.* (*Oxford*) **3**, 69.
Anderson, J., Clark, J. H., and Peck, E. J. (1972). *Biochem. J.* **126**, 561.
Ballard, P. L. (1979). *In* "Monographs on Endocrinology: Glucocorticoid Hormone Action" (J. D. Baxter, and G. G. Rousseau, eds.), Vol. 12. Springer-Verlag, Berlin and New York.
Bardin, C. W., Musto, N., Gunsalus, G., Kotite, N., Cheng, S-L., Larrea, F., and Becker, R. (1981). *Annu. Rev. Physiol.* **43**, 189.
Bordin, S., and Petra, P. H. (1980). *Proc. Natl. Acad. Sci. U.S.A.* **77**, 5678.
Brown, G. M., Grota, L. J., Penney, D. P., and Reichlin, S. (1970). *Endocrinology* **86**, 519.
Burke, C. W. (1969). *Biochim. Biophys. Acta* **176**, 403.
Chader, G. J., and Westphal, U. (1968). *Biochemistry* **7**, 4272.
Chopra, I. J., Abraham, G. E., Chopra, U., Solomon, D. H., and Odell, W. D. (1972). *N. Engl. J. Med.* **286**, 124.
Chrousos, G. P., Vingerhoreds, A., Brandon, D., Eil, C., Pugeat, M., Loviaux, D. L., and Lipsett, M. B. (1982). *N. Engl. J. Med.*, in press.

Clark, J. H., and Peck, E. J. (1979). *In* "Monographs on Endocrinology: Female Sex Steroids, Reception and Function" (F. Gross *et al.*, eds.), Vol. 14. Springer-Verlag, Berlin and New York.

Coe, C. L., Chen, J., Lowe, E. L., Davidson, J. M., and Levine, S. (1981). *Horm. Behav.* **15**, 36.

Colowick, S. P., and Womack, F. C. (1969). *J. Biol. Chem.* **244**, 774.

Davidson, B. J., Gambone, J. C., LaGasse, L. B., Castaldo, T. W., Hammond, G. L., Siiteri, P. K., and Judd, H. (1980). *J. Clin. Endocrinol. Metab.* **52**, 404.

Davidson, B. J., Ross, R., Paganini-Hill, A., Hammond, G. L., Siiteri, P. K., and Judd, H. (1982). *J. Clin. Endocrinol. Metab.* **54**, 115.

DeKloet, E. R., and McEwen, B. S. (1976). *Biochim. Biophys. Acta* **421**, 115.

DeMoor, P., and Joossens, J. V. (1970). *Steroidologia* **1**, 129.

DeMoor, P., Heirwegh, K., Heremans, J. F., and Deelerck-Raskin, M. (1962). *J. Clin. Invest.* **41**, 816.

Do, Y. S., and Feldman, D. (1980). *Endocrinology* **107**, 1370.

Dunn, J. F., Nisula, B. E., and Rodbard, D. (1981). *J. Clin. Endocrinol. Metab.* **53**, 58.

Feldman, D., Funder, J. W., and Edelman, I. S. (1973). *Endocrinology* **92**, 1492.

Forest, M. G., Cathiard, A. M., and Bertrand, J. A. (1968). *Steroids* **22**, 323.

Funder, J. W., Feldman, D., and Edelman, I. S. (1973). *Endocrinology* **92**, 1006.

Giannopoulos, G. (1976). *J. Steroid Biochem.* **7**, 553.

Giorgi, E. P. (1980). *Int. Rev. Cytol.* **65**, 49.

Giorgi, E. P., and Stein, W. P. (1981). *Endocrinology* **108**, 688.

Goldstein, J. L., and Brown, M. S. (1977). *Annu. Rev. Biochem.* **46**, 897.

Greenstein, B. D., Puig-Duran, E., and Franklin, M. (1977). *Steroids* **30**, 331.

Guériguian, J. L., Sawyer, M. E., and Pearlman, W. H. (1974). *J. Endocrinol.* **61**, 331.

Gunsalus, G. L., Musto, N. A., and Bardin, C. W. (1978). *Science* **200**, 65.

Gurpide, E. (1975). *In* "Monographs on Endocrinology: Traler Methods in Hormone Research" (F. Gross *et al.*, eds.), Vol. 18. Springer-Verlag, Berlin and New York.

Gurpide, E., Stolee, A., and Tseng, L. (1971). *Karolinska Symp. Res. Methods Reprod. Endocrinol., 3rd* p. 247.

Hammond, G. L., Nisker, J. A., Jones, L. A., and Siiteri, P. K. (1980). *J. Biol. Chem.* **255**, 5023.

Harrison, R. W., and Yeakley, J. (1979). *Mol. Cell. Endocrinol.* **15**, 13.

Harrison, R. W., Fairfield, S., and Orth, D. N. (1974). *Biochem. Biophys. Res. Commun.* **61**, 1262.

Harrison, R. W., Fairfield, S., and Orth, D. N. (1975). *Biochemistry* **14**, 1304.

Harrison, R. W., III, Fairfield, S., and Orth, D. N. (1977). *Biochim. Biophys. Acta* **466**, 357.

Hossner, K. L., and Billiar, R. B. (1979). *Biochim. Biophys. Acta* **585**, 543.

Hossner, K. L., and Billiar, R. B. (1981). *Endocrinology* **108**, 1780.

Igbal, M. J., and Johnson, M. W. (1977). *J. Steroid Biochem.* **8**, 927.

Judd, H. L., Lucas, W. E., and Yen, S. C. C. (1976). *J. Clin. Endocrinol. Metab.* **43**, 272.

Keller, W., Richardson, U. I., and Yates, F. E. (1969). *Endocrinology* **84**, 49.

Kirschner, M. A., Cohen, F. B., and Ryan, C. (1978). *Cancer Res.* **38**, 4029.

Kley, H. K., Bartman, E., and Krüskemper, H. L. (1977a). *Acta Endocrinol.* **85**, 209.

Kley, H. K., Bartman, E., and Krüskemper, H. L. (1977b). *J. Clin. Chem. Clin. Biochem.* **15**, 465.

Koblinsky, M., Beato, M., Kalimi, M., and Feigelson, P. (1972). *J. Biol. Chem.* **247**, 7897.

Koch, B., Lutz, B., Briaud, B., and Mialhe, C. (1976). *Biochim. Biophys. Acta* **444**, 497.

Koch, B., Sakly, M., and Lutz-Bucher, B. (1981). *Meet. Endocrine Soc., 63rd, Cincinatti* Abstr. No. 691.

Krieger, D. T., and Zimmerman, E. A. (1977). *In* "Clinical Neuroendocrinology" (L. Martini and G. M. Besser, eds.). Academic Press, New York.

Linkie, D. M., and LaBarbeora, H. R. (1979). *Proc. Soc. Exp. Biol. Med.* **161**, 7.

Lippman, M., and Thompson, E. B. (1974). *J. Steroid Biochem.* **5**, 461.

Litwack, G., Filler, R., Rosenfield, S. A., Lichtash, N., Wishman, C. A., and Singer, S. (1973). *J. Biol. Chem.* **248**, 7481.

Lobo, R. A., Granger, L., Goebelsmann, U., and Mishell, D. K. (1981). *J. Clin. Endocrinol. Metab.* **52**, 159.

MacDonald, P. C., Edman, C. D., Hemsell, D. L., Porter, J. C., and Siiteri, P. K. (1978). *Am. J. Obstet. Gynecol.* **130**, 448.

Mayer, N., Kaiser, N., Micholland, N., and Rosen, F. (1975). *J. Biol. Chem.* **250**, 1207.

Mendoza, S. P., Lowe, E. L., Davidson, J. M., and Levine, S. (1978). *Horm. Behav.* **11**, 295.

Mickelsen, K. E., and Petra, P. H. (1974). *FEBS Lett.* **44**, 34.

Mickelsen, K. E., and Westphal, U. (1979). *Biochemistry* **18**, 2685.

Milgrom, E., and Baulieu, E. E. (1970). *Endocrinology* **87**, 276.

Milgrom, E., Atger, M., and Baulieu, E. (1973). *Biochim. Biophys. Acta* **320**, 267.

Moll, G. W., and Rosenfield, R. L. (1977). *Biochem. Med.* **18**, 344.

Moll, G. W., and Rosenfield, R. L. (1978). *J. Clin. Endocrinol. Metab.* **46**, 501.

Moore, J. W., Clark, G. M., Bulbrook, R. D., Hayword, R. D., Murai, J. T., Hammond, G. L., and Siiteri, P. K. (1982). *Eur. J. Cancer,* in press.

Nisker, J. A., and Siiteri, P. K. (1981). *In* "Clinical Obstetrics and Gynecology" (R. J. Worley, ed.), Vol. 24, p. 301. Harper, New York.

Nisker, J. A., Hammond, G. L., Davidson, B. J., Frumar, A. M., Takai, W. K., Judd, H. L., and Siiteri, P. K. (1980). *Am. J. Obstet. Gynecol.* **138**, 637.

Pardridge, W. M. (1981). *Endocr. Rev.* **2**, 103.

Payne, D. W., Peng, L., and Pearlman, W. H. (1976). *J. Biol. Chem.* **251**, 5272.

Perrot-Applanat, M., and Milgrom, E. (1979). *Biochemistry* **18**, 5732.

Peterson, R. E. (1977). *In* "Endocrinology of Pregnancy" (F. Fuchs and A. Klopper, eds.), p. 157. Harper, New York.

Petrakis, N. L. (1981). *In* "Banbury Report 8" (M. C. Pike, P. K. Siiteri, and C. W. Welsch, eds.). Cold Spring Harbor Lab., Cold Spring Harbor, New York.

Plager, J. E., Schmidt, K. G., and Staubitz, W. (1964). *J. Clin. Invest.* **43**, 1066.

Rao, M. L., Rao, G. S., Höller, M., Breuer, H., Schaatenberg, P. J., and Stein, W. D. (1976). *J. Physiol. Chem.* **357**, 573.

Raymoure, W. J., and Kuhn, R. W. (1980). *Endocrinology* **106**, 1747.

Raymoure, W. J., and Kuhn, R. W. (1982). *Endocrinology,* in press.

Robbins, J., and Rall, J. E. (1957). *Recent Prog. Horm. Res.* **13**, 161.

Rosner, W. (1972a). *J. Steroid Biochem.* **3**, 531.

Rosner, W. (1972b). *J. Clin. Endocrinol. Metab.* **34**, 983.

Rosner, W. (1976). *In* "Trace Components of Plasma: Isolation and Clinical Significance" (G. A. Jamieson and T. J. Greenwalt, eds.), p. 377. Liss, New York.

Rosner, W., Beers, P. C., Tayyiba, A., and Khan, M. S. (1976). *J. Clin. Endocrinol. Metab.* **42**, 1064.

Sakly, M., and Koch, B. (1981). *Endocrinology* **108**, 591.

Sandberg, A. A., Slaunwhite, W., and Carter, A. (1960). *J. Clin. Invest.* **39**, 1914.

Santi, D. V., Sibley, C. H., Perriard, E. R., Tomkins, G. M., and Baxter, J. D. (1973). *Biochemistry* **12**, 2412.

Seal, V. S., and Doe, R. P. (1966). *In* "Steroid Dynamics" (G. Pincus, T. Nakao, and J. E. Tait, eds.), p. 63. Academic Press, New York.

Siiteri, P. K. (1981). *J. Endocrinol.* **89**, 119P.

Siiteri, P. K., and MacDonald, P. C. (1973). *In* "Handbook of Physiology, Section 7" (S. R. Geiger, E. B. Astwood, and R. O. Greep, eds.), p. 615. American Physiological Society, New York.

Siiteri, P. K., Hammond, G. L., and Nisker, J. A. (1981). *J. Clin. Endocrinol. Metab.* **52**, 404.

Sirbasku, D. A. (1981). *In* "Banburg Report 8, Hormones and Breast Cancer" (M. C. Pike, P. K. Siiteri, and C. W. Welsch, eds.). Cold Spring Harbor Lab., Cold Spring Harbor, New York.

Soto, A. M., and Sonnenschein, C. (1979). *J. Steroid Biochem.* **11**, 1185.

Spangler, A. S., Antoniades, H. N., Sotman, S. L., and Inderbitizin, T. M. (1969). *J. Clin. Endocrinol. Metab.* **29**, 650.

Sternberger, L. A. (1979). "Immunocytochemistry." Prentice-Hall, New York.

Strum, J. M., Feldman, D., Taggart, B., Marver, D., and Edelman, I. S. (1975). *Endocrinology* **97**, 505.

Suyemitsu, T., and Terayama, H. (1975). *Endocrinology* **96**, 1499.

Svec, F., Yeakley, J., and Harrison, R. W., III (1980). *J. Biol. Chem.* **255**, 8573.

Szego, C., and Pietras, R. (1981). *In* "Biochemical Actions of Hormones" (G. Litwack, ed.), Vol. III, p. 307. Academic Press, New York.

Tait, J. F., and Burstein, S. (1964). *In* "The Hormones" (G. Pincus, K. V. Thimann, and E. B. Astwood, eds.). Academic Press, New York.

Vaitukaitis, J. L., Robbins, J. B., Nieschlag, E., and Ross, G. T. (1971). *J. Clin. Endocrinol.* **33**, 988.

Vermeulen, A. (1977). *In* "Androgens and Antiandrogens" (L. Martini and M. Mota, eds.), p. 53. Raven, New York.

Vermeulen, A., Stoica, T., and Verdonck, L. (1971). *J. Clin. Endocrinol. Metab.* **33**, 759.

Vigersky, R. A., Kono, S., Sauer, M., Lipsett, M. B., and Loriaux, D. L. (1979). *J. Clin. Endocrinol. Metab.* **49**, 899.

Vingerhoeds, A. C., Thijissen, J. H., and Schwarz, F. (1976). *J. Clin. Endocrinol. Metab.* **43**, 1128.

Wang, D. Y., and Bulbrook, R. D. (1969). *Eur. J. Cancer* **5**, 247.

Weiser, J. N., Do, Y. S., and Feldman, D. (1979). *J. Clin. Invest.* **68**, 461.

Werthamer, S., and Amaral, L, (1973). *Fed. Proc. Fed. Am. Soc. Exp. Biol.* **32**, 865A.

Werthamer, S., Samuels, A. J., and Amaral, L. (1973). *J. Biol. Chem.* **248**, 6398.

Werthamer, S., Govindoraj, S., and Amaral, L. (1976). *J. Clin. Invest.* **57**, 1000.

Westphal, U. (1971). "Monographs on Endocrinology: Steroid Protein Interactions" (F. Gross *et al.*, eds.), Vol. 4. Springer-Verlag, Berlin and New York.

Wolfe, G., Armstrong, E. G., and Rosner, W. (1981). *Endocrinology* **108**, 805.

Wu, C. H., Motohashi, H. A., Abdel-Rahman, L. A., Flickinger, G. L., and Mikhail, G. (1976). *J. Clin. Endocrinol. Metab.* **43**, 436.

Wynder, E. L., and Hill (1977). *Lancet* **ii**, 840.

Yarus, M., and Berg, P. (1970). *Anal. Biochem.* **35**, 450.

Yeakley, J. M., Balasubramanian, K., and Harrison, R. W. (1980). *J. Biol. Chem.* **255**, 4182.

Young, J. R., and Jaffe, R. B. (1976). *J. Clin. Endocrinol. Metab.* **42**, 432.

Zimmerman, E. A., Stillman, M. A., Recht, L. D., Antunes, J. L., Carmel, P. W., and Goldsmith, P. C. (1977). *Ann. N.Y. Acad. Sci.* **297**, 405.

DISCUSSION

D. Tulchinsky: Dr. Siiteri, you measured sex hormone binding capacity rather than measuring sex hormone binding globulin itself or CBG. Do you see any disadvantage to that, particularly when one deals with a new breast fluid where you are measuring something that you presume to be CBG or SHBG. If you have the purified CBG or SHBG it would not be too difficult to develop a radioimmunoassay.

P. K. Siiteri: Yes, your question is very important of course. I tried to indicate that we at present have no evidence to indicate that these binders are in fact either CBG or SHBG. We do not presently have a radioimmunoassay for SHBG but we have collaborated with Dr. Rosner who has recently developed a radioimmunoassay for human SHBG. We have done correlations with about 150 serum samples and the binding assays agree very nicely with his radioimmunoassay. We plan to do breast fluid assays as soon as possible but I neglected to point out that if we get 15 μl of breast fluid, we are deliriously happy because that is a lot.

W. W. Leavitt: I was particularly interested in the studies you have done on breast fluid and intrigued by the binding specificity results on the components contained therein. You made the point that the binding specificity of the material in breast fluid did not conform to what was present in the serum. Do you have evidence that the serum binding proteins are indeed present in the breast fluid? And if so, what would their function be?

P. K. Siiteri: We have no direct evidence at the present time that the binding molecules in breast fluid are in fact CBG or SHBG. My view of the matter is that we have concentrated so much on what is present in blood, we have tended to exclude other body fluids such as breast fluid and more importantly, the whole lymph vasculature. I did not have time to present our data but there is a concentration gradient between blood and lymph for both CBG and SHBG as measured by binding assays. It is much more difficult to study differences in binding specificity but we are pursuing this quite vigorously.

W. W. Leavitt: I was curious as to whether there is steroid associated with the binding proteins in the breast fluid, for example, could this be a delivery system for transporting steroid to the mammary epithelium.

P. K. Siiteri: Well, there is a lot of steroid present and the presumption is that it is bound. My view is that the fluid represents what might be called a normal transudate across the epithelial cells of the breast arising from blood.

S. W. Spaulding: I am afraid you have not headed off all of the thyroid people by your comments on your attempts to study thyroid hormone binding. Some years ago we attempted to use some similar techniques to look at thyroid free hormone levels and encountered a variety of difficulties, particularly with binding of hormone to filters. Perhaps the filters you have come up with are less sticky. One thing I didn't see with our technique that you had reached hydrostatic equilibrium: it would appear to me that your serum binding proteins are becoming more concentrated the longer you spin. One other problem that I could see would be maintaining pH on your serum samples. I don't know the story about SHBG, but certainly with thyroxine binding proteins, the effects of pH are rather critical. I wonder if you could comment about your technique and in particular whether the filters you use bind hormone or could release inhibitors of binding.

P. K. Siiteri: The technique was published in detail last June (*J. Biol. Chem.* **255**, 5023, 1980). We have addressed each of the questions that you asked. We have used an ordinary dialysis membrane which under these circumstances does not bind a significant amount of steroid. We have proved that by achieving equilibrium from both sides of the membrane. Furthermore, our technique is independent of volume changes as compared to ordinary ultrafiltration or dialysis systems. As far as pH is concerned, we were concerned about this and did a few studies to indicate that steroid binding to SHBG and CBG and percentage free steroid is stable in the physiologic pH range. Perhaps you noticed in the diagram that we have a small volume (200 μl) and the system is closed. In earlier studies, we were gassing with CO_2 and oxygen prior to capping it but it is not necessary.

L. P. Bullock: You correlated the active form of the steroid with that bound to its high affinity serum binding protein. Can you comment on sex hormone activity in those species that are considered to have low levels of TEBG such as the rodents?

P. K. Siiteri: Well, obviously the rodents are a very special case because they don't have an SHBG as such. They do, however, have in the circulation an androgen binding protein as very elegantly demonstrated by Wayne Bardin. Now the function of this protein is thought to be restricted to the male reproductive tract. The fact is that it does get into the circulation and the concentration of binding sites is in the range of what the serum testosterone levels are. Conversely, it is commonly said there is no estrogen binder in adult rat serum but this is not correct. Dr. Daniel Linkie has published information to show that there is sufficient α-fetoprotein in the circulation of adult female rats to bind the estradiol found during the proestrus surge of the estrus cycle. So it is a myth to believe that you don't have to worry about the rodents because there are no serum binding proteins.

H. L. Bradlow: I want to come back to the breast secretion question again. We have looked extensively at breast cyst fluid and to a lessor extent at nipple secretions together with Dr. Peter Hill. One of the things that is true about both is that there is no albumin in either fluid. The only proteins in both are globulins so that some of the differences which you are seeing could be due simply to the fact that there is no albumin to bind to any of the other steroids you are adding in the test system. Consequently, everything is free to bind to the serum binding proteins. Also, the total steroid levels in cyst fluids or nipple secretions are far higher than one could account for by their being exudates. One finds steroid levels of androgens and estrone sulfate and estradiol sulfate that are up to 20 to 100 times higher than plasma levels. So there has got to be something more complicated than a simple exudation system going on here.

P. K. Siiteri: I don't necessarily agree with that. I think breast cyst fluid is quite a different matter than what I am referring to. Breast cyst fluid is derived from an enclosed compartment in which the steroid proteins or what have you can accumulate over a long period of time. I'm not surprised that you find the very high levels of estrogen sulfates that you and Morty Levitz have found there. I don't think it represents the same biological situation as normal breast fluid, number one. Two, as far as the presence or absence of albumin is concerned, the assays are done at high dilution (1 : 100) and we get very significant suppression of binding at a half molar excess of the synthetic steroids. Furthermore, Dr. Petrakis has found considerable amounts of all serum proteins in this fluid.

H. L. Bradlow: The other thing I would like to ask is, in comparing the cancer patients to the normal subjects you came up with a difference of about eight-tenths of a percent 1.5 versus 2.3 if I recall correctly. Do you think this is physiologically meaningful? Do you mean this relatively or in terms of the small amount of steroid present?

P. K. Siiteri: I tried to make the point that the percentage free is a function of not only the binding to a high affinity protein but also the affinity of the steroid for albumin. The maximal value for percentage free estradiol with albumin is only about 3%. Now, if we take these data and calculate the distribution of estradiol among the free, the albumin, and the SHBG bound, then you find that the percentage of estradiol bound to SHBG varies about 5-fold over the physiologic range of SHBG concentrations. The very fact that free estradiol levels are lower than those required to saturate estrogen receptors raised real doubts in my mind about the free hormone concept in general.

J. H. Oppenheimer: I have some reservations, not about your pregnancy data, but your interpretation of these data. The concept that the high affinity transport protein enters the cell as a complex with the hormone ligand would run counter to the accumulated findings in various fields and over a period of about 25 years. Thus, one would have to postulate that patients with a congenitally high TBG would have thyrotoxicoxis and those with congenital low TBGs, hypothyroidism. Pregnant women would be both thyrotoxic and Cushinoid!

Quite to the contrary, there is every reason to think that the specific binding proteins effectively compete with cells for the hormone. Not only has this been demonstrated in the intact organism, this has equally effectively shown in tissue culture system. Moreover, there is no reason to suppose that the effective space of distribution of any known binding protein includes any significant cellular domain. The demonstration of such proteins in an intra-cellular location by immunofluorometric techniques does not guarantee a substantial exchangeable pool of protein. Localization in liver and kidney could simply represent the sites of synthesis and/or catabolism.

Lastly, I should like to emphasize that the metabolic clearance rate of a hormone is not determined uniquely by the characteristics of its binding to plasma transport proteins. The contributions of cellular protein binding and cellular irreversible processing of hormone must be taken into account, as we have pointed out in a previous Laurentian Hormone Conference (1968).

P. K. Siiteri: Two things: first, you are assuming that if in fact the bound steroid enters a target cell that it is irreversibly cleared and that is certainly not what I suggested. Perhaps I was not clear. Our correlation of MCR values with percentage free plus albumin fractions suggests to me that non-SHBG or CBG bound hormone is rapidly metabolized irreversibly in the liver. Changes in the levels of CBG or SHBG are associated with reciprocal changes in the free fractions of their ligands. We are accustomed to thinking that the free fraction equates with biological activity but the obverse may in fact be true. Drs. Slaunwhite and Sandberg demonstrated that 50% of the CBG is outside of the vascular tree.

J. H. Oppenheimer: I am talking about the interstitial plus vascular, the albumin or the protein compartment, there is a distinction between the two, half of the albumin is outside the compartment, and the distributions of TBPA and TBG are precisely that of albumin.

P. K. Siiteri: Exactly. All I am suggesting to you is that steroids bound to CBG or SHBG in the interstitial fluid can get into target cells. There are many observations that say that these proteins get into cells. Our preliminary results suggest that rat CBG enters GH₃ cells by a steroid and temperature-dependent process and becomes concentrated in the cell nucleus.

G. P. Chrousos: Thank you very much for acknowledging us and our work. As you know, we looked at the binding capacity and affinity of both CBG and the glucocorticoid receptor in various species spanning prosimians, Old World primates, including man, and New World primates. When we plotted the affinities of the CBG against the affinities of the glucocorticoid receptor, we found a striking correlation (correlation coefficient greater than 0.9). Do you think that the CBG and the glucocorticoid receptor are in any way molecularly or otherwise related to each other and if that could explain why these two molecules have such a strong relationship.

P. K. Siiteri: I can only answer by saying that we have been trying very hard to establish such a relationship. We have not yet succeeded but neither have we given up. I suspect that there may well be one.

G. P. Chrousos: The other comment I have is: you mentioned high plasma progesterone levels during the luteal phase in the squirrel monkey and we now have evidence that may explain why it is elevated. We have a paper in press in which we studied the progesterone receptor in the uterus of this species. Estrogen-induced progesterone receptor in the ovariec-tomized squirrel monkey is 10 times less than what it is in cynomolgus monkeys studied in parallel. Thus, elevated plasma progesterone levels may be explained by end-organ resis-tance to this hormone secondary to a progesterone receptor abnormality.

P. K. Siiteri: That is very interesting. Thank you.

G. W. Moll, Jr.: You have presented some interesting and provocative data. We have described a flow dialysis technique in biochemical medicine in 1977 which employs inulin as an internal standard. In the May 1981 issue of *Journal of Clinical Endocrinology and Metab-*

$$f_E = \frac{f_T \cdot A}{B + f_T}$$

$$A = \left(1 - \left(\frac{K_{tE}}{K_{tT}}\right) + K_{aE}\,[a] - \left(\frac{K_{tE}}{K_{tT}}\right)K_{aT}\,[a]\right)^{-1}$$

$$B = \left(\frac{K_{tE}}{K_{tT}}\right)A$$

FIG. A.

olism we published a well-defined relationship between the fraction free estradiol and fraction free testosterone which is shown here (Fig. A). The fraction free estradiol FE and fraction free testosterone FT are related by two constants: A which has the value of 9.3 plus or minus 0.9 and B which has the value of 4.8 plus or minus 0.8. These constants involve only the ratio of the respective TeBG association constants, the respective albumin association constants, and albumin concentration. Figure B shows a similar analysis for fraction-free DHT and fraction-free testosterone simultaneously measured by flow dialysis technique under physiologic conditions in plasmas from individuals with a variety of clinical presentations. The data again fit a model involving TeBG and albumin as significant binding species, addition of increasing amounts of cold DHT or cold testosterone represented by the X's altered the fraction-free DHT and fraction-free testosterone in the predicted manner.

Our simple relationships can be employed to analyze plasma fraction free DHT, fraction free estradiol, and fraction free testosterone data. Any significant deviation of measured fraction free estradiol or fraction free DHT from their predicted values, based upon fraction free testosterone measurements or vice versa should be investigated as to the applicability of the methodology and/or the plasma may have alterations in binding site properties or significant addition of binding species other than TBG and albumin. Thank you.

P. K. Siiteri: I'm aware of your excellent paper that came out recently and I apologize for not mentioning it.

B. Robaire: I would like to make two points about androgen binding protein (ABP) as they relate to the hypothesis you presented. First, ABP has been shown to be a nearly identical protein to SHBG. Second, recent studies by Dym and his colleagues have shown that ABP is internalized exclusively in the initial segment of the rat epididymis, a region of

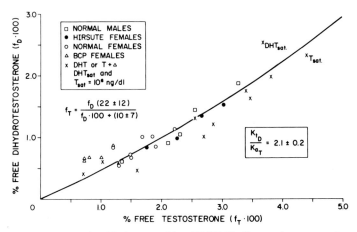

FIG. B. Relationship between T and DHT binding to plasma proteins.

the tissue where we have hypothesized [*in* "Bioregulators of Reproduction" (G. Jiagello, ed.). Academic Press, New York, 1981] a biological role for ABP. I think this system is highly compatible with your hypothesis.

P. K. Siiteri: That is very interesting. I might add that in our culture studies the cells were incubated for 48 hours in a serum free medium before the probe was added.

H. J. Ringold: I'm intrigued by your hypothesis but bothered immediately by the fact that the very potent glucocorticoids, in particular the synthetic ones, are in general very poorly bound by CBG. Does this bother you?

P. K. Siiteri: Well, not really. The fact that we see differences in binding specificity in certain fluids suggests to me that there may be a change in binding specificity of CBG either upon entry or intracellularly. For example, if you imagine an uptake mechanism analogous to the LDL system where you get internalization and inclusion into a lysosome, carbohydrate could be removed from the serum protein or other changes could occur which would alter the steroid specificity so that it binds synthetics like dexamethasone. The other thing I would say is that Dr. Feldman has been doing very careful studies of glucocorticoid binding and he finds that bovine serum has a high affinity binder for triamcinolone acetonide. As you know, fetal calf serum is commonly used in cell culture work and I think a lot of glucocorticoid studies are going to have to be repeated.

J. F. Dunn: In our methodology, we basically adsorb TEBG and CBG with a solid phase matrix of Con A-sepharose, wash away any interfering proteins that also bind, such as albumin, and then we can determine their equilibrium constants for binding to a number of steroids by their relative abilities to displace either tritiated testosterone from TEBG or tritiated cortisol from CBG. Using these association constants which I should emphasize are determined at equilibrium conditions and physiological temperature we can use a computer model, based on the law of mass action developed in association with Dr. Rodbard to calculate the plasma distribution of each of 21 steroids. Shown are TEBG bound, illustrated in the green, CBG bound, illustrated in yellow, or albumin-bound fractions, illustrated in the blue, or unbound which is the black spaces at the top of each bar. It can be seen that androstendiol, dihydrotestosterone are primarily bound by TEBG. Approximately 44% of testosterone is bound by TEBG and we would emphasize in normal man with equilibrium studies on undiluted plasma we agree that at least 20% of the estradiol is bound to TEBG. About 90% of cortisol is bound to CBG, approximately 6% is bound to albumin, and approximately 4% is unbound agreeing well with Dr. Siiteri's data obtained with isodialysis. We also agree with Dr. Moll's data obtained with flow dialysis. I should emphasize that these data were obtained before we were aware of Dr. Siiteri's method. We developed these methods independently and then were able to see the remarkable correlations shown by Dr. Siiteri when we determined unbound testosterone and unbound estradiol concentrations in the same sample. One of the advantages of a computer model like this is that you can examine what happens when you change one or another of the variables. Also illustrated is what happens to the plasma distribution of cortisol in a normal man or a normal woman when you increase the cortisol concentration. Again 90% of the cortisol is bound to CBG and approximately 6% albumin and approximately 4% is unbound in peripheral vein blood. As you increase the cortisol concentration to levels associated with pulsatile release cortisol, you see profound changes in the plasma distribution of serum cortisol. Finally, I would just like to confirm Dr. Siiteri's data on the distribution of estradiol in a normal woman as opposed to previous groups at the NIH. We find that 40% of the circulating estradiol is bound to TEBG, about 60% albumin, and about 2% is unbound agreeing with his figures by isodialysis. This also shows that as you increase or decrease the TEBG concentration in a normal woman, this results in profound change in the plasma distribution of estradiol. I think this illustrates the necessity of carefully measuring these different parameters.

J. E. A. Tyson: I can't let the opportunity escape to respond to some of the things related to the breast for it seems to be taken by the audience that a physiologic secretion from the female breast can be obtained with ease from 50% of women. Since 1972 we have not been successful in isolating significant "physiologic secretion from the nonpregnant/nonpuerperal woman." If we do obtain secretion from the breast of such women it is a traumatic transudate. In some instances where we have obtained fluid, the protein is less than 1% as you have heard from Dr. Bradlow. Now you state as much as 50 μl of fluid can be retrieved and such fluid contains estrogen. I'd like to know how the breast samples were collected by Dr. Petrakis and what groups of women were sampled? Were these women taking oral contraceptives or other agents? In what stage of the menstrual cycle and their ages?

P. K. Siiteri: A number of investigators have shown that breast fluid can be aspirated from the nipples of nonpregnant, nonlactating adult women (G. B. Papanicolaou *et al.*, *Cancer* **11**, 377, 1958; O. W. Sartorius, *J. Natl. Cancer Inst.* 1977; N. L. Petrakis *et al.*, *J. Natl. Cancer Inst.* **54**, 829, 1975; G. C. Buehring, *Cancer* **43**, 1788, 1979; Miller *et al.*, *J. Steroid Biochem.* **13**, 145, 1980). Employing the aspiration technique of Sartorius, we have attempted aspiration in over 5000 women of all ages and racial groups, including women with clinically normal breasts, women with benign breast disease, and women with breast cancer (N. L. Petrakis *et al.*, *J. Natl. Cancer Inst.* **67**, 277, 1981). These women did not have galactorrhea or other evidence of endocrinologic abnormality. The technique involves the use of a small nipple cup attached to a 10-ml syringe. On retraction of the syringe to 6–8 ml for not more than 5–15 seconds, accompanied by gentle but firm compression of the breast by the woman, fluid appears at the nipple surface in about 75% of women between 40 and 50 years of age. Differences were found related to demographic, reproductive, and other characteristics. Overall, 53% of nulliparous women yielded fluid. The quantity of fluid obtained averaged about 30 μl. The aspiration is definitely not, as suggested by Dr. Tyson, a "traumatic event" and the fluid obtained is not a transudate. Perhaps the minute quantities obtained do not seem "significant," but 10–15 μl of fluid is a significant quantity when employing microanalytic techniques.

That the aspirated fluid is a true breast secretion is indicated by its chemical composition which is similar to, but more concentrated than, colostrum. We have found aspirates to contain a variety of chemical substances, including lactose, cholesterol, fatty acids, protein, estrone, and immunoglobulins, as well as certain exogenously-derived substances (N. L. Petrakis, "Banbury Report 8: Hormones and Breast Cancer," pp. 243–255, 1981). In addition, the fluid contains exfoliated breast epithelial cells, colostrum corpuscles (foam cells), and apocrine cells (E. B. King *et al.*, *Am. J. Clin. Pathol.* **64**, 729, 1975, and E. B. King *et al.*, *Am. J. Clin. Pathol.* **64**, 739, 1975).

It must be stressed that the technique of aspiration employed is very important. We avoid prolonged application of the nipple aspirator. We believe that prolonged application of negative pressure to a nipple (e.g., up to 10 minutes) as employed by Wynder *et al.* (*Cancer* **47**, 1444, 1981) may very likely lead to local trauma and transudation with dilution of breast fluid by tissue fluid. However, the brief application of negative pressure (5–15 seconds) as employed by us does not.

J. E. A. Tyson: It is inappropriate at this time to present our data, however, I still maintain that the negative pressures created by the pump will produce a traumatic transudate not a physiologic secretion!

B. E. P. Murphy: I like your isodialysis method; the one problem I can see that might arise would be the control of temperature. You didn't mention the effects of temperature. We've been working with an even simpler approach recently; this consists of dialyzing heated undiluted plasma against unheated undiluted plasma. We have also shown that you do get some binding of estradiol to SHBG at 37°C. I'll be interested to compare our data with yours, using your method. Another point is that there are some odd specificities of the CBGs apart from the human, for example, cat CBG binds S (11-desoxycortisol) better than F (cortisol), chicken CBG binds E (cortisone) better than F, the monkey CBG binds B (corticosterone) better than F. I wonder how these observations fit into your very interesting and thought-provoking hypothesis. Third, how do you interpret the rises of CBG, SHBG, and so on in pregnancy in some species and not in others?

P. K. Siiteri: The temperature effect was described in our *JBC* paper. The rate of egress decreases very markedly with temperature as expected from equilibrium binding studies. The percentage of free steroid is also temperature sensitive. As far as variations in binding specificity, I think one of the most interesting that you didn't mention is the evidence for dexamethasone binding in the serum of chickens. So those who do glucocorticoid work with chickens might well be aware of it. The situation in pregnancy is complicated by the presence of progesterone and I'd rather not speculate at this time.

R. N. Andersen: As you know, Jim Givens in Memphis has been studying hyperandrogenism for a number of years, primarily in polycystic ovarian disease. We find lower TeBG binding capacities and elevated free testosterone in most of these patients in agreement with your data and that of others. He has used combination oral contraceptives to try to suppress the total androgen. With the right kinds of combination contraceptives, the binding capacity is increased. We have interpreted our data to suggest that the progression of hirsutism is arrested with this treatment because the free testosterone has been reduced. If I understand your last figure, we should reinterpret those data to say that when the free testosterone is elevated the binding globulin (TeBG) is more completely saturated and therefore would enter the cells in higher proportion than when the binding capacity goes up and the total testosterone goes down. Under the latter condition, the binding globulin would be less heavily saturated and would not enter the cells as readily. Is that a reasonable interpretation based on the concept you have presented?

P. K. Siiteri: Not exactly. The model suggests that the elevated free testosterone is caused by lowered total SHBG levels resulting from greater uptake of testosterone–SHBG complexes by target cells.

Note Added in Proof: In order to study steroid receptors we have established fibroblast cell lines from squirrel monkey and human genital skin. Whole cell receptor binding studies carried out by Dr. Eldon Schriock have shown that the glucocorticoid receptor affinity measured with [^{3}H]dexamethasone is about 3-fold lower in squirrel monkey cells ($K_D = 10 \pm 3.1$ nM) than in human cells ($K_D = 3.1 \pm 0.7$ nM). It can be calculated that over the physiologic range of free plasma cortisol concentration (3–30 nM), 10–60% of receptors are saturated in normal human cells. However, under all conditions, greater than 98% of glucocorticoid receptors would be saturated by plasma-free cortisol (2–10 μM) in squirrel monkeys. In marked contrast, the range of plasma CBG bound cortisol concentration (100–1000 nM) is virtually the same in both species. Androgen receptor binding affinity measured with ^{3}H-R-1881 is similar ($K_D \simeq 0.15$ nM) in both species. Interestingly, the number of androgen binding sites per cell (1–2000) for both squirrel monkey and a patient with testicular feminization is about 10-fold lower than that found in normal human cells. The concentrations of plasma-free testosterone in humans and squirrel monkeys is sufficient to saturate only 2–5% of androgen receptors. The concentration of free plus albumin bound testosterone, however, is sufficient to saturate greater than 85% of androgen receptors in the human and about 70 or 95% during the nonbreeding and breeding seasons in squirrel monkeys, respectively. Interestingly, the plasma concentration of SHBG bound testosterone increases 10-fold in the breeding season to levels 5- to 10-fold greater than those found in normal human plasma. All of these results are consistent with our working hypothesis which suggests that plasma bound steroid hormones are the physiologically active form.

Insulin Mediators and Their Control of Metabolism through Protein Phosphorylation

JOSEPH LARNER, KANG CHENG, CHARLES SCHWARTZ,
KUNIMI KIKUCHI, SHINRI TAMURA, STEVEN CREACY,
ROBERT DUBLER, GAIL GALASKO, CLAIRE PULLIN, AND MARK KATZ

Department of Pharmacology, University of Virginia, School of Medicine, Charlottesville, Virginia

I. Introduction

Since the discovery of insulin in 1911 (and again in 1920) (see discussion by Larner, 1980), many of its effects in sensitive tissues have been defined over the years. Insulin initiates three types of actions: (1) a rapid (seconds) set of actions at the cell membrane which increases hexose transport, ion transport, and the transport of other monomeric metabolites including amino acids, fatty acids, and nucleosides; (2) a slower (minutes to hours) direction of metabolism into an anabolic mode both by enhancing anabolic pathways and by decreasing catabolic pathways including lipolysis, proteolysis, glycogenolysis, and gluconeogenesis; and (3) a still slower (hours) stimulation of cell growth. The questions we will address are "How is this complex set of events initiated at the cell membrane by insulin? How are these actions coordinated? How does insulin initiate this complex set of events at the cell membrane?

In a provocative article, the late Gordon Tompkins and his colleagues (Hershko *et al.*, 1971) termed this coordinated regulatory program the "pleiotypic" response. They compared it with the stringent response in bacteria where an analogous set of reactions is controlled by the availability of required amino acids. An unusual guanine nucleotide ppGpp accumulated in stringent (controlled) but not in relaxed (uncontrolled) strains of bacteria under conditions of amino acid starvation, and the nucleotide disappeared when the amino acid starved bacteria were treated with chloramphenicol. This suggested that ppGpp might be the mediator of at least some of the reactions of the pleiotypic response of stringent strains. By analogy, an unusual nucleotide was suggested as a mediator in eukaryotic cells controlled by insulin according to the scheme in Fig. 1. The resting cell membrane provokes mediator formation which regu-

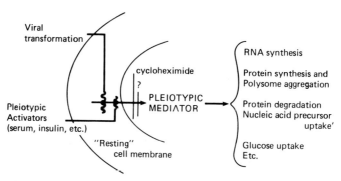

FIG. 1. Hypothetical mechanism of pleiotypic control. The "resting" cell membrane is presumed to promote the appearance of the pleiotypic mediator, which in turn regulates the reactions of the pleiotypic response as shown. Pleiotypic activators are postulated to prevent reversibly the resting membrane from stimulating mediator formation. Viral transformation is assumed to interfere in a more permanent way with membrane control of mediator appearance. Cycloheximide may reverse the pleiotypic reaction by inhibiting the synthesis of the mediator.

lates the pleiotypic response. Pleiotypic activators such as insulin prevent mediator formation by the membrane.

In 1972, we also had proposed a novel cyclic nucleotide as a mediator of the action of insulin (Larner, 1972) by analogy to cAMP formation as a second messenger for glucagon and epinephrine action (Fig. 2). This hypothesis was based on the fact that insulin could depress tissue cyclic AMP concentrations elevated by lipolytic hormones, but did not affect basal concentrations of cyclic AMP. Both of the above proposals suggested a chemical signal formed from the membrane and regulated by insulin. As I will demonstrate, insulin does act via chemical signals formed

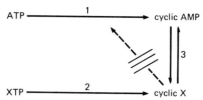

FIG. 2. ATP is converted to cyclic AMP by adenyl cyclase (reaction 1), and XTP to cyclic X by another cyclase or similar enzyme (reaction 2). Cyclic AMP and cyclic X are interconvertible (reaction 3). Cyclic X inhibits reaction 1. Glucagon and epinephrine stimulate reaction 1; insulin would stimulate reaction 2. Insulin alone would stimulate cyclic X formation (reaction 2) and increase cyclic X levels. Should these become high enough, cyclic AMP levels might increase by reaction 3. Preincubation with insulin would inhibit reaction 1 because of the accumulation of cyclic X. Analogously, preincubation with glucagon would lead to increased cyclic AMP. Addition of insulin would increase cyclic X and decrease cyclic AMP levels by inhibiting reaction 1.

from the cell membrane. However, these signals are not nucleotide but rather peptide in nature.

Our work has focused on the control by insulin of glycogen synthesis, the first anabolic action of insulin to be discovered (Best, 1963), and its relationship to increased hexose transport. Over the years, the principles worked out with glycogen synthase, which is controlled by insulin through covalent phosphorylation, have been broadly applied to other intracellular enzyme systems. Today, we recognize that in five areas of metabolism, namely, glycogenesis, lipogenesis, cholesterol synthesis, protein synthesis, and gluconeogenesis, the key enzymes involved are controlled by covalent phosphorylation in a manner analogous to glycogen synthase. We consider this phosphorylation mechanism as having the significance of a "language" which allows us to understand how a hormonal signal can direct metabolism in an overall manner within the cell. The basis for the language concept is that covalent phosphorylation can be considered to be made up of words like serine-P threonine-P or tyrosine-P; sentences composed of enzymes with multiple or single phosphorylation sites like glycogen synthase and phosphorylase and especially when arranged in enzyme cascades; and whole articles comprising the coordinate control of multiple enzyme-P in a number of areas of metabolism to direct the cell toward anabolism or catabolism.

Preceding the control of metabolism are the initial actions of insulin at the cell surface. We have systematically worked to understand the metabolic action of insulin or glycogenesis within the cell and traced that action outward to the cell membrane. Recently, we have defined the nature of the chemical signals or mediators formed by the initial action of insulin at the cell membrane as peptides. This has allowed us to attack the problem of their formation at the cell membrane, and thus begin to define the very initial biological actions of insulin. In this article, I will discuss three areas of our work: first, the chemical topography of the insulin molecule in terms of its binding and biological activity functions and the influence of insulin fragments on the binding of insulin and degraded insulin to the receptors; second, the elucidation of two separate mechanisms for activating glycogen synthase synergistically without and with glucose present; and third, the isolation of mediator peptides, their chemical composition, and the mechanism of their formation.

II. The Insulin Molecule and Its Receptor-Mediated Functions

Two general biochemical mechanisms can be devised to understand the interaction of the insulin molecule with its receptor. In the first, there is a separation of the binding domain from the biological activity domain; in the second, there is no separation and these functions coexist in the same portions of the molecule. In Fig. 3 a mechanism involving separate domains in the insulin molecule is shown. Precedents for this model include the peptide hormones ACTH (Hofmann *et al.*, 1970), glucagon (Wright *et al.*, 1978), PTH (Segre *et al.*, 1979), the glycoprotein hormones TSH, LH, FSH, and HCG, and bacterial toxins (Neville and Chang, 1978). In Fig. 4 a mechanism involving multiple domains with coexisting binding and activity functions is shown. A precedent for this model is the β-adrenergic receptor (Bilezekian *et al.*, 1971). In both models, binding is hypothesized to coincide with the release of an inhibitory subunit (Harmon *et al.*, 1980). Subsequent to binding of insulin, activation of the inactive insulin–receptor complex occurs by a separate event, hypothesized as S–S crosslinking.

To understand whether the insulin molecule has separate domains for binding to the receptor and for biological activity, we studied two degraded insulins, desoctapeptide insulin (DOP) (trypsin) and desalanine desasparagine insulin (DAA) (carboxypeptidase), as well as two C-terminal B-chain peptides, B22–26 (Arg-Gly-Phe-Phe-Tyr) and B23–29 (Gly-Phe-Phe-Tyr-Thr-Pro-Lys) (Kikuchi *et al.*, 1980). Peptides were

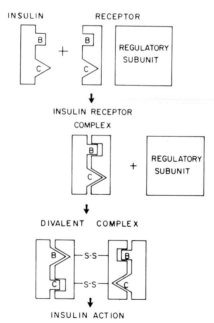

FIG. 3.   Model of insulin-receptor interaction with separate domains on the insulin molecule for binding and biological activity. B, Binding domain; C, catalytic domain.

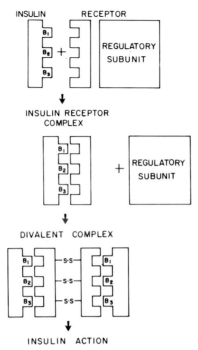

FIG. 4. Model of insulin–receptor interaction without separate binding and biological activity domains. Three mixed binding and catalytic activity domains are shown, each of which contributes partially to the binding and activity.

studied alone and in the presence of suboptimal concentrations of insulin or DOP. Two "insulin-like" agents concanavalin A, (Con A) and nonsuppressible insulin-like activity-P (NSILA-P) were also studied.

DOP, purified by three physical methods and by one biological method (IM9 lymphocyte receptor depletion), was resolved free of trace insulin contamination and shown to be as fully active as insulin (Fig. 5) in stimulating glucose oxidation but reached maximal efficacy at much higher (3 log units) concentrations than insulin. The same was true for DAA, but the dose–response curve was shifted to the right one to two log units. ^{125}I-labeled insulin displacement curves with DOP paralleled biological activity (Fig. 6). Thus both degraded insulins were fully efficacious but did not bind to the receptor as well as insulin.

C-terminal B-chain peptides (Fig. 7) were inactive alone at all concentrations tested. In the presence of suboptimal insulin concentrations, small synergistic enhancement of biological activity was observed at 10^{-7} to 10^{-6} M peptide and major synergistic enhancement at 10^{-4} to 10^{-3} M

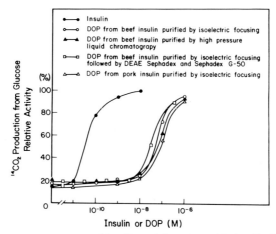

FIG. 5. Dose–response curves of insulin and desoctapeptide insulin (DOP) purified by three independent methods. Cells were isolated and washed in Krebs–Ringer phosphate buffer, pH 7.4, containing 30 mg/ml of bovine serum albumin. Glucose conversion to CO_2 was measured after incubating cells with insulin or desoctapeptide insulin for 1 hour at 37°C in medium containing 0.2 mM D-[1-^{14}C]glucose. The results are presented as percentages of the controls. ●, Insulin; ○, desoctapeptide insulin purified by isoelectric focusing; ▲, desoctapeptide insulin purified by high pressure liquid chromatography; □, desoctapeptide insulin purified by isoelectric focusing followed by DEAE-Sephadex G-50 gel filtration; △, desoctapeptide insulin from pork insulin purified by isoelectric focusing.

peptide. Enhancement at 10^{-7} to 10^{-6} M peptide was *not* associated with increased insulin binding, and thus differed mechanistically from the marked enhancement at 10^{-4} to 10^{-3} M peptide which was associated with increased insulin binding (Kikuchi *et al.*, 1981b).

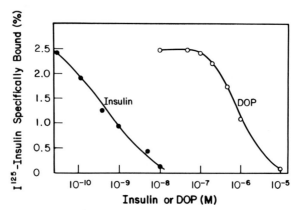

FIG. 6. Fat cells (0.5 × 10^6) were incubated with ^{125}I-labeled insulin (0.7 × 10^{-10} M) in the presence of increasing concentrations of insulin (●) or desoctapeptide insulin (DOP) (○).

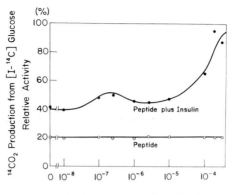

FIG. 7. Effect of the β-alanylpentapeptide amide on [^{14}C]glucose oxidation in the absence and presence of insulin. Cells were incubated at 37°C for 1 hour in a medium containing 0.2 mM D-[1-^{14}C]glucose with the indicated concentrations of the β-alanylpentapeptide amide without (○) or with (●) $10^{-10}\,M$ insulin.

Studies of insulin degradation showed that the decrease in degradation with peptide present was too small an effect to account for the major enhancement of biological activity. With bacitracin added, insulin degradation was fully blocked, yet the peptides still enhanced insulin binding and action markedly (Fig. 8). Thus, the peptides did not act by protecting insulin from degradation but by a different mechanism.

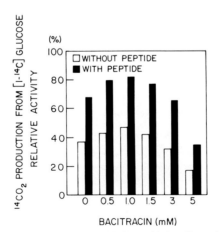

FIG. 8. Effect of peptide on glucose oxidation with insulin and bacitracin. Cells were incubated with the indicated concentrations of bacitracin without (white bars) and with 0.6 mM N-acetylpentapeptide amide (black bars). All incubations were done with $10^{-10}\,M$ insulin. Other conditions were as described in the legend to Fig. 7.

[125]I-labeled insulin binding was studied in rat adipocytes with three different pentapeptide derivatives (B22–26) and with heptapeptide (B23–29). Peptides alone did not affect the action of labeled insulin in the presence of maximal concentrations of unlabeled insulin (60 μg/ml) (Fig. 9). In the presence of submaximal insulin ($10^{-10}\,M$), pentapeptides containing arginine markedly enhanced insulin binding with the rank order, pentapeptide amide β-alanyl pentapeptide amide N-acetyl pentapeptide amide. This order followed reasonably well the order on biological activity (Kikuchi *et al.*, 1981b). Heptapeptide, which does not contain arginine was inactive even in the presence of a submaximal insulin concentration, suggesting a requirement for arginine in the peptide enhancement effect. Studying the time course with various insulin concentrations revealed that the peptides enhanced initial rates of binding and decreased lag times, as well as increasing long-term equilibrium binding (up to 8 hours). Shown in Fig. 10 are displacement curves without and with peptide (A), Scatchard plots without and with peptide (B), and Hill plots without and with peptide (C). Little or no change in total number of binding sites occurred (B). The Hill coefficient of 0.85 (C) indicates "negatively cooperative" phenomenology, with no change in the Hill number in the presence of peptide. Equilibrium dissociation constants, K_D calculated from Hill plots, decreased 2-fold in the presence of peptide.

When dissociation rates (k_{-1}) were separately studied no differences were seen without and with peptide (Fig. 11). Enhanced dissociation was

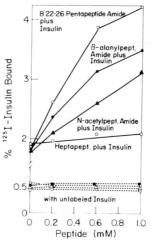

FIG. 9.   Effect of peptide on ^{125}I-labeled insulin binding to adipocytes. Cells (5×10^5) were incubated at 25°C for 30 minutes with ^{125}I-labeled insulin ($0.7 \times 10^{-10}\,M$) with the indicated concentrations of ●, β-alanyl-Arg-Gly-Phe-Phe-Tyr-NH$_2$; ○ Arg-Gly-Phe-Phe-Tyr-NH$_2$; △, N-acetyl-Arg-Gly-Phe-Phe-Tyr-NH$_2$; □, Gly-Phe-Phe-Tyr-Thr-Pro-Lys.

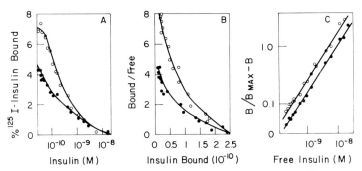

FIG. 10. (A) Displacement of ^{125}I-labeled insulin by native insulin. ^{125}I-labeled insulin binding to adipocytes was determined at 25°C for 2 hours of incubation without (○) and with (●) 0.6 mM B22-26 pentapeptide amide in the presence of 10^{-10} M ^{125}I-labeled insulin supplemented with amounts of native insulin to make insulin concentrations as shown. Nonspecific binding has been subtracted. (B) The bound-to-free ratio of ^{125}I-labeled insulin is plotted as a function of insulin bound (Scatchard Plot). ○,●, same condition as shown in (A). (C) $B/(B_{max} - B)$ is plotted as a function of free hormone (Hill Plot), where B is the insulin bound at an indicated free insulin concentration, and B_{max} is the calculated maximal binding value obtained from the curve shown in (B).

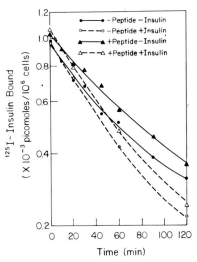

FIG. 11. Dissociation curves of ^{125}I-labeled insulin binding in the absence and presence of peptide. Cells were incubated with 1.4×10^{-10} M ^{125}I-labeled insulin at 25°C for 1 hour, then washed 2 times and incubated at 25°C for the indicated times without (●,○) or with (▲,△) 0.6 mM N-acetylpentapeptide amide in the absence and presence of native insulin (60 μg/ml).

observed with the addition of unlabeled insulin in keeping with "negatively cooperative" phenomenology, again with no difference in rates without and with peptide. k_{-1} values were 1.2 and 1.1 × 10^{-2} min^{-1} without and with peptide, respectively.

When association rates (k_{+1}) were determined, a marked dose dependent effect of peptide was observed (Fig. 12). Association rate constants were 0.5 × 10^7 and 1.0 × 10^7 $min^{-1} M^{-1}$ without and with peptide, respectively. Equilibrium dissociation constants (K_D), calculated from the velocity constants decreased from 2.4 × 10^{-9} to 1.1 × $10^{-9} M$ without and with peptide, respectively.

As shown in Table 1, equilibrium dissociation constants (K_D) decreased 2-fold with peptide present whether calculated from the Hill plot or from the ratio of the velocity constants.

Pentapeptide shifted insulin and DOP dose–response curves about 1 log unit to the left (Fig. 13) when 2-deoxyglucose transport was studied in rat adipocytes. Similar responses were observed for glucose oxidation. Thus, the peptide, itself inactive, can amplify markedly the action of a suboptimal concentration of insulin or DOP. Enhancement of insulin action by peptide was specific for insulin, since binding and action of several other hormones tested was not influenced. Further tests of specificity included studies with three detergents and a ganglioside, all of which were shown to be inactive.

The kinetic mechanism of the enhanced insulin binding appears to involve increased velocity of binding (k_{+1}) without decreased velocity of dissociation (k_{-1}), with a net result of a decreased equilibrium dissociation constant (K_D). These studies suggest a mechanism by which there is mul-

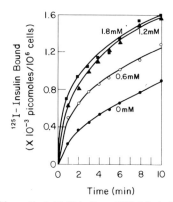

FIG. 12.   Effect of peptide on the initial binding of ^{125}I-labeled insulin to adipocytes. Cells were incubated for the indicated times with ^{125}I-labeled insulin (2 × $10^{-10} M$) in the absence (●) and presence (○, 0.6 mM, ▲, 1.2 mM, ■, 1.8 mM) of N-acetylpentapeptide amide.

TABLE I

Kinetic Constants of Binding of Insulin at 25 °C with the Insulin-Receptor of Adipocytes

Kinetic constant	Units	Peptide	
		Without	With
Association rate constant $(k_{+1})^a$	$min^{-1} M^{-1}$	0.5×10^7	1.0×10^7
Dissociation rate constant $(k_{-1})^b$	min^{-1}	1.2×10^{-2}	1.1×10^{-2}
Dissociation constant from Hill plots^c	M	4.6×10^{-9}	2.8×10^{-9}
Dissociation constant from k_{-1}/k_{+1}	M	2.4×10^{-9}	1.1×10^{-9}

[a] Calculated from the data presented in Figs. 10B and 12.
[b] Calculated from the data presented in Fig. 11.
[c] Calculated from the data presented in Fig. 10.

tivalent cooperative binding of insulin to the receptor with the peptide being able to substitute for one or more of the insulin molecules, and further that there may be separate domains in the molecule for binding and for biological activity.

Our studies are entirely in keeping with experiments on the point substituted human insulin. Substitution of B24 phenylalanine with leucine produced a molecule with properties almost identical to DOP, i.e., poor binding but with maximal efficacy at high concentration. A similar mechanism

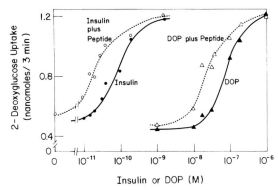

FIG. 13. Effect of peptide on 2-deoxyglucose transport in the presence of varying concentrations of insulin or desoctapeptide insulin. Cells were preincubated at 25°C for 1 hour without or with 0.6 mM N-acetylpentapeptide amide in the presence of varying concentrations of insulin or desoctapeptide insulin. ●, Insulin; ○, insulin plus peptide; ▲, desoctapeptide insulin; △, desoctapeptide insulin plus peptide.

involving multivalent binding of insulin to the receptor has been hypothesized by Olefsky *et al.* (1980) to explain the unusually low biological activity of this human insulin compared with its binding to the receptor. All of the above studies suggest that the C-terminal end of the B-chain is, at least in part, the binding domain and that the remainder of the molecule contains the active center domain.

III. Insulin Action on Hexose Transport and Glycogen Synthesis: Identification of Two Mechanisms for Activating Glycogen Synthase

The action of insulin to enhance hexose transport is one of its earliest and best established actions, due in no small part to the work of Dr. Levine and his colleagues (Levine *et al.*, 1949). However, in balance studies with eviscerate dogs Soskin and Levine (1940) found that when insulin was administered with glucose, glycogen breakdown was obliterated, but lactic acid was still produced. In other words, insulin was acting to redistribute the glucose taken up by the muscle mass, rather selectively into glycogen (Table II). To quote from this paper: "The additional insulin prevented the breakdown of glycogen usually seen in our experiments on non-insulinized normal animals, and in some cases even increased the muscle glycogen." To again quote: "This indicates that insulin acts by promoting the conversion of glucose into some intermediate substance which is necessary for both storage and utilization. The present state of our knowledge of the intermediate steps in glycogen formation and breakdown strongly suggests that the intermediate substance, the formation of which is facilitated by insulin, is one of the phosphorylated hexoses." How prophetic these words were!

Our studies on the mechanism of insulin-mediated glycogen synthesis began over 20 years ago. The question originally asked was, "Does insulin promote glycogen synthesis as a consequence of increased glucose transport through the cell membrane, or is there a specific intracellular mechanism directly influencing glycogen synthesis, set into motion by insulin?"

TABLE II

Condition	Muscle glycogen			Lactic acid	
	Average initial (mg%)	Average final (mg%)	Average decrease (mg%)	Average final (mg%)	Average increase (mg%)
Normal	511	355	43.1	106.7	15.2
Depancreatized	337	217	38.4	183.2	21.0
Insulinized	763	761	0.5	79.6	10.6

It was promptly concluded that the latter was true based upon two pieces of evidence obtained in our laboratory (Larner, *et al.*, 1960):

1. The yields of glycogen synthesized from glucose under the influence of insulin were so high as to be in effect quantitative (i.e., the yields were over 90%). It did not seem likely that increased transport alone could explain, by a "push" mechanism, such extraordinarily high yields of one product of glucose metabolism, namely glycogen, in the face of other competing pathways.

2. When the then known intermediates between glucose and glycogen, namely glucose 6-phosphate and glucose 1-phosphate, were analyzed, evidence was found for a "pull" mechanism operating in addition to a "push." Evidence for the "push" was obtained by virtue of the increased concentration of glucose 6-phosphate observed in the insulin-treated tissue.

Evidence for the "pull" consisted of the finding that tissue concentrations of glucose 1-phosphate which had been expected to also be elevated in the insulin-treated as compared to the control tissue were not.

Considering the increased glycogen concentrations and the increased glucose 6-P concentrations, the lack of an increase in glucose 1-phosphate concentrations was in effect a crossover point. We concluded in our paper, "Glucose 1-phosphate levels are smaller than hexose 6-phosphate, and in contrast to the latter there is no increase with insulin. An interpretation of this finding is that the rise in glucose 1-phosphate which might be expected concomitantly with the increase in hexose 6-phosphate, is counterbalanced by a rapid removal of glucose 1-phosphate, presumably to glycogen. The speed and quantitative aspects of the glycogen synthesis observed here open the question of the mechanistic relationship of the stimulated glycogen formation to the stimulated conversion of extracellular glucose to intracellular hexose 6-phosphate; that is, whether an increase in transport alone is sufficient to account for the glycogen synthesis noted."

We then went on to analyze the enzymes involved in glycogen synthesis and degradation. It was found that only one enzyme of the four examined had been influenced by insulin, namely, glycogen synthase; that insulin activated glycogen synthase, and that the activation was stable to extraction of the enzyme into a cell-free extract (Villar-Palasi and Larner, 1960, 1961). As shown in Fig. 14, this activation of the enzyme by insulin treatment of rat diaphragms did not require glucose in the medium. It was not observed at low temperatures, indicating that it was temperature-dependent and, therefore, likely to be an enzyme-catalyzed reaction. We

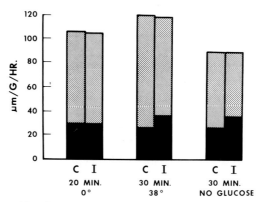

FIG. 14.   Effect of insulin on glycogen synthase in rat diaphragm. C, Control; I, insulin
(0.1 μg/ml). Filled in black bar, enzyme activity without glucose 6-P; total bar, enzyme
activity in the presence of 40 mM glucose 6-P.

were able to observe the activation because the enzyme was assayed in
the absence as well as in the presence of glucose 6-phosphate. The effect
of insulin was seen only when the assay was performed in the absence of
added glucose 6-phosphate. When the enzyme was assayed with added
glucose 6-phosphate, which stimulated the enzyme maximally, the control
and insulin-treated enzyme activities were identical. This suggested that
insulin had not caused a synthesis of new enzyme, but rather had acted in
a manner to convert the enzyme from a less active to a more active form,
without changing the "total" enzyme content. The activation by insulin of
this enzyme constituted the "pull" which had been suggested by the
hexose phosphate measurements.

   With J. Lawrence (Lawrence and Larner, 1978) and Y. Oron (Oron and
Larner, 1980), we established that there are in fact two separate but
synergistic mechanisms in adipocytes by which insulin activates glycogen
synthase with and without glucose present. Without glucose, insulin activated glycogen synthase in rat adipocytes within 1 minute (Fig. 15); the
effect was maximal at about 4 minutes and was stable for at least 20
minutes. This was similar to the classic effect observed originally in diaphragm and which we now term mechanism 1. In adipocytes, glucose alone
activated the enzyme rapidly; the maximal stimulation was at 2 minutes
and the effect slowly decreased with time. Insulin and glucose together
activated glycogen synthase synergistically, with the maximal effect at 4
minutes which slowly decreased with time up to 20 minutes. In the presence of cytochalasin B or phloridzin, the synergistic stimulation observed
with glucose and insulin was reduced to the stimulation observed with
insulin alone, but not to the basal level (Table III), suggesting that there
were two separate mechanisms present.

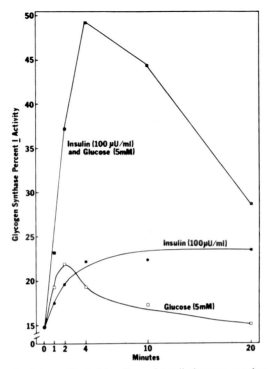

FIG. 15. The stimulatory effect of insulin on fat cell glycogen synthase in the presence and absence of glucose. Fat cells were incubated in 5 ml of medium (8.1 × 10⁵ cells/ml) at 37°C for 20 minutes before the cells were centrifuged and homogenized. The additions indicated were made after the appropriate period of this incubation to obtain the times of exposure indicated.

TABLE III

Effect of Cytochalasin B on Response of Fat Cell Glycogen Synthase to Insulin and Glucose[a]

Additions	Control	Cytochalasin B, (10 μg/ml)
	(% glycogen synthase I)	
None	14.0 ± 0.8	12.0 ± 0.8
Glucose (1 mM)	14.4 ± 0.2	13.0 ± 0.8
Insulin (50 μU/ml)	20.9 ± 0.8	17.9 ± 1.0
Insulin (50 μU/ml)+ glucose (1 mM)	28.4 ± 1.2	19.3 ± 0.8

[a] Cells were incubated with or without 10 μg/ml of cytochalasin B for 10 minutes at 23°C. Insulin and glucose were added to yield the concentrations indicated, and glycogen synthase activity was determined after incubation at 37°C for 15 minutes. The values presented represent the means ± SE of four experiments performed on different days.

Using various hexoses, it was proven that only those which were phosphorylated in the six position were capable of activating glycogen synthase. Thus, 2-deoxyglucose was a powerful activator, but 3-O-methyl glucose, whose transport was also accelerated by insulin, but which was not subsequently phosphorylated, did not activate (Lawrence and Larner, 1978). The new mechanism, termed mechanism 2, was established by two separate lines of evidence: correlation of glucose 6-phosphate, or 2-deoxyglucose 6-phosphate concentrations in tissues with glycogen synthase activation state (Fig. 16); and, direct activation of glycogen synthase phosphatase in extracts by glucose 6-phosphate concentrations which were shown to be present in the tissues (Fig. 17). The two separate mechanisms were identified first in fat, then in muscle (Oron and Larner, 1980) and thus are likely to be general.

As shown in the model in Fig. 18, in the presence of glucose, glucose 6-phosphate became a feed-forward signal molecule in its own right

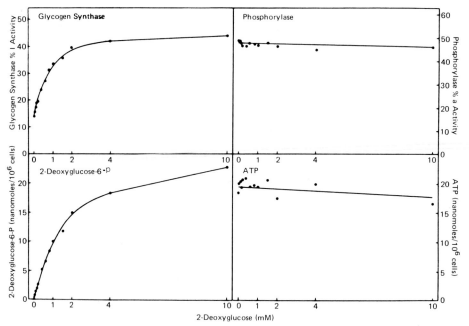

FIG. 16. Dependence of adipocyte glycogen synthase I activity, phosphorylase a activity, and the concentrations of 2-deoxyglucose 6-P and ATP on the concentration of 2-deoxyglucose. Fat cells were incubated at 37°C with the indicated concentrations of 2-deoxyglucose. After 5 minutes, the incubations were terminated and glycogen synthase and phosphorylase activities and the concentrations of 2-deoxyglucose 6-P and ATP were determined.

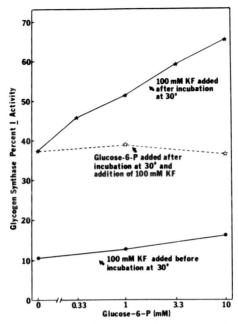

FIG. 17. Effect of glucose 6-P on the activity of glycogen synthase phosphatase using endogenous adipocyte glycogen synthase as substrate. Extracts from isolated fat cells were incubated at 30°C with the indicated concentrations of glucose 6-P for 5 minutes. Details of the incubation are described in the text.

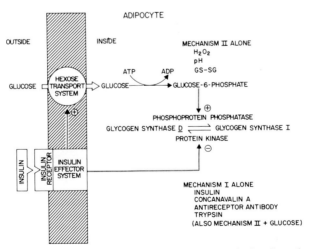

FIG. 18. Two mechanisms of glycogen synthase activation by insulin and other agents in the absence and presence of glucose.

(mechanism 2), in contrast to the direct activation by insulin of glycogen synthase without glucose (mechanism 1). Glucose 6-phosphate is now recognized as a more general signal in metabolism; e.g., in the initiation of cell-free protein synthesis (Ernst *et al.*, 1978) and in the increased uptake of Ca^{2+} by skinned muscle fibers (Brautigan *et al.*, 1980). Concanavalin A (Fig. 19) and antireceptor antibody (Fig. 20) are also insulin-like in that they activate glycogen synthesis in mechanism 1 without glucose. In the presence of glucose, all three agents also activate mechanism 2. As will be shown subsequently, we have recently added trypsin to this list. Physiologically, with both insulin and glucose present, probably neither mechanism 1 nor mechanism 2 exists alone, only both together, amplifying each other as feed-forward signals. It is conceivable that they may operate separately in pathologic states; e.g., in diabetics without insulin present, mechanism 2 might operate; or in type 1 glycogen storage disease with low or absent blood glucose, mechanism 1 might operate. As we will show later, mechanism 1 is related to peptide mediator signal generation by proteolysis.

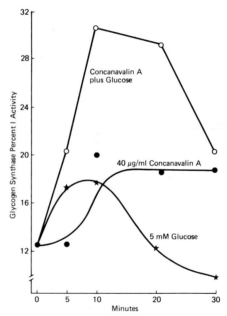

FIG. 19.   Time course of adipocyte glycogen synthase activation by concanavalin A in the absence and presence of glucose. Adipocytes were incubated in 5 ml of medium (0.7 × 10^6 cells/ml) at 37°C for 30 minutes before the incubations were stopped. Concanavalin A (40 μg/ml), glucose (5 m*M*), or concanavalin A plus glucose were added after the appropriate times to give the periods of exposure indicated before termination of the incubations.

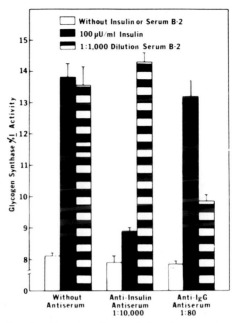

FIG. 20. Effects of antiinsulin and antihuman IgG antisera on the activation of glycogen synthase by insulin and serum B-2. Tubes containing insulin (200 μU) and serum B-2 (2 μl) were incubated at 23°C in 1 ml of medium containing no antisera, antiinsulin antiserum (1 part antiserum per 5000 parts medium), or antihuman IgG antiserum (1 part antiserum per 40 parts medium). After 15 minutes, adipocytes (1 ml) were added to the tubes and incubated at 37°C. The incubations were terminated after 15 minutes, and glycogen synthase activities were assayed. The results presented represent the mean values + SE from 3 experiments performed on different days.

We have recently identified a set of chemical reagents which activate transport without activating glycogen synthase, i.e., mechanism 2 alone. The first shown in our laboratory with J. C. Lawrence was H_2O_2 (Lawrence and Larner, 1978). In contrast to insulin, H_2O_2 without glucose did not activate glycogen synthase in rat adipocytes, but did activate glucose transport. With K. Kikuchi, we recently studied the effect of increased pH and of oxidized and reduced glutathione in rat adipocytes, and found that they act similarly to H_2O_2 (Kikuchi and Larner, 1981).

As is well known, increased pH enhances insulin binding to the receptor (Fig. 21). With increase in pH, the effect on binding is related to an enhanced velocity of association k_{+1}, rather than to a decreased velocity of dissociation k_{-1} (Figs. 22 and 23). This has also been shown recently by Gliemann's group (Sonne et al., 1981). Increased pH also enhances transport of glucose as indicated by oxidation of labeled glucose to $^{14}CO_2$ (Fig.

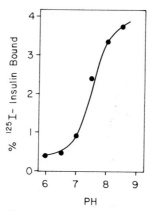

FIG. 21. Effect of pH on ^{125}I-labeled insulin binding to rat adipocytes. Binding of ^{125}I-labeled insulin was carried out by incubating fat cells (0.5×10^6 cells) in labeled insulin ($0.7 \times 10^{-10}\,M$) for 60 minutes at 25°C at indicated pH values and determined.

24) and by increased transport of 2-deoxyglucose (Fig. 25). In contrast, there is no effect of pH to activate glycogen synthase without (Fig. 26A) or with glucose (Fig. 26B). In the presence of glucose, there is a much larger effect of insulin itself but essentially no effect of pH alone. But without glucose present, there is no activation of glycogen synthase with increased pH (Fig. 26).

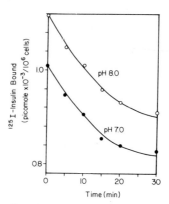

FIG. 22. Effect of pH on dissociation kinetics of ^{125}I-labeled insulin from rat adipocytes. Dissociation curves of ^{125}I-labeled insulin binding at pH 7 and 8. Dissociation was conducted after cells (0.5×10^6 cells) had been incubated with ^{125}I-labeled insulin ($1.4 \times 10^{-10}\,M$) at 25°C for 60 minutes. Cells were washed 2 times with 10 ml of Krebs–Ringer phosphate buffer containing 30 mg/ml BSA and incubated for the indicated times at 25°C at the indicated pHs.

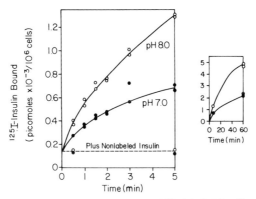

FIG. 23. Effects of pH on association kinetics of ^{125}I-labeled insulin to rat adipocytes. Initial velocity of ^{125}I-labeled insulin binding at pH 7 and 8. Cells (0.5 × 10^6 cells) were incubated with ^{125}I-labeled insulin (1.4 × 10^{-10} M) for the indicated times at pH 7 and 8 and binding determined. Unlabeled insulin was added at a concentration of 60 μg/ml in order to correct for nonspecific binding.

Analogous results have been obtained with oxidized glutathione. This compound increased binding of labeled insulin to receptors in rat adipocytes in a dose-dependent manner (Fig. 27). Increased oxidation of labeled glucose to $^{14}CO_2$ and increased transport of 2-deoxyglucose were

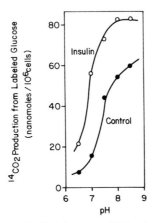

FIG. 24. The effect of pH on labeled glucose oxidation in the absence and presence of insulin. Cells were isolated and washed in Krebs–Ringer phosphate buffer, pH 7.4, containing 30 mg/ml BSA. [^{14}C]Glucose oxidation was measured after incubating 50 μl cells (pH 7.4) at 37°C for 1 hour with 450 μl of medium containing 0.2 mM D-[1-^{14}C]glucose in the absence (●) and presence (○) of maximal insulin (10^{-8} M) at the indicated pH values. Mean values of duplicate tubes were presented.

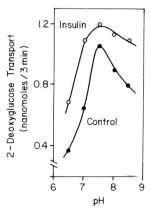

FIG. 25. The effect of pH on 2-deoxyglucose transport without and with insulin. Cells
(50 μl) (pH 7.4) were preincubated at 25°C for 1 hour with 450 μl of medium at the indicated
pH values without (●) and with (○) insulin ($10^{-8} M$). Assays were carried out without and
with 0.05 mM cytochalasin B and the values obtained with cytochalasin B were subtracted
from the values obtained without cytochalasin B and presented.

also noted (Figs. 28 and 29). However, oxidized glutathione did not activate glycogen synthase in the absence of glucose (Fig. 30A) and only
minimally with glucose (Fig. 30B). Reduced glutathione was inhibitory
under all circumstances. Thus it would appear that these three agents,

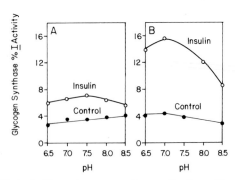

FIG. 26. The effect of pH on glycogen synthase activation without and with glucose.
Cells (2.5×10^6) (0.5 ml) were incubated without (A) and with (B) 5 mM glucose with 4.5 ml
of a medium at the indicated pH values for 15 minutes at 37°C, without (●) and with (○)
insulin ($10^{-8} M$), and then centrifuged for 15 seconds in a clinical centrifuge. After aspirating
the medium, cells were washed with 10 ml of medium (pH 7.4) and the incubation terminated
by adding 0.5 ml of cold buffer (100 mM KF and 10 mM EDTA, pH 7.0), and homogenization
at 0°C. After centrifugation at 10,000 g for 15 minutes, supernatants were used for enzyme
assay.

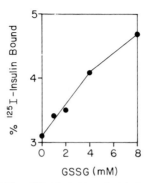

FIG. 27. The effect of GSSG on ^{125}I-labeled insulin binding to rat adipocytes. Rat adipocytes (0.5 × 10⁶ cells) were incubated with ^{125}I-labeled insulin (0.7 × 10⁻¹⁰ M) in the presence of the indicated concentrations of GSSG at room temperature for 60 minutes and binding determined.

H₂O₂, increased pH, and oxidized glutathione are only partially insulin-like. They act to enhance membrane-related functions, but do not activate intracellular metabolic functions as judged by glycogen synthase. We would propose that they act to perturb the cell membrane, but do not act proteolytically to generate mediator from the membrane to transmit chemical signals intracellularly.

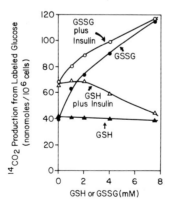

FIG. 28. The effect of reduced (GSH) and oxidized glutathione (GSSG) on labeled glucose oxidation without and with insulin. Rat adipocytes were isolated and washed in Krebs–Ringer phosphate buffer, pH 7.4, containing 30 mg/ml BSA. [¹⁴C]Glucose oxidation measured after incubating cells at 37°C for 1 hour in a medium containing the indicated concentrations of GSH (▲,△) or GSSH (●,○) and 0.2 mM D-[1-¹⁴C]glucose in the absence and presence of insulin (10⁻⁸ M). Mean values of duplicate tubes were presented.

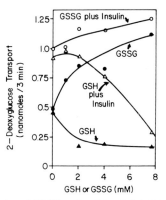

FIG. 29. The effect of reduced (GSH) and oxidized glutathione (GSS) on 2-deoxyglucose transport without and with insulin. Cells were preincubated at 25°C for 1 hour in a medium containing the indicated concentrations of GSH (▲,△) or GSSG (●,○) without and with insulin ($10^{-8} M$). All assays were carried out without and with 0.05 mM cytochalasin B and the values obtained with cytochalasin B were subtracted from the values obtained without cytochalasin B and presented.

IV. Insulin Mediator

Two lines of evidence from our laboratory provided the stimulus for postulating an insulin mediator: first, a dissociation of the effects of insulin on glucose transport and on glycogen synthase activation suggested that they were normally coupled possibly by a chemical signal (Larner, 1972); second, the insulin-like or insulin-antagonistic action of two proteins larger in size than insulin, pituitary diabetogenic peptide (Miller and Larner, 1972) and human antireceptor antibody (Lawrence et al., 1978),

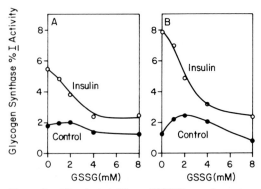

FIG. 30. The effect of oxidized glutathione (GSSG) on glycogen synthase activation without (A) and with (B) glucose. Conditions were the same as those in Fig. 26, except that cells were incubated in a medium at pH 7.4 containing the indicated concentrations of GSSG.

both of which presumably act initially at the cell surface, suggested that a chemical signal was very likely required to link receptor binding and intracellular effects of insulin.

A necessary requirement for seeking a mediator is a suitable assay.

V. Mediator Not Related to Cyclic Nucleotide Concentrations

A number of experiments in muscle, liver, and fat failed to detect any consistent effect of insulin to alter basal cyclic AMP concentrations or for that matter cyclic GMP tissue concentrations (Larner et al., 1979a). Recently the group which has most strongly championed the lowering of cyclic AMP concentrations as the mechanism of action of insulin has bowed to the fact that in muscle insulin acts with no change in cAMP concentrations (Shikama et al., 1981). We determined that insulin acted more directly on the cAMP-dependent protein kinase to convert it to the holoenzyme which was desensitized with regard to its activation by cyclic AMP (Walkenbach et al., 1978, 1980). As a result of our work with the insulin-inhibited protein kinase, it is now possible to understand how insulin is able to lower elevated cyclic AMP concentrations. In our model (Fig. 31) the cyclic AMP-dependent protein kinase can be influenced by two separate hormonal inputs: cyclic AMP, which dissociates the enzyme, activating it and shifting the equilibrium to the right; and the insulin mediator peptide which catalyzes the formation of the desensitized inactivated holoenzyme species, shifting the equilibrium to the left. Thus with insulin action, the inactive holoenzyme is formed, and coincident with its formation, cyclic AMP bound to the regulatory subunit (2 mol/mol subunit) is released into solution. Bound cyclic AMP is known to be unavailable to phosphodiesterase, whereas cyclic AMP in solution is susceptible

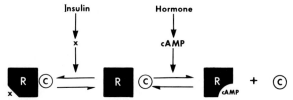

FIG. 31. Hormonal control of cAMP-dependent protein kinase. Hormones acting to increase cyclic AMP concentrations activate the protein kinase by dissociation. Insulin inactivates the protein kinase by a mechanism involving mediator (x) formation and reassociation to the holoenzyme with release of bound cyclic AMP which then becomes available to degradation by phosphodiesterase. In the model mediator is shown bound to the regulatory subunit of the kinase holoenzyme, leading to a new species desensitized to cyclic AMP. An alternate hypothesis can be formulated without the necessity of bound mediator in the desensitized holoenzyme species.

to phosphodiesterase action (O'Dea *et al.*, 1971). Therefore, the formation of holoenzyme by subunit reassociation releases bound cyclic AMP, making it accessible to phosphodiesterase action. In addition, recent work by Jarett's group has demonstrated that insulin mediator specifically activates insulin-sensitive phosphodiesterase (Jarett *et al.*, 1981). Thus, there is a mediator-dependent fail-safe mechanism for insulin to decrease tissue cAMP concentrations; namely, reassociation and desensitization of cyclic AMP-dependent protein kinase holoenzyme, with release of bound cyclic AMP; and second, activation of insulin-sensitive phosphodiesterase leading to cAMP hydrolysis.

VI. Insulin Mediator Identification and Purification

Our initial assay for the insulin mediator was based on the inhibition of protein kinase. We detected insulin mediator in extracts of skeletal muscle of control and insulin-treated hind limbs or diaphragms deproteinized by acid or by heat (Table IV) (Larner *et al.*, 1976). The next 4 years were spent in learning to stabilize active mediator. I determined that four conditions were essential; acid pH, the presence of a metal chelator such as EDTA, an SH compound such as cysteine or mercaptoethanol, and the absence of O_2 produced by the introduction of N_2. During this time, with L. Huang we found that mediator was not a nucleotide, since when nucleotides were removed by chromatography, mediator (detected by inhibition of protein kinase and relying on a control-insulin difference) was still present (Fig. 32). Because of the presence of nonspecific inhibitors in the crude extracts, i.e., inhibitors which did not display the control-insulin difference, we were unable to quantitate recovery of insulin mediator and had to proceed qualitatively using only the control-insulin difference as marker.

With G. Galasko, we next found that mediator was present in a specific peak (fraction 2) on a Sephadex G-25 sizing column (Fig. 33). This peak

TABLE IV

Presence of Acid-Stable Protein Kinase Inhibitor in Insulin-Perfused Rabbit Skeletal Muscle

Perfusion time (min)	Glycogen synthase % I form in		Protein kinase activity with added cyclic AMP in the presence of		
	Control muscle (%)	Insulin-perfused muscle (%)	Control extract (cpm)	Insulin extract (cpm)	Inhibition (%)
6	26.9	37.3	1029	1191	
10	26.1	37.2	603	318	47.3

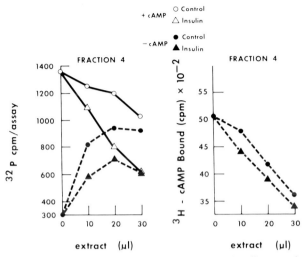

FIG. 32. Presence of heat-stable protein kinase inhibitor in insulin-treated rabbit skeletal muscle. Heat-inactivated extracts of rabbit muscle were prepared and fractionated as previously described (Larner *et al.*, 1976, 1979a). The activities of control and insulin-treated fractions were compared to protein kinase activity (left) and [³H]cyclic AMP binding (right) as a function of amount of extract added.

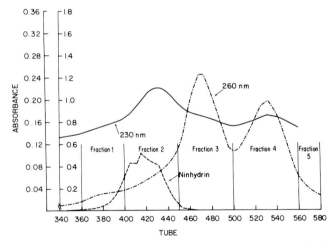

FIG. 33. Sephadex G-25 chromatogram of a skeletal muscle extract that had been deproteinized and from which the major nucleotides had been removed by paper chromatography. Frozen muscle powder (25 g) was heat-treated, extracted, and chromatographed on paper. After elution, lyophilization, and reconstitution, 5 ml of the purified paper eluate was applied to the column; the column was washed twice with equal volumes of 0.05 N formic acid and then developed with the same solution; 2.5 ml fractions were collected at a flow rate of 15 drops per minute in a fraction collector and then analyzed for absorbance at 230 and 260 nm and for ninhydrin reactivity.

contained essentially all of the ninhydrin reactive material and the bulk of
the 230 nm absorption. This suggested that mediator was peptide in nature
and that it had a molecular weight of about 1000–2000 (Larner *et al.*,
1979a). Cheng *et al.* (1980) then found that peak 2 was altered in its
morphology when control and insulin-treated muscle extracts were compared (Fig. 34). This then constituted the first biochemical marker of
insulin mediator, further assuring us that mediator was present in or
around peak 2 (Cheng *et al.*, 1980).

Further purification of peak 2 proceeded along 2 main lines, high voltage
electrophoresis, and high performance liquid chromatography. With high

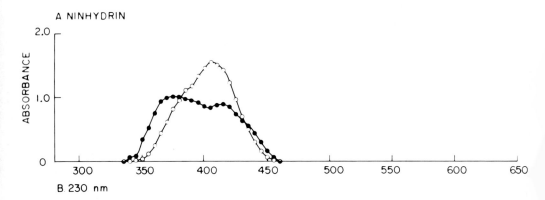

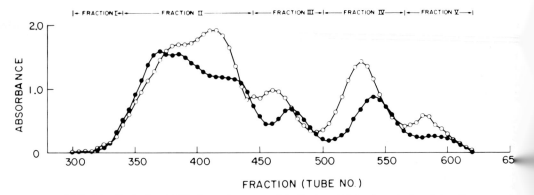

FIG. 34. Sephadex G-25 chromatograms of both deproteinized control and insulin-
treated muscle extracts. Materials eluted from Whatman 3 MM filter paper sheets were
lyophilized and redissolved in 5 ml of 50 m*M* formic acid and applied to a Sephadex G-25
column (5 × 85 cm). The column was eluted with 50 m*M* formic acid containing 0.1 m*M*
EDTA and 0.01 m*M* cysteine with a flow rate of 15 seconds/drop and 50 drops per fraction.
(○), Control muscle extract from 61 g of original muscle; (●), insulin-treated extract from 55
g of original muscle. This result has been observed consistently in 3 experiments.

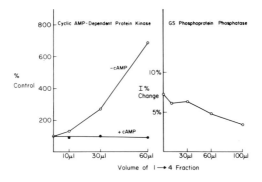

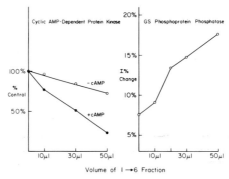

FIG. 35. Effect of fractions 1 → 4 and 1 → 6 on cyclic AMP-dependent protein kinase and glycogen synthase phosphoprotein phosphatase. The control activities of protein kinase in the absence and presence of cyclic AMP were 0.06 and 1.5 nmol/min/mg protein, respectively. The final concentration of cyclic AMP is 2.5 μM, when present.

voltage electrophoresis, Cheng isolated from peak 2 separate peptides which controlled dephosphorylation (mediator) (Fig. 35) or increased phosphorylation, both being well-recognized actions of insulin. The latter we now term antimediator. Mediator is assayed by inhibition of the cAMP-dependent protein kinase, and by stimulation of the synthase phosphatase. The phosphorylation-promoting peptide, antimediator is assayed by its stimulation of the cAMP-dependent protein kinase in the absence of added cyclic AMP and its inhibition of the synthase phosphatase. Mediator peptide is now known to inhibit cyclic AMP-dependent protein kinase, stimulate glycogen synthase phosphoprotein phosphatase (Cheng *et al.*, 1980) and mitochondrial pyruvate dehydrogenase phosphatase (Kiechle *et al.*, 1981), stimulate endoplasmic reticulum cAMP phosphodiesterase (Jarett *et al.*, 1981), and activate the high affinity (Ca²⁺

+ Mg^{2+}) ATPase and the ATP-dependent Ca^{2+} transport in adipocyte plasma membrane (McDonald *et al.,* 1981). Thus, its effects are widespread within the cell and the term mediator seems well justified.

Mediator peptide has recently been obtained in our laboratory by K. Cheng and M. Katz using high voltage electrophoresis (Larner *et al.,* 1981b). Amino acid composition demonstrates the presence of Phe Lys His Ala Asp Gly Leu Ser. Peptides also provisionally contain carbohydrate, indicating their origin from membrane glycoproteins. Further work will determine their sequence and carbohydrate structure.

VII. Proteolytic Formation of Mediator

Two types of evidence have been obtained which indicate that mediator is generated by proteolysis. First, mediator is generated in intact rat adipocytes by very mild trypsin action. Since this action is blocked by soy bean trypsin inhibitor, trypsin is probably acting proteolytically. As shown in Fig. 36 (Kikuchi *et al.,* 1981a), trypsin acting for 30 seconds on rat adipocytes maximally enhances cell membrane transport, as indicated by enhanced $^{14}CO_2$ production (upper curve). With 60 seconds of trypsin action, without glucose in the medium, glycogen synthase is already maximally activated (lower curve), perhaps somewhat more slowly than

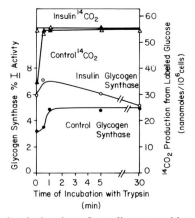

FIG. 36.   Effect of preincubation time of rat adipocytes with trypsin on the activation of glucose oxidation and glycogen synthase activation without and with insulin. Cells were preincubated with trypsin (0.05%) without glucose in the medium for the glycogen synthase experiment at room temperature for the indicated times. For the glucose oxidation experiment 0.2 mM [^{14}C]glucose was present. After washing extensively, cells were then divided and incubated in Krebs–Ringer phosphate buffer containing 30 mg/ml BSA without and with (10^{-8} M) insulin for 15 minutes at room temperature. Cells were then collected, extracts prepared after homogenization, and glycogen synthase activity determined.

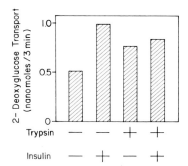

FIG. 37. Effect of pretreatment of rat adipocytes with trypsin on 2-deoxyglucose transport. Cells were pretreated without and with trypsin (0.05%, 3 minutes at room temperature)
without glucose in the medium. After washing extensively, 2-deoxyglucose transport was
measured after incubation of cells for 60 minutes at room temperature in the absence and
presence of insulin ($10^{-8}\,M$).

membrane transport. Insulin acting after trypsin does not further stimulate transport (upper curve), but does further stimulate glycogen synthase
(lower curve). That membrane transport is directly activated by trypsin is
shown by its stimulation of 2-deoxyglucose transport in an insulin-like
manner (Fig. 37). That trypsin is acting by generating peptide mediator is
shown by the data of Fig. 38. Here, the Sephadex G-25 elution profile of
heat-inactivated, charcoal-treated, extracts of rat adipocytes of control,
insulin-treated and trypsin-treated cells are shown. The column profiles of
the active 230 nm absorption peaks of the adipocyte extracts were clearly
altered by insulin or trypsin treatment. In both cases, there has occurred
the redistribution similar to that noted previously in muscle (Fig. 34). This
altered profile is associated with increased mediator activity in the leading
portion of the peaks (1) in both insulin and trypsin peaks as determined by
its ability to activate synthase phosphatase (Table V). Mediator assayed
by this method was greater in the insulin as compared with the trypsin
peak 1. Peak 1A of insulin was inactive. Peak 2 of insulin showed a
different pattern from that of trypsin, inhibiting the phosphatase in contrast to trypsin which stimulated the enzyme. The inhibitor in the insulin
peak 2 is quite likely related to the phosphatase inhibitory peptide (antimediator) previously separated from mediator peptide (Cheng *et al.*,
1980), and could be generated either by processing of mediator or by its
simultaneous formation with mediator by a cooperative proteolytic action
initiated by insulin (vide infra). The fact that trypsin does not reproduce
faithfully the effects of insulin on peaks 1 and 2 suggests that the pattern of
proteolysis and mediator formation catalyzed by insulin is not faithfully
duplicated by trypsin.

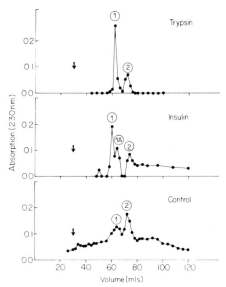

FIG. 38. Sephadex G-25 column profiles of extracts of control, insulin-treated, and trypsin-treated rat adipocytes. Rat adipocytes were incubated in Krebs–Ringer phosphate buffer pH 7.4 containing 10 mg/ml BSA without or with insulin (1.0 mU/ml) for 25 minutes at 37°C, or in 30 mg/ml BSA with trypsin (0.05%) for 3 minutes at room temperature. Cells were heated at 80°C in extraction buffer (50 mM formic acid, 0.1 mM EDTA, 0.1 mM cysteine pH 3.5) for 4 minutes, centrifuged, then treated with 15 mg/ml activated charcoal to remove nucleotides. After centrifugation and lyophilization, the redissolved extracts (0.8 ml) were applied to a Sephadex G-25 column (1.4 × 36 cm) equilibrated in 50 mM formate containing 0.1 mM EDTA and 0.1 mM mercaptoethanol, and 40 drop fractions collected and analyzed.

TABLE V

Mediator Activity: Glycogen Synthase Phosphoprotein Phosphatase[a]

	Peak 1 (GSI) activity (%)	[ΔGSI] (%)	Peak 1A (GSI) activity (%)	Peak 2 (GSI) activity (%)	[ΔGSI] (%)
Control	17.4	—	—	36.8	—
Insulin	29.1	[+11.7]	18.4	28.2	[−8.6]
Trypsin	22.9	[+5.5]	—	41.5	[+4.7]

[a] Peak tubes form the G-25 column of control, insulin-treated, and trypsin-treated fat cell extracts were pooled and lyophilized, then tested for their ability to affect the phosphoprotein phosphatase conversion of glycogen synthase. The activity ratio of glycogen synthase (%I) was obtained using the low G6P/high G6P assay of Guinovart *et al.* (1979).

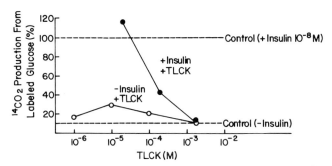

FIG. 39. The effect of TLCK on insulin action in rat adipocytes. Adipocytes were preincubated with various concentrations of TLCK in Krebs–Ringer phosphate buffer pH 7.4 containing 3% BSA, with 1.25 mM D-[1-^{14}C]glucose for 20 minutes at 37°C. Cells were then incubated with (●) or without (○) insulin at a final concentration of 10^{-8} M for 60 minutes at 37°C, and $^{14}CO_2$ production determined by standard methods.

VIII. Insulin Action Is Blocked by TLCK

Further evidence that insulin acts proteolytically is indicated by the fact that TLCK blocks its action (Larner *et al.*, 1981a). As shown in Fig. 39 brief treatment of intact adipocytes with increasing concentrations of TLCK was able to completely block the action of insulin to stimulate glucose oxidation. Similar effects of TLCK were also observed on several other parameters of insulin action including the activation of hexose transport and of glycogen synthase. No effect of TLCK was observed on binding of labeled insulin to the receptor. A number of additional proteolytic inhibitors were tested including soybean trypsin inhibitor, α_2-macroglobulin, antipain, chymostatin, and ovomucoid and were ineffective in blocking insulin action.

IX. Cooperative Mechanism of Proteolysis

Trypsin, like insulin, produces mediator which acts extremely rapidly intracellularly. Therefore, we suggest that the proteolytic event or events occur at the external surface of the cell. Furthermore, we feel that mediator(s) must enter the cell in a free rather than vesicular-bound form to be rapidly available to the intracellular systems. Because our evidence indicates that mediator is oligoglycopeptide, it must be formed by cleavage of membrane glycoprotein. Since the carbohydrate moieties of membrane glycoproteins face the external surface, the question is thus raised as to how mediators are transferred across the plasma membrane. One possible way this could occur is by mutual hydrophobic shielding. After removal of the glycopeptide moiety, the remaining hydrophobic polypeptides in the membrane could interact with each other to an enhanced degree. Hydrophobic shielding could be further enhanced by the bi- or multivalent nature of the activated insulin–receptor complex (see Figs. 1 and 2). Evidence for a multivalent insulin–receptor active complex is accumulating. For example, Goren (1979) demonstrated that chemical cross-linking agents exhibited insulin-like effects when incubated with adipocytes. Stronger evidence is provided by the work of Kahn *et al.* (1978) who have used antiinsulin receptor antibodies which have insulin-like action. The FAB fragments of these antibodies must be divalent to be active; monovalent fragments bind to the receptor, but are inactive. Similar evidence of multivalency has been provided for insulin itself. An interesting hypothetical possibility to consider is that the bi- or multivalent state of the insulin–receptor complex may in fact constitute the active form of the protease.

X. Mediator Internalization

A possible mechanism for mediator internalization is derived from the work of Cullis and co-workers (1979), who demonstrated that phospholipids are transferred across the cell membrane by a mechanism involving the formation of an "inverted" phase such as the hexagonal phase. A similar mechanism was hypothesized by Robertson and Thompson (1977), for Cl⁻ flux across the lipid bilayer. Although this is not directly relevant to the transfer of large molecules across a plasma membrane, aspects can be used to supply a mechanism for the transfer of glycopeptide. External proteolysis (Fig. 40) with two (or more) cleavages catalyzed by insulin-linked receptor dimer would cause formation of a pore in the membrane with phospholipids at each boundary arranged in a hexagonal phase. This would permit ionic bonding and dipole–dipole interaction between hydrophilic oligoglycopeptides. Cleaved hydrophobic residues would interact with each other, allowing for the transfer of the glycopeptides into the cytoplasm. The rate of lateral diffusion of membrane bound proteins (e.g., antigen) in the liquid crystalline membrane is of the order of 7×10^{-9} cm²/second (Wolf *et al.*, 1977). Hence, across a distance of about 50 Å this redistribution would be predicted to occur within milliseconds, allowing mediator(s) to control metabolism rapidly by regulating the phosphorylation state of enzymes (Larner *et al.*, 1981b). Redistribution of mediator into mitochondria and possibly other cell organelles would lead to control of metabolism analogously in these sites as well. One question raised by this hypothesis is why oligoglycopeptides would not be released into the medium rather than be internalized. A small hydrophobic anchor-

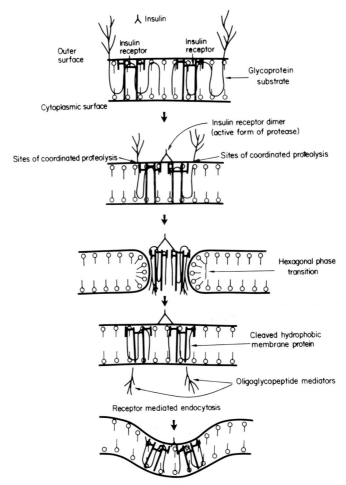

FIG. 40.   Model of coordinated proteolytic mechanism of insulin action to form mediator oligoglycopeptides. The 2 coordinated proteolytic events at the outer membrane surface are initiated by the crosslinking by insulin of the insulin receptors. This leads to pore formation with hexagonal phase phospholipid interacting with oligopeptide mediators, and rapid internalization of mediators in free form into the cytoplasm. The restored membrane now contains the proteolytically cleaved hydrophobic polypeptides. This initiates the receptor-mediated endocytosis which causes membrane to investigate forming residues. Vesicles are cycled through Golgi and lysosomes restoring glycopeptide mediator to cleaved hydrophobic peptides, and vesicles are reinserted into the cell membrane, restoring its original composition.

ing segment near the proteolytic cleavage point might be present to minimize this event.

An alternate mechanism not involving rapid phospholipid redistribution could occur via a hydrophilic pore formed in the membrane by a protein in helical configuration with one side relatively hydrophilic and the other hydrophobic (Hughes, 1975). Provided the carbohydrate moieties were positioned close to or within the pore, the altered protein conformation after limited surface proteolysis could lead to a rapid transit of the oligoglycopeptide through the hydrophilic pore directly into the cytoplasm. In this mechanism, there would not exist a theoretical requirement for bivalency or multivalency, but because of the reasons stated above a cooperative mechanism is attractive.

XI. Hexose Transport and Other Insulin-Activated Events

The membrane-bound hydrophobic segments of the mediator precursor glycoprotein could conceivably be the activated form of the hexose transporter, or could serve to activate the hexose transporter. This activation could occur by a redox state alteration (Czech, 1977) or by a mechanism involving redistribution of the transport units from within the cell interior to the cell membrane (Cushman and Wardzala, 1980; Suzuki and Kono, 1980).

If the insulin-mediated membrane events were coupled with a change in K^+ ion flux, this proteolysis might be expected to lead to rapid alteration in the resting membrane potential. Membrane hyperpolarization observed with insulin action, while still debated in terms of mechanism (Zierler and Rogus, 1981), is supported by a considerable body of evidence, including recent experiments with labeled lipid soluble ions used for measuring membrane potential (Cheng et al., 1981). The proteolytic events previously described could lead to an alteration in membrane potential secondary to an altered ion flow. Localized electrical hyperpolarization is insulin-like in its action (Zierler and Rogus, 1980). Whether electrical hyperpolarization mediates all of the actions of insulin, including activation of glycogen synthase, or whether electrical hyperpolarization is similar to H_2O_2, increased pH, and oxidized glutathione is unknown.

XII. Reversibility Considerations and Receptor-Mediated Endocytosis

Irreversibility of the proteolytic events leads to a consideration of the overall reversibility of the process. Recently there has been much work documenting the mechanism of internalization of polypeptide hormones. At the morphological and the biochemical levels, internalization of a number of hormones and other proteins is now clearly established (Carpentier et al., 1979). In some cases this occurs via specific mechanisms which involve coated pits and clathrin (Anderson et al., 1980). Insulin and apparently intact receptors are internalized in vesicles and cycled through the Golgi apparatus, lysosomes, and fused lysosomes. Finally, vesicles containing receptors are thought to be reinserted into the plasma membrane, with the discharge of degraded insulin fragments into the surrounding environment (Hofmann et al., 1980). No definitive evidence has demonstrated that internalization is required for any aspect of insulin action; however, no mechanism has yet been ruled out.

If the rate of restoration of insulin receptors is slower than that of initial proteolytic events, one would predict that a temporary state of insulin resistance should be observed. Such a state has been demonstrated following long-term incubation of adipose tissue with insulin in vitro (Livingston et al., 1978). Therefore, in our view, internalization of the insulin–receptor complex via vesiculation would be a prime candidate for the replacement mechanism used to renew spent hydrophobic membrane components formed by the initial proteolysis which initiated the internalization. The spent membrane glycoproteins could be regenerated de novo by complete resynthesis from amino acids, although an ATP-dependent regeneration via a peptide ligation mechanism is also conceivable.

The detailed action and metabolism of the glycopeptide mediators will not be considered here except in the most general of terms. It is conceivable that they act at various sites within the cell without further metabolism. It is also possible that further alteration of the carbohydrate or peptide portions occurs to make mediators more accessible to intracellular sites or to terminate their activity.

XIII. Growth Promotion

The coordinated proteolytic theory developed here has other attractive features. It explains a considerable body of work dealing with the release of cultured cells from growth arrest by the action of proteolytic enzymes on the cell surface (Burger, 1970; Carney and Cunningham, 1978). Given the evidence presented in this article, it is conceivable that stimulation of growth may occur via mediator-like oligopeptides. Further support of this hypothesis comes from the action of insulin itself, which acts directly to promote cell growth. The importance of this promotion is demonstrated by an essentially universal requirement for this hormone by cells in completely defined tissue culture medium (Hayashi et al., 1978). For example, growth promotion is very clearly seen in the case of the liver tumor cell line which requires physiological concentrations of insulin (Koontz and

Iwahashi, 1981). Since we have now demonstrated that insulin and trypsin act analogously via mediator peptide formation to control metabolic events, it is equally possible that they also act analogously to control cell growth. Taken further, this could imply that the growth-promoting properties of insulin are related to the growth-promoting properties of externally acting proteases, perhaps via mediator oligopeptides.

XIV. Evolutionary Aspects

Insulin is known to be an "ancient" protein which is widely distributed in the phylogenetic tree. Rieser and Rieser, 15 years ago, first demonstrated the insulin-like effects of proteolytic enzymes in whole animals and isolated tissues (Rieser, 1967). Steiner *et al.* (1973) have proposed that insulin is derived from a precursor gut proteolytic enzyme. This hypothesis has received experimental support from the work of DeHaen *et al.* (1976), who used computer modeling techniques to demonstrate an amino acid sequence homology of insulin to that of the serine proteases. Thus the concept of a proteolytic mechanism of action for insulin is strengthened by the findings that it may have been derived genetically from a proteolytic enzyme. Our present work takes this concept a step forward by allowing one to hypothesize that insulin acts to initiate proteolytic events at the plasma membrane which through cooperative mechanisms lead to the generation of mediator glycopeptides. In essence insulin would be a "cofactor" for an intrinsic membrane protease, possibly activating it by directly cross-linking the insulin receptors.

XV. Summary and Conclusions

Studies with DOP insulin and DAA insulin indicate that these molecules are as fully efficatious metabolically as insulin itself, but differ in that they do not bind as effectively to the insulin receptor as insulin. C-terminal B-chain peptides B22–26 Arg-Gly-Phe-Phe-Tyr and B23–29 Gly-Phe-Phe-Tyr-Thr-Pro-Lys are inactive alone but significantly enhance suboptimal insulin and DOP insulin action. Small synergistic enhancement of biological activity was observed at 10^{-7} to 10^{-6} M peptide and major synergistic enhancement at 10^{-4} to 10^{-3} M peptide. The enhancement at 10^{-7} to 10^{-6} M peptide was not associated with increased insulin binding, and thus differed mechanistically from the marked enhancement at 10^{-4} to 10^{-3} M peptide which was associated with increased insulin binding. The enhancement at higher peptide concentration was not due to protection of insulin from degradation since degradation protection was too small to account for biological activity enhancement and since peptide enhancement occurred with bacitracin present when insulin degradation fully blocked.

When enhanced binding was studied kinetically, an effect of peptide to increase association rate (k_{+1}) in a concentration-dependent manner was observed. No effect of peptide on dissociation rate (k_{-1}) was noted. Association rates in the absence and presence of peptide were 0.5×10^7 and 1.0×10^7 min^1 M^1. Dissociation rates were 1.2 and 1.1×10^{-2} min^{-1} without and with peptide, respectively. Equilibrium dissociation constants (K_D) calculated from velocity constants decreased from 2.4×10^{-9} to $1.1 \times 10^{-9} M$ without and with peptide, respectively.

These studies are in keeping with the studies on the point substituted (B24 leucine in place of phenylalanine) human insulin recently described. They suggest that C-terminal B-chain peptides may act by binding to the insulin receptor themselves and thus enhance further binding of insulin thus predicting multivalent binding of insulin to the receptor. They further suggest that there may exist on the insulin molecule a binding domain composed at least in part of the C-terminal of the B-chain which is separate from the biological activity domain located in the remaining portion of the molecule.

In the interaction of insulin with the receptor to promote increased hexose transport and glycogen synthase activation, two separate mechanisms have been identified which are synergistic. In adipose tissue and in muscle, insulin (as well as concanavalin A, antireceptor antibody, and trypsin) activate glycogen synthase directly via mediator formation in the absence of glucose-termed mechanism 1. In the presence of glucose these agents also promote increased glucose transport and resultant formation of glucose 6-phosphate which itself acts as a feed-forward signal to promote additional glycogen synthase activation by activation of glycogen synthase phosphoprotein phosphatase-termed mechanism 2. Whether mediator is directly involved in activating hexose transport is still unknown. Another class of agents including H_2O_2, alkaline pH, and oxidized glutathione activate hexose transport (mechanism 2) but do not activate glycogen synthase in the absence of glucose (mechanism 1) and hence are thought to act by perturbing the cell membrane without mediator formation.

Insulin mediator assayed by inhibition of cyclic AMP-dependent protein kinase, stimulation of glycogen synthase phosphoprotein phosphatase, stimulation of pyruvate dehydrogenase phosphoprotein phosphatase, stimulation of insulin-sensitive cyclic nucleotide phosphodiesterase appears to be a peptide of molecular weight about 1000–2000. Preliminary data indicate the presence of carbohydrate as well (glycopeptide). Mediator from rat muscle has been purified and fractionated into mediator and antimediator fractions, which promote dephosphorylation and phosphorylation, respectively. Both mediator and antimediator are formed with insulin action in adipocytes.

Trypsin acts presumably proteolytically to form mediator and to activate glycogen synthase in adipocytes, but preliminary studies indicate that trypsin mediator is not identical with insulin mediator. These findings suggest the insulin also acts proteolytically to produce mediator. Further support for this hypothesis is that TLCK is able to block insulin action in rat adipocytes but does not affect insulin binding to the receptor.

A mechanism of action of insulin is proposed involving multiple "hit" proteolysis at the outer surface of the membrane with rapid internalization of the glycopeptides formed with them acting as mediators to regulate metabolism by controlling phosphorylation states of proteins within the cell.

ACKNOWLEDGMENTS

This work was supported by United States Public Health Service Grants AM22125 and AM14334 and the University of Virginia Diabetes Research and Training Center. It was also supported in part by a generous gift from Mr. and Mrs. C. Gerald Harris to the University of Virginia Diabetes Research and Training Center.

REFERENCES

Anderson, R. G. W., Goldstein, J. I., and Brown, M. S. (1980). *Receptor Res.* **1**, 17–39.
Best, C. H. (1963). "Selected Papers." Univ. of Toronto Press, Toronto, Canada.
Bilezikian, J. P., Dornfeld, A. M., and Gammon, D. E. (1971). *Biochem. Pharmacol.* **27**, 1445–1454, 1455–1461.
Brautigan, D. L., Kerrick, W. G. L., and Fischer, E. H. (1980). *Proc. Natl. Acad. Sci. U.S.A.* **77**, 936–939.
Burger, M. M. (1970). *Nature (London)* **227**, 170–171.
Carney, D. H., and Cunningham, D. D. (1978). *Cell* **14**, 811–823.
Carpentier, J. L., Gorden, P., Freychet, P., LeCam, A., and Orci, L. (1979). *J. Clin. Invest.* **63**, 1249–1261.
Cheng, K., Galasko, G., Huang, L., Kellogg, J., and Larner, J. (1980). *Diabetes* **29**, 659–661.
Cheng, K., Groarke, J., Osotimekin, B., Haspel, H. C., and Sonenberg, M. (1981). *J. Biol. Chem.* **256**, 649–655.
Cullis, P. R., and DeKruijff, B. (1979). *Biochim. Biophys. Acta* **559**, 399–420.
Cushman, W. W., and Wardzala, L. J. (1980). *J. Biol. Chem.* **255**, 4758–4762.
Czech, M. (1977). *Annu. Rev. Biochem.* **46**, 359–384.
DeHaen, C., Swanson, E., and Teller, D. C. (1976). *J. Mol. Biol.* **106**, 639–661.
DeLisi, C. (1981). *Nature (London)* **289**, 322–323.
Ernst, V., Levin, D. H., and London, I. M. (1978). *J. Biol. Chem.* **253**, 7163–7172.
Goren, J. H. (1979). *Diabetes* **28**, 391 (Abstr.).
Guinovart, J. J., Salavert, A., Massaque, J., Cuidad, C. J., Salsas, E., and Itarte, E. (1979). *FEBS Lett.* **106**, 284–288.

Harmon, J. T., Kahn, C. R., Kempner, E. S., and Schlegel, W. (1980). *J. Biol. Chem.* **255**, 3412–3419.

Hayashi, I., Larner, J., and Sato, G. (1978). *Cell* **14**, 23–30.

Hershko, A., Hamont, P., Shields, R., and Tomkins, G. M. (1971). *Nature (London) New Biol.* **232**, 206–211.

Hofmann, K., Wingender, W., and Finn, F. M. (1970). *Proc. Natl. Acad. Sci. U.S.A.* **67**, 829–836.

Hofmann, C., Marsh, J. W., Miller, B., and Steiner, D. F. (1980). *Diabetes* **29**, 865–874.

Hughes, R. C. (1975). *Essays Biochem.* **11**, 1–36.

Jarett, L., Kiechle, F. L., and Parker, J. C. (1981). *Fed. Am. Soc. Exp. Biol. Symp.* (in press).

Kahn, C. R., Baird, K. L., Jarret, D. B., and Flier, J. S. (1978). *Proc. Natl. Acad. Sci. U.S.A.* **75**, 4209–4213.

Kiechle, F. L., Jarett, L., Kotagal, N., and Popp, D. A. (1981). *J. Biol. Chem.* **256**, 2945–2951.

Kikuchi, K., and Larner, J. (1981). *Mol. Cell. Biochem.* **37**, 109–115.

Kikuchi, K., Larner, J., Freer, R. J., Day, A. R., Morris, H., Dell, A., Marshall, S., and Olefsky, J. (1980). *J. Biol. Chem.* **255**, 9281–9288.

Kikuchi, K., Schwartz, C., Creacy, S., and Larner, J. (1981a). *Mol. Cell. Biochem.* **37**, 125–130.

Kikuchi, K., Larner, J., Freer, R. J., and Day, A. R. (1981b). *J. Biol. Chem.* **256**, 9441–9444.

Koontz, J. W., and Iwahashi, M. (1981). *Science* **211**, 947–949.

Larner, J. (1972). *Diabetes* **21**, 428–438.

Larner, J. (1980). "Goodman and Gilman's The Pharmacologic Basis of Therapeutics," 6th Ed., Ch. 64, pp. 1497–1523. Macmillan, New York.

Larner, J., Villar-Palasi, C., and Richman, D. J. (1960). *Arch. Biochem. Biophys.* **86**, 56–60.

Larner, J., Takeda, Y., Brewer, H. B., Huang, L. C., Hazen, R., Brooker, G., and Murad, F. (1976). "Metabolic Interconversion of Enzymes, 1975," pp. 71–85. Springer-Verlag, Berlin and New York.

Larner, J., Galasko, G., Cheng, K., DePaoli-Roach, A. A., Huang, L., Daggy, P., and Kellogg, J. (1979a). *Science* **206**, 1408–1410.

Larner, J., Lawrence, J. C., Roach, P. J., DePaoli-Roach, A. A., Walkenbach, R. J., Guinovart, J., and Hazen, R. J. (1979b). *Cold Spring Harbor Conf. Cell Prolif.* **6**, 95–112.

Larner, J., Cheng, K., Schwartz, C., Kikuchi, K., Tamura, S., Creacy, S., Dubler, R., Galasko, G., Pullin, C., and Katz, M. (1981a). *Fed. Am. Soc. Exp. Biol. Symp.* (in press).

Larner, J., Cheng, K., Galasko, G., Huang, L., Lawrence, J., Walkenbach, R. J., Roach, P. J., and DePaoli-Roach, A. A. (1981b). "The Regulation of Carbohydrate Formation and Utilization in Mammals." (C. M. Veneziale, ed.), pp. 1–21. Univ. Park Press, Baltimore, Maryland.

Lawrence, J. C., Jr., and Larner, J. (1978). *J. Biol. Chem.* **253**, 2104–2113.

Lawrence, J. C., Jr., Larner, J., Kahn, C. R., and Roth, J. (1978). *Mol. Cell. Biochem.* **22**, 153–157.

Levine, R., Goldstein, M., Klein, S., and Huddlestun, B. (1949). *J. Biol. Chem.* **179**, 985–986.

Livingston, J. N., Purvis, B. J., and Lockwood, D. H. (1978). *Nature (London)* **273**, 394–396.

McDonald, J. M., Pershadsingh, H. A., Kiechle, F. L., and Jarett, L. (1981). *Biochem. Biophys. Res. Commun.* **100**, 857–864.

Miller, T. B., and Larner, J. (1972). *Proc. Natl. Acad. Sci. U.S.A.* **69**, 2774–2777.

Neville, D. M., Jr., and Chang, T.-M. (1978). *Curr. Top. Membr. Transp.* **10**, 65–150.

O'Dea, R. F., Haddox, M. K., and Goldberg, N. D. (1971). *J. Biol. Chem.* **246**, 6183–6190.

Olefsky, J. M., Saekow, M., Tager, H., and Rubenstein, A. H. (1980). *J. Biol. Chem.* **255**, 6098–6105.

Oron, Y., and Larner, J. (1980). *Mol. Cell. Biochem.* **32**, 153–160.

Riesser, P. (1967). "Insulin Membranes and Metabolism." Williams & Wilkins, Baltimore, Maryland.

Robertson, R. N., and Thompson, T. E. (1977). *FEBS Lett.* **76**, 16–19.

Schlessinger, J., Schechter, Y., Willingham, M. C., and Pastan, I. (1978). *Proc. Natl. Acad. Sci. U.S.A.* **75**, 5353–5357.

Segre, G. V., Rosenblatt, M., Reiner, B. L., Makaffey, J. E., and Potts, J. T., Jr. (1979). *J. Biol. Chem.* **254**, 6980–6986.

Shikama, H., Chiasson, J.-L., and Exton, J. H. (1981). *J. Biol. Chem.* **256**, 4450–4454.

Sonne, O., Gliemann, J., and Linde, S. (1981). *J. Biol. Chem.* **256**, 6250–6254.

Soskin, S., and Levine, R. (1940). *Am. J. Physiol.* **129**, 782–786.

Steiner, D. F., Peterson, J. D., Tager, H., Endin, S., Ostberg, Y., and Falkmers, S. (1973). *Am. Zool.* **13**, 591–604.

Suzuki, K., and Kono, T. (1980). *Proc. Natl. Acad. Sci. U.S.A.* **77**, 2542–2545.

Tarone, G., Hamasaki, N., Fukuda, M., and Marchesi, V. T. (1979). *J. Membr. Biol.* **48**, 1–12.

Villar-Palasi, C., and Larner, J. (1960). *Biochim. Biophys. Acta* **39**, 171–173.

Villar-Palasi, C., and Larner, J. (1961). *Arch. Biochem. Biophys.* **94**, 436–442.

Walkenbach, R. J., Hazen, R., and Larner, J. (1978). *Mol. Cell. Biochem.* **19**, 31–41.

Walkenbach, R. J., Hazen, R. J., and Larner, J. (1980). *Biochim. Biophys. Acta* **629**, 421–430.

Wolf, D. E., Schlessinger, J., Elson, E. L., Webb, W. W., Blumenthal, R., and Henkart, P. (1977). *Biochemistry* **16**, 3476–3483.

Wright, D. E., Hruby, V. J., and Rodbell, M. (1978). *J. Biol. Chem.* **253**, 6338–6340.

Zierler, K., and Rogus, E. M. (1980). *Am. J. Physiol.* **239**, B21–29.

Zierler, K., and Rogus, E. M. (1981). *Fed. Proc. Fed. Am. Soc. Exp. Biol.* **40**, 121–124.

DISCUSSION

U. Zor: I would like to raise an extreme caution about using TLCK as a protease inhibitor. I would like to remind the audience that TPCK and TLCK are a very active alkylating agent and they for example inhibit protein kinase activity as shown by Shaltiel and by Pastan. In the ovary, Ryan suggested (*Biochem. J.*, 1980) that proteases are involved in the stimulatory effect of hCG on adenylate cyclase; he based his suggestion mainly on the inhibition of hCG action by high doses of TPCK and TLCK. We measured the same activity and found (SSR meeting, 1980, Ann Arbor) that TPCK completely blocked the stimulatory effect of all the hormones that we measured, namely, catacholamine, LH, FSH, prostaglandin E on ovarian adenylate cyclase. Nevertheless other protease inhibitors were inactive in this respect. We are thinking therefore that the activation of an adenylate cyclase by hCG and other hormones is not related to an activation of plasma membrane protease. I don't like in any way to exclude the possibility that insulin works through activation of protease, but to emphasize that TLCK is a very dangerous substance in high doses, and the interpretation of the data should be done with a lot of reservation. I would like to ask why you need to take 1 mM of TLCK. Is 1 μM not enough to inhibit protease? The second question which is more important, is whether insulin really activates plasma membrane protease?

J. Larner: This is a very good point. We have used another inhibitor bacitracin which also blocks insulin degradation and at high concentration bacitracin will also block insulin action, and Czeck's group has reported in Atlanta, that several other members of the serine protease inhibitor group also block insulin action at millimolar concentrations. We have simply worked with TLCK because it was the first one we found. We will broaden our studies, but that is a very, very good point. In addition, DeHaen in Seattle also reported in Cincinnati that he had studied several other protease inhibitors of the serine protease class that also blocked the action. Now why we have to use millimolar concentrations is because I think this is a cell bound protease not a soluble protease and this concentration is what experimentally we find is necessary for a cell bound enzyme.

U. Zor: Do you find activation of proteases by insulin?

J. Larner: We are looking for that right now. We are just setting up to do those experiments.

H. H. Samuels: The rate at which you can stimulate glucose transport with insulin is obviously quite rapid. What about the off response, that is, as you remove insulin from the system, how rapidly does the decrease in glucose transport occur? The reason I ask this question is in terms of assessing at the functionality of these peptides which would predict that they must be turned over rapidly in the cell. Do you have any correlation between the appearance and disappearance of these peptides both from the onset of stimulation glucose uptake by insulin and the decay of the response, after removal of insulin from the system.

J. Larner: As you can well imagine, these types of experiments now, with these bioassays require large numbers of rats, about 30 rats required for each point on those assays, so it is not possible to do yet kinetic types of experiments on and off, but we have it in mind to do that as soon as it becomes feasible. With regard to the kinetics of activation and deactivation we haven't studied these ourselves.

J. E. Rall: Thank you. That was a splendid exposition of an enormous corpus of work. Two questions: one, it seemed to me you said that in the glycogen synthase molecule those 2 phosphates closest to the carboxy terminal were the ones which were phosphorylated with cyclic AMP-dependent protein kinase. Those same phosphates also seemed to be the ones that your inhibitor effect most strongly. This seems a little strange.

J. Larner: It is very funny, but let me simply mention that in addition to the direct action of the cyclic kinase to phosphorylate those two sites, it also has the indirect action of phosphorylating phos B kinase, and that is the calcium sensitive one that phosphorylates on serine-7 which is the most potent, so I think it is kind of a two-way action and I think maybe physiologically the action via the indirect route of phosphorylating phos B kinase may be physiologically the most important.

J. E. Rall: One other question. You had a model in which you showed the regulatory subunit binding one of these mediators. Do you have any direct evidence to suggest that this is the case?

J. Larner: Yes, we have a little bit of indirect evidence in our lab that is compatible with this idea. But it is very preliminary.

J. K. Findlay: Can you tell me whether growth hormone or the somatomedins will stimulate the production of the mediators in the rat adipocytes?

J. Larner: We have not worked with any other hormones as yet.

G. D. Aurbach: That was a really elegant presentation and review of the history of this subject and the hard work that you and your colleagues have put into it. I have two questions: one, further characterization of the activator, namely, you presented data primarily on gel filtration on a G-25 column but also mentioned paper electrophoresis. I wonder if you get a single spot in paper electrophoresis and several different pHs for compounds. The second question has to do with the fact that there are now many systems known with insulin receptors including mammalian red cells, turkey erythrocytes, and other systems from which one could get fairly clean plasma membranes. I wonder if you can add insulin to such purified membranes and generate the activator.

J. Larner: With regard to the first question, yes. We do have single bands and we were very excited about this, but the single bands turned out not to be homogeneous, so that is why I am rather cautious about it. We don't get good molar ratios from the single bands yet, so I am sure they are not homogeneous but they are well along the way, I would think. So I am very hopeful. In answer to your second question, that is a very good idea we have had. We have made one or two tries with turkey erythrocytes to generate the mediator with insulin and with trypsin so far unsuccessfully. We may not be sophisticated enough in handling that but I would really like to push that type of work.

J. Kallos: It is a very impressive study in term of how insulin affects the sensitivity of protein kinase; I would like to ask, have you been able to show in any of these instances, like activators, how do they affect specific phosphorylation of specific sites on specific proteins. In other words, have you seen any unusual type of phosphorylation like tyrosine or other types which can be correlated with phosphorylation in term of structure and function.

J. Larner: We have looked for specifically tyrosine phosphorylation with insulin action in, I am trying to remember whether we did it in the diaphragm or in fat cells, but one or the other and could find none, but we have not examined the actions of the mediator yet in terms of its ability to promote unusual phosphorylations.

J. Kallos: Let me elaborate further, have you looked at any new type of substrate in terms of phosphorylation, that is to say, looking at two-dimensional gels, appearance or disappearance of phosphoproteins?

J. Larner: You mean with insulin in intact cells or the mediator?

J. Kallos: Yes, let's say for instance putting in the mediator; does it promote phosphorylation of new proteins or block phorphorylation of other proteins.

J. Larner: That is a very nice experiment. We have not done those experiments in crude extracts yet, however I see what you mean.

S. W. Spaulding: Have you looked at the effects of any proteolytic or glycoside hydrolytic agents on your mediator?

J. Larner: Yes, as I mentioned we can find no sensitivity to trypsin. We find sensitivity to subtilisin. Sometimes it is sensitive, sometimes it is not. I think the explanation is that the carbohydrate present prevents proteolysis and only one lab, that I am aware of, has claimed that the mediator is sensitive to proteases and that is Czeck's lab; both our laboratory and Jarret's laboratory can find no consistent effect of proteases to destroy the mediator simply, so we use acid hydrolysis.

H. Friesen: Have you had an opportunity to look at any of the various fibroblast cell lines derived from patients with insulin resistance to see whether they generate this mediator?

J. Larner: Yes, we're starting. We have just started these studies in collaboration with Dr. James Craig and we have a cell line that was investigated by Arthur Rubinstein and co-workers in which it was claimed that the receptor binding from an infant with leprecaunism was normal, but that the transport of glucose was abnormal. We were very excited about that but we find that in this cell line, in our hands, under our conditions, we can find both a markedly depressed insulin binding and insulin action.

H. Friesen: Does this mediator work in intact cells, and if it does, does that imply there are surface receptors for the mediator?

J. Larner: We have about two successful experiments now in which we have added mediator to a fibroblast culture dish and found activation of synthase. That is very preliminary and I would not want to say much more about it than that. Other than that, we have observed positives.

J. C. Penhos: Do you foresee any possibility that this insulin mediator has any role in the production of diabetes?

J. Larner: I would say it is theoretical. Many, many years ago, I thought glycogen storage disease was a single disease. When I started working on it in the Cori laboratory I realized that it was a disease of every conceivable enzyme involved in glycogen metabolism as well as a number of others that are not involved in glycogen metabolism. So my philosophy is every polypeptide chain is a potential inborn error of metabolism. I would also say yes, there the prediction would be a severe insulin resistant end organ type of diabetes, but where?

M. H. G. Raj: Naturally occurring antibodies in insulin-resistant patients have been shown to have an insulin-mimicking action. Dr. Kahn from NIH alluded to this in the previous Conference and his data also show very well that these could cause insulin-like effects. So my question is, do you suppose that there are particular types of specific binding or a particular interaction that is occurring? If so, can very different molecules like immunoglobulins also mimic it? Do you suppose a crosslinking of the receptors by insulin, and to a degree we could conceive of it if we think of a bivalent antibody sitting just like insulin would at this interphase. Can you reconcile your model to such a situation?

J. Larner: I feel that it is entirely possible that both the antireceptor antibody and the Con A act by crosslinking the receptor. I didn't want to go into this, but we have data on the binding of insulin to the receptor in terms of specific portions of the insulin molecule, and I think it is entirely possible that insulin may bind to the receptor in at least two ways: (1) a regular type of binding, and (2) a crosslinking type of binding. I think the crosslinking type of binding is the type that may be imitated by Con A and by the antireceptor antibody.

R. Levine: How do you relate the two factors, one which promotes dephosphorylation of many enzyme proteins and favors anabolic reactions and the other which favors phosphorylation with Houslay's demonstration that in the membrane insulin seems to lead to phosphorylation of the external membrane proteins and to dephosphorylation of the internal proteins. In other words are they generated, one on the outer surface of the membrane, and one on the inner and the inner one is the anabolic mediator, and the outer one is the surface mediator that accounts for Wallaas' protein and for Houslay's results?

J. Larner: In all honesty, I have not really thought about that seriously.

C. Monder: In the model that you showed in your final figure, you refer to the formation of the mediator. I assume that means both mediators. Is that correct?

J. Larner: Yes, there are two possibilities for that. Either both could be formed simultaneously or else the other possibility is that one if formed, one type is formed and then it is processed subsequently.

C. Monder: The final picture in that sequence indicated that insulin remained external to the cell. There is a body of evidence that demonstrates the internalization of insulin. Would you comment on that?

J. Larner: I would like to comment on that. That figure was just an overall one. It was not meant to be complete, but what I think I am going to do to modify that, and, again, I have not had a chance to present the data for this to you, but I think that there may be multivalent binding of insulin to the receptor, that is to say the stoichiometry of insulin binding is greater than one. I think it is entirely possible that there is insulin bound to the receptor in one binding site and insulin bound to the receptor as a cross-linker in another binding site. What I showed was the latter type. I did not show the former type. You are absolutely right, insulin is internally degraded but there is also evidence that there is an external receptor linked protease which is blocked, for example, by bacitracin rather specifically and that was the type of thing I was trying to show in that figure.

M. Saffran: Is there evidence that the holoenzyme binds the mediator?

J. Larner: This we do not know.

M. Saffran: If it does bind the mediator, this would be a means of enrichment and purification of the mediator.

J. Larner: Yes, we have thought of that.

S. Solomon: Dr. Larner, do you need insulin or will the receptor do in acting to stimulate the phosphorylation of the two proteins?

J. Larner: That is a very good question. There is a very brief abstract in the literature which states that chemical crosslinking agents alone are insulin-like. This is the work of Goren and Kahn at NIH and I think it is being continued by Goren in Canada. So there is just an abstract which suggests that chemical crosslinking, these were experiments, it is hard to tell from the abstract, but in essence what was done was chemical crosslinking agents were added to fat cells and they turned out to be insulin-like. Now, this could be just nonspecific or it could be specific in terms of crosslinking the receptors.

S. Solomon: From what little I know about the internalization of the insulin–receptor complex and the data you presented here it would seem possible that insulin once it activates the receptor is not further needed on the internal membrane and that the activated receptor stimulates phosphorylation which would help explain what Carl Monder is getting at.

R. Chatterton: I wonder if you could speculate about inhibition of some of the effects of insulin on adipocytes by cortisol. Do you think that cortisol might inhibit formation or internalization of the mediator?

J. Larner: I hesitate to speculate further on that, but anything is possible.

J. H. Oppenheimer: Have you had a chance to study insulin analogs?

J. Larner: Yes, we have and I did not, unfortunately, have time to go into that work. We have had experience with analogues.

J. H. Oppenheimer: Do you find the appropriate correlations between biologic activity and the mediator?

J. Larner: Yes.

Organization of the Thyroid Hormone Receptor in Chromatin

HERBERT H. SAMUELS, ANDREW J. PERLMAN, BRUCE M. RAAKA,
AND FREDERICK STANLEY

Division of Molecular Endocrinology, Department of Medicine,
New York University Medical Center, New York, New York

I. Introduction

Abundant evidence supports the concept that most if not all of the significant cellular responses elicited by thyroid hormone are mediated by a cellular receptor localized to the cell nucleus (Samuels, 1978; Oppenheimer and Dillmann, 1978). This conclusion is derived from *in vivo* studies in intact animals (Schadlow *et al.*, 1972; Oppenheimer and Dillmann, 1978; Latham *et al.*, 1978) as well as with cultured GH_1 cells, a rat somatotrophic cell line (Samuels *et al.*, 1973; Samuels and Tsai, 1973) in which physiological concentrations of thyroid hormone stimulates the synthesis of growth hormone (Tsai and Samuels, 1974; Samuels and Shapiro, 1976). Evidence from several systems indicates that thyroid hormone stimulates the synthesis of proteins by increasing the accumulation of their respective mRNA molecules (Kurtz *et al.*, 1976; Roy *et al.*, 1976; Seo *et al.*, 1977; Martial *et al.*, 1977; Shapiro *et al.*, 1978; Towle *et al.*, 1980). The modulation of specific mRNA molecules by thyroid hormone likely reflects a transcriptional or posttranscriptional nuclear event which appears to be controlled by the thyroid hormone–receptor complex.

A. THYROID HORMONE RECEPTOR LEVELS CAN BE INFLUENCED BY A VARIETY OF FACTORS

Unlike steroid hormones (O'Malley and Means, 1974), a cytoplasmic form of the receptor has not been identified (Samuels *et al.*, 1974; Oppenheimer and Surks, 1975). Furthermore, thyroid hormone does not appear to elicit an increase in the concentration of nuclear associated receptors as a result of a cytosolic to nuclear translocation as has been reported for the steroid hormones. Evidence supporting this comes from the observation that the concentration of nuclear associated receptors is not decreased in the hypothyroid state compared to the euthyroid state in rat liver (Oppenheimer *et al.*, 1975). GH_1 cells cultured in the absence of thyroid hormone contain approximately 15,000 copies of receptors per

557

cell nucleus, and the level of the receptor is reduced by thyroid hormone in a time and dose-dependent fashion. This reduction of receptor involves a mechanism which is dependent on the association of hormone with the receptor binding site (Samuels et al., 1976, 1977, 1979b). In GH₁ cells, in addition to thyroid hormones, sodium butyrate and other short chain aliphatic carboxylic acids elicit a reduction in receptor which appears to be inversely related to the extent of acetylation of chromosomal proteins which is increased by these compounds (Samuels et al., 1980).

Evidence that the receptor does not represent a static population also comes from the observation that a variety of factors may influence the concentration of hepatic receptors *in vivo*. Starvation or a decrease in carbohydrate intake decreases the level of nuclear associated receptors (DeGroot et al., 1977; Burman et al., 1977). Furthermore, administration of pharmacological concentrations of glucagon elicits a rapid reduction in hepatic receptor (Dillmann et al., 1978a), and a decrease in concentration of receptor is observed in rat liver after partial hepatectomy which results in liver regeneration (Dillmann et al., 1978b). Furthermore, the administration of cycloheximide, an inhibitor of protein synthesis, to rats results in a rapid decrease in hepatic levels of receptor to approximately 50% of the control level within 5 hours of administration (Jaffe and Means, 1977). Therefore, both *in vivo* studies in animals as well as studies in cultured GH₁ cells indicate that the thyroid hormone nuclear receptor likely represents a dynamic rather than a static population in which the concentration of receptor may be influenced by a variety of physiological and pharmacological factors.

These observations raise a number of questions regarding the dynamics of the receptor in the cell. Do receptor concentrations reflect steady-state values which are solely dependent on the rate of receptor synthesis and degradation? If receptor concentrations represent steady-state values, is there evidence for equilibrium of nuclear bound receptor with a significant pool of cytoplasmic receptor which cannot be detected, but develops an affinity for ligand after association with chromatin. Is there evidence for several populations of chromatin bound receptors having different affinities for chromatin or do all chromatin associated receptors turn over with an identical half-life? If the level of nuclear associated receptor reflects a steady-state is the modulation of receptor due to changes in receptor synthesis, degradation, or a combination of both parameters?

B. QUESTIONS RELATING TO CHROMATIN INTERACTIONS OF THYROID HORMONE RECEPTOR

The thyroid hormone nuclear receptor can be extracted from chromatin by high ionic strength buffer conditions (Samuels et al., 1974; Latham et *al.*, 1976). The salt extracted form of the receptor from rat liver has been estimated to have a sedimentation coefficient of 3.5 S and a Stokes radius of 3.5 nm (Latham *et al.*, 1976). Assuming a partial specific volume of 0.725 cm^3/g, a molecular weight (M_r) for the rat liver receptor was estimated to be 50,500. Similar parameters have been observed for salt solubilized receptor from GH_1 cell chromatin which has an estimated sedimentation coefficient of 3.8 S, a Stokes radius of 3.3 nm, and an M_r of 54,000 (Perlman *et al.*, 1982). Although these studies provide some information regarding the basic structure of the receptor binding site, they provide no information as to whether receptor is organized in a subunit structure in chromatin with other protein components since this would likely be disaggregated by high salt conditions.

Although the receptor can only be identified in nuclei in cells, very little is understood regarding the interaction of the receptor with chromatin components. Pertinent questions to be resolved are: (1) is the receptor heterogeneously organized in chromatin and localized to restricted chromatin domains; (2) although the salt extracted receptor can associate with DNA *in vitro* (MacLeod and Baxter, 1976) the question remains whether the receptor associates with DNA in the intact cell; and (3) in addition to possible interactions with DNA, does the receptor interact with other unique regulatory proteins which may play an important role in the action of the thyroid hormone–receptor complex?

This article reviews recent developments in which the dynamics of receptor synthesis and degradation have been quantitated and the mechanism of receptor regulation explored. In addition, studies are also reviewed in which the interaction of the receptor with chromatin components has been probed using nuclease digestion. Evidence is presented to indicate that the level of nuclear bound receptor is solely determined by the rate of receptor synthesis and receptor degradation and that the receptor may be organized in chromatin in a multimeric form.

II. Quantitation of Receptor Half-Life and Estimation of Synthetic Rates Using Dense Amino Acid Labeling in GH_1 Cells

A. PRINCIPLES OF DENSE AMINO ACID LABELING OF RECEPTORS

As described above, the nuclear concentration of thyroid hormone receptor appears to be influenced by a variety of parameters *in vivo* and by thyroid hormone and certain aliphatic carboxylic acids in GH_1 cells. The modulation of receptor levels could occur by several mechanisms. These include (1) an increase in receptor degradation; (2) a decrease in the rate of receptor synthesis; (3) an alteration in the conformational state of the receptor such that it no longer recognizes the ligand; and (4) modification in the structure of chromatin such that newly synthesized receptor does not associate. Clarification of the parameters that regulate thyroid hormone nuclear receptor levels may improve our understanding of the biology of the receptor as well as provide information regarding the association of receptor with chromatin components and possibly its action. The standard techniques used to quantitate the rate of synthesis or degradation of a protein involve radioactive amino acid incorporation followed by selective isolation of the peptide with specific antiserum, identification by gel electrophoresis, or a combination of both procedures. If the peptide is present in low abundance (e.g., receptor proteins) it may be technically difficult to quantitate synthetic and/or degradation rates using this approach even if highly purified antisera is used.

It is possible to directly quantitate the half-life of the receptor and estimate the rate of receptor synthesis by density labeling cell proteins with amino acids uniformly labeled with the nonradioactive dense isotopes ^{15}N, ^{13}C, and ^{2}H. Newly synthesized proteins will be of higher density than the preexisting proteins and can be separated using gradient centrifugation techniques (Hunttermann and Wendelberger, 1976). The densities of most proteins are approximately 1.3 to 1.4 g/cm^3. The total substitution of amino acids containing all three heavy isotopes results in a maximal density shift of 0.123 g/cm^3 which increases the density of proteins approximately 8%. The velocity of sedimentation of a particle is directly related to the difference between the particle density (ρ) and the density of the gradient (ρ_0). The density of most proteins is approximately 1.35 g/cm^3 and an 8% increase will yield protein with a density of 1.47 g/cm^3. If a gradient can be constructed such that the average density is 1.2 g/ml, the value of ρ-ρ_0 for the dense protein is 0.27 while the value for the protein of normal density is 0.16.

Thus under the correct gradient conditions an 8% increase in the density of the protein can result in a 1.5-fold increase in the velocity of sedimentation. To achieve a gradient density of approximately 1.2 g/ml sucrose gradients can be constructed using D_2O instead of H_2O. The newly synthesized protein of higher density can be separated from the preexisting protein of normal density by velocity sedimentation and the respective populations of dense and normal receptor are identified using radiolabeled ligand. This approach was initially used to quantitate the half-life and the synthetic rate of the acetylcholine receptor (Devreotes *et al.*, 1977) and the position of receptor of different densities was identified using ^{125}I-labeled α-bungarotoxin.

This approach has been adapted to quantitate thyroid hormone receptor synthesis and half-life in cultured GH_1 cells (Raaka and Samuels, 1981). As described in the previous section physiological concentrations of the thyroid hormones stimulate growth hormone synthesis and mRNA in GH_1 cells (Tsai and Samuels, 1974; Samuels and Shapiro, 1976; Shapiro *et al.*, 1978; Samuels *et al.*, 1979a). In addition to modulating the growth hormone response, thyroid hormone also reduces the concentration of its receptor in GH_1 cells and the kinetics of disappearance appear to be a direct linear function of the occupancy of the receptor by L-triiodothyronine (L-T3) as well as other thyroid hormone analogs (Samuels *et al.*, 1977, 1979b). Dense amino acid labeling was utilized in GH_1 cells to quantitate receptor half-life and synthetic rates, and to examine the mechanism by which thyroid hormone modulates receptor levels in these cells. Using this approach receptor half-life is measured without the use of protein synthetic inhibitors such as cycloheximide which may itself alter the rate of protein turnover (Hershko and Tomkins, 1971). Since purification of the protein of interest is not required, density labeling is particularly useful in studies of receptor proteins of low abundance.

B. SEPARATION AND QUANTITATION OF NORMAL AND DENSE THYROID HORMONE RECEPTORS IN SUCROSE-D_2O GRADIENTS

GH_1 cells were cultured in medium containing dense amino acids for 1.5, 5, or 20 hours (Raaka and Samuels, 1981). One hour prior to harvesting the cells, 5 nM L-$[^{125}I]$T3 was added to the culture medium to identify and quantitate the receptor. This concentration of L-T3 occupies greater than 95% of the receptor population and gives an estimate of total receptor levels (Samuels *et al.*, 1976). Normal and dense receptors were then extracted from isolated GH_1 cell nuclei with 0.4 M KCl and separated by velocity sedimentation in 17–32% sucrose gradients constructed in D_2O (Fig. 1). After 1.5 hours in dense amino acid medium approximately 90% of the receptor is of normal density and only a small, faster sedimenting peak corresponding to newly synthesized dense receptor is detected. After 5 hours in dense medium, the receptor of normal density is reduced and an almost equal amount of dense receptor is present. Finally after 20 hours about 95% of the receptor is of high density. By quantitating the amount of receptor of normal density after different times of incubation with dense amino acids the receptor half-life can be determined. Furthermore, by following the kinetics of appearance of receptor of high density, the rate of receptor synthesis can be calculated.

Figure 2 illustrates the disappearance of receptor of normal density over a 20 hour incubation of cells with dense amino acid medium. The receptor

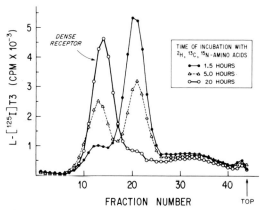

FIG. 1.   Separation of normal and dense thyroid hormone receptors in sucrose gradients. GH₁ cells were cultured in medium without thyroid hormones for a total of 43 hours. Normal medium was replaced with dense medium 1.5, 5, or 20 hours prior to harvesting the cells. The dense medium was supplemented with 5 n*M* L-[¹²⁵I]T3 1 hour before harvesting the cells to identify the receptor. Extraction of hormone–receptor complexes from isolated nuclei and conditions for sucrose gradient centrifugation are described in the text. The direction of sedimentation is from right to left. From Raaka and Samuels (1981).

of normal density disappears with a half-life of about 5 hours when the cells are cultured in the absence of L-T3 but received L-[¹²⁵I]T3 for only 1 hour to estimate receptor levels. After 20 hours in dense amino acid medium less than 5% of the total receptor is of normal density. The receptor

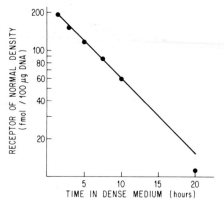

FIG. 2.   Half-life of receptor of normal density in cells cultured in dense medium. GH₁ cells were cultured for a total of 44 hours in medium without thyroid hormone. Normal medium was replaced with dense medium at the times indicated prior to harvesting the cells. The dense medium was supplemented with 5 n*M* L-[¹²⁵I]T3 1 hour before harvesting the cells to identify the receptor. Dense and normal receptors were separated and quantitated as described in Fig. 1. From Raaka and Samuels (1981).

decay curve indicates that the receptor of normal density begins to decrease after lag time of less than 30 minutes following addition of dense amino acids to the cells. Since the concentration of total receptor during the experiment remains constant at 205 fmol/100 μg DNA, the concentration of receptor reflects a steady-state determined by the 5 hour half-life and the synthetic rate.

The synthetic rate (k_s) can be calculated from the degradation rate constant (k_d) [$k_d = 0.693/t_{1/2}$] and the steady-state amount of receptor (R) by the formula $k_s = k_d R$ (Schimke, 1975). The k_s was calculated to be 29 fmol of receptor/100 μg DNA/hour which is equivalent to the synthesis of 1700 molecules of receptor/hour/cell. This value was directly confirmed by examining the kinetics of appearance of newly synthesized receptor and is described below. Furthermore the virtual absence of a lag period and the straight line semilogarithmic plot indicates that an appreciable storage pool of extranuclear receptor which cannot be detected but can associate with nuclei and become activated to bind thyroid hormone does not exist. Moreover greater than 95% of the receptor falls off with an identical half-life indicating that no appreciable nuclear associated receptor pools exist with varying half-lives. This does not exclude the possibility that a very small chromatin associated pool (less than 5%) may be tightly bound to chromatin and be associated with a subset of chromatin components (Raaka and Samuels, 1981).

C. EFFECTS OF THYROID HORMONE ON RECEPTOR HALF-LIFE AND APPEARANCE RATE DURING STEADY-STATE CONDITIONS

The dense amino acid labeling technique (Raaka and Samuels, 1981) was utilized to study the mechanism by which L-T3 and other iodothyronine compounds cause a dose-dependent reduction in the amount of thyroid hormone receptor in GH$_1$ cells (Samuels *et al.*, 1976, 1977, 1979b). To observe receptor depletion, cells are first cultured for 24 hours in medium which lacks thyroid hormone. Following addition of 5 nM L-[^{125}I]T3, the amount of receptor gradually decreases reaching a new steady-state level after 24 hours which is 55 to 60% of the value in cells cultured without thyroid hormone (Fig. 3). This reduction in receptor is not a result of a redistribution of receptor within the cell, a change in the affinity of the receptor for hormone, or a decrease in cell uptake of iodothyronine (Samuels *et al.*, 1976). The steady-state amount of receptor appears to be determined by the rate of receptor synthesis and the rate of receptor degradation. Therefore in order to reduce the level of nuclear receptor, thyroid hormone must affect one or both of these processes.

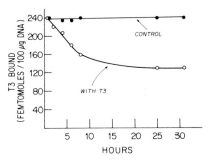

FIG. 3. Time course of receptor depletion in cells incubated with 5 nM L-[^{125}I]T3. GH$_1$ cells were cultured for 24 hours in Ham's F-10 medium without thyroid hormone. At zero time on the figure, the medium was supplemented with 5 nM L-[^{125}I]T3 in the cell cultures shown with open circles. Cells were harvested at the times indicated and radioactivity bound to the cell nuclei was determined. Control cells, shown with closed circles, were treated identically except that 5 nM L-[^{125}I]T3 was added to the culture medium only 1 hour before harvesting the cells to identify and quantitate the receptor. From Raaka and Samuels (1981).

To distinguish between these possibilities dense amino acid labeling was used to compare receptor half-life in control cells cultured without thyroid hormone to cells cultured with 5 nM L-[^{125}I]T3 for a total of 29 hours to reduce the steady-state amount of receptor (Fig. 4). Receptor half-life was

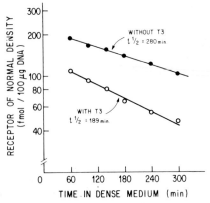

FIG. 4. Measurement of thyroid hormone receptor half-life under steady-state conditions in cells cultured with or without 5 nM L-[^{125}I]T3. GH$_1$ cells that had been previously depleted of thyroid hormone were cultured in medium containing 5 nM L-[^{125}I]T3 for 29 hours before harvesting. At times ranging from 1 to 5 hours before harvesting the cells, normal amino acid medium was replaced with dense medium. Control cells were treated identically except that 5 nM L-[^{125}I]T3 was added to the culture medium only 1 hour before harvesting the cells. Normal and dense receptors were separated and quantitated as described in Fig. 1 (Raaka and Samuels, 1981).

280 minutes in control cells cultured without hormone, and 189 minutes in cells cultured with 5 nM L-[^{125}I]T3. The steady-state amounts of receptor in control and hormone-treated cells were 206 and 123 fmol/100 μg of DNA, respectively. If the rate of appearance of newly synthesized receptor was not affected by thyroid hormone, the observed decrease of receptor half-life would reduce the steady-state amount of receptor to (189/280 minutes) $\times$ 100 or 68% of the control value. Since the observed amount of receptor in the presence of hormone was (123/206) $\times$ 100 or 60% of the control value these results suggest that the rate of receptor appearance was also influenced by hormone exposure.

D. EFFECTS OF THYROID HORMONE ON RECEPTOR DURING APPROACH TO STEADY-STATE CONDITIONS

The mechanism by which L-T3 shortens the half-life of its receptor is not known. The change in half-life could be an immediate result of the binding of hormone to receptor to induce a conformational change which could decrease the affinity of the receptor for chromatin and increase the susceptibility of receptor to proteolytic cleavage. Alternatively the change in half-life could be due to a delayed effect of the binding interaction such as a gradual modification of chromatin structures to which the receptor binds, or to the induction of a receptor-specific protease.

To distinguish between immediate and delayed effects, the density labeling technique was used to estimate receptor half-life under non-steady-state conditions in cells cultured for a total of 6 or 15 hours with 5 nM L-[^{125}I]T3 (Raaka and Samuels, 1981). As can be seen from Fig. 3 a substantial reduction of receptor occurs within 6 to 15 hours of L-T3 incubation. During these incubation times receptor reduction occurred without any substantial change in receptor half-life. Receptor half-life in cells incubated for a total of 6 hours with L-T3 was identical to control cells and cells incubated for 15 hours with hormone demonstrated a half-life which was only 9% decreased (Raaka and Samuels, 1981). This demonstrates that a change in receptor half-life does not occur immediately upon binding of hormone to the receptor, and a significant decrease in the amount of the receptor occurs before any change in receptor half-life occurs. Figure 5 demonstrates that the decrease in the amount of receptor occurring at early times during incubation of cells with L-T3 is primarily due to a decrease in the accumulation of newly synthesized receptor. The rates of appearance of newly synthesized receptor during the final 5 hours of 6, 15, and 29 hour incubations with L-[^{125}I]T3 were calculated from the accumulation data and these rates were 13.6, 18.7, and 26.1 fmol/100 μg of DNA/ hour, respectively. The rate in control cells cultured without thyroid hor-

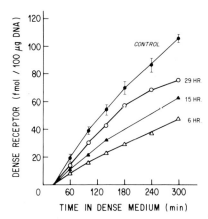

FIG. 5. Accumulation of newly synthesized dense receptor in cells incubated with 5 nM L-[^{125}I]T3 for 6, 15, or 29 hours. The rates of appearance of newly synthesized dense receptor (k_s) can be calculated from the accumulation results using the formula $k_s = k_d R_t / (1 - e^{-k_d t})$, where R_t is the amount of newly synthesized dense receptor present in the nucleus at any time (t) after addition of dense amino acids to cells. The degradation rate constants ($k_d = 0.693/t_{1/2}$) for the 6 hour, 15 hour, 29 hour, and control experiments were calculated from the half-life values given in the text (Raaka and Samuels, 1981).

mone was 31.2 fmol/100 μg of DNA/hour. Therefore L-T3 initially inhibits the accumulation of newly synthesized receptor by as much as 56%, but the magnitude of this inhibition gradually diminishes to about 16% during the final 5 hours of a 29 hour L-T3 incubation. This rapid inhibition of receptor appearance is not due to a general inhibition of protein synthesis since 5 nM L-T3 does not alter the rate of incorporation of L-[^{3}H]leucine into total cell protein (Samuels and Shapiro, 1976).

A dose–response study further demonstrated that during a 5 hour incubation, thyroid hormone reduces the accumulation of newly synthesized receptor without affecting the half-life of preexisting receptor (Fig. 6). Cells were incubated for 6 hours in dense amino acid medium. During the first 5 hours of this incubation the medium contained the indicated concentrations of L-[^{125}I]T3. The hormone concentration was adjusted to 3.8 nM in each cell culture for the final hour of the incubation which gives a good estimate of total receptor levels. Half-maximal depletion of total receptor occurred at about 0.3 nM L-T3. This value was similar to the L-T3 concentration giving half-maximal occupancy of receptor binding sites (Samuels et al., 1976) confirming that receptor occupancy is necessary for receptor depletion. From the amounts of total receptor and receptor of normal density in the cells cultured without L-T3, the receptor half-life was 280 minutes which is in the expected range in cells cultured without hormones

(Fig. 4). Since the amount of receptor of normal density remained constant as the hormone concentration was increased, receptor half-life was not influenced by L-T3 during the 6 hour incubation. A hormone-dependent decrease in the accumulation of newly synthesized dense receptor completely accounted for the decrease in total receptor levels.

The reduction of receptor caused by L-T3 can be reversed by removing the hormone (Fig. 7). GH$_1$ cells were cultured in medium containing 1 nM L-[^{125}I]T3 for 24 hours. This resulted in a 55% decrease in the amount of receptor compared to control cells which were not incubated with hormone. After removing hormone from cells by exchanging the culture medium several times over a 30-minute period with hormone-free medium, the cells were cultured in dense medium without hormone. The amount of receptor progressively increased after hormone removal and at 18 hours attained 92% of the value in control cells. Although the total amount of receptor increased, the amount of receptor of normal density decreased with a half-life of about 198 minutes during the first 9 hours after the removal of hormone which is characteristic of receptor in cells cultured for 24 hours or longer with L-T3 (Fig. 4).

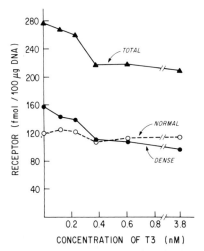

FIG. 6. Effect of L-[^{125}I]T3 concentration on accumulation of newly synthesized dense receptor. GH$_1$ cells were grown in normal amino acid medium without thyroid hormone for 24 hours. Exactly 6 hours before harvesting the cells, the normal medium was replaced with dense medium containing the indicated concentration of L-[^{125}I]T3. The concentration L-[^{125}I]T3 was adjusted to 3.8 nM in each culture 1 hour before harvesting the cells to identify and quantitate receptor. Normal and dense receptors were separated and quantitated as described in Fig. 1. The contribution of normal and dense receptors to the total amount of nuclear receptor at each concentration of L-T3 is shown on the figure (Raaka and Samuels, 1981).

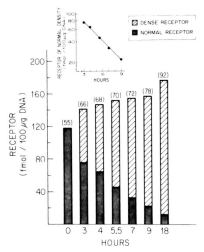

FIG. 7.   Reappearance of receptor after removal of L-[¹²⁵I]T3 from cells. GH₁ cells that had been previously depleted of thyroid hormone were incubated for 24 hours with normal amino acid medium containing 1 nM L-[¹²⁵I]T3. Hormone was then removed from the cell cultures by replacing the culture medium 3 times over a 30-minute period with hormone-free medium. After this washing procedure, which removed greater than 97% of the radioactivity from the cultures, cells were incubated with dense medium for the times indicated. All cells were incubated with 5 nM L-[¹²⁵I]T3 for 1 hour prior to harvesting to identify receptor. The numbers in parentheses indicate the amount of receptor in hormone-treated cells as a percentage of receptor in control cells that did not receive hormone but were otherwise treated identically (Raaka and Samuels, 1981).

Therefore, when hormone is removed from cells, receptor half-life does not immediately increase to the value of 280 minutes found in cells cultured without thyroid hormone. The increase in amount of receptor following removal of hormone is solely due to accumulation of newly synthesized dense receptor (Fig. 7). The rate of appearance of receptor during the first 9 hours of removal of hormone from cells was calculated to be 31.5 fmol/100 μg of DNA/hour using a receptor half-life value of 198 minutes. This rate is essentially identical to the rate found in cells cultured without thyroid hormone indicating that the rate of receptor appearance rapidly increases following removal of hormone from cells. Thus, during both the onset of and the recovery of thyroid hormone-mediated receptor depletion, the change in the appearance rate of newly synthesized receptor occurs rapidly whereas the change in receptor half-life occurs more slowly. With longer incubation times receptor half-life decreases approximately 30% while the appearance rate in newly synthesized receptor partially recovers but does not completely return to that observed in control cells.

E. POSSIBLE MECHANISMS AND IMPLICATIONS OF RECEPTOR LEVEL REGULATION

A model to explain the observed results must account for the observation that L-T3, as a result of binding to its nuclear receptor, causes a rapid but partially transient decrease in the rate of appearance of newly synthesized receptor and a slow increase in the rate of receptor degradation. One possible model assumes that the expression of the gene for the receptor protein is negatively controlled by the thyroid hormone–receptor complex, and that the cytosolic mRNA for the receptor protein has a short half-life. When L-T3 is added to cells previously depleted of hormone, the production of receptor mRNA rapidly decreases and cytosolic mRNA levels consequently decrease causing a reduction in receptor synthesis. This would account for the decreased rate of appearance of newly synthesized receptor in the nucleus after short incubation times with hormone. As the receptor concentration in the nucleus falls, the amount of hormone–receptor complex present may no longer be sufficient to exert maximal negative control on receptor gene expression. This would cause a partial increase in receptor mRNA levels and a consequent increase in receptor synthesis to a level which would approach that of control cells cultured without hormone.

This partial recovery of receptor synthesis does not lead to an increase in the amount of receptor since it is compensated for by the slower increase in the rate of receptor degradation. When thyroid hormone is removed from the cells, hormone rapidly dissociates from the receptor and the negative control of receptor gene would be completely relieved. This would cause a rapid increase in receptor synthesis to a level identical to that with control cells cultured without hormone. Again, the change in receptor half-life would occur more slowly following removal of hormone by reversal of the process responsible for shortening receptor half-life in the presence of hormone.

Although the binding of 5 nM L-T3 to the nuclear receptor reaches equilibrium within 1 hour, the increase in receptor degradation occurs more slowly and is not seen until after 15 hours of incubation. For this reason the shortened half-life is not a direct consequence of the binding of hormone to receptor which would elicit a conformational change which would make the receptor more susceptible to proteolytic degradation. Although the time course of change in the receptor half-life is consistent with the L-T3 induction of a protease specific for receptor, the change in half-life might be an indirect result of other late effects induced by thyroid hormone. For example, increases in the rate of cell growth and glucose consumption become measurable about 20 hours after addition of L-T3 to

GH$_1$ cells (Samuels *et al.*, 1973). Such general changes in cell metabolism might alter the amounts or activity of many cellular proteins including those responsible for receptor degradation.

In summary, in cultured GH$_1$ cells, chromatin associated thyroid hormone receptors are a dynamic population in which the steady-state value is solely dependent upon rates of receptor synthesis and degradation. Thyroid hormone appears to decrease steady-state levels of receptor by initially inhibiting the appearance rate of newly synthesized receptor and subsequently elicits a change in receptor half-life. Evidence that receptor concentrations *in vivo* reflect a dynamic rather than a static population comes from the observation of Jaffe and Means (1977) in which the hepatic receptor decreases rapidly after administration of cycloheximide. Other studies have demonstrated that the receptor can be reduced quite rapidly after pharmacologic doses of glucagon (Dillmann *et al.*, 1978a) or after partial hepatectomy (Dillmann *et al.*, 1978b).

With a half-life of approximately 5 hours over 95% of the receptor is exchanged in a 24-hour period. Therefore, receptor does not remain fixed to specific regions of chromatin but is constantly exchanged both by loss of receptor from specific chromatin domains and replenishment by newly synthesized receptor. In addition it is likely that mobility of receptor occurs within chromatin from one region to another. Although the parameters of receptor turnover have recently been defined (Raaka and Samuels, 1981) an important aspect involving thyroid hormone action relates to the interaction of the receptor with chromatin components. Although the receptor can be extracted in a soluble form by high salt conditions, very little is understood regarding the specific chromatin domains or structures with which the receptor interacts. Recent developments from several laboratories have provided some insights in this area.

III. Organization of the Receptor in Chromatin

A. ORGANIZATION OF CHROMATIN

1. Nucleosome Structure

It is now generally accepted that DNA in chromatin is organized into repeating subunits referred to as nucleosomes (Kornberg, 1977; Felsenfeld, 1978). This repeating subunit structure can be identified in extended chromatin by electron microscopy in which the nucleosome particles appear to be connected by strands of linker DNA (Olins and Olins, 1974). Further evidence for this structure comes from digestion of nuclei or chromatin with nucleases. Micrococcal nuclease digestion of chromatin or nuclei followed by chelation of divalent ions with EDTA releases a soluble chromatin fraction which when isolated on sucrose gradients yields a series of particles varying between 11 and 30 S (Noll, 1974; Kornberg, 1974).

Analysis of the DNA size of the individual particles indicates that the 11–11.5 S species represents mononucleosome particles containing between 140 and 240 base pairs of DNA, and the DNA sizes of the larger sedimenting fractions appear to be multiples of these values (Kornberg, 1977). Analysis of the protein composition of the mononucleosome fraction formed during micrococcal nuclease digestion demonstrates that it is associated with histones H2A, H2B, H3, and H4, as well as histone H1.

In rat liver nuclei Noll and Kornberg (1977) showed that the average DNA repeat of this species is approximately 160 base pairs of DNA and upon further digestion this is trimmed down to a core particle which contains only histones H2A, H2B, H3, and H4 and 140 base pairs of DNA. The loss of approximately 20 base pairs from the species is associated with the release of histone H1.

Although the DNA size of nucleosomes released during early micrococcal nuclease digestion varies between 140 and 240 base pairs in a variety of species as well as from the same cell, further digestion with micrococcal nuclease in each case yields a core nucleosome particle containing 140 base pairs which is devoid of H1 histone (Morris, 1976a,b). The variability of the length of DNA in the nucleosome, therefore, appears to derive entirely from variation in the length of the DNA linker regions associated with the core particle rather than the core particle itself. These studies indicate, therefore, that micrococcal nuclease shows preference for cleaving linker DNA regions releasing core nucleosome particles, nucleosome particles containing linker DNA, and nucleosome particles connected by linker DNA such as dinucleosomes, trinucleosomes, and larger polynucleosomes (Fig. 8). In association with the cleavage of linker DNA regions is the release of fragments of linker DNA associated with specific chromosomal proteins (Varshavsky et al., 1978). These proteins may represent low abundant receptor proteins or high abundant nonhistone proteins such as the high mobility group proteins (HMG) initially described by Goodwin and Johns (1973). These proteins are approximately one-tenth as abundant as the histones and appear to be enriched in domains of chromatin that are involved in or have a history of being transcribed. In contrast with micrococcal nuclease, pancreatic deoxyribonuclease I (DNase I) does not show significant preference for DNA linker regions and cleaves the DNA of both the linker and the core particle generating smaller DNA fragments. The characteristics of

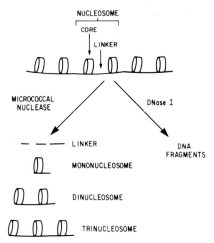

FIG. 8.   Chromatin digestion by micrococcal nuclease and DNase I.

chromatin digestion by micrococcal nuclease and DNase I are illustrated schematically in Fig. 8.

2. Transcriptionally Competent Chromatin

Although micrococcal nuclease and DNase I are nonspecific nucleases and cleave DNA without specific base sequence recognition they show preference for digesting domains of chromatin which are transcriptionally competent. For example, DNase I digests the globin genes of immature erthyrocytes at a greater rate than total chromatin DNA (Weintraub and Groudine, 1976). The increased sensitivity to DNase I digestion is not directly related to the transcriptional process since the enzyme also preferentially digests gene sequences which have been but are no longer transcribed (Weintraub and Groudine, 1976; Miller et al., 1978), and also digests genes that are transcribed at different rates with equal sensitivity (Garel et al., 1977). Therefore, the altered conformation of chromatin recognized by DNase I is imposed by specific genes as they are transcriptionally active and remain associated with these sequences following their inactivation. In contrast, Bloom and Anderson (1978, 1979) have shown that micrococcal nuclease recognizes transcriptionally active genes which appears to be related to alterations in the expression of their sequences. Furthermore, unlike DNase I which destroys active genes, micrococcal nuclease excises but does not degrade nucleosomes from transcriptionally active regions of chromatin (Bloom and Anderson, 1978, 1979; Levy et al., 1979).

Since micrococcal nuclease and DNase I are nonspecific nucleases the enhanced sensitivity of transcriptionally competent chromatin to these enzymes implies that these chromatin domains exist in an altered conformation which are cleaved more rapidly than that of the bulk of chromatin. Therefore, both enzymes digest and/or excise transcriptionally competent chromatin preferentially during early digestion times, while with more extensive digestion other domains of chromatin which are accessible to these nucleases are either destroyed by DNase I or excised as mononucleosome particles by micrococcal nuclease. Even with extensive digestion, particularly at 4°C, a residual fraction of chromatin remains which is relatively insensitive to nuclease digestion. This fraction presumably represents the heterochromatin fraction observed by electron microscopy which has a highly compact structure. Chromatin which is more accessible to nuclease digestion appears to have a more extended structure and likely represent the dispersed euchromatin fraction observed by ultrastructural analysis. Therefore, sensitivity to nuclease digestion represents a continuum in which certain chromatin domains (e.g., transcriptionally competent chromatin) are attacked most rapidly by micrococcal nuclease and DNase I followed by cleavage of chromatin domains which presumably exist in an extended conformation but are not necessarily enriched for transcriptionally active genes. Lastly, the fraction of chromatin which presumably reflects a highly compact domain is more resistent to cleavage by nucleases.

The precise factors which organize chromatin into domains with increased sensitivity to nonspecific nucleases are not completely defined, but increasing evidence suggests that the HMG proteins may play an important role in this organization. Several of these proteins have been purified and their amino acid sequence fully defined. Four major classes appear to be present in virtually all chromatin and are designated HMG-1 (M_r = 26,500), HMG-2 (M_r = 26,000), HMG-14 (M_r = 8000–10,000), and HMG-17 (M_r = 9247) (Goodwin et al., 1975). HMG proteins are highly abundant at approximately 10^6 copies per nucleus (Goodwin and Johns, 1973) and their amino acid sequences have been highly conserved during evolution (Romani et al., 1979). Jackson et al. (1979) demonstrated that mononucleosome fractions excised by micrococcal nuclease which were enriched for transcriptionally active genes lacked histone H1 and instead were associated with stoichiometric amounts of HMG-1 and HMG-2. These HMG proteins are likely associated with DNA linker regions since mild micrococcal nuclease digestions, which do not cleave the DNA of core particle, release large amounts of HMG-1 and HMG-2 (Jackson et al., 1979). Each protein sediments at approximately 5 to 6 S in sucrose gradients which based on their M_r of approximately 26,000 suggests they remain bound to excised linker DNA (Varshavsky *et al.*, 1978). This is further supported by the observation that after micrococcal nuclease digestion, chromatin fractions which sediment at 4 to 7 S in sucrose gradients contain DNA fragments of 30–70 base pairs (Rill *et al.*, 1975).

In addition to the micrococcal nuclease studies, evidence that the HMG proteins are in some fashion involved with gene activation comes with the observation that under mild digestion with DNase I (Vidali *et al.*, 1977) a high proportion of total chromatin associated HMG proteins is excised. In contrast to HMG-1 and HMG-2, the lower molecular weight HMG-14 and HMG-17 proteins appear to be associated with the DNA of a core particle and not with linker DNA (Mathew *et al.*, 1979). Furthermore, extraction of HMG proteins with 0.35 M NaCl prevents the selective digestion of transcriptional competent genes by nonspecific nuclease. Addition of purified HMG-14 and HMG-17 to nuclei which have been extracted by salt demonstrated that these HMG proteins were fully effective in restoring nuclease sensitivity to transcriptionally competent genes (Weisbrod and Weintraub, 1979). Therefore, the HMG proteins represent a class of chromatin proteins which may play an important role in modifying domains of chromatin to generate altered conformations which are associated with gene transcription and also show increased sensitivity to micrococcal nuclease and DNase I.

B. INTERACTION OF THYROID HORMONE RECEPTORS WITH CHROMATIN COMPONENTS

From the above analysis it is apparent that major advances in understanding chromatin structure have been achieved in the past 5 years. Most of this work, however, has related to the fundamental structure of the nucleosomal core particle and an examination of the organization of the HMG proteins with this basic structure. Other fundamental questions to be resolved relate to how the very low abundant nuclear associated receptor proteins (e.g., thyroid and steroid hormone receptors) are organized within this basic structure to modulate changes in chromatin function and possibly its structure. For example: (1) Is the thyroid hormone receptor homogeneously distributed throughout all chromatin domains or is it primarily restricted to chromatin conformations which are transcriptionally competent? (2) Is the receptor associated solely with linker DNA regions or is it associated primarily with the core nucleosome particle? (3) Does the receptor associate with chromatin primarily by directly binding to DNA or is the receptor organized with other specific chromosomal proteins to form a multimeric component which is both structurally and functionally important in the action of the thyroid hormone–receptor complex? Such a putative functional multimeric species would not be detected by 0.4 M KCl extraction of nuclei since its structure would likely be disaggregated by high salt conditions. By examining what chromatin forms of the receptor are excised by micrococcal nuclease and/or DNase I as a function of total chromatin digestion the above questions may be resolved. Furthermore, since nuclease digestion can be carried out at low ionic strength, an assessment can be made as to whether the receptor interacts primarily with linker DNA, DNA of the core particle, or with other unique chromosomal proteins within these chromatin domains. Recently several laboratories have examined the organization of the receptor in chromatin using micrococcal nuclease or DNase I as a probe (Samuels et al., 1980; Jump and Oppenheimer, 1980; Groul, 1980; Perlman et al., 1982).

C. MICROCOCCAL NUCLEASE EXCISES THE RECEPTOR AS A PREDOMINENT 6.5 S FORM AND AS A LESS ABUNDANT 12.5 S SPECIES FROM GH$_1$ CELL NUCLEI

Using low ionic strength conditions, Samuels et al. (1980) first reported that micrococcal nuclease excises the receptor from GH$_1$ cells as an abundant 6.5 S form and as a less abundant 12.5 S species which sediments slightly more rapidly than the bulk of the mononucleosomes generated (11.5 S). Similar studies on thyroid hormone receptors in rat liver were subsequently reported by Jump and Oppenheimer (1980) and by Groul (1980). These investigators reported that micrococcal nuclease released the receptor as a particle of approximately 6.0 S. These results contrast with the observation that 0.4 M KCl extraction of GH$_1$ cell and rat liver nuclei yields a receptor species which sediments as 3.8 S and 3.5 S, respectively (Samuels et al., 1980; Latham et al., 1976). Based on micrococcal nuclease digestion of GH$_1$ cell nuclei, we suggested that the 12.5 S receptor form represents receptor excised in association with a subset of mononucleosome particles while the 6.5 S form represents receptor excised in association with linker DNA regions and possibly other protein components (Samuels et al., 1980).

Figure 9 illustrates an isokinetic sucrose gradient of chromatin solubilized from GH$_1$ cell nuclei after a 10 minute digestion at 0°C followed by centrifugation at 32,000 rpm in an SW 41 rotor for 16 hours. In all studies intact GH$_1$ cells are first incubated with L-[^{125}I]T3 for 1–2 hours followed by nuclear isolation and chromatin digestion (Samuels et al., 1980). In this experiment approximately 10% of the total chromatin was excised as a soluble fraction based on the $A_{260\text{ nm}}$ units released. Ultracentrifugation resolves the released chromatin fraction into bulk nucleosomal

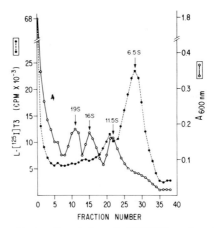

FIG. 9.   Isokinetic gradient sedimentation of L-[^{125}I]T3 bound to chromatin solubilized by micrococcal nuclease digestion. GH$_1$ cells cultured in roller bottles were incubated with L-[^{125}I]T3 for 1 hour. Isolated nuclei equivalent to 35 A_{260nm} units were digested in 0.7 ml for 10 minutes with 15 units of enzyme/1 A_{260nm} unit at 0°C. Solubilized chromatin (250 μl) was centrifuged in isokinetic gradients at 0°C at 32,000 rpm for 16 hours. The gradient was fractionated into 38 equal fractions and trichloroacetic acid was added to each fraction to achieve a final concentration of 15% (w/v). The L-[^{125}I]T3 bound (●) was determined in a refrigerated Auto-Gamma spectrometer and the samples were then centrifuged at 3000 g for 20 minutes. The dry pellets were then analyzed for DNA content (○) by the method of Burton (1956) by measuring the absorbance at 600 nm. One unit of absorbance at 600 nm is equal to 75 μg of DNA. From Samuels *et al.* (1980).

species which can be quantitated by the DNA content within the gradient. The study in Fig. 9 resolves the excised chromatin into 11.5 S mononucleosomes, 16 S dinucleosomes, and 19 S trinucleosomes, while higher molecular weight forms sediment toward the bottom of the gradient. Fifty percent of the excised L-[^{125}I]T3 sediments as a predominant 6.5 S peak and a less abundant peak of 12–12.5 S is also observed and sediments slightly more rapidly than the bulk of the mononucleosomes generated (11.5 S). There is also a suggestion of a small L-[^{125}I]T3 peak of 17 S migrating slightly faster than the 16 S dinucleosome. Figure 10A indicates that the L-[^{125}I]T3 peak of 12.5 S is a discrete form and can be resolved from the abundant 6.5 S receptor form. Figure 10B illustrates the sedimentation profile of receptor which was extracted from nuclei with 0.4 M KCl and then sedimented in the low salt isokinetic sucrose gradient. In this case only a 3.8 S form is resolved (Samuels *et al.*, 1980).

These observations on the sedimentation profile of the micrococcal nuclease excised thyroid hormone receptor are similar to that reported for the estradiol receptor in rat uterine chromatin by Senior and Frankel (1978) and hen oviduct chromatin by Massol *et al.* (1978). In both studies the

level of estradiol receptor was observed to be greater in the mononucleosome region compared to the dinucleosome and trinucleosome fractions,
and an estradiol peak sedimented somewhat more rapidly than the bulk of
the mononucleosome generated. In addition, the estradiol receptor was
released as a 6.9 S form which sedimented more rapidly than the estradiol
receptor dissociated from nuclei with high salt (Senior and Frankel, 1978).
Excluding the thyroid hormone receptor associated with the high molecular weight chromatin at the bottom of the gradient, the 6.5 S form represents approximately 80% and the 12.5 S form 10% of the receptor resolved
in the gradient. In addition, assuming one receptor moiety per nucleosome
species, the subset of 12.5 S mononucleosomes associated with receptor

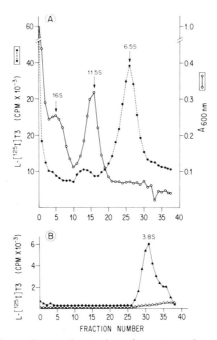

FIG. 10. Isokinetic gradient sedimentation of receptor released from chromatin solubilized by micrococcal nuclease digestion (A) and receptor extracted from nuclei with 0.4 M
KCl (B). The soluble chromatin fraction was prepared by enzyme digestion at 0°C using
nuclei derived from cells incubated with L-[^{125}I]T3 for 1 hour. The incubation conditions
were the same as described in the legend to Fig. 9 except that nuclei equivalent to 54 $A_{260\,nm}$
units were digested for 20 minutes. In a parallel study, thyroid hormone receptors were
solubilized from nuclei by extraction with 0.4 M KCl and then dialyzed at 0°C to lower the
salt concentration. Both the enzyme solubilized chromatin fraction and the nuclear extract
were centrifuged at 37,000 rpm for 16 hours at 0°C. (A) absorbance at 600 nm (○); L-[^{125}I]T3
(●). (B) L-[^{125}I]T3 (▲); L-[^{125}I]T3 plus a 1000-fold excess of nonradioactive L-T3 (△). From
Samuels *et al.* (1980).

represents approximately 0.006% of the bulk mononucleosomes generated.

Martin *et al.* (1977) have demonstrated that micrococcal nuclease digestion yields mononucleosomes of heterogeneous size and that polynucleosomes, which have longer DNA linker regions, are processed to mononucleosomes more rapidly than those with short linker regions. Furthermore, the DNA repeat lengths of these mononucleosomes are greater than 140 base pairs and appear to have intact linker DNA associated with histone H1 and nonhistone proteins (Todd and Garrard, 1979). Therefore, the 12.5 S L-T3 receptor peak may represent a species in which the thyroid hormone receptor is associated with mononucleosomes with intact linker DNA regions. Since micrococcal nuclease shows preference for cleavage and excision of linker DNA regions, the abundant 6.5 S receptor species likely represents the 3.8 S receptor in association with linker DNA fragments and/or other chromatin components.

D. KINETICS OF EXCISION OF CHROMATIN RECEPTOR FORMS BY MICROCOCCAL NUCLEASE

Since the studies in Figs. 9 and 10 examined the forms of the receptor excised with minimal micrococcal nuclease digestion at a single time, no inferences can be made as to whether the thyroid hormone receptor is uniformly distributed throughout the total chromatin or whether it is heterogeneously organized such that a high percentage of total receptor is excised when only a small fraction of total chromatin is digested. Furthermore, it does not establish whether both the 6.5 S and 12.5 S receptor forms are generated from the same chromatin domain or represent the release of receptor from discrete and different regions of chromatin. Therefore, kinetic studies were carried out to examine the rate of appearance of 12.5 S and 6.5 S receptor in relation to the digestion of total chromatin [as measured by the percentage of total DNA rendered perchloric acid (PCA) soluble] and to the generation of the bulk mononucleosomes. Figure 11 illustrates the effect of micrococcal nuclease on the kinetics of release of the total L-[^{125}I]T3 receptor, total solubilized chromatin released, and the extent of digestion as assessed by the percentage of total $A_{260\,nm}$ absorbance units which are rendered PCA soluble. As shown in Figure 11A the total L-[^{125}I]T3 receptor excised by micrococcal nuclease parallels the percentage of total chromatin solubilized by the enzyme. Although not illustrated, digestion of only 2–5% of total chromatin yields a similar parallelism in the release of chromatin and receptor. Figure 11B compares the concentration of receptor per $A_{260\,nm}$ absorbance units in the released chromatin fraction, and in the residual fraction which

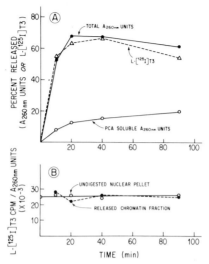

FIG. 11. Kinetics of release of receptor and chromatin by micrococcal nuclease. GH_1 cells were incubated with 1 nM L-[^{125}I]T3 for 1 hour. The derived nuclei were incubated at 0°C with micrococcal nuclease at 15 units of enzyme/$A_{260\,nm}$ units of nuclei. At 10, 20, 40, and 90 minutes 10 mM EDTA was added to stop the reaction. The samples were centrifuged at 3000 g for 15 minutes. The absorbances of the supernatant and residual pellet were determined at 260 nm and an alliquot of the supernatant was precipitated with 5% perchloric acid (PCA). (A) Percentage of total receptor and chromatin ($A_{260\,nm}$ units) released. (B) Concentration of L-[^{125}I]T3 in the released and insoluble chromatin fractions.

was not solubilized by micrococcal nuclease digestion. At all digestion times the concentration of receptor is the same and identical to that of the starting nuclear (zero time) preparation prior to digestion. This indicates that the bulk of the receptor is homogeneously dispersed throughout the chromatin.

However, it remains possible that a small fraction of the total receptor exists in a chromatin domain which is preferentially excised by micrococcal nuclease. To explore this possibility the kinetics of appearance of the nuclease derived receptor forms was examined using isokinetic sucrose gradients. Figure 12 illustrates the gradient profile of receptor and chromatin released by micrococcal nuclease digestion from the experiment in Fig. 11. Between 10 and 90 minutes of digestion, the 6.5 S receptor form progressively increases in magnitude and appears to parallel the abundance of the bulk mononucleosome peak generated from chromatin. In contrast the 12.5 S receptor form plateaus within 10 minutes of digestion and remains relatively constant thereafter. Figure 13 compares the kinetics of appearance of the 6.5 S receptor, the rate of formation of the

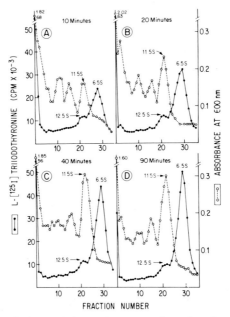

FIG. 12.   Kinetics of release of chromatin receptor forms by micrococcal nuclease. The supernatant fractions from the study in Fig. 11 were centrifuged in isokinetic sucrose gradients at 32,000 rpm for 16 hours in an SW-41 rotor. Micrococcal nuclease digestion times: (A) 10 minutes, (B) 20 minutes, (C) 40 minutes, (D) 90 minutes.

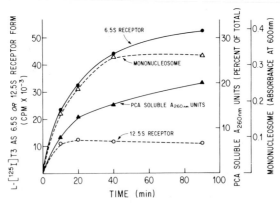

FIG. 13.   Comparison of the rate of appearance of the 6.5 S receptor, 11.5 S bulk mononucleosomes, and 12.5 S receptor. The results were derived from Figs. 11 and 12.

bulk mononucleosomes, and the kinetics of appearance of the 12.5 S receptor form.

At virtually all digestion times the kinetics of formation of the 6.5 S receptor form parallels the excision of the mononucleosomes from the bulk of chromatin. These rates also parallel the rates of total digestion as assessed by the percentage of chromatin which is rendered PCA soluble by micrococcal nuclease. In contrast, the 12.5 S receptor species is generated rapidly and attains a plateau value within 10 minutes of incubation. In other studies (not illustrated) the 12.5 S receptor form was shown to attain a maximal value within 3 minutes of micrococcal nuclease digestion. Therefore, if the 12.5 S receptor form represents receptor in association with mononucleosome particles, this species is excised at a rate far more rapidly than that of the mononucleosomes of bulk chromatin. This suggests that it is derived from a chromatin domain which is exceedingly sensitive to micrococcal nuclease digestion. Based on the studies of Bloom and Anderson (1978) the 12.5 S receptor form likely represents receptor in association with mononucleosomes which are derived from a putative transcriptionally active region of chromatin. Although this is suggested by the digestion kinetics this will have to be confirmed by determining the rate of appearance of transcriptionally active sequences in the mononucleosome region as a function of the kinetics of appearance of the 12.5 S form.

E. THE 6.5 S RECEPTOR FORM CONTAINS A DNA FRAGMENT AND MAY EXIST AS A MULTIMERIC SPECIES

The observation that the kinetics of appearance of the 6.5 S form parallels that of the bulk mononucleosomes generated suggest that most of this receptor form is derived from a separate domain in chromatin than the 12.5 S receptor. If the 6.5 S receptor represented receptor bound to linker DNA regions and was homogeneously dispersed throughout the chromatin, the kinetics of appearance of this form and the bulk mononucleosome species would be expected to be parallel since cleavage of DNA linker regions would excise the 6.5 S receptor and also release chromatin particles as mononucleosomes. The 12.5 S receptor form is of too low abundance to isolate and further characterize. However, the 6.5 S form can be totally isolated from other forms of the receptor excised by micrococcal nuclease digestion. This can be achieved either by isolating this receptor form by density gradient centrifugation or by micrococcal nuclease digestion in the presence of 5 mM MgCl$_2$. At this concentration of Mg^{2+}, mononucleosome particles and higher chromatin forms remain insoluble and the receptor is released only as a 6.5 S species. Studies were therefore performed to (1) characterize the 6.5 S receptor, (2) determine if it is excised in association with a DNA fragment, and (3) assess whether this structure may represent a multimeric species of 3.8 S salt extracted receptor in association with other protein components.

This was initially assessed by determining the influence of increasing salt concentrations on the sedimentation profile of the 6.5 S receptor (Perlman *et al.*, 1982). Figure 14 illustrates the sedimentation profile of the 6.5 S receptor which was adjusted to KCl concentrations between 10 and 200 mM prior to sedimentation in gradients containing the same KCl concentration. At KCl concentrations of 60 mM or less (Fig. 14A–C) the receptor sediments as a 6.5 S form. Above 60 mM KCl (Fig. 14D–F) there is a progressive stepwise decrease in the sedimentation coefficient. The 6.5 S receptor sediments as a 5.3 S species at 100 mM KCl and as a 4.4 S form at 150 mM KCl. At 200 mM KCl the 6.5 S receptor sediments as a 3.9 S form which is essentially identical to that extracted from nuclei by high salt conditions (3.8 S). The decrease in the sedimentation coefficient with increasing salt concentrations does not reflect a conformational change of a single component species since at high salt concentrations the receptor component would be more compact and would sediment at an increased and not decreased rate (Sherman *et al.*, 1980). If the 6.5 S

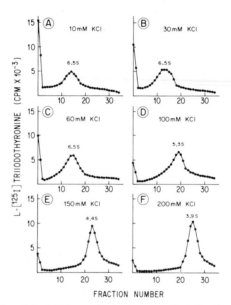

FIG. 14.   Conversion of the 6.5 S receptor to slower sedimenting forms by increasing KCl concentrations. From Perlman *et al.* (1982).

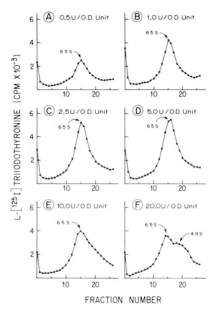

FIG. 15. Effect of DNase I concentration on the release of the receptor from GH₁ cell nuclei. From Perlman *et al.* (1982).

receptor was only 3.8 S receptor bound to only one other component (i.e., a DNA fragment), increasing KCl concentrations would result only in a decrease in the magnitude of the 6.5 S receptor with a reciprocal increase in the 3.8 S species. Therefore, the stepwise change in the sedimentation coefficient with increasing KCl concentrations is compatible with the notion that the 6.5 S receptor is in association with at least two other components which are progressively and sequentially disaggregated by high salt conditions.

Evidence that one of these components is a DNA fragment comes from studies which examined the receptor forms released by DNase I (Perlman *et al.*, 1982). Figure 15 illustrates the effect of DNase I concentrations on the magnitude and the sedimentation profile of the receptor forms released. In contrast with micrococcal nuclease, receptor forms sedimenting greater than 6.5 S are not observed. With DNase I concentrations from 0.5 to 5 enzyme units, the 6.5 S species is symmetrical and progressively increases in magnitude (Fig. 15A–D). At 10 enzyme units (Fig. 15E) the 6.5 S peak broadens and decreases in height. At 20 enzyme units (Fig. 15F) the 6.5 S peak is reduced in magnitude and an apparent 4.9 S shoulder is also present. Therefore, DNase I appears to initially excise the receptor only as a 6.5 S species and at high enzyme concentrations, the magnitude of the 6.5 S form diminishes within an apparent conversion to a slower sedimenting species. With further DNase I digestion the 6.5 S receptor is converted to a 3.8 S form (see Fig. 16). These results suggest that DNase I initially excises the receptor as a 6.5 S form which contains a DNA fragment. Further digestion of the DNA fragment converts the 6.5 S receptor to a series of slower sedimenting forms and upon complete cleavage of the DNA fragment yields 3.8 S receptor which has the same sedimentation properties as the receptor extracted from nuclei by high salt conditions.

Further documentation that the 6.5 S receptor form contains a DNA fragment comes from studies which examined the ability of receptor species of various S values to associate with highly polymerized DNA (Perlman *et al.*, 1982). Figure 16 illustrates a study which examined the DNase I digestion of the 6.5 S species and the DNA binding characteristics of the derived forms. Nuclei were first incubated with 50 units of DNase I for 30 minutes at 0°C. The supernatant fraction was divided into three groups and the digestion was inhibited in one group with 10 mM EDTA to yield "mild digestion." "Moderate" and more "extensive" digestion were obtained by additional incubation with 2500 units of DNase

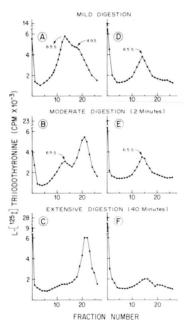

FIG. 16. Interaction of DNase I generated receptor forms with duplex DNA. From Perlman *et al.* (1982).

I for 2 minutes and 40 minutes after which the nuclease activity was inhibited. Each digestion was divided into two parts. To one part of each (A, B, and C) 50 μl of nuclease buffer was added. To parallel samples (D, E, and F) 50 μl of buffer containing 300 μg of purified highly polymerized duplex calf thymus DNA was added. The samples were incubated for 30 minutes at 0°C and were centrifuged in isokinetic gradients at 37,000 rpm for 40 hours. DNase I progressively reduced the size of the 6.5 S receptor to a limit value of 3.8 S (Fig. 16B and C) and at early times both a 6.5 S and a shoulder estimated at 4.9 S are present (Fig. 16A). The 6.5 S form does not appear to bind to exogenous DNA while the slower sedimenting forms sediment with the DNA to the bottom of the gradient. (Fig. 16D–F). In similar studies (data not illustrated) the 6.5 S receptor form excised with micrococcal nuclease did not associate with exogenous duplex DNA while the 3.8 S receptor isolated by 0.4 M KCl was a DNA binding species. These studies suggest that the 6.5 S chromatin derived receptor form contains a DNA fragment which is cleaved by progressive DNase I digestion and exposes regions of the receptor component(s) which have high affinity for duplex DNA.

F. ESTIMATION OF THE PARTICLE DENSITY, STOKES RADII, AND MOLECULAR WEIGHTS OF THE 3.8 S AND 6.5 S RECEPTOR FORMS: IMPLICATIONS FOR THE STRUCTURE OF THE RECEPTOR IN CHROMATIN

Other evidence that the 6.5 S receptor contains a DNA fragment comes from the high density of the 6.5 S species compared to the 3.8 S form (Perlman *et al.*, 1982). The density of each of the receptor species was estimated by ultracentrifugation in isokinetic sucrose gradients where the density was varied by replacing H_2O by D_2O (Edelstein and Schachman, 1967). Devreotes *et al.* (1977) and Meunier *et al.* (1972) have used this approach to estimate the density of the acetylcholine receptor. The velocity of sedimentation of a particle is directly related to the difference between the particle density (ρ) and the density of the sedimentation medium (ρ_0). Since the density of D_2O is 10.56% greater than H_2O, a particle will sediment slower in sucrose gradients constructed in D_2O compared to H_2O. Figure 17 illustrates the sedimentation of the 6.5 S receptor in isokinetic sucrose gradients constructed in either 100% D_2O or 100% H_2O. The receptor sediments approximately 1.5-fold further when the gradient is constructed with H_2O compared to D_2O.

The distance that a particle sediments from the meniscus in millimeters $(X_m) = (X_0tK/\rho)(\rho - \rho_0)$, where X_0 is the distance from the center of rotation to the meniscus, t is the time of centrifugation in hours, K is a

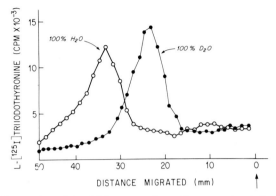

FIG. 17.   Sedimentation of the 6.5 S receptor in gradients constructed with 100% H_2O or 100% D_2O. The samples were centrifuged at 44,000 rpm at 5°C for 17.5 hours in an SW-60 rotor.

constant determined by rotor speed, temperature, and M_r, ρ_0 is the average density of the gradient, and ρ is the density of the macromolecule. Therefore, if the particle is sedimented into a series of gradients having different densities, linear plots of X_m vs ρ_0 intersect the horizontal axis at the solvent density at which the macromolecule does not migrate. This gives an estimate of the density of the macromolecule since when $X_m = 0$, $\rho = \rho_0$. Figure 18 illustrates a study in which the 6.5 S and 3.8 S receptor forms were sedimented into gradients composed of H_2O, D_2O, or $D_2O : H_2O$ mixtures of 25, 50, or 75% D_2O (Perlman *et al.*, 1982). Based on

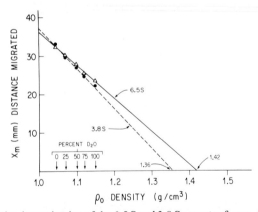

FIG. 18.   Density determination of the 6.5 S and 3.8 S receptor forms. Sedimentation was in 5–20% sucrose gradients of various D_2O/H_2O proportions, and average densities (ρ_0) of 0% D_2O = 1.045 g/ml, 25% D_2O = 1.07 g/ml, 50% D_2O = 1.10 g/ml, 75% D_2O = 1.12 g/ml, 100% D_2O = 1.15 g/ml. Other details are given in the text. From Perlman *et al.* (1982).

the intersection with the horizontal axis, the estimated anhydrous density of the 6.5 S form was 1.42 g/cm³ ± 0.02 ($p < 0.01$) and the 3.8 S form was 1.36 g/cm³ ± 0.03 ($p < 0.01$). The density of most proteins is approximately 1.36 g/cm³ (Sherman *et al.*, 1980), while that for DNA is 1.8 g/cm³ (Luzzati *et al.*, 1967). Therefore the 3.8 S receptor form has a density characteristic of protein while the density of the 6.5 S species falls between that of protein and DNA. Assuming that the density increment of the 6.5 S form is due to an associated DNA fragment it can be calculated that the 6.5 S species consists of 15% DNA and 85% protein.

The Stokes radii were calculated by the elution profile of the 6.5 S and 3.8 S receptor on Sephrose CL-6B and Fig. 19 illustrates these results. The distribution coefficient (K_d) was determined for each elution fraction and for protein standards of known Stokes radius (R_s). As illustrated in the inset to Fig. 19, a plot of $(K_d)^{1/3}$ vs R_s for the four protein standards is linear in agreement with the observations of Siegel and Monty (1966). Based on the K_d for the receptor forms, the R_s of the 3.8 S and the 6.5 S receptor species were calculated to be 3.3 and 6.0 nm, respectively. Using the sedimentation coefficient, the R_s values and the partial specific volumes ($\bar{v}$) derived from the estimated anhydrous density ($\bar{v} = 1/\rho$), the M_r values were calculated to be 54,000 for the 3.8 S receptor and 149,000 for the 6.5 S form. The M_r and the R_s for the salt extracted receptor from GH₁ cell nuclei are in good agreement with those reported by Latham *et al.* (1976) for the thyroid hormone receptor extracted from rat liver nuclei ($M_r = 50,500; R_s = 3.5$ nm).

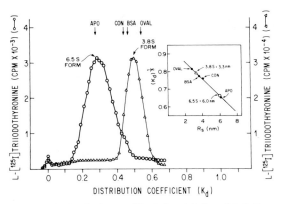

FIG. 19. Estimation of the Stokes radii of the 6.5 S and 3.8 S receptor forms by Sepharose CL-6B chromatography. The results are plotted as the distribution coefficient (K_d) of the receptor forms and protein standards of known Stokes radius (R_s). The inset shows the relationship between the R_s and the $(K_d)^{1/3}$ (Siegel and Monty, 1966) which was used to calculate the R_s of the receptor forms. From Perlman *et al.* (1982).

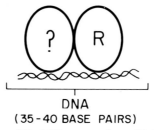

DNA
(35 - 40 BASE PAIRS)

FIG. 20.   Possible structure of the 6.5 S receptor form. (R) denotes the 3.8 S receptor. (?) represents additional chromosomal proteins with which the 3.8 S receptor interacts or another 3.8 S receptor molecule. The protein components are associated with DNA which is excised as a 35–40 base pair fragment by micrococcal nuclease.

The DNase I digestion studies (Fig. 16) suggest that the 6.5 S receptor contains a DNA fragment and from the density measurement it can be calculated that the 6.5 S receptor is composed of 85% protein and 15% DNA. Based on the total M_r of the 6.5 S species of 149,000 this yields an M_r value for the protein component of 127,000. The M_r for the putative DNA component is therefore 22,000 which would be equivalent to 36 base pairs of DNA and is the size length expected if the 6.5 S receptor form were derived from linker DNA regions in chromatin. The estimated M_r of 127,000 for the protein component of the 6.5 S receptor is significantly greater than the M_r (54,000) for the hormone binding activity extracted from nuclei by 0.4 M KCl suggesting that the receptor exists as a multimer in chromatin (Fig. 20). This is also supported by the stepwise reduction in sedimentation coefficient seen with increasing salt concentrations (Fig. 14). The structure of the 6.5 S receptor form could represent the 54,000 M_r (3.8 S) receptor in dimeric form alone, or in association with other unique protein components bound to DNA. Alternatively, it could represent a single 54,000 M_r (3.8 S) receptor in association with other unique chromatin protein components which interact as a multimer with DNA (Figure 20).

Whether these proteins are abundant chromosomal proteins (e.g., HMG proteins) or unknown proteins of low abundance will require purification of the chromatin forms of the receptor. Clearly, identification of the protein composition of the 6.5 S receptor as well as the 12.5 S receptor form may provide important insights as to how the hormone–receptor complex initiates thyroid hormone action at the molecular level.

IV. Summary and Conclusions

Numerous studies indicate that the thyroid hormones stimulate the accumulation of specific mRNA molecules in cell culture as well as in tissues *in vivo*. This response appears to be mediated by a chromatin associated receptor which presumably regulates a transcriptional and/or post-transcriptional event in the cell nucleus which is rate limiting for mRNA accumulation. The receptor can be extracted by high salt conditions from liver or GH_1 cell nuclei. This receptor form from liver has a Stokes radius of 3.5 nm, and a sedimentation coefficient or 3.5 S (Latham *et al.*, 1976). From GH_1 cells, the KCl extracted receptor has an estimated Stokes radius of 3.3 nm and a sedimentation coefficient of 3.8 S (Samuels *et al.*, 1980; Perlman *et al.*, 1982). The difference in the physical parameters of the salt extracted receptor from rat liver and GH_1 cells likely reflects differences in experimental measurements rather than intrinsic differences in the receptor binding component.

The half-life and synthetic rate of the 3.8 S receptor component has been estimated in GH_1 cells using a dense amino acid labeling technique (Raaka and Samuels, 1981). These studies show that the nuclear receptor level is solely a reflection of the rate of receptor degradation and the rate of accumulation in newly synthesized receptor. Furthermore, there is no evidence for a significant pool of masked cytoplasmic receptor which cannot bind the ligand prior to association with nuclei. Thyroid hormone lowers receptor levels in GH_1 cells (Samuels *et al.*, 1976, 1977) although there is no evidence that hormone mediated receptor regulation occurs in the liver *in vivo* (Oppenheimer *et al.*, 1975). Using dense amino acid labeling we have shown that the reduction of receptor elicited by thyroid hormone in cultured GH_1 cells is primarily due to an inhibition in the accumulation of newly synthesized dense receptor at early incubation times with hormone. At longer incubation times (greater than 24 hours) thyroid hormone also results in a shortening of receptor half-life. This decrease in receptor half-life does not appear to result as a direct consequence of the hormone binding to the receptor but appears to reflect late and delayed effects of thyroid hormone on the cell which may result from changes in cell metabolism and/or chromatin structure. A model to explain the rapid thyroid hormone mediated decrease in accumulation of newly synthesized receptor is presented and it is suggested that the nuclear thyroid hormone receptor complex can inhibit the production rate of its own mRNA. Clearly, documentation of this model will require direct quantitation of the mRNA for the receptor.

Since the receptor has a half-life of about 5 hours the total nuclear receptor population appears to fully exchange within a 24-hour period. Therefore, the receptor does not remain fixed to specific regions of chromatin but is constantly exchanged both by loss of receptor from specific chromatin domains and replenishment by newly synthesized receptor. Studies using nuclease digestion demonstrated that the thyroid hormone receptor can be excised from nuclei as a predominant 6.5 S form and is a less abundant 12.5 S species (Samuels *et al.*, 1980; Perlman *et al.*, 1982). Studies in rat liver (Oppenheimer and Jump, 1980; Groul, 1980) also indicate that the predominant excised form of the receptor sediments at about 6.0 S. The 12.5 S form of the receptor likely represents association of receptor with a subset of mononucleosome particles which appear to be excised more rapidly than the bulk of the mononucleosomes generated. Based on kinetics of excision this fraction of nuclear bound receptor may represent receptor in association with mononucleosome particles that are derived from a transcriptionally competent region of chromatin. In GH_1 cells the remainder of receptor population appears to be homogeneously distributed throughout the chromatin as assessed by micrococcal nuclease digestion. Whether this type of receptor distribution occurs *in vivo* will require further analysis.

Evidence is presented that the 6.5 S receptor form represents the 3.8 S receptor in association with other chromatin protein components which are excised as a complex bound to a DNA fragment of approximately 35 base pairs. Clearly studies of this type provide some basic information regarding the organization of the receptor in chromatin. Future approaches will require an analysis both on a functional and structural level. Such an analysis should include (1) a determination as to whether the thyroid hormone–receptor complex directly regulates the transcriptional process or influences posttranscriptional modifications of specific genes transcripts; (2) isolation of the mRNA for the receptor, synthesis of a cDNA, and cloning by recominent DNA techniques; this will allow quantitation of the receptor mRNA as well as a function as a probe for isolation and analysis of receptor gene sequences in chromatin; and (3) studies to determine if the mononucleosome bound form of the receptor represents receptor in association with mononucleosome particles that are being actively transcribed. In addition, further analysis is required of the protein composition of the micrococcal nuclease excised form of the receptor since this may represent a functionally important multimer in which the receptor binding component is a subunit of a regulatory complex which plays an important role in mediating the action of thyroid hormone at the nuclear level.

ACKNOWLEDGMENTS

Experimental work from the author's laboratory reported in this article was supported by research grant AM 16636 from the National Institutes of Health. A. J. Perlman and B. M. Raaka are recipients of Individual National Research Service Award Postdoctoral Fellowships from the National Institutes of Health. We thank Mary McCarthy for her patience and assistance in typing this manuscript.

REFERENCES

Bloom, K. S., and Anderson, J. N. (1978). *Cell* **15**, 141–150.
Bloom, K. S., and Anderson, J. N. (1979). *J. Biol. Chem.* **254**, 10532–10539.
Burman, K. D., Lukes, V., Wright, D. F., and Wartofsky, L. (1977). *Endocrinology* **101**, 1331–1334.
Burton, K. (1956). *Biochem. J.* **62**, 315–323.
DeGroot, L. J., Coleoni, A. H., Rue, P. A., Seo, H., Martino, E., and Refetoff, S. (1977). *Biochem. Biophys. Res. Commun.* **79**, 173–178.
Devreotes, P. N., Gardner, J. M., and Fambrough, D. M. (1977). *Cell* **10**, 365–373.
Dillmann, W. H., Bonner, R. A., and Oppenheimer, J. H. (1978a). *Endocrinology* **102**, 1633–1636.
Dillmann, W. H., Schwartz, H. L., and Oppenheimer, J. H. (1978b). *Biochem. Biophys. Res. Commun.* **80**, 259–266.
Edelstein, S. J., and Schachman, H. K. (1967). *J. Biol. Chem.* **242**, 306–311.
Felsenfeld, G. (1978). *Nature (London)* **271**, 115–122.
Garel, A. M., Zolam, M., and Axel, R. (1977). *Proc. Natl. Acad. Sci. U.S.A.* **74**, 4867.
Goodwin, G. H., and Johns, E. W. (1973). *Eur. J. Biochem.* **40**, 215–219.
Goodwin, G. H., Schooter, K. V., and Johns, E. W. (1975). *Eur. J. Biochem.* **54**, 427–433.
Groul, D. J. (1980). *Endocrinology* **107**, 994–999.
Hershko, A., and Tomkins, G. M. (1971). *J. Biol. Chem.* **246**, 710–714.
Hunttermann, A., and Wendelberger, G. (1976). *Methods Cell Biol.* **13**, 153–170.
Jackson, J. B., Pollock, J. M., Jr., and Rill, R. L. (1979). *Biochemistry* **18**, 3739–3748.
Jaffe, R. C., and Means, A. B. (1977). *Endocrinology* **101**, 447–452.
Jump, D. B., and Oppenheimer, J. H. (1980). *Science* **209**, 811–813.
Kornberg, R. D. (1974). *Science* **184**, 868–871.
Kornberg, R. D. (1977). *Annu. Rev. Biochem.* **46**, 931–954.
Kurtz, D. T., Sippel, A. E., and Feigelson, P. (1976). *Biochemistry* **15**, 1031–1036.
Latham, K. R., Ring, J. C., and Baxter, J. D. (1976). *J. Biol. Chem.* **251**, 7388–7397.
Latham, K. R., MacLeod, K. M., Papavasiliou, S. S., Martial, J. A., Seeburg, P. H., Goodman, H. M., and Baster, J. D. (1978). *In* "Receptors and Hormone Action" (B. W. O'Malley and L. Birnbaumer, eds.), Vol. 3, pp. 76–100. Academic Press, New York.
Levy, B. W., Connor, W., and Dixon, G. H. (1979). *J. Biol. Chem.* **254**, 609–620.
Luzzati, V. E., Masson, F., Mathis, A., and Saludjian, P. (1967). *Biopolymers* **5**, 491–508.
MacLeod, K. M., and Baxter, J. D. (1976). *J. Biol. Chem.* **251**, 7380–7387.
Martial, J. A., Baxter, J. D., Goodman, H. M., and Seeburg, P. H. (1977). *Proc. Natl. Acad. Sci. U.S.A.* **74**, 1816–1820.
Martin, D. Z., Todd, R. D., Lang, D., Pei, P. N., and Garrard, W. T. (1977). *J. Biol. Chem.* **252**, 8269–8277.
Massol, N., Lebeau, M.-C., and Baulieu, E.-E. (1978). *Nucleic Acids Res.* **5**, 723–738.
Mathew, C. G., Goodwin, G. H., and Johns, E. W. (1979). *Nucleic Acids Res.* **6**, 167–179.
Meunier, J. C., Olsen, R. W., and Changeux, J. P. (1972). *FEBS Lett.* **24**, 63–68.
Miller, D. M., Turner, P., Nienhuis, A. W., Axelrod, D. E., and Gopalkrishnan, T. V. (1978). *Cell* **14**, 511–521.
Morris, N. R. (1976a). *Cell* **9**, 627–632.
Morris, N. R. (1976b). *Cell* **8**, 357–363.
Noll, M. (1974). *Nature (London)* **251**, 249–251.
Noll, M., and Kornberg, R. D. (1977). *J. Mol. Biol.* **109**, 393–404.
Olins, A. L., and Olins, D. E. (1974). *Science* **183**, 330–332.
O'Malley, B. W., and Means, A. R. (1974). *Science* **183**, 610.

Oppenheimer, J. H., and Surks, M. I. (1975). In "Biochemical Action of Hormones" (G. Litwack ed.), Vol. 3, pp. 119–157.

Oppenheimer, J. H., Schwartz, L., Koerner, D., and Surks, M. I. (1975). Endocrinol. Res. Commun. 2, 309–325.

Oppenheimer, J. H., and Dillmann, W. H. (1978). In "Receptors and Hormone Action" (B. W. O'Malley and L. Birnbaumer, eds.), Vol. 3, pp. 1–33. Academic Press, New York.

Perlman, A. J., Stanley, F., and Samuels, H. H. (1982). J. Biol. Chem., in press.

Raaka, B. M., and Samuels, H. H. (1981). J. Biol. Chem. 256, 6883–6889.

Rill, R. L., Oosterhof, D. K., Hozier, J. C., and Nelson, D. A. (1975). Nucleic Acids Res. 2, 1525–1539.

Romani, M., Rodman, T. C., Vidali, G., and Bustin, M. (1979). J. Biol. Chem. 254, 2918–2922.

Roy, A. K., Schiop, M. J., and Dowbenko, D. J. (1976). FEBS Lett. 64, 396–399.

Samuels, H. H. (1978). In "Receptors and Hormone Action" (B. W. O'Malley and L. Birnbaumer, eds.), Vol. 3, pp. 35–74. Academic Press, New York.

Samuels, H. H., and Shapiro, L. E. (1976). Proc. Natl. Acad. Sci. U.S.A. 73, 3369–3373.

Samuels, H. H., and Tsai, J. S. (1973). Proc. Natl. Acad. Sci. U.S.A. 70, 3488–3492.

Samuels, H. H., Tsai, J. S., and Cintron, R. (1973). Science 181, 1253–1256.

Samuels, H. H., Tsai, J. S., Casanova, J., and Stanley, F. (1974). J. Clin. Invest. 54, 853–865.

Samuels, H. H., Stanley, F., and Shapiro, L. E. (1976). Proc. Natl. Acad. Sci. U.S.A. 73, 3877–3881.

Samuels, H. H., Stanley, F., and Shapiro, L. E. (1977). J. Biol. Chem. 252, 6052–6060.

Samuels, H. H., Stanley, F., and Shapiro, L. E. (1979a). Biochemistry 18, 715–721.

Samuels, H. H., Stanley, F., and Casanova, J. (1979b). J. Clin. Invest. 63, 1229–1240.

Samuels, H. H., Stanley, F., Casanova, J., and Shao, T. C. (1980). J. Biol. Chem. 255, 2499–2508.

Schadlow, A. R., Surks, M. I., Schwartz, H. L., and Oppenheimer, J. H. (1972). Science 176, 1253.

Schimke, R. T. (1975). Methods Enzymol. 40, 241–266.

Senior, M. B., and Frankel, F. R. (1978). Cell 14, 857–863.

Seo, H., Vassart, G., Brocas, H., and Refetoff, S. (1977). Proc. Natl. Acad. Sci. U.S.A. 74, 2054–2058.

Shapiro, L. E., Samuels, H. H., and Yaffe, B. M. (1978). Proc. Natl. Acad. Sci. U.S.A. 75, 45–49.

Sherman, M. R., Tuazon, F. B., and Miller, L. K. (1980). Endocrinology 106, 1715–1727.

Siegel, L. M., and Monty, K. J. (1966). Biochim. Biophys. Acta 112, 346–362.

Todd, R. D., and Garrard, W. T. (1979). J. Biol. Chem. 254, 3074–3083.

Towle, H. C., Mariash, C. N., and Oppenheimer, J. H. (1980). Biochemistry 18, 579–585.

Tsai, J. S., and Samuels, H. H. (1974). Biochem. Biophys. Res. Commun. 59, 420–428.

Varshavsky, A. J., Bakayev, V. V., Nedospasov, S. A., and Georgiev, G. P. (1978). Cold Spring Harbor Symp. Quant. Biol. 42, 457–473.

Vidali, G., Boffa, L. C., and Allfrey, V. G. (1977). Cell 12, 409–415.

Weintraub, H., and Groudine, M. (1976). Science 193, 848–853.

Weisbrod, S., and Weintraub, H. (1979). Proc. Natl. Acad. Sci. U.S.A. 76, 630–634.

DISCUSSION

D. B. Jump: I should like to present some data which represent an extension of our previous study demonstrating the release of a T3 receptor containing chromatin fragment (5.8 S) following mild micrococcal nuclease or DNase I digestion of rat liver nuclei. In the

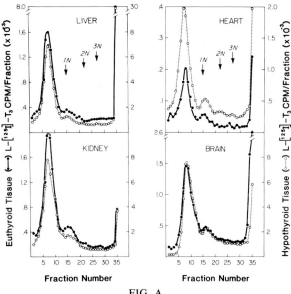

FIG. A.

present study, we were interested in determining whether T3 receptors in various euthyroid and hypothyroid tissues were associated with chromatin in the same manner as we found in euthyroid rat liver. Isolated nuclei from *in vivo* labeled (^{125}I-T3) euthyroid and hypothyroid rat brain, heart, kidney, and liver were digested with micrococcal nuclease and the soluble chromatin fragments separated by velocity sedimentation (Fig. A). Sedimentation direction is from left to right and the position of the mononucleosome, dinucleosome, and trinucleosome is denoted by 1N, 2N, and 3N, respectively. Micrococcal nuclease excises a predominant T3 receptor containing fragment (5.5–6.0 S) migrating slower than mononucleosomes from chromatin of all tissues examined. In addition, a minor fragment (12–14 S) migrating nearly coincident with mononucleosomes was also detected. I believe these structures are analogous to those you have found in GH$_1$ cell nuclei. Thus, in rat pituitary tumor cells, liver, heart, kidney, and brain, the thyroid hormone receptor appears to be associated with the same binding domain, i.e., the DNA between nucleosomes. In addition, our studies indicate that neither thyroidal status nor receptor occupancy influences the association of the thyroid hormone receptor with chromatin in rat liver.

You have provided evidence that T3 receptors are homogeneously distributed in chromatin in GH$_1$ pituitary cell nuclei. A number of studies in our laboratory suggest that receptors are not uniformly distributed and are associated with internucleosomal DNA in regions of chromatin highly susceptible to endonuclease digestion. For example, we have found that the specific activity of T3 receptors decreases as the size of receptor-containing chromatin increases from mononucleosomes to octanucleosomes. Second, under very mild digestion conditions in which 2% of the total nuclear DNA appears in the mononucleosomal fraction, 25–30% of the total nuclear receptor is excised as the 5.5 S fragment. If T3 receptors were homogeneously distributed in chromatin, only 2–3% of the T3 receptors would be excised under these conditions. And lastly, a fraction of chromatin that consists of mononucleosomes through tetranucleosomes containing 20% of the total nuclear DNA was found to contain 70% of the total nuclear T3 receptor, thus leading to an enrichment in T3 binding capacity over that found in nuclei. These data indicate to us that T3 receptors are associated with a select region of chromatin in rat liver nuclei which differs from your observations with GH_1 pituitary cells. Perhaps you may like to comment on these observations.

H. H. Samuels: Although I think one possible explanation is that we are studying different cell types, the data that you obtained in liver are completely different in their characteristics from our results obtained in GH_1 cells. From what you observed the kinetics of appearance of the 6 S form of the receptor is very different than that of the bulk of mononucleosome particles. I don't know if you have any data on the 12 S form of the receptor. It is possible, for example, that liver chromatin is in a more extended conformation and that the receptor may be organized differently in the liver than it is in the GH_1 cells. For example, we don't know what the receptor half-life is in liver and whether it is exchanged very rapidly. I think that additional studies in both systems will probably clarify the differences in our observations.

D. Moore: I have a comment relating to a rather different system which has a similar idea. Dr. Farhang Payvar working in the laboratories of Keith Yamamoto and Howard Goodman using steroid receptor imported from Sweden has recently shown that he can detect specific binding of that protein hormone complex to the DNA of mouse mammary tumor virus. There are three binding sites that he has located: one near the promoter region and two others downstream. The most relevant point, with regard to the sorts of studies you have described, is that this DNA is just bare, pure DNA, no chromatin, no histones, etc. Obviously this is a different system, but would you have any comment on these results?

H. H. Samuels: I think the issue you raise that the glucocorticoid receptor may associate with unique DNA sequences is interesting. We have some results in GH_1 cells which suggest that the thyroid hormone receptor may bind to a unique DNA sequence and not just randomly with DNA. If the 6.5 S receptor is incubated under high salt conditions to dissociate the 3.8 S binding component, the 6.5 S receptor can be fully regenerated by sedimenting the chromatin preparation into a gradient of low ionic strength. This regeneration of the 3.8 S to the 6.5 S receptor is not significantly inhibited by a marked excess of exogenous calf thymus DNA. We have isolated the DNA from the chromatin that is released, and after purification have separated the DNA based on size using sucrose gradients. If the various size fractions of DNA are examined for the ability to reconstitute the 6.5 S receptor from the 3.8 S receptor, the fragment that specifically regenerates the 6.5 S receptor was in the range of about 40 base pairs. There is no regeneration of the receptor using DNA fragments, for example, of greater than 100 base pairs or less than 20 base pairs. Furthermore, fragments greater than 100 base pairs do not generate a species larger than 6.5 S and fragments less than 20 pairs do not generate a species intermediate between 3.8 and 6.5 S. This implies that the receptor binding components may associate with a unique DNA sequence and that sequence is protected from digestion and is excised along with the receptor by micrococcal nuclease. So I think that the notion that nuclear associated receptors may not bind to specific DNA sequences may have to be reexamined. I think that the same may hold true for steroid and thyroid hormone receptors although the results in our system may not be as well defined as studies on the glucocorticoid receptor with the mouse mammary tumor viral system.

S. W. Spaulding: With regard to the diametrically opposed data presented by Dr. Jump, one must consider the sensitivity of chromatin confirmation to minor changes in divalent cation concentration, pH, salt concentration, etc. and the way you make your nuclei. I wonder whether you and he have used the same techniques? Also, what about the possibility that you might be obtaining translocation of the receptor due to the conditions you use for extracting and digesting?

H. H. Samuels: We carry out the digestion at a total salt concentration of about 20 mM. Donald Jump may wish to comment, however, the studies which he and Jack Oppenheimer published in *Science* were carried out at a salt concentration of about 120 mM. We find that at 120 mM salt that the receptor sediments at 5.3 S which is close to the sedimentation value which Dr. Jump has reported from his studies with rat liver nuclei. I have not seen the data and Ed Rall may wish to comment but Vera Nikodem has told me that using the same low ionic strength buffer conditions as we have, she identified that micrococcal nuclease excised the receptor from rat liver as a 6.5 S form. Therefore, the ionic conditions may account for some of the differences in sedimentation values. We feel that the difference in sedimentation value is due to the salt dissociation of a component of the 6.5 S receptor which yields a slower sedimenting species at 120 mM salt. Nevertheless, the nuclease digestion patterns are similar, and in both GH$_1$ cells as well as liver the receptor is excised as a species which sediments at about 6 S and as a component of about 12 to 14 S which may represent mononucleosome associated receptor. With regard to your question relating to the difference in the kinetics of release of the receptor of approximately 6 S with the extent of digestion of GH$_1$ cell and liver chromatin it is possible that it is related to the salt concentration. We have not used Dr. Jump's buffer conditions in our cells and I don't know whether he has used our buffer conditions in his digestion studies with liver nuclei.

B. S. McEwen: Do you have any information on how the presence or absence of T3 on the receptor influences its affinity for chromatin or DNA?

H. H. Samuels: In GH$_1$ cells when T3 binds to the receptor there is no change in receptor half-life for up to 10 hours of incubation. However, after 24 hours of T3 incubation there is a 30% shortening of the receptor half-life. This decrease in half-life is not due directly to the binding of T3 to the receptor because T3 fully occupies the receptor in 1 hour and between 1 and 10 hours the receptor half-life is unchanged whether the receptor is occupied by T3 or not. Nevertheless there may be an increase in the affinity of a small fraction of receptor for chromatin. Although we don't know the parameters that modify the half-life, I don't think that there is any good evidence to indicate that T3 modifies the affinity of the majority of the receptor population for chromatin components. In addition, studies which have examined the salt extracted form of the receptor in terms of binding to calf thymus DNA show no effect of T3 on the general affinity of receptor for total DNA. However, T3 might increase the affinity of the receptor for unique DNA sequences which are present at such low abundance that we cannot quantitate this interaction.

J. H. Oppenheimer: Also, relevant in this regard are Dr. Jump's studies which showed no difference in receptor distribution in chromatin from the livers of hypothyroid and euthyroid animals.

J. Larner: I wondered if you had any information on the stoichiometry of binding of T3 to the two forms of the receptor of the 6.4 or 6.5 S in the lower molecular weight 3.8 S.

H. H. Samuels: You mean is there a difference in the affinity of T3 for 6.5 S receptor compared to the receptor obtained by salt extracted?

J. Larner: Not only affinity, but do you have any information as to how many moles of T3 are bound per mole of receptor?

H. H. Samuels: We can't make that measurement because the receptor hasn't been fully purified so we don't know its absolute mass. If Scatchard plots were carried out with purified receptor we would know for each mole of receptor how many moles of T3 bound and that assessment could be made. Therefore, we really can't know whether the receptor has only a single binding site or has multiple binding sites for hormone.

J. Larner: Do you have information with regard to the polypeptide chains in these fractions?

H. H. Samuels: Dr. Angel Pascual, who is a visiting scientist from Spain in my laboratory, has synthesized a radioactive photoaffinity probe which can bind to the receptor in intact cells and upon UV irradiation will covalently crosslink with the receptor. We have used the probe to estimate the molecular weight of the receptor by SDS gel electrophoresis and have identified a major radiolabeled component of 47,000 as well as a minor labeled component of 57,000. Both appear to represent the same receptor protein based on affinity for ligand. We have excluded the possibility that the 47,000 receptor is derived from the 57,000 species as a result of proteolysis or ultraviolet light cleavage. We don't know if the two receptor forms represent some type of postsynthetic modification of the receptor so that it migrates differently on gels. Ultraviolet light can cross-link proteins in physical contact and the 57,000 receptor protein may represent UV crosslinking of the binding component to a subunit or another adjacent protein giving two molecular size forms. Preliminary studies using peptide mapping with specific proteases suggest that both binding components represent the same protein species.

J. Larner: That should allow a definition of the stoichiometry in the future then, stoichiometry of binding. In other words the number of moles of T3 bound per mole of receptor.

H. H. Samuels: Yes it might, but the mapping studies may not be conclusive. For example, tryptic or chymotryptic digestion of the 47,000 molecular weight species followed by SDS gel electrophoresis may result in several radiolabeled peaks. This might suggest the possibility that there are multiple binding sites because if the photoaffinity label crosslinked to a single amino acid component of the receptor then one would expect to identify one radioactive peak with a limit digest. This may not be the case since the receptor binding site may be constructed of amino acids derived from various regions of the primary structure of the receptor molecule. If the receptor protein were sequenced you might find that amino acids 10, 20, and 50 from the N-terminal were organized, as a result of the secondary structure, to form the hormone binding site. There is no way to be sure that upon photolysis the photoaffinity label covalently links with only a single amino acid in the binding site. If this were established you could draw some conclusions about the number of binding sites per receptor molecule. The crosslinking may occur to 4 or 5 possible amino acids which are derived from different regions of a primary structure of the receptor. If this occurred, peptide mapping may generate several radiolabeled peaks with a limit digestion. So I don't think that the photoaffinity label probe will allow us to draw any conclusions about the number of binding sites, and this is a question that will have to await receptor purification to be resolved.

J. E. Rall: Just a comment with respect to the latter point that Dr. Larner raised. Vera Nikodem and Jane Cheng did bromoacetyl affinity labeling of the receptor and basically you get a labeled receptor that has a molecular weight of about 56,000. Furthermore, on SDS mercaptoethanol gel there was a single polypeptide chain. They have been doing some more recent experiments with some slightly different labeling techniques and have run into a certain amount of instability in the receptor in terms of its breaking down into smaller molecular weight fragments. The DNA in mammalian nuclei consist of of about 2 billion base pairs and this means that there are on the order of 10 million nucleosomes.

H. H. Samuels: Well there are about 10 pg of DNA per cell.

J. E. Rall: Three?

H. H. Samuels: Well, it may be different in the GH_1 cell. I once did the calculation and I think I derived approximately 10^7 to 10^8 nucleosomes per cell but I don't remember the exact number which I calculated.

J. E. Rall: There are about a thousand more nucleosomes and hence linkers than there are T3 receptors. This means that only one in the thousand linker regions has a T3 receptor associated with it. Do you think there is some specificity to this association?

H. H. Samuels: Some of these questions have been raised in studies in bacterial systems which have examined the interaction of the lactose repressor protein with lactose operator

DNA sequences in the bacterial genome. The lactose repressor has a very high affinity for lactose operator DNA but it also has a significant affinity for other nonspecific DNA sequences. The relative distribution between binding to the lactose operator region and other DNA sequences is thermodynamically influenced by the concentration of the unique sequences relative to the total mass of nonspecific DNA sequences which are in marked excess. The thyroid hormone receptor is not fixed in chromatin but is rapidly turning over and exists in a dynamic steady-state. Clearly the receptor can interact and probe structures in chromatin and presumably identify components or DNA sequences for which it has a higher affinity. Therefore, we don't know what percentage of total chromatin associated receptor may interact with such putative sequences. An excess of receptor may provide a sufficient concentration of the receptor protein such that unique DNA sequences remain occupied with receptor. This is the explanation that Keith Yamamoto and Bruce Alberts have proposed to explain the apparent excess of steroid hormone receptors relative to the number of genes that are regulated.

J. H. Oppenheimer: Do you suppose that the inhomogeneity in distribution might be related to the proportion of the genomic domain under thyroid hormone control.

H. H. Samuels: It certainly may. In the GH_1 cells there are not many peptides that are under control by thyroid hormone, while in the liver you have shown that there are an abundant number of different peptides under thyroid hormone control. It is possible, for example, that there are domains of chromatin which may have an altered conformation and the receptor has a higher affinity for that structure. Under these conditions the receptor would not cause the altered conformation but its interaction is influenced by a preexisting chromatin conformational change such that the receptor associates with those regions. For the liver such a chromatin conformation may be a more extensive component of the total chromatin compared to GH_1 cell chromatin.

J. Kallos: Two questions. First have you looked for the hormone binding that might affect the chromatin conformation? For instance, have you considered carrying out a similar type of nuclease digestion in the absence of hormone and binding hormone, and do you have any drastic differences in chromatin conformation as seen by any of the probes?

H. H. Samuels: We have done those studies. We have compared short incubation times of 1 hour to very long hormone incubation times such as 24 hours and there is no apparent change in chromatin distribution. All of the studies we have presented have been carried out in intact cells which are incubated with T3 and therefore, any changes in chromatin conformation may occur within seconds. We have carried out studies after *in vitro* binding of T3 to isolated nuclei, and nuclease digestion gives the same general pattern of receptor release that is observed in the intact cell. I think Jack Oppenheimer and Donald Jump may have made the same observation with isolated rat liver nuclei. We have to recognize that we only are assessing gross changes of receptor interaction with chromatin and it does not seem that there are any major changes caused by thyroid hormone incubation in cells. This does not exclude the fact that thyroid hormone may modulate subtle alterations which we cannot resolve with precision. A similar conclusion in the animal also comes from the observation that no major differences in digestion occurred in hypothyroid animals compared to euthyroid animals as just described by Donald Jump.

J. Kallos: Does for instance any polymerase binding studies show a difference in chromatin conformation?

H. H. Samuels: We did those studies years ago and I had no confidence in them so we never published our results. RNA polymerase binding studies are complicated to interpret because we find that if you take the same cells and homogenize them with two different homogenizing tubes even with the same pestle that we obtain different results. Slight differences in the clearance or environment of the pestle and homogenizing tubes are such that subtle differences in shearing of chromatin likely occurs and influences the RNA polymerase titrations. The differences we observed are in the range of 5 to 10% and there was too much variability for us to have sufficient confidence to publish those results.

W. W. Leavitt: Have you looked at the role that SH groups play in the interaction of receptor with DNA and chromatin? The reason I ask is that Dr. Richard MacDonald and I have been studying activation of progesterone receptor, and SH groups are particularly important for the activation and DNA binding of this and other steroid receptors.

H. H. Samuels: In the intact cell we know nothing about whether the nuclear receptor is in an oxidized or reduced state with regard to SH groups. If one attempts to extract the receptor from nuclei by salt approximately 50% of the receptor can be solubilized with $0.4 M$ KCl. The efficiency of extraction is increased by the presence of 1 to 2 mM mercaptoethanol or dithiothreitol. So clearly, there may be some effect on the reduction of disulfide bonds that may play an important role in the interaction of the receptor with chromatin. It may be that the receptor can form a disulfide bond with some other adjacent protein which retards extraction. Reduction of those bonds will result in an increase in the efficiency of extraction by high salt conditions. Nevertheless, although dithiothreitol or mercaptoethanol will increase the efficiency of extraction they are not absolutely required to extract a reasonable percentage of the total nuclear receptor.

A. L. Barofsky: You are looking at cells that derive from a tissue that normally responds to thyroid hormone in a feedback regulatory mechanism and presumably contains receptors appropriate for that response. I wonder if you have any information or could speculate about a possible role for the receptor that you are examining in feedback regulation of the pituitary cell by thyroid hormone.

H. H. Samuels: The cells we have examined are a well differentiated somatotrophic tumor cell line. Studies that have been carried out in intact animals on the induction of growth hormone show that the kinetics of induction are identical in the GH_1 cell culture system as in the somatotroph *in vivo*. I think the question you are addressing relates to the inhibition of TSH secretion by thyroid hormone and there are cell culture systems where this has been examined. Dr. Marvin Gershengorn at NYU has been studying cultured mouse thyrotrophic tumor cells which synthesize TSH. Unfortunately it is difficult to study the kinetics of TSH secretion in these cells. It has been suggested that the inhibition of TSH secretion by thyroid hormone can be prevented by inhibiting protein or RNA synthesis suggesting that thyroid hormone induces some factor which inhibits TSH secretion. I think this was suggested in a paper by Bower's group a number of years ago. GH_1 cells also synthesize prolactin and thyroid hormone can inhibit the rate of prolactin production. With steroid hormones, in addition to responses that are stimulated, there are several responses which are inhibited. The inhibition of effects by steroid hormones can result from a decrease in the accumulation of a specific mRNA molecule or from the induction of a protein which, for example, inhibits mRNA translation. I think the mechanism by which thyroid hormone inhibits TSH secretion is highly important because it clearly plays a critical role in controlling and modulating the maintenance of the normal thyroidal state. Little is known about the mechanism by which thyroid hormone inhibits TSH secretion except to say that there is good evidence that the inhibition appears to be mediated by the interaction of thyroid hormone with the nuclear receptor in the thyrotroph.

K. Sterling: I have a comment and a question. The comment is that I don't think it is any detraction from the excellence of these studies to point out that there are *other* receptors for thyroid hormone in the cell, namely, in the plasma membrane and the mitochondria and that these exert their physiological functions despite complete blockade of protein synthesis by cyclohexamide. Now the question: as I understand it, Eberhard and Baxter have evidence that corehistone tends to stabilize these nuclear receptors for T3; therefore could these digestion fragments have any contribution by histone, or have you ruled that out?

H. H. Samuels: With regard to your comment, I don't think that those investigators studying the biology of the nuclear receptor and its possible action are biased in excluding other possible pathways of thyroid hormone action. There are binding components in other cell organelles that have been reported. Whether or not the interaction of hormone with those components elicits physiological responses of significant magnitude for them to function as receptors remains open to question. Regarding your question, one problem is that there is no way of determining whether there is any histone present as a component of the 6.5 S receptor since it has not been purified. There are approximately 15,000 receptors per cell nucleus and approximately 70% of those can be released as a 6.5 S form by micrococcal nuclease digestion. Analysis of the protein composition in the region of the gradient where the 6.5 S receptor sediments demonstrates a number of abundant chromatin proteins varying from H1 histone to the high mobility group proteins. The problem is that one cannot conclude whether they are associated with the 6.5 S receptor because they are highly abundant while the 6.5 S receptor is a very low abundant species. The fact that these proteins sediment in the same region of the gradient does not allow us to conclude that histones or other abundant chromatin proteins are a component of the 6.5 S receptor. Therefore, we do not know whether or not histone is associated with the 6.5 S receptor which is released from chromatin by micrococcal nuclease digestion.

Characteristics of the Guanine Nucleotide-Binding Regulatory Component of Adenylate Cyclase

MURRAY D. SMIGEL, JOHN K. NORTHUP, AND ALFRED G. GILMAN

Department of Pharmacology, University of Texas Health Science Center at Dallas, Dallas, Texas

I. Introduction

Cyclic AMP was discovered more than two decades ago by Earl Sutherland and Theodore Rall, and much of the basic phenomenology of adenylate cyclase—the enzyme responsible for synthesis of the cyclic nucleotide—was described in a classical series of papers that was published in 1962 (Sutherland *et al.*, 1962; Rall and Sutherland, 1962; Murad *et al.*, 1962; Klainer *et al.*, 1962). Nearly a decade passed, however, before Rodbell and his colleagues (1971) described an additional crucial property of hormone-sensitive adenylate cyclase—the fact that low concentrations of guanine nucleotides (particularly GTP) are essential for observation of the stimulatory effects of hormones on enzymatic activity.

We now realize that hormone-sensitive adenylate cyclase is a multiprotein enzyme complex (Ross and Gilman, 1980). Its activity is regulated by various hormones, neurotransmitters, and autacoids when the components of the system are properly embedded and organized in the matrix of the plasma membrane. At least three proteins (or categories of proteins) are known to be essential: receptors with externally oriented ligand binding sites; a catalytic protein (C), responsible for the synthesis of cyclic AMP from ATP; and a guanine nucleotide-binding regulatory protein, which we term G/F. G/F serves as an essential coupling factor between the receptor and the catalyst and as an activator of the catalyst. In the absence of G/F, the activity of C (in the presence of MgATP as substrate) is essentially nil.

This model of hormone-sensitive adenylate cyclase evolved independently from work in two laboratories. Pfeuffer (1977) demonstrated that a putative guanine nucleotide-binding protein could be partially resolved from the catalytic component of adenylate cyclase by affinity chromatography with GTP-Sepharose. Enzymatic activity that was not adsorbed by the affinity support could only be weakly stimulated by guanine nucleotide

601

analogs; this activity was partially restored by addition of a catalytically inactive fraction that was eluted from the column with a guanine nucleotide.

In the interim, Bourne and co-workers (1975) had isolated a genetic variant of the murine S49 lymphoma cell line that was phenotypically deficient in adenylate cyclase activity (cyc⁻). Ross and Gilman (1977a) then developed techniques for the reconstitution of hormone-sensitive enzymatic activity in membranes of this variant and subsequently demonstrated that the cyc⁻ phenotype was due to a deficiency of G/F rather than C (Ross and Gilman, 1977b; Ross et al., 1978). These studies established that G/F was needed for the expression of the activity of C in the presence of its physiological substrate, MgATP, identified G/F as a site of action of both guanine nucleotides and fluoride, and demonstrated that G/F was required for transmission of stimulatory signals from receptors to C.

Reconstitution of adenylate cyclase activity in cyc⁻ membranes also provided a method for the quantitative assay of the regulatory protein, G/F. Given this capability and the greater stability of G/F compared to C, purification of the regulatory protein was undertaken. In this article we would like to describe some of the techniques, results, and theories that have evolved from the work of members of our group who have undertaken the study of G/F. A review of considerably broader scope has been published recently by Ross and Gilman (1980).

II. Purification and Physical Properties of G/F

As mentioned, membranes derived from the cyc⁻ cell line provide a convenient means for assaying the activity of G/F. These membranes contain the catalytic protein (C) and competent hormone receptors but lack functional G/F. In a recent publication we have described the details of the execution and interpretation of this reconstitution assay (Sternweis et al., 1981). We note here that the degree of reconstituted adenylate cyclase activity observed depends on the relative proportions of G/F and C in the assay and on the choice of activating ligand and detergent used. We have developed procedures for the purification of G/F from a number of disparate sources, including plasma membranes derived from rabbit liver, turkey erythrocytes, and human erythrocytes (Table I). The procedures include extraction of G/F activity from the membranes with sodium cholate and chromatography of the extracts in cholate and sodium fluoride on DEAE Sephacel, Ultrogel AcA-34, and heptylamine Sepharose. The protein is then diluted and again absorbed onto DEAE. The detergent is switched to Lubrol 12A9, and the activity is eluted from the column with salt. Finally, protein is bound to hydroxylapatite, deactivated by removal

TABLE I

Purification of the Regulatory Component of Adenylate Cyclase

Step	Protein (mg)	Total activity (nmol/min)	Recovery (%)	Specific activity[a] (nmol/min/mg)
A. Rabbit liver				
Cholate extract of membranes	7000	8500	100	1.2
DEAE Sephacel	380	6100	72	16
AcA34	38	3900	46	103
Heptylamine- Sepharose	2.4	2500	29	1040
DEAE Sephacel	0.77	1240	15	1600
B. Turkey erythrocyte				
Cholate extract of membranes	2000	6800	100	3.4
DEAE Sephacel	305	5220	77	17
AcA34	25	4200	62	168
Heptylamine- Sepharose	4.3	2710	40	631
DEAE Sephacel	0.57	1220	18	2140
Hydroxyapatite	0.2	680	10	3400

[a] Measured in the presence of fluoride; higher values are obtained with GTPγS.

of fluoride, eluted with phosphate, and desalted by a final gel filtration. The procedures result in the isolation of near milligram quantities of pure G/F in a form that is stable to storage over a period of months at −80°C. Details of the purification procedures for rabbit liver and turkey erythrocyte G/F have recently been published (Northup *et al.*, 1980; Sternweis *et al.*, 1981; Hanski *et al.*, 1981).

The G/F isolated from rabbit liver shows, by SDS polyacrylamide gel electrophoresis, prominent bands at apparent molecular weights of 52,000, 45,000, and 35,000, while that isolated from turkey erythrocytes shows peptides only at 45,000 and 35,000 daltons. The 52,000-dalton band from liver and the 45,000-dalton bands from liver and turkey prove to be substrates for cholera toxin-mediated ADP ribosylation (Northup *et al.*, 1980; Hanski *et al.*, 1981). An almost pure protein of molecular weight 35,000 arises during purification as an early eluting species on the second DEAE column. This protein appears to be identical, by the criteria of its behavior during isoelectric focusing and protease digestion, to the 35,000-dalton subunit of the active G/F complex. We refer to this early eluting protein as "free 35K protein." Its biochemical behavior will be discussed in the following sections.

The hydrodynamic behavior of purified G/F has been studied by gel filtration and sedimentation in cholate and Lubrol-containing solutions. Emanuel Hanski has determined that the G/F from turkey erythrocytes behaves like a particle of molecular weight 80,000 (Hanski *et al.*, 1981). When the G/F is incubated with GTPγS or NaF and hydrodynamic behavior is measured under conditions that maintain activation by these ligands, the apparent molecular weight is reduced to ~50,000. Measurements in H₂O and D₂O show that this change is not due to alteration of the partial specific volume of the particle. Similar results are obtained with G/F derived from liver (Sternweis *et al.*, 1981). These results are consistent with the view that G/F is a heterodimer with 35,000- and 45,000-dalton subunits. They also suggest that incubation of G/F with guanine nucleotide analogs or fluoride is accompanied by a dissociation of these subunits.

III. Phenomenology of Activation of G/F

A. ACTIVATION BY GUANINE NUCLEOTIDE ANALOGS

Experiments with crude preparations of G/F indicated that it could be "activated" by incubation with certain guanine nucleotide analogs or fluoride (Howlett *et al.*, 1979). By activation we mean the production of a state of G/F that is capable of reconstituting a high level of MgATP-dependent adenylate cyclase activity (when combined with C) in the absence of an effective concentration of free ligand. Shortly after the procedures for the purification of liver G/F were established, John Northup began to study the kinetics of its interaction with GTPγS and Gpp(NH)p. In these experiments a relatively concentrated solution of G/F was incubated with the activating guanine nucleotide and Mg²⁺. At various times, aliquots were removed and diluted with enough GTP (a nonactivating ligand) to stop any further activation. Sets of tubes representing time courses of activation were then accumulated on ice, reconstituted with cyc⁻ membranes, and assayed with an adenylate cyclase reaction mixture that did not contain any activating ligands. The activated state proved to be stable, and the carryover of stimulatory ligands into the assay stage proved negligible.

The activation process is slow; liver G/F typically requires 120 minutes at 30°C in 30 mM Mg²⁺ and 10 μM GTPγS to achieve optimal reconstitutive activity (Sternweis *et al.*, 1981). Hanski's studies of the activation of turkey erythrocyte G/F show an even more pronounced requirement for Mg²⁺, with 100–200 mM needed for optimal activation (Hanski *et al.*, 1981).

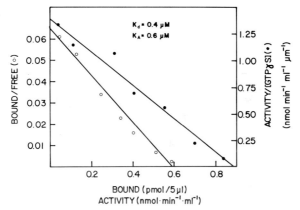

FIG. 1. Comparison of activation of G/F by GTPγS with nucleotide binding to the regulatory protein. G/F (4 μg/ml) was incubated with 0.03–10 μM [³⁵S]GTPγS and 30 mM MgCl₂ at 30°C. Aliquots were withdrawn at several times and diluted into 100 μM GTP for subsequent assay of adenylate cyclase or were filtered on S&S B85 membranes to assess binding of [³⁵S]GTPγS. Steady-state levels of binding and activation were obtained from the time courses, and these values were used for the Scatchard (○) or Hoffstee (●) analysis of binding and activation, respectively.

As shown in Fig. 1, increasing the concentration of the guanine nucleotide analog caused a hyperbolic increase of the level of activation of G/F reached at steady state. The data are consistent with the dependence expected for a reversible binding equilibrium:

$$E + N \rightleftharpoons EN$$

with a dissociation constant

$$K_d = E \cdot N/EN$$

When the activating guanine nucleotide was mixed with a variety of nonactivating nucleotides (e.g., GTP), competitive inhibition of the activation process was observed (Table II).

In order to measure the interaction of G/F with guanine nucleotide directly, John Northup utilized [³⁵S]GTPγS as a radioligand. The ligand–protein complex is effectively trapped on a cellulose nitrate membrane. The steady-state binding of [³⁵S]GTPγS to G/F appears to be a simple saturable process, characterized by a dissociation constant that is in good agreement with that determined from the studies of the activation reaction (Fig. 1; Table II).

The ability of other nucleotides to compete for [³⁵S]GTPγS binding sites has been compared with their capacity to activate G/F (GPP[NH]P) or to inhibit GTPγS-mediated activation (GTP, GDP, etc.). Again, the

TABLE II

Nucleotide Specificity of G/F [a]

Nucleotide	K_a (μM)	K_i (μM)	K_D (μM)
GTPγS	0.75 ± 0.39	—	0.71 ± 0.33
Gpp(NH)p	5.0 ± 1.7	—	4.7 ± 1.5
GTP	—	3.6 ± 1.9	1.3 ± 0.8
GDP	—	13 ± 8	3.0 ± 0.5
ITP	—	200 ± 100	220 ± 20

[a] For nucleotides that activate G/F (GTPγS, Gpp[NH]p) K_a is the half maximal concentration for such activation. The other nucleotides were tested for their ability to inhibit activation by GTPγS (K_i). K_D was obtained by Scatchard analysis of [35S]GTPγS binding or by assessment of competition for such binding. Values of K_i and $K_D > 1000 \mu M$ were obtained for GMP, ATP, XTP, UTP, CTP, NAD, cAMP, and cGMP.

correlation is excellent (Table II). These studies indicate that the binding site that is measured is the same as that responsible for activation of G/F.

The number of guanine nucleotide binding sites on G/F is an issue of considerable interest, since there is the possibility of multiple sites of action of GTP. These studies are complicated by the existence of denatured G/F in our purified preparation. There is, however, a good correlation between the capacity to bind [35S]GTPγS and the reconstitutive specific activity of the protein (Fig. 2). The best preparation of G/F that has been studied had a specific activity of approximately 15 μmol min^{-1} mg^{-1} (when activated with GTPγS) and bound 1 mol [35S]GTPγS per mol protein (assumed $M_r = 80,000$). These data suggest the existence of but one binding site for [35S]GTPγS on G/F.

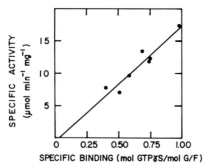

FIG. 2. Correlation between specific activity and binding capacity of G/F. Different preparations of G/F were assayed for reconstitutive activity after activation with GTPγS or for [35S]GTPγS binding activity.

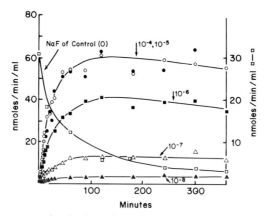

FIG. 3. Time courses of activation of G/F by various concentrations of GTPγS. G/F (8 μg/ml) was incubated at 30°C for the indicated times in a Lubrol-containing buffer with 10 mM MgCl₂ and the indicated concentrations of GTPγS. At the indicated times, aliquots were withdrawn, diluted into buffer containing 100 μM GTP, reconstituted with cyc⁻ membranes, and assayed for adenylate cyclase activity. The incubation performed in the absence of GTPγS was assayed in the presence of 10 mM fluoride (□).

Several anomalies were soon found to complicate this pleasingly simple story. Attempts to reverse the activated state by dilution of G/F into warm GTP-containing solutions were not successful. Furthermore, attempts to add additional GTPγS to suboptimally activated G/F showed little or no increases in activity. As shown in Fig. 3 and Table III, measurement of the variation of the rates of activation with nucleotide concentration revealed

TABLE III

Variation of Fractional Activation Rate Constant (R)
with Concentrations of GTPγS [a]

GTPγS (M)	V_{inf} (nmol min⁻¹ ml⁻¹)	$R(\times 10^2)$ (min⁻¹)
10^{-8}	1.94(1.61–2.23)	2.37(1.35–3.53)
10^{-7}	11.1(10.2–11.9)	3.22(2.58–3.93)
10^{-6}	37.5(35.4–39.4)	3.66(3.10–4.26)
10^{-5}	56.9(53.9–59.8)	4.63(3.95–5.34)
10^{-4}	55.6(53.0–58.1)	4.46(3.84–5.12)

[a] Data from Fig. 3 were fit by a Gauss–Newton algorithm to a single exponential (see Section III). V_{inf} is the reconstitutive activity of G/F calculated at infinite time and R is the exponential rate constant $(a)/V_{inf}$. Ranges for the 95% confidence limits are shown in parentheses.

more difficulties; the rate was independent of the nucleotide concentration over several orders of magnitude around the apparent K_d. If we assume a binding equilibrium as proposed above and if the total concentration of enzyme is well below that of nucleotide:

$$E_T = E + EN \ll N_T = N + EN$$

then, at a time t, we expect:

$$EN(t) = EN_{inf}(1 - e^{-at})$$

where

$$a = k_1 N_T + k_{-1}$$

and k_1 and k_{-1} are the microscopic rate constants that characterize the equilibrium constant K_d. Thus, we have an initial rate of activation:

$$\left. \frac{dEN(t)}{dt} \right|_{t=0} = (k_1 N_T + k_{-1}) EN_{inf}$$

and we have a fractional rate of activation, R, given by:

$$R = \frac{1}{EN_{inf}} \cdot \left. \frac{dEN(t)}{dt} \right|_{t=0} = k_1 N_T + k_{-1}$$

Since no reversal was seen, $k_{-1} \ll k_1 N_T$; thus we expect $R = k_1 N_T$. This clearly is not what is observed (Table III).

Faced with these phenomena, we began to look at other models of the activation process. Introduction of an irreversible step after binding of nucleotide obviously supplies the observed lack of reversibility of the activated state, but this fails to explain the graded nature of the increase in steady-state activity with increasing concentrations of nucleotide. The data mentioned above suggested the need to include both an irreversible activating step, with rate constant k^*, and irreversible denaturation of the unliganded protein, characterized by rate constant k^+, as shown in the following diagram.

$$E + N \underset{}{\overset{K_d}{\rightleftharpoons}} EN \overset{k^*}{\rightarrow} EN^*$$
$$k^+ \downarrow$$
$$E^+$$

Conservation of total enzyme is expressed by

$$E_T = E + EN + EN^* + E^+$$

where E^+ is the concentration of denatured G/F and EN^* is that of the irreversibly activated species. If we make the steady-state assumption that k_1N and $k_{-1} \gg k^*$ and k^+ then:

$$\frac{dEN}{dt} = k_1N(E) - (k_{-1} + k^*)EN = 0$$

$$(EN)_{s.s} = \frac{k_1N(E_T - E^+ - EN^*)}{k_{-1} + k^* + k_1N}$$

$$\frac{dEN^*}{dt} = \frac{k^*k_1N(E_T - E^+ - EN^*)}{k_{-1} + k^* + k_1N}$$

and

$$\frac{dE^+}{dt} = \frac{k^+(k_{-1} + k^*)}{k_{-1} + k^* + k_1N} (E_T - E^+ - EN^*)$$

Assuming that there is no activated and no denatured enzyme at $t = 0$, then the time course of activation is given by

$$EN^*(t) = \frac{k^*k_1N}{k^+(k_{-1} + k^*)} E^+(t)$$

$$EN^*(t) = \frac{k^*k_1N(E_T)}{k^*k_1N + k^+(k_{-1} + k^*)} (1 - e^{-at})$$

where

$$a = \frac{k^*k_1N + k^+(k_{-1} + k^*)}{k_{-1} + k^* + k_1N}$$

and, at $t = $ infinity, we have the steady-state level of activation

$$(EN^*)_{s.s} = E_T \bigg/ \left(1 + \frac{k_{-1}}{k_1N}\left[\frac{k^+}{k^*} + \frac{k^+}{k_{-1}}\right]\right)$$

Since we have assumed that $k^+ \ll k_{-1}$ and letting

$$K_{eq1} = k_{-1}/k_1$$

$$(EN^*)_{s.s} = E_T \bigg/ \left(1 + \frac{K_{eq1}}{N} \cdot \frac{k^+}{k^*}\right)$$

This expression gives the observed hyperbolic dependence of the extent of activation upon concentration of nucleotide. This hyperbola is characterized by a $K_{apparent} = K_{eq1} (k^+/k^*)$, which is altered from the binding constant by the ratio of the rates of denaturation and activation. Examining the predicted initial rates of activation, we find:

$$\frac{dEN^*}{dt}\bigg|_{t=0} = \frac{k^*k_1NE_T}{k_{-1} + k^* + k_1N} = k^*E_T \bigg/ \left(\frac{K_{eq1}}{N} + \frac{k^*}{k_1N} + 1\right)$$

Assuming $k^* \ll k_1 N$ and using our expression for the extent of activation, we compute the fractional rate of activation, R, as

$$R = \frac{1}{(EN^*)_{s.s}} \cdot \frac{dEN^*}{dt}\bigg|_{t=0} = k^* \left[1 + \frac{K_{eq1}}{N} \cdot \frac{k^+}{k^*} \right] \bigg/ \left[1 + \frac{K_{eq1}}{N} \right]$$

Thus, if the rate of activation is approximately equal to the rate of denaturation, then R will be independent of the concentration of nucleotide. To test these ideas, measurements of the rate of denaturation of G/F in detergent solution were undertaken. They revealed that the thermal denaturation of G/F was a distinctly non-first-order process; the rapid component was characterized by a rate constant roughly comparable in magnitude to that of the activation rate constant measured under similar conditions. These data will be discussed in more detail in a later section.

B. ACTIVATION OF G/F BY FLUORIDE

Work by Paul Sternweis on the mechanism of interaction of G/F with fluoride has shown that incubation of purified G/F in the presence of F^- and Mg^{2+} alone is insufficient to cause activation of the protein. Months of inconsistent and anomalous results led to clear documentation that various experimental manipulations introduced cofactors that were necessary for the activation of G/F by fluoride. Three sources of such factors have been identified: tap water, disposable glass test tubes, and a variety of commercial preparations of nucleotides. There is little activation of G/F by fluoride when glass distilled water is used, experiments are performed in plastic or washed glass tubes, and there is no nucleotide present (Fig. 4). Introduction of tap water, extracts of test tubes, or certain nucleotides (e.g., ATP) markedly facilitates activation of G/F by F^- and Mg^{2+}.

While the identity of the active cofactors remains unknown, certain facts are clear. Nucleotide per se is not responsible; active materials can be resolved from ATP. Factors derived from nucleotide preparations and from glass test tubes appear to be inorganic, based on their resistance to ashing and to acid or alkaline hydrolysis. Identification of such factors should provide insight into the mechanism of activation of adenylate cyclase by fluoride—long a mystery.

C. ACTIVATION OF G/F BY ADP-RIBOSYLATION

The 45,000- and 52,000-dalton subunits of purified rabbit liver G/F and the 45,000-dalton subunit of turkey and human erythrocyte G/F can be labeled (presumably ADP-ribosylated) by incubation with activated cholera toxin and $[^{32}P]NAD^+$. However, in initial experiments Leonard Schleifer showed that it was necessary to reconstitute the purified pro-

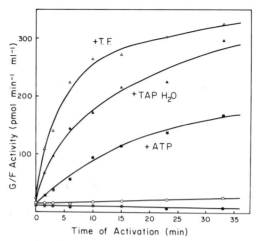

FIG. 4. Requirement for cofactors for activation of G/F by fluoride. G/F was incubated in the absence of NaF and Mg^{2+} (●) or in the presence of 10 mM NaF and 10 mM Mg^{2+} (○,■,▲,△). The following additions were also included as indicated: 1 mM ATP (■); 70% (v/v) tap water (▲); an aqueous extract of disposable 13 × 100-mm glass test tubes (△; 0.5 tube equivalent). After incubation for the times shown reaction mixtures were diluted, reconstituted with cyc⁻ membranes, and assayed for adenylate cyclase activity.

tein into cyc⁻ plasma membranes; in the absence of such membranes, almost no labeling was observed (Northup *et al.*, 1980). Further experiments by Schleifer and Richard Kahn indicated that this requirement for cyc⁻ membranes could be met by the inclusion of cholate extracts of cyc⁻ or of wild type S49 membranes, and that a protease-sensitive, thermolabile factor present in such extracts appeared to be essential. (This putative protein has been termed ADP-ribosylation factor or ARF.) The activity of such a factor can be detected either by monitoring the extent of incorporation of ³²P into the protein in the presence of cholera toxin and [³²P]NAD or by measurement of the altered activity of the modified G/F. As previously reported, there is a marked enhancement of GTP-stimulated adenylate cyclase activity when G/F is ADP-ribosylated with NAD⁺ and cholera toxin (Levinson and Blume, 1977; Ross *et al.*, 1977). The effect of the factor on the rate of modification of G/F by the toxin is shown in Fig. 5. The time course represents the length of treatment of G/F with toxin, NAD⁺, GTP, and partially purified factor before a 20-fold dilution was performed to terminate the modification reaction. The diluted samples were then reconstituted with cyc⁻ membranes and the GTP-dependent adenylate cyclase activity was assayed.

Gel filtration of a cholate extract of wild type membranes, which contains both G/F and the factor necessary for ADP-ribosylation of G/F by cholera toxin, indicates that the factor behaves as a monodisperse species

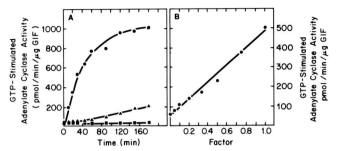

FIG. 5. Effect of ADP-ribosylation factor (ARF) on covalent modification of G/F by cholera toxin. (A) G/F and NAD⁺ were incubated without toxin (■), with toxin (▲), or with toxin and a partially purified preparation of ARF (●) for the indicated times. Reconstitution and assessment of GTP-stimulated adenylate cyclase activity followed. (B) Effect of varying concentrations of ARF during a 20-minute incubation. The highest concentration of factor shown (1.0) represents 5.5 μg/ml protein.

with a Stokes radius of approximately 3.2 nm (corresponding to a globular protein with a molecular weight of 50,000). The factor is clearly resolvable from G/F on this column. The significance of this factor is not known. Assessment of its possible contribution to the physiological function of hormone-sensitive adenylate cyclase will require resolution from the other components of the system. Attempts to obtain factor-deficient S49 cell mutants have, to date, failed.

IV. Evidence for Dissociation of Subunits upon Activation of G/F

Since G/F can be activated by a variety of agents, one is lead to wonder whether there is an underlying event common to all such processes. The technical advantages of studying the guanine nucleotide analog-mediated activation of G/F (slow reversibility and availability of radiolabeled re-agents) and our underlying interests in the physiological activation of the enzyme by hormones and GTP have prompted us to work extensively on this pathway of activation of G/F. The remainder of this article will attempt to describe our progress and plans in that pursuit.

During the course of his studies of the activation of G/F by guanine nucleotides, Northup made many attempts to reverse the Gpp(NH)p- and GTPγS-activated states. Experiments usually involved incubation of a relatively concentrated solution of G/F with Mg^{2+} and an activating ligand (the activation phase) and then dilution of an aliquot into a GTP-containing solution in order to stop the activation and/or to initiate its reversal. This protocol, as mentioned above, was uniformly unsuccessful in reversing the activated state. In an experiment comparing the effect of removal of nucleotide by dilution with that achieved by gel filtration, deactivation was observed in the gel-filtered sample. This result and the highly suggestive changes observed in the rate of sedimentation of G/F upon activation led us to formulate a model in which activation was a result of a dissociation of the subunits of G/F. Since SDS gel electrophoresis of G/F indicated the presence of peptides of molecular weights 35,000 and 45,000 (ignoring the presence of variable amounts of a 52,000-dalton peptide in liver G/F), we speculated that these were the two interacting species:

$$AB + N \xrightleftharpoons{K_{eq1}} ABN \xrightleftharpoons{K_{eq2}} AN + B$$

Demonstration of the labeling of a 45,000-dalton peptide by a guanine nucleotide photoaffinity label (Cassel and Pfeuffer, 1978) led us to believe that the A subunit was the 45,000-dalton peptide and the B subunit the 35,000-dalton peptide. The activated species that associates with C is hypothesized to be AN, corresponding to the EN* form of G/F discussed above. In this model the lack of reversal of the activated state upon dilution is blamed on the dilution of the B subunit (coincident with the dilution of the nucleotide) and a very slow rate constant for the dissociation of AN.

In an attempt to find evidence for the dissociation of the subunits of G/F in detergent solution, we measured the kinetics of the thermal denaturation of rabbit liver G/F as a function of protein concentration. The dilute enzyme proved to be quite labile at 30°C in 10 mM Mg^{2+} ($t_{1/2} \sim 5$ minutes), whereas concentrated solutions of G/F were markedly more stable. As shown in Fig. 6, stabilization of dilute G/F could be achieved by the addition of the free 35K protein isolated during the purification of G/F.

If the binding of an activating guanine nucleotide to G/F causes a dissociation of its subunits and if this dissociation is the slow step in the none too rapid activation of the protein, then a dilute solution of the protein might well be activated more rapidly by GTPγS or Gpp(NH)p. This proved to be true. Further, free 35K protein retards the rate of activation of dilute G/F (Fig. 7). These results suggested that the activation and denaturation of G/F could be represented as follows:

$$AB + N \underset{k_{-1}}{\overset{k_1}{\rightleftharpoons}} ABN \qquad K_{eq1} = \frac{(AB)N}{ABN} = \frac{k_{-1}}{k_1}$$

$$k_4 \Big\updownarrow k_{-4} \qquad k_{-2} \Big\updownarrow k_2 \qquad K_{eq2} = \frac{(AN)B}{ABN} = \frac{k_{-2}}{k_2}$$

$$A + B + N \underset{k_3}{\overset{k_{-3}}{\rightleftharpoons}} AN + B \qquad K_{eq3} = \frac{(A)(N)}{AN} = \frac{k_{-3}}{k_3}$$

$$k^+ \Big\downarrow$$

$$A^+ \qquad\qquad\qquad K_{eq4} = \frac{(A)(B)}{AB} = \frac{k_{-4}}{k_4}$$

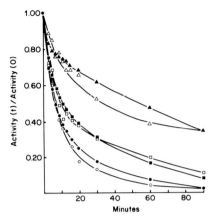

FIG. 6.   Time course of decay of G/F activity. G/F (0.16 μg/ml) was incubated at 30°C in a Lubrol-containing solution with 10 mM MgCl$_2$ and either 0 (○), 2.5 (□), or 5.0 (△) μg/ml of free 35K protein. At the times indicated aliquots were withdrawn and G/F activity was determined by reconstitution with cyc$^-$ membranes and assessment of adenylate cyclase activity. Closed symbols represent simulations of the inactivation kinetics using methods and parameters described in the text.

In a cyclic model the free energies summed around the loop must add to zero, implying that

$$K_{eq1}K_{eq4} = K_{eq2}K_{eq3}$$

Thus, if the binding of N causes dissociation, i.e., if

$$K_{eq2} > K_{eq4}$$

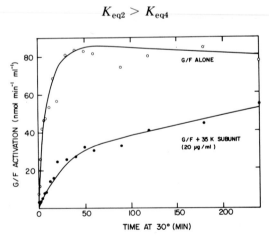

FIG. 7.   Effect of the 35,000-dalton subunit of G/F on the rate of activation of G/F by GTPγS. G/F was activated with GTPγS as in Fig. 3 in the presence or absence of added 35K protein, as indicated.

then

$$K_{eq1} > K_{eq3}$$

This implies that the free A subunit should have a higher affinity for the nucleotide than does the AB complex. The apparent irreversibility of the activation observed experimentally is rationalized by assuming poor affinity of AN for B, low concentration of B after dilution of N, and tight binding of N to A. The model then predicts that addition of B subunit (presumed to be free 35K protein) should cause reversal of the activated state. Recent work in this laboratory has confirmed this prediction.

To summarize the evidence for this model and the identification of the B subunit as the free 35K protein, we note the following phenomena:

1. The decrease in the sedimentation rate and hydrodynamic molecular weight of G/F upon activation of the protein.

2. The labilization of G/F to thermal denaturation upon dilution of the protein.

3. The stabilization of the activity by addition of free 35K protein.

4. The acceleration of GTPγS- and Gpp(NH)p-mediated activation of G/F upon dilution of G/F.

5. The retardation of the activation upon addition of free 35K protein.

6. The reversal of the guanine nucleotide analog-induced activated state by the addition of free 35K protein.

7. The absence of reconstitutive or guanine nucleotide-binding activity of free 35K protein.

V. Estimation of Parameters

The study of adenylate cyclase has affected scientists in a variety of ways. Some admit to feelings of despair, while others retreat from reality, as evidenced by a need to build elaborate models. The literature abounds with reasons for this state of affairs; prominent among them are the inability to solubilize, let alone purify, a hormonally sensitive adenylate cyclase from any source, the variety of stimulators and inhibitors known to alter enzymatic activity in various tissues and preparations, and the wide range of parameters (pH, metal ion type and concentration, temperature, and viscosity, to name but a few) amenable to experimental manipulation. Given these difficulties, almost all workers in the field eventually succumb to bouts of kinetics; these may be brief, lasting only a few months, but, when severe, may develop into an end stage disease. We are certainly not immune to this syndrome. Since the prognosis is uncertain, many may wish to pass over this section of the article.

Heartened by the qualitative success of the model presented above in rationalizing a number of the more obvious features of the activation and denaturation of G/F, we were encouraged to try to develop experimental procedures and analytical approaches that would allow us to determine the equilibrium and kinetic constants needed for a quantitative understanding of its behavior. A number of questions might be resolved by this approach. Do various guanine nucleotide analogs activate G/F to differing extents and at differing rates because of differences in their intrinsic affinities for G/F or do they have differing efficacies in inducing dissociation of subunits? How does activation by fluoride differ from that caused by guanine nucleotides? What is the role of Mg^{2+} in the activation and denaturation processes? How similar are Mg^{2+}- and hormone-stimulated pathways in the activation of G/F? These and other questions of mechanism require a more detailed determination of the parameters underlying the activation process.

A quantitative model of the kinetics of denaturation of unliganded G/F in detergent solution seemed a good place to begin, since no nucleotide binding constants come into play. Our working model for the subunit associations becomes

$$AB \underset{k_4}{\overset{k_{-4}}{\rightleftharpoons}} A + B \overset{k^+}{\longrightarrow} A^+ + B$$

where

$$K_{eq4} = A \cdot B/AB = k_{-4}/k_4$$
$$E_T = AB + A + A^+$$
$$B = A + A^+ + B_e$$

and B_e represents the concentration of free 35K protein added to a solution of G/F. The differential equations characterizing the model become

$$dA/dt = k_{-4}(E_T - A - A^+) - k_4(A + A^+ + B_e)A - k^+A$$
$$dA^+/dt = k^+A$$

At time zero we assume that there is no denatured A subunit and that the concentration of free A is given by

$$A(0) = fE_T$$

Unfortunately, f is not known, since it probably is a function of $[Mg^{2+}]$ and temperature, the variables whose alterations define the start of the time course. The experiments are generally done with very dilute solutions of G/F, such that f is presumably relatively large.

Examination of the time course of decay of G/F activity at a variety of concentrations of added free 35K protein reveals that the initial rates of denaturation are almost independent of the level of B_e, while the amount of activity remaining after 45 minutes is altered dramatically (Fig. 6). This is understandable if k_4B is slow when compared to k^+, the rate constant for denaturation. This would imply that when G/F is diluted into a solution containing $[Mg^{2+}]$, a considerable amount of A is denatured before the AB complex can form. Thus, the initial rate of denaturation is a good measure of the rate constant for the process. The rate of decay of activity in the presence of high concentrations of free 35K protein is sensitive to the rate constant for dissociation of the complex, and the variation of the amount of activity remaining at long times reflects the equilibrium constant, given by the ratio k_{-4}/k_4.

Numerical solution of the differential equations governing the model allows assignment of the following values for the kinetic and equilibrium constants:

$$k^+ = 0.17/\text{minute}$$
$$k_{-4} = 0.030/\text{minute}$$
$$k_4 = 2.7 \times 10^6 \text{ liters/minute} \cdot \text{mol}$$
$$K_{\text{eq4}} = 1.1 \times 10^{-8} M$$
$$f = 0.66$$

These constants were estimated by a Gauss–Newton nonlinear fitting procedure. The elements of the approximate Hessian matrix were computed by extending the coupled differential system to include terms giving rise to the appropriate partial differentials, as suggested by Bard (1974). Eight time courses of decay, each at a different level of B_e (consisting of approximately 100 data points in all) were fit to the four free parameters k^+, k_{-4}, k_4, and f.

The full kinetic model is too complex to allow assignment of parameters using such an unconstrained nonlinear curve fitting procedure. Our approach to the problem is to devise experimental protocols that will allow us first to determine the equilibrium constants and then to exploit them to allow us to determine the remaining kinetic constants. The strategy used will be explained below; the experimental work is in progress.

There are two conditions under which the denaturation of G/F is slow enough (hopefully) to be ignored; if either enough free 35K protein or enough guanine nucleotide is present, there will be little A subunit available for thermal denaturation. To focus the discussion of the resulting equilibrium version of the model, we have the following interconversions:

$$
\begin{array}{ccc}
\text{AB} + \text{N} & \xrightleftharpoons{K_{\text{eq1}}} & \text{ABN} \\
K_{\text{eq4}} \Big\updownarrow & & \Big\updownarrow K_{\text{eq2}} \\
\text{A} + \text{B} + \text{N} & \xrightleftharpoons{K_{\text{eq3}}} & \text{AN} + \text{B}
\end{array}
$$

with equilibrium constants defined as in the full model and conservation relationships as follows:

$$E_T = AB + ABN + AN + A$$
$$B = A + AN + B_e$$

The cyclic nature of the model determines one of the equilibrium constants in terms of the other three, so that

$$K_{eq2} = \frac{K_{eq1}K_{eq4}}{K_{eq3}}$$

We solve the simultaneous equilibria for AN as follows:

$$AB = \frac{K_{eq3}AN}{K_{eq4}N}\left[\frac{K_{eq3}AN}{N} + AN + B_e\right]$$

$$ABN = \frac{K_{eq3}AN}{K_{eq1}K_{eq4}}\left[\frac{K_{eq3}AN}{N} + AN + B_e\right]$$

$$AN = \frac{-C_2 + (C_2 + 4C_1E_T)^{1/2}}{2C_1}$$

with

$$C_1 = \frac{K_{eq3}(K_{eq3} + N)(K_{eq1} + N)}{K_{eq1}K_{eq4}NN}$$

$$C_2 = \frac{K_{eq3}B_e(K_{eq1} + N)}{K_{eq1}K_{eq4}N} + \frac{N + K_{eq3}}{N}$$

If we now compute the degree of activation, L, measured at saturating concentrations of nucleotide, we have

$$L = \frac{AN}{E_T}\bigg|_{N=\inf}$$
$$= 2\bigg/\left(\frac{K_{eq3}B_e}{K_{eq1}K_{eq4}} + 1 + \left[\left[\frac{K_{eq3}B_e + K_{eq1}K_{eq4}}{K_{eq1}K_{eq4}}\right]^2 + \frac{4K_{eq3}E_T}{K_{eq1}K_{eq4}}\right]^{1/2}\right)$$

Solving this expression for Q, the ratio of K_{eq3} to K_{eq1}, we find that:

$$\frac{K_{eq3}}{K_{eq1}} = \frac{K_{eq4}(1 - L)}{L(E_T L + B_e)} = Q$$

Since we know K_{eq4} from the variation in the kinetics of the denaturation of G/F with added 35K protein, we can compute the ratio K_{eq3}/K_{eq1} from the depression, by added 35K protein, of the steady state of activation reached after long times of incubation with high concentrations of guanine nucleotide analogs.

We must next disentangle K_{eq1} from K_{eq3}. To do this we determine the nucleotide saturation curve of G/F in the presence of a high concentration of 35K protein. If we examine the concentration of nucleotide that half activates the mixture ($N_{1/2}$), we know that

$$\left. \frac{AN}{E_T} \right|_{N=N_{1/2}} = \frac{L}{2} = \frac{2}{C_2 + (C_2{}^2 + 4C_1E_T)^{1/2}}$$

Thus when $N = N_{1/2}$

$$\frac{4}{L^2} = E_T \frac{K_{eq3}(K_{eq3} + N)(K_{eq1} + N)}{K_{eq1}K_{eq4}N^2} + \frac{2}{L} \cdot \frac{K_{eq3}B_e(K_{eq1} + N)}{K_{eq1}K_{eq4}N} + \frac{K_{eq3} + N}{N}$$

$$K_{eq1} = \frac{2C_5}{C_4 + (C_4{}^2 + 4C_3C_5)^{1/2}}$$

where

$$C_3 = E_T \left[\frac{K_{eq4}(1 - L)}{L(E_TL + B_e)} \right]^2 = E_T Q^2$$

$$C_4 = \left[E_T Q(1 + Q) + \frac{2Q(K_{eq4} + B_e)}{L} \right] N_{1/2}$$

$$C_5 = \left[\frac{4K_{eq4}}{L^2} - E_T Q - \frac{2}{L} [K_{eq4} + B_e Q] \right] N^2{}_{1/2}$$

Thus, from the depression, by free 35K protein, of the steady state of activation reached at high concentrations of guanine nucleotide and from the half saturating concentration of guanine nucleotide needed to activate that mixture, we can uniquely determine K_{eq1} and K_{eq3}. Since we already have determined K_{eq4}, we can calculate K_{eq2}. In principle, all of the equilibrium constants in the model can thus be determined.

The experimental aspects of this approach require some comments. If we express the steady-state activity (depressed by high concentrations of 35K protein) L, as a function of B_e, we have, in the limit of large B_e

$$L = 1 \left/ \left(1 + \frac{B_e}{K_{eq4}} \cdot \frac{K_{eq3}}{K_{eq1}} \right) \right.$$

Thus if $K_{eq3} \ll K_{eq1}$, that is, if the nucleotide binds much more tightly to A than to AB, then concentrations of free 35K protein much larger than K_{eq4} will be required to give an easily measureable depression of L. Another difficulty is the effect of large amounts of B_e to slow the rate of activation of G/F. This makes it difficult to know that steady state has been achieved. In spite of these technical difficulties, we are proceeding with work to attempt to determine these constants. The power of being able to estimate the equilibrium constants under conditions of a very slow rate of denaturation makes the approach worthy of pursuit.

Once the equilibrium constants are in hand, a number of the kinetic constants should be experimentally measureable. For example, measurement of the rate of reversal of the activation of G/F as a function of added B_e will give a good idea of k_2, since deactivation seems to proceed through ABN:

$$AN + B \underset{k_{-2}}{\overset{k_2}{\rightleftharpoons}} ABN$$

Measurement of the rate of activation of the dilute enzyme will give a notion of k_3, since activation will proceed mainly via

$$A + N \underset{k_{-3}}{\overset{k_3}{\rightleftharpoons}} AN$$

The rate constants contributing to K_{eq1} may well be too rapid for experimental determination.

The full kinetic model is as follows:

$$d\,AB/dt = -k_1N(AB) + k_{-1}ABN - k_{-4}AB + k_4A(B)$$
$$d\,ABN/dt = k_1N(AB) - (k_{-1} + k_{-2})ABN + k_2AN(B)$$
$$d\,A/dt = k_{-4}AB + k_{-3}AN - k_4A(B) - k_3N(A) - k^+A$$
$$d\,A^+/dt = k^+A$$
$$d\,AN/dt = k_{-2}ABN - k_2AN(B) - k_{-3}AN + k_3N(A)$$

with

$$E_T = A + AB + AN + ABN + A^+$$
$$B = AN + A + A^+ + B_e$$

Straightforward numerical integration of this system of nonlinear differential equations poses certain technical difficulties. They are caused by the disparity of the rate constants for the various steps and manifest themselves as "stiffness" of the system (Garfinkel *et al.*, 1977). This means that an adaptive integration routine starts to take what seem to be excessively small steps to compensate for numerical instabilities caused by the mismatched rates. One approach to dealing with these stiff equations is to use an algorithm that uses iterative methods to fit the solution to a power series over a region of the solution. Codes such as Gear's Algorithm 407 (Gear, 1971) are of this type. Alternatively, one can attempt to use physical knowledge to decompose the system into fast and slow processes. For instance, one can make steady-state assumptions about certain of the variables to convert the differential equation defining their time evolution to algebraic equations for their steady-state values. We are currently exploring these approaches to the solution of the simulation problem.

Certain care in this matter is required; in any mechanized approach to the problem of assignment of parameters to a differential model, many numerical solutions of the system of differential equations, with potentially wide variation of the parameters, are called for. This requires both considerable efficiency and "robustness" on the part of the method of solution.

As the above discussion probably makes all too clear, the problems, both experimental and numeric, in system identification that are presented by such a collection of interacting proteins are formidable. The reader may well wonder whether the results of such a program will be enlightening or even believable. We feel, on a good day, that the processes are sufficiently well understood to allow the design of experiments that will reduce the complexity of the interactions and provide relatively unambiguous tests of the model's structure. This uncoupling of interactions is the motivation for our layered approach of first modeling the denaturation of the unliganded protein, second determining the equilibrium constants of the system, and finally assigning as many of the kinetic constants as possible.

As for the hope of enlightenment by this process, we must confess to a certain feeling that we are searching for our lost keys under one of the few available street lamps. These measurements are being made on a protein in detergent solution, not on one in a biological membrane. The values of the constants determined will reflect this circumstance. We can only hope that the patterns of interaction will facilitate understanding the activation of G/F in other milieu. In defense of our approach, the complexities revealed, despite our efforts to simplify the number of interacting components, give some inklings of those possible in a system containing catalyst and hormone receptors. We do assert a somewhat reductionist faith that knowledge gained in the study of resolved systems can be of use in understanding both reconstituted and natural ones.

ACKNOWLEDGMENTS

This research was supported by United States Public Health Service Grant NS18153 and by American Cancer Society Grant BC240C. We thank Pamela Van Arsdale for superb technical assistance, Wendy Deaner for excellent editorial work, and our colleagues whose work is described in this article.

REFERENCES

Bard, Y. (1974). "Nonlinear Parameter Estimation," Ch. 8. Academic Press, New York.
Bourne, H. R., Coffino, P., and Tomkins, G. M. (1975). *Science* **187**, 750–752.
Cassel, D., and Pfeuffer, T. (1978). *Proc. Natl. Acad. Sci. U.S.A.* **75**, 2669–2673.
Garfinkel, D., Marbach, C. B., and Shapiro, N. Z. (1977). *Annu. Rev. Biophys. Bioeng.* **6**, 525–542.

Gear, C. W. (1971). *Commun. ACM* **14**, 185–190.

Hanski, E., Sternweis, P. C., Northup, J. K., Dromerick, A. W., and Gilman, A. G. (1981). *J. Biol. Chem.* **256**, 12911–12919.

Howlett, A. C., Sternweis, P. C., Macik, B. A., Van Arsdale, P. M., and Gilman, A. G. (1979). *J. Biol. Chem.* **254**, 2287–2295.

Klainer, L. M., Chi, Y.-M., Friedberg, S. L., Rall, T. W., and Sutherland, E. W. (1962). *J. Biol. Chem.* **237**, 1239–1243.

Levinson, S. J., and Blume, A. J. (1977). *J. Biol. Chem.* **252**, 3766–3774.

Murad, F., Chi, Y.-M., Rall, T. W., and Sutherland, E. W. (1962). *J. Biol. Chem.* **237**, 1233–1238.

Northup, J. K., Sternweis, P. C., Smigel, M. D., Schleifer, L. S., Ross, E. M., and Gilman, A. G. (1980). *Proc. Natl. Acad. Sci. U.S.A.* **77**, 6516–6520.

Pfeuffer, T. (1977). *J. Biol. Chem.* **252**, 7224–7234.

Rall, T. W., and Sutherland, E. W. (1962). *J. Biol. Chem.* **237**, 1228–1232.

Rodbell, M., Birnbaumer, L., Pohl, S. L., and Krans, M. J. (1971). *J. Biol. Chem.* **246**, 1877–1882.

Ross, E. M., and Gilman, A. G. (1977a). *Proc. Natl. Acad. Sci. U.S.A.* **74**, 3715–3719.

Ross, E. M., and Gilman, A. G. (1977b). *J. Biol. Chem.* **252**, 6966–6970.

Ross, E. M., and Gilman, A. G. (1980). *Annu. Rev. Biochem.* **49**, 533–564.

Ross, E. M., Maguire, M. E., Sturgill, T. W., Biltonen, R. L., and Gilman, A. G. (1977). *J. Biol. Chem.* **252**, 5761–5775.

Ross, E. M., Howlett, A. C., Ferguson, K. M., and Gilman, A. G. (1978). *J. Biol. Chem.* **253**, 6401–6412.

Sternweis, P. C., Northup, J. K., Smigel, M. D., and Gilman, A. G. (1981). *J. Biol. Chem.* **256**, 11517–11526.

Sutherland, E. W., Rall, T. W., and Menon, T. (1962). *J. Biol. Chem.* **237**, 1220–1227.

DISCUSSION

U. Zor: In many systems one could find more than one hormone that activates the adenylate cyclase in one specific cell type, e.g., in the isolated rat granulosa cell there are at least four different hormones. Can you speculate a little bit about the regulation of the coupling between the GTP regulatory protein and the specific receptor to hormone?

A. G. Gilman: The easiest way out of the multiple receptor problem is probably to speculate that there are more molecules of G/F than there are total R or C. If, for example, there were 10^3 molecules of any one cyclase-linked receptor per cell, 10^4 molecules of G/F, and 10^3 molecules of C, it would be easier to envision how any one of several hormones that act independently could activate adenylate cyclase maximally.

U. Zor: I am specifically referring to the phenomenon of homologous desensitization which some scientists believe has some kind of uncoupling between the receptor and the GTP-regulatory protein taking place during this process. How is it possible that one hormone will uncouple the common G-unit?

A. G. Gilman: You need to unleash some receptor-mediated reaction wherein each agonist–receptor complex could ultimately influence multiple molecules of G/F. For example, an agonist–receptor complex could cause activation of an enzyme responsible for covalent modification and uncoupling of G/F.

W. Moyle: Do you have any evidence that occupied hormone receptors promote dissociation of the 35K subunit from the G/F protein complex?

A. G. Gilman: All of the experiments that we have done that bear on the question of dissociation of subunits have been done in detergent-containing solutions and have not, therefore, involved hormone.

W. Moyle: Do you know of any mutants that might be used to show dissociation of the 35K subunit?

A. G. Gilman: Not that I can think of.

G. D. Aurbach: After the G-unit, particularly the 45 or 55K subunit interacts with the catalytic unit, the system gets deactivated and the G-unit either dies or gets recycled. Which do you think happens? The second question is more technical. The turkey erythrocyte system seems to have a much higher affinity for G nucleotides, particularly GDP, and is much less readily exchangeable when in the basal state. You indicated in the relative affinities of various G nucleotides that GDP had a rather low affinity relative to GDP. Was that for the liver system or does that apply to the turkey also?

A. G. Gilman: To answer the second question first: the data shown were for the liver system; we have not yet done those experiments with the turkey erythrocyte protein. Is your first question really just a clever way to ask if there is GTPase activity in our preparation or are you searching for something more than that? We have not found GTPase activity in purified G/F from either turkey erythrocytes or rabbit liver. However, I remain thoroughly intrigued by the hypothesis of Cassel and Selinger that there is a GTPase and that hydrolysis of GTP is the mechanism of deactivation. The fact that we cannot find the GTPase activity in the purified protein is perhaps relatively meaningless, since it would make sense if the GTPase activity was manifest only in the presence of another protein—presumably the catalyst.

R. W. Downs: In the figure that you showed on the partial resolution of 52K and 45K subunits on the heptylamine Sepharose column, it is not immediately apparent to me why there should be a notch in the iso plus GTP curve, since the 52K labeled band appeared to be decreasing continuously rather than decreasing and then increasing again.

A. G. Gilman: The amount of 45K is going up at that point. You can certainly see responses to hormones in the absence of the 52K protein. We just think that the 52K subunit is a little better than the 45.

R. W. Downs: So, you are saying that it is the sum of the two that affects coupling?

A. G. Gilman: We presume that it's the sum of the concentration of each multiplied by an efficacy factor, and that factor would be better for 52K than for 45K.

R. W. Downs: Ken Seamon and John Daly at the NIH have recently described a diterpine compound called forskolin which stimulates adenylate cyclase activity, and I wonder if you have had the chance to examine it in your system to determine whether it may possibly interact in any way at all with G/F.

A. G. Gilman: We've not looked at it yet. As I'm sure you know, Daly's data indicate that it acts on C. It stimulates cyclic AMP production in cyc⁻ S49 cells, and it works on detergent extracts of membranes of those cells.

J. E. Rall: I am interested in this adenosyl ribosylating factor which is off on one side of your diagram. Is this required for the normal hormonal stimulation pathway or is it involved only under special circumstances?

A. G. Gilman: We wish we knew—but we don't. We have tried to select for ARF-deficient mutants of the S49 cell but have had no luck to date. In the absence of a mutant, resolution of all of the components of the system from the ADP-ribosylating factor will probably be necessary.

P. J. Olsiewski: Have you been able to prepare antibodies using any of these purified preparations?

A. G. Gilman: Yes, but the titers are low, and the antibodies have not yet proven useful.

K. Sterling: I think all the material on G/F regulatory units was very impressive. What I wanted to ask is a sort of naive general question that has bothered me for about three decades, ever since Rall and Sutherland discovered the role of cAMP as a second messenger. The thing that bothers me about the whole adenylate cyclase system is that you have got the same sort of signal whether the hormone is ACTH, parathyroid hormone, or epinephrine. Now, can the vast differences between these hormones and their effects be ascribed solely to the distribution of receptors and firmness and duration of receptor binding, or are there some other elements that would account for the differences?

A. G. Gilman: The receptors help, of course, but there are other obvious and major elements. Cyclic AMP particularly influences differentiated cellular functions, and the specificity is thus built in by differentiation.

G. D. Aurbach: Your data indicate that the 55K or 45K subunit when combined with the catalytic unit is the active one.

A. G. Gilman: All we need is the isolated subunit to prove that.

G. D. Aurbach: If that is so, then in AC minus, the 45 bank or 55 must be defective since one cannot detect labeling with choleratoxin. I wonder in view of your experiments showing that the 35K subunit can inhibit effects of activated GF whether there is a good 35K subunit in AC minus which can inhibit the effects of GF?

A. G. Gilman: What you're saying is that we have an assay for the 35K subunit and, using that assay, can we detect the protein in cyc$^-$? I want to state it in that way because everything hinges on whether or not you believe the assay. The most sensitive assay involves activating G/F with fluoride, diluting the reaction mixture, and looking at the rate of reversal of the activation as a function of added 35K protein. Activity is, of course, detected by reconstitution into cyc$^-$ membranes at various times after initiation of deactivation. Using this protocol we can detect 35K activity in cyc$^-$, but only if we incubate extracts with Mg^{2+} prior to assay. This is the same condition that "releases" 35K protein in G/F. So, if you wanted to push the speculation to the limit, you would say that cyc$^-$ has 35K protein but that it is bound to something. Perhaps cyc$^-$ has a normal 35K and a defective 45K subunit.

G. D. Aurbach: That is a terrific observation. One might further push one step beyond that—hormone also presumably would facilitate dissociation of the 35K subunit from AC minus membranes. Have you tested that hypothesis?

A. G. Gilman: No, but it's a good idea. We'll try that.

INDEX